CHINA AT WORK

CHINA AT WORK

AN ILLUSTRATED RECORD OF THE PRIMITIVE INDUSTRIES OF CHINA'S MASSES, WHOSE LIFE IS TOIL, AND THUS AN ACCOUNT OF CHINESE CIVILIZATION

BY

RUDOLF P. HOMMEL

PUBLISHED FOR

THE BUCKS COUNTY HISTORICAL SOCIETY

DOYLESTOWN, PENNSYLVANIA

BY

THE JOHN DAY COMPANY · NEW YORK

PRINTED IN THE UNITED STATES OF AMERICA BY THE CORNWALL PRESS, CORNWALL, N. Y.

Records of

Chinese, Oriental and Other Primitive Industries

Being the Results of an Expedition

begun in the year 1921,
planned, equipped and directed by

Henry Chapman Mercer.

Dedicated to the Memory of

Timothy Bigelow Lawrence
of Boston

by his nephew

Henry Chapman Mercer.

"Nunc ad res transeo, in quibus
maxime sunt personis juncta,
quae agimus, ideoque prima
tractanda: in omnibus porro,
quae fiunt, quaeritur aut
Quare? aut
Ubi? aut
Quando? aut
Quomodo? aut
Per Quae?
facta sunt."

(Now we shall deal with actions
which closely affect human beings,
and must therefore be considered first.
In regard, then, to everything
that is done, it should be asked,
either why, or where, or when,
in what manner, or by
whom it was done.)

"De Institutione Oratoria,"
Liber V, 10, 32.
MARCUS FABIUS QUINTILIANUS.

"I keep six honest serving men,
They taught me all I know;
Their names are What and Why and When,
And How and Where and Who."

RUDYARD KIPLING.

PREFACE

IT WAS my good fortune to be able to live in China for eight years (from 1921 to 1926, and from 1928 to 1930), and not only to be there and travel about the country, but to live among the Chinese people and get to know them. In spite of many hardships, which a Chinese likewise has to endure who travels about his country, I came to respect the Chinese people and their civilization. The task set me by Dr. Henry C. Mercer, who to my great sorrow did not live to see the completion of it (he passed away on the ninth of March 1930), was to record by photographs and descriptions the tools and implements of the Chinese people. This formidable task was greatly hampered by the innate aversion of the people to the camera. This extended not only to photographing the people but also to their belongings. In spite of all the handicaps, augmented by the Chinese internecine war, raging for many years, I gathered enough pictures and information to produce a volume whose aim it is to give a fairly complete picture of Chinese life, as lived by millions of people today, a life in which there has been no considerable change for thousands of years. While in this way the book gives a picture of modern Chinese life, the past is projected into it and we get by studying the handicrafts a History of Human Progress or Civilization. We are today sufficiently advanced to interpret civilization in that broad sense which takes into account the doings of peasant and tradesman, who together form nine tenths of the population.

The tool pictures, photographed from their originals in China, with their descriptions have been arranged in related groups according to the classification of the 18th century tools adopted in the Mercer Museum of the Bucks County Historical Society at Doylestown, Pennsylvania, U.S.A., namely as

> Primary Tools for (1) Making Tools, or Iron Working, the basis for all tool making, (2) Food, (3) Clothing, (4) Shelter, (5) Transport.

The description of Secondary Tools, pertaining to Language, Religion, Science, Commerce, Government, Art, Amusement, would amply furnish material for another volume.

We are dealing here primarily with Chinese tools. A sojourn in Japan for about a year (during 1927), when turmoil in China prevented altogether any systematic working, gave me the opportunity to study Japanese tools to some extent, and for this reason I am enabled to show now and then Japanese tools for comparison. At the same time such introduction should help to dispel the western tendency to confound Chinese with Japanese civilization. Chinese civilization is by far the older, in fact, at the time of the Tang Dynasty (618 to 907 A.D.), when Japan was just emerging from barbarism, China was considered the most civilized country in the world. Chinese influence extended to Japan mainly in intellectual pursuits, and she even adopted the Chinese script. Agricultural methods, tools and industries of Japan, however, were scarcely touched by this influence but had their own autochthonous development.

The measurements given in most of the pictures can be only approximate on account of the perspective variation of depth in a photograph. They have been taken as nearly as possible along a horizontal center line of the article or articles depicted. It was felt that this makeshift was better than no indication of measurements at all. The taking of measurements with a footrule was almost as offensive to the Chinese as the taking of photographs. There must have seemed to be a fatal finality about measuring anything with a footrule, perhaps comparable to the measuring of the corpse for the coffin. To get around the objection I had secret marks of feet and inches on my cane and holding it casually against the article or laying it upon it I obtained the dimensions wanted.

Of books that have been of help to me in compiling this work I name the following:

H. Blümner, Technologie & Terminologie der Gewerbe & Kuenste bei Griechen & Roemern, Leipzig & Berlin, 1912.

F. M. Feldhaus, Die Technik der Vorzeit etc., Leipzig & Berlin, 1914.

R. Forrer, Real-Lexikon, Berlin & Stuttgart, 1907.

H. A. Giles, A Chinese Biographical Dictionary, London, 1898.

H. A. Giles, A Chinese-English Dictionary, London & Shanghai, 1912.

F. Hirth, Ancient History of China, New York, 1908.

F. H. King, Farmers of Forty Centuries, Madison, Wis., 1911.
B. Laufer, The Beginnings of Porcelain in China, Chicago, 1917.
Lettres Edifiantes et Curieuses, Paris, 1780-1783.
A. Neuburger, Die Technik des Altertums, Leipzig, 1920.
A. Rich, Dictionnaire des Antiquités Romaines et Grecques, Paris, 1861.
G. A. Stuart, Chin. Materia Medica, Shanghai, 1911.
E. T. C. Werner, Chinese Sociology, London, 1910.
S. W. Williams, The Middle Kingdom, New York, 1883.
Sir Henry Yule, The Book of Ser Marco Polo, London, 1921.

Grateful acknowledgement for his collaboration and inspiring enthusiasm goes first to my dear departed friend, Dr. Henry Chapman Mercer, who originated and endowed this undertaking for studying the primitive industries in foreign countries, before they become submerged by modern processes and machinery, as has happened in the United States of North America. Dr. Mercer founded a Museum in Doylestown, Pennsylvania, which houses his collection of nearly 25,000 tools and utensils imported by the European immigrants or constructed after European types, and used until about 1820, or approximately the time of the introduction of steam and modern machinery.

On my inland travels in China it was many a time a godsend to receive the hospitality of missionaries and have the benefit of their knowledge of local conditions, and an all-including thanks is extended to them. Ch'en Mao Chih of Peking, a venerable gentleman and scholar of the old school, was ever ready to unravel problems the language proffered and has aided in every way with his prodigious knowledge of Chinese literature. I bow to him in profoundest respect. Not less I wish to thank Wu Tsung T'ai of Tsingtao, whose store of knowledge of Chinese customs and lore was ever at my command. In the preparation of these pages for the printer I had the invaluable help of Professor P. M. Palmer, Dean of the College of Arts and Science of Lehigh University (Bethlehem, Pa.), who with the greatest patience read the manuscript with me and suggested many improvements in diction and presentation of complicated technical description. I thank him heartily for his friendship and help.

The field of my investigations was mainly the region of Central China, the adjoining provinces of the lower Yangtse Valley, up to Hankow and into Hunan province, also in the north, Shantung and Chihli provinces. I have throughout this work given the locality where I obtained my pictures and information, and this is necessary to avoid the common mistake of generalizing about China. A case in instance. Are there Persian cats in China? Generally speaking, no, but still there is a place, south of Tientsin, where an old Mohammedan family is breeding a beautiful kind of long-haired cats, like the famous Persians. They sell only gelded specimens, and in that way have kept the business within their clan for perhaps centuries. Similarly there may be many surprises in this book, even to old residents of China, who as a rule do not venture beyond the confines of coastal cities. Of the sinologues I ask indulgence; my transliteration of Chinese names is not always uniform, and I surely do not wish to pose as learned in the Chinese language.

In conclusion I wish to thank the Chinese authorities for non-interference with my work, and I hope that any who may peruse these pages will feel the admiration I have for Chinese civilization, and that my aim was to investigate and not to criticize. I add to this the wish that a possible continuation of my work in China may be looked upon with favor by the authorities, as it can only serve to increase the understanding of old Cathay by western nations.

Rudolf P. Hommel.
"Gargoyle," Richlandtown, Pa.
May 25, 1937.

CONTENTS

CHINA AT WORK

Chapter I

TOOLS TO MAKE TOOLS

WE TRY to illustrate Human History, the History of Civilization, by means of Tools, which help man to contend with nature and procure the requirements of life. Tools are the means of doing anything, everything. When the uncultured savage took a stick for defense or a stone to break open a nut, the first tools were invented. By prehistoric man the stone was gradually fashioned to cut or indent and fashion other tools, and long before any definite trades catered to specific wants there was the need for tools that make tools.

The stone had to be found, pried from the rock, shaped and edged by hitting with stones or by slow abrasion, and it had to be mounted for better handling. Later with the use of bronze, there was the same order, the finding of the raw material (mining the ore), intermediate processes with various implements to get finally the bronze tool. With the Dawn of History, in the so-called Iron Age, iron became the basis of all tools and, little as we realize it, it is today, and has become the master of all processes. Therefore, before proceeding to the description of tools for specific purposes we fittingly deal with tools that make tools and following the order of procuring the raw material, preliminary preparation, final preparation we begin with the description of mining, stone blasting and quarrying which are just as applicable to procuring iron ore, as to getting coal or building stone.

Liu Añ (died 122 B.C.), Prince of Huai-nan, and grandson of the founder of the Han dynasty (206 B.C. to 25 A.D.), in his writings first referred to coal, which he called Ice Charcoal. Later on it was also called Earth or Stone Charcoal. If the statement is correct that Roman authors refer to impure coal [1] in the second century B.C., we must conclude that coal was discovered at about the same time in Europe and China. Marco Polo noticed the use of Chinese coal and described it in such manner that we might believe that it was utterly unknown to him or his contemporaries. He says "It is a fact that all over the country of Cathay there is a kind of black stones existing in beds in the mountains, which they dig out and burn like firewood. If you supply the fire with them at night, and see that they are well kindled, you will find them still alight in the morning; and they make such capital fuel that no other is used throughout the country. It is true that they have plenty of wood also, but they do not burn it, because those stones burn better and cost less."

England seems to be the first European country in which coal was used to any considerable extent. A Roman cellar discovered at Housesteads in 1833 was filled with stone coal, and when the water reservoir was made at Benwell some years ago the workingmen exposed ancient coal workings, which were thought to go back to Roman times.[2] In the Anglo-Saxon period, as early as 825 A.D., coal was in some districts an article of household consumption. Its use may be traced back still further by stone-implements, said to have been found in some old English coal-mines, from which we may conclude that the knowledge and use of coal preceded that of iron.[3]

We are justified in reasoning that a find of stone-implements is to be considered *prima facie* evidence that the users thereof were living in the stone age. In China, however, we may well use caution in making sweeping deductions. One of our first investigations was devoted to pottery, and when we found, in the mountains of Chekiang, potters unacquainted with the potter's wheel, we, of course, would have been entirely wrong had we concluded from this evidence, that the Chinese as a people do not know the potter's wheel. This was merely a striking indication of a tenacious conservatism fostered by isolation and poor means of intercommunication. A further example was our finding stone hammers in present use for driving wedges in a primitive oil press, more than 3,000 years after the Chinese emerged from the stone age.

The following notes dealing with coal mining in

[1] W. F. Collins, in "Encyclopedia Sinica," Shanghai, 1917.

[2] This information was kindly supplied by Reginald A. Smith of the British Museum, and H. Askew, upon my inquiry in "Notes & Queries," Vol. 151, pp. 140 & 214.

[3] R. L. Galloway in his "Annals of Coal Mining" (First Series), 1898, p. 3, doubts, however, that the finds referred to can be linked to ancient British utilisation of stone coal.

Fig. 1. A Chinese Coal Mine. Surface structures of a coal mine at Kong Tong, Kiangsi. Thatched straw huts, the miners' dwellings, are built over the mine shafts. A large half-timbered house is seen to the left.

Fig. 2. Coal Miner's Windlass. There are two units of rope in use upon the cylinder of the windlass. When the one is wound, the other is unwound, with the effect that by turning the cranks one rope winds to pull up a load, while the other unwinds to let down an empty basket into the shaft of the mine.

China, show methods which are primitive and indicate very little development. It is surprising how the Chinese discovered coal at a depth of from 100 to 150 feet. But as the shafts and the method of sinking them are very similar to well-digging, it seems probable that in the search for water the Chinese pierced the overlying stratum of loose sand-stone and accidentally discovered coal, which they had known already from surface outcrops.

COAL MINING

While in Feng Chen, a small town on the Kan River in Kiangsi province, I heard of coal being mined near a village, called Kong Tong, about 20 li (a li is one third of a mile) distant in a north-westerly direction. Being assured that the mining was carried on in primitive Chinese manner, we started out for the place and arrived after about two hours' walking. The area where the shafts are sunk is owned by a man

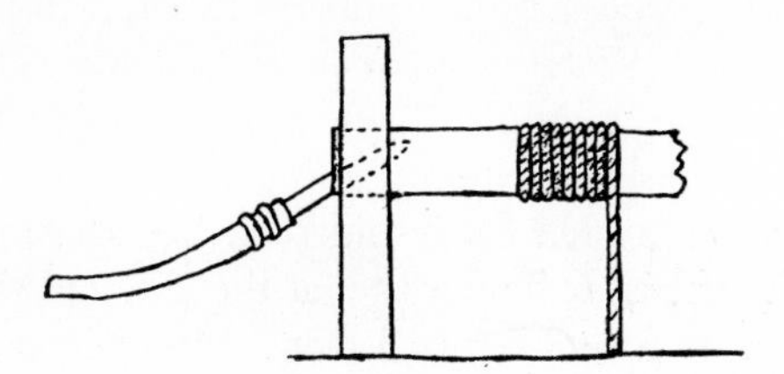

Fig. 3. Rudimentary Crank of a Coal Miner's Windlass.

who rents out plots to the miners for a share in the proceeds. After the claims are fenced in, the digging begins. The shafts are about 5 feet in diameter and the sides are protected by bamboo wicker-work, which is applied as the excavation proceeds. Coal seams are struck at a depth of from 100 to 150 feet. Over the shaft a derrick with a windlass is erected similar to the one used in well digging and shown in Fig. 172. Over the derrick a straw hut is built to protect the operation at the shaft and to serve at the same time for a habitation for the miners.

Fig. 1 presents a view of the mining district we visited, with a house of half-timbered construction at the left and various straw huts built over the mine shafts. A derrick over the mouth of a shaft is shown in Fig. 2. Two men are needed to turn the wooden cranks at either end of one and the same beam. The rope on the beam is arranged in such manner that an empty basket descends at the same time that a full one is pulled up. Miners going down stand in the basket, one at a time, and hold on to the rope. The cranks of the windlass are shown but dimly. They are only rudimentary cranks. Into the ends of the beam or cylinder upon which the rope winds a strong piece of wood is set obliquely and to this is tied a curved branch of a tree. The accompanying sketch, Fig. 3, will make this quite clear.

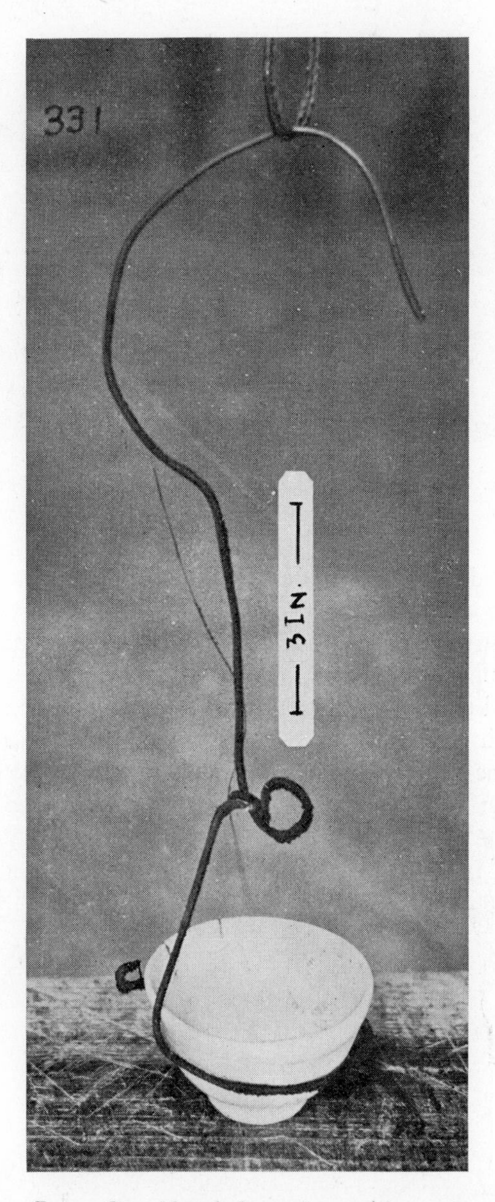

Fig. 4. Coal Miner's Lamp. A porcelain cup is suspended on a bent wire which is easily hooked into the mine wall. One such lamp is carried by each miner, with a bamboo bottle of vegetable oil for fuel.

The miner's lamp, Fig. 4, is a simple contrivance. A wire is bent to form a loop, in which rests a small porcelain cup. Another wire bent to form a hook is joined to the former and this constitutes the lamp, which can be easily hooked to a hole in the wall, wherever the miner is working. Vegetable oil is

Fig. 5. Coal Miner's Water Basket. This basket, lined with oiled cloth, is used to remove water from the coal mines.

burned and each miner carries down with him a bamboo bottle filled with oil, and a few rush wicks. For striking light flint and steel are used. The miners stay underground continuously for about 3 hours, and to tell the time they carry with them an incense stick which glows for about 3 hours. The Chinese call it "Time-piece." In other districts where the danger of inflammable gases is greater the miners dare not use open lights and instead get a semblance of light with rotten wood or a kind of resin which burns without flame. Out of 24 hours they have two three-hour periods of work underground and two periods of nine hours above ground for recreation. In every shaft two men and a small boy are at work.

When coal is reached the seam is taken out, but not much lateral digging is done on account of the danger of inflammable gases, against which the Chinese do not know how to protect themselves. Rather than make extensive horizontal passages underground, the Chinese dig a new shaft, sometimes quite near the other to exploit this fresh one. Mine timbers are not employed. Water is taken out in baskets lined with oiled cloth, an example of which is shown in Fig. 5.

Similar baskets without lining are employed for removing excavated earth and coal. See specimen on the right of Fig. 6. The basket at the left, and the one in Fig. 7 are for taking coal from drifts which are so low that the miners have to work in them lying down. The baskets, as is evident, are proportionately

Fig. 6. Coal Miner's Baskets. The left basket is pushed and pulled by hand to transport coal from side drifts to the shaft where it is dumped into the windlass basket (right) to be hoisted to the surface.

low in shape. To raise the large windlass baskets, they are tied with a knot to the rope of the windlass, or sometimes hung on a hook fastened to the windlass rope, Fig. 8. Two men at the windlass raise the basket, and, as mentioned before, lower at the same time an empty one. When the basket has reached the surface it is carried away on a pole by two men to be dumped nearby. The pole with which this is done, is shown in Fig. 9. To the center of the pole a rope is attached which carries at its loose end a bamboo stick. This stick is passed through the handles of the basket, and then brought up vertically against the rope and held there by one of the carriers, who grasps stick and rope with one hand. Both men are then ready to carry the load away. This device, simple as it is, suspends the basket and releases it by letting go the stick.

Of tools employed by the coal miner there is more variety than one might expect. For breaking up large pieces of rock the sledge-hammer, Fig. 10, is used, with a head about 10 inches long. It is not used under ground for want of space. The pick-axe, Fig. 11, serves for digging the shaft. A shovel is not used at all. When digging a basket is placed in readiness, and loosening the material, it drops into it, or the dirt is scooped into the basket which is then laid on its side. The coal mined at Kong Tong is a good grade of anthracite, and it is pried from the solid seam with wedges. Where the space permits a wedge with a handle, a miner's gad, is used, see Fig. 12, held by one man, while another swings the hammer, Fig. 13, to hit the flat gad-face. In lateral mining, where the miner works lying down, the wedge without a handle, the hand-gad, Fig. 14, is held with one hand and driven down with the curious hammer, Fig. 15. It consists of a round iron disk about 4 inches in diameter with a handle in the center. The lumps of coal detached in this manner are picked up by hand, and deposited in a shallow basket which is dragged along the low passage to the vertical shaft, and there deposited in a large basket to be hoisted up.

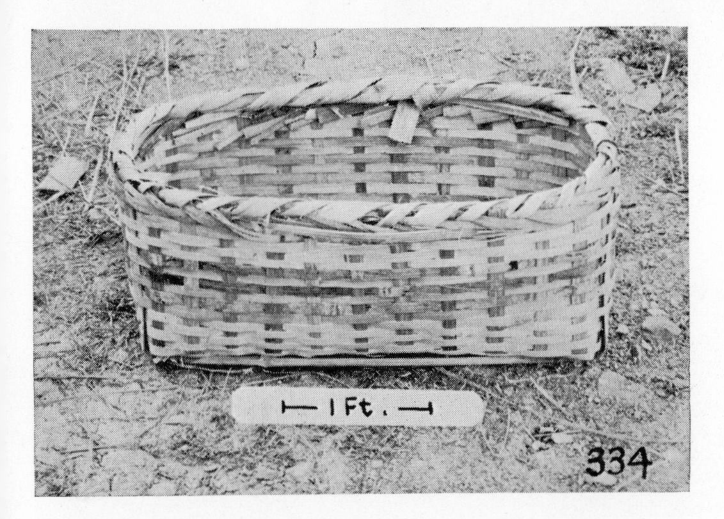

Fig. 7. Coal Miner's Drift Basket. Used like the basket on the left of Fig. 6, for shifting by hand lumps of excavated coal from lateral drifts.

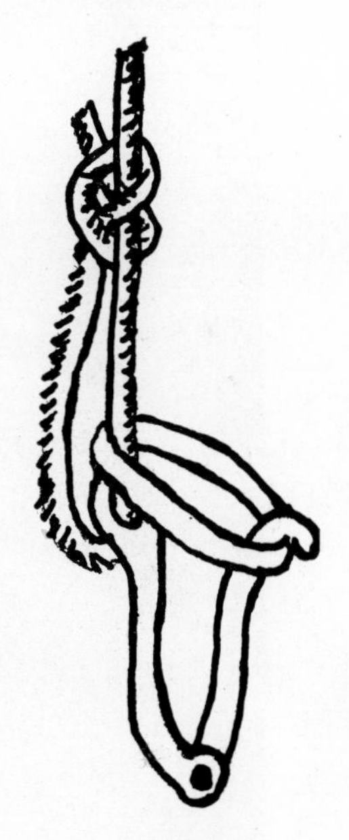

Fig. 8. Hook on Coal Miner's Windlass Rope. The sketch shows the hinged iron hook, attached to the windlass rope, upon which the coal baskets are lifted from the mine to the surface.

MINER'S ROPE MAKING

The rope used by the miners on their windlasses must needs be very strong, it has to raise and lower coal and men. The rope is twisted of three strands of bamboo strips. No doubt, experience taught the Chinese that such ropes have a limit of usefulness, and they are accordingly used not longer than from ten to fifteen days. The village shown in the background of Fig. 1, is the place where these ropes are manufactured, and Figs. 16 and 17, illustrating their manufacture, were photographed there. Long thin strips of bamboo are first twisted upon a wheel similar to the hemp-wheel shown in Fig. 248. Three of these strands are then fastened singly upon the hooks shown in Fig. 17. The other ends of these strands are hooked upon the single hook on the sled-like frame with two uprights, shown in Fig. 16. The twisting is performed by turning the cranks, the three at the one end and the one at the other end, respectively, upon the two parts of the rope machine. The spacing block, seen lying on the platform in Fig. 16, with three radial end channels is held by two men, one at each handle, close to the place where the three strands are fastened to the one hook on the machine, Fig. 16, so that the strands pass through the channels. As the twisting progresses they walk backward leaving before them the twisted rope until the whole length of the strands have been united to a strong, firmly twisted rope. The contrivance for twisting the other end of the rope, shown in Fig. 17, is held against two upright

Fig. 9. Carrying Pole for Taking Coal in Baskets Away From the Mouth of the Mine Shaft.

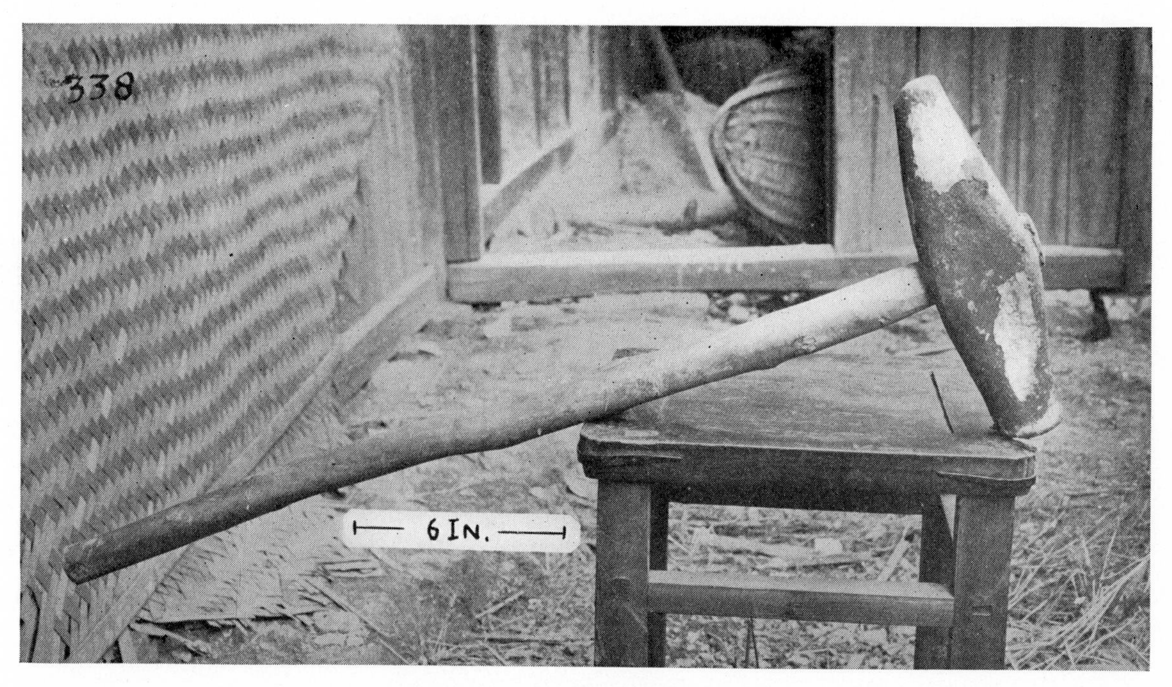

Fig. 10. Coal Miner's Sledge Hammer.

FIG. 11. COAL MINER'S PICK-AXE. The single pointed pick-axe, flat-faced on one end of the head, is used for digging and enlarging the shaft.

posts, rammed into the ground, by a man who turns all three hooks at once by means of a wooden bar, loosely penetrated by the turning cranks which form the rear of each hook. Through continuous turning, the strands and the resulting rope become shorter and drag the sled-like frame of the machine upon the ground, which is weighted down by the man standing upon it and turning the single crank. Unfortunately the crank does not show clearly because its iron arm coincides with a black wall joint in the background of the picture. The sled-like frame has two uprights which are propped against the frame in the direction in which the sled is pulled. The upper cross-piece between the uprights is perforated in the middle for the passage of the above mentioned single crank with its unseen hook similar to those shown in Fig. 17. To

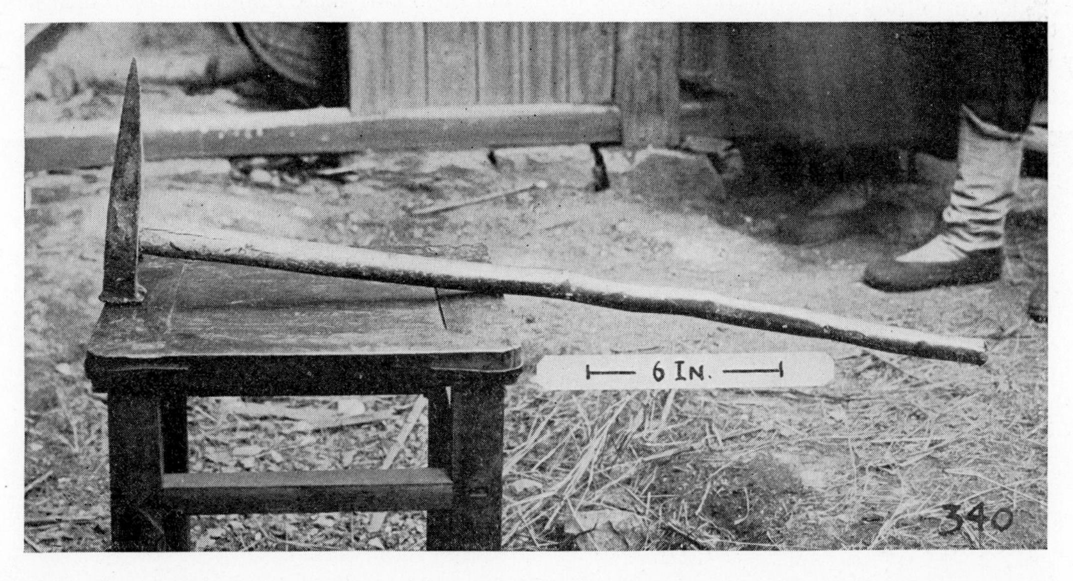

FIG. 12. COAL MINER'S HANDLED WEDGE OR GAD. Where space permits, one man holding the instrument by its handle, sets its sharp point upon the solid coal, while another drives the iron point into the seam to split it by striking the flat face of this tool with the iron hammer shown in Fig. 13.

FIG. 13. COAL MINER'S LONG HANDLED GAD HAMMER. One miner holds the point of the handled iron gad, Fig. 12, against the solid coal seam, while another miner strikes the flat gad-face with this hammer.

this hook are fastened the three strands above noted which in the process of twisting become a rope. Twisted rope can be seen clearly dangling from the back of the upper cross-piece of the frame. In front the iron crank extends downward and its handle can be recognized by closely looking at the picture. On the sled lies the "laying top" or spacing block above described.

STONE BLASTING

In and around Kuling, Kiangsi province, a great deal of blasting with gun powder is carried on by Chinese workmen to secure building stone. It is done in such a primitive way that we might be misled to believe that it is a native practice, not introduced recently by foreigners.

The honor of having invented gunpowder is credited to the Chinese. Their chroniclers tell us that already during the Wei dynasty (220-265 A.D.), "crackling and exploding staves" were used, to which were added fireworks of gunpowder by the Emperor Yang Ti (reigned from 605-617 A.D.) of the Sui dynasty The use of these for warfare is not proven. The trend, however, was for such application, and experimenting was carried on along those lines. "Thunderbolt projectiles" made of paper filled with lime and sulphur were used by Yu Yun-wen, a general of the Sung dynasty, in 1161 A.D., at the battle of Ts'ai Shih, near Nanking. When these touched the water, fire lept from them and dense fumes rose up which helped to defeat the enemy. At about the same time another general of the Sung dynasty, Wei Sheng, employed

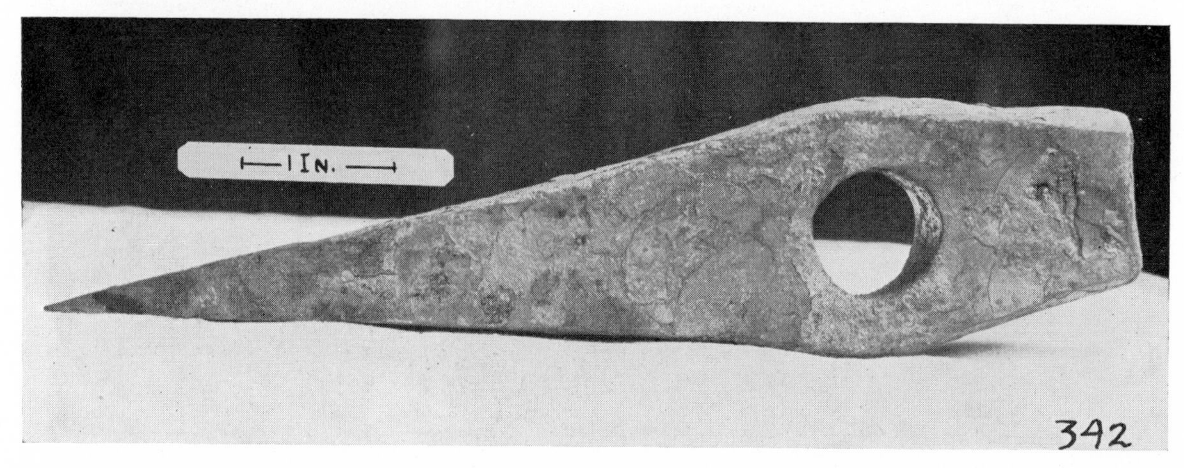

FIG. 14. COAL MINER'S HAND-GAD, OR EXCAVATING CHISEL. A one-man tool, used to excavate coal in contracted drifts. The miner sets with his left hand the point of the iron instrument against the solid coal seam and strikes its flat head with the discoidal iron hammer, Fig. 15, which is well adapted for swinging in restricted space.

means to throw "Fire-Stones" a considerable distance and the Chinese historians expressly state that this "fire-drug" was made of nitre, sulphur, and willow charcoal. Arab traders brought the secret of this combination to Western Asia, and here, it is said, it was adapted to warfare as a propellant for missiles. The use of gunpowder for blasting is another application of far greater importance, and yet the Chinese annalists are silent on this point as on most of the primitive trades.

FIG. 15. COAL MINER'S HAMMER. A thick iron disc mounted on a wooden handle, used for striking the gad point, Fig. 14, against the solid coal seam in the side drifts of the mine.

To return to the present mode of blasting, as practiced in Kiangsi. The first thing in blasting is to drill a hole in the rock, next comes the charging with gunpowder, and finally the setting off or firing of the charge. The drill or chisel used is a steel rod from one to two feet long which fits into a holder. The cutting end has been flattened and ends in a rounded edge, which having been sharpened in forging by hammering shows a bevel on each side. Fig. 18 shows, in the center, a chisel in its holder, and next to it a loose chisel. The holder is formed of an iron sleeve with sockets at both ends. One receives the drill and the other holds permanently a wooden shaft, whose free end is protected by two rings of intertwisted rawhide. The chisel is held with the left hand by the wooden part and hit with a stubby iron hammer. The rawhide rings are a

FIG. 16. PART OF COAL MINER'S ROPE MAKING MACHINE. A single iron twist crank, imperfectly seen, with a wooden handle plainly visible, penetrates the top cross bar of a wooden frame, propped vertically on a heavy wooden platform. The spacing block is seen lying on the platform.

wonderful protection for the wood, which wears down smoothly together with the protective ring without ever getting ragged. While hammering the workman turns the drill. A hole is thus started in the rock until the depression is well marked. Then the workman builds with wet clay or mud a wall around the hole and pours water into the enclosure. Now he resumes his hammering with continued turning of the drill until the hole is about a foot to a foot and a half deep. As the hole gets deeper more water is poured in to keep its level above the edge of the hole. Holes are usually drilled vertically down into the rock, or sideways slanting downward. This is necessary so that the hole will retain the water. If a slanting hole is drilled a mud-wall is built around the lower part of the orifice only, as this is sufficient to retain the water. In this wet drilling the particles of crushed stone get mixed with water and are withdrawn together with the water. To effect this, use is made of a small bamboo tube, open at both ends, which is inserted open into the hole, whereupon, when its upper end is closed with the thumb, it can be withdrawn with the liquid in the tube. Finally, when most of the water has been thus withdrawn the workman pushes the tube into the hole once more and sucking with his mouth the remaining water into the tube withdraws it in this manner. The hole is still moist from the water and is now wiped dry with the frayed end of a rope which is pushed into it with the bamboo tube.

The hole is now ready to receive the charge. At Kuling the workman keeps the gunpowder in a tin can. The gunpowder is of native make and appears ill-triturated and lumpy. The long iron wire, 2 feet 2½ inches long and 1/16 inch thick is put into the hole with the looped end extending, and powder poured in to fill about 2 inches of the hole which is barely 1 inch in diameter. The powder is then rammed down tightly with the long iron rod shown next above the iron wire in the picture. The plugging of the hole is done with small pieces of crumbling rock which are first pulverized and then thrown into the hole and rammed down as was the powder. Thus the hole is filled to the top. The iron is still in the hole and must now be carefully withdrawn without caving in the material to leave a vent for the insertion of the fuse. The workman takes one of the chisels, inserts it into the loop of the wire and hits the chisel close to the loop with his hammer. Holding the chisel steady and tapping in an upward direction, parallel to the

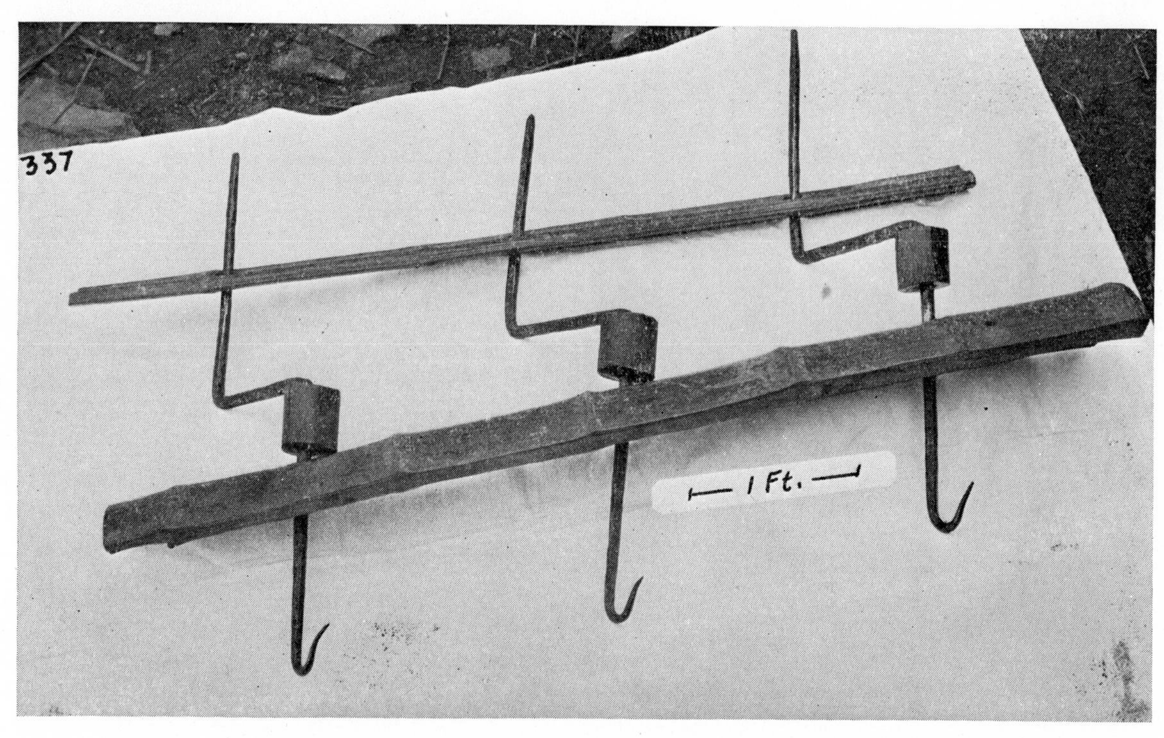

FIG. 17. PART OF COAL MINER'S ROPE MAKING MACHINE. The picture shows the loose turning device, belonging to the machine for making bamboo windlass rope. The handle-bar, ingeniously set upon the handles of the three cranks, enables the worker to turn all three at the same time.

wire, the latter will come out leaving a smooth hole, which extends clear down to the powder. The fuse is rolled of thin Chinese paper in strips half an inch wide, and filled with powder. It is easily inserted into the hole. The workman lights the extending end with an incense stick and then runs for safety. After a few seconds follows a report and in most cases the blasting of a piece of rock is accomplished. Very rarely does the powder throw out the plug without doing the intended blasting.

holder for drills or chisels, and the mode of protecting the wood against fraying. The drills are held in the holder by friction and when one becomes dull, it is easily removed by tapping with the hammer against the metal part of the holder. The rawhide rings for the protection of the wood fulfill their purposes exceedingly well. Our carpenters have sometimes a metal ring for protecting the wooden handles of their chisels, an attempt in the same direction, with much inferior results.

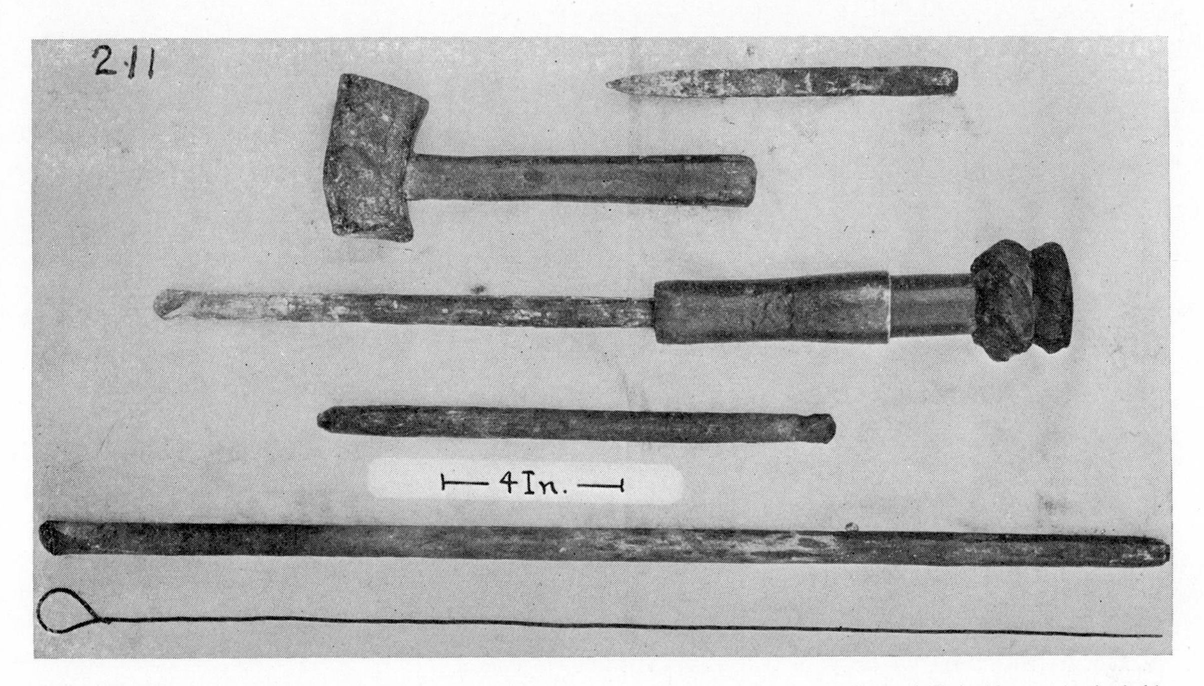

Fig. 18. Stone Quarrying Tools. There is the drill-hammer and drill-holder with three different drills besides one in the holder and the blasting needle.

Fig. 18 was photographed in Kuling, Kiangsi. The head of the drill-hammer is a rough block of iron, one face has been considerably worn down from continuous hitting. It is strange that iron does wear away from merely hitting against wood and rawhide. The drills, of which four are shown, are always used with the holder. The drill next above the hammer is used for dressing the rough quarried stones. The working end is more or less squared and forged into a tapering point. The drill-holder (middle), with inserted drill is 21 inches long, the holder alone 9½ inches long, and the wooden shaft has a diameter of 1½ inches. Originally the wooden shaft was about as long as the metal part of the holder, and the end to receive the rawhide rings had a somewhat smaller diameter. The rawhide rings are applied wet and upon drying cling firmly to the wood.

Interesting details of the process are the use of this

Besides the tools shown a sledge hammer is used and iron crowbars. The sledge hammer is elliptic in shape and has the characteristic flexible handle. In lifting it up to deal a blow the worker grasps the end with the left hand and holds the right hand round the handle near the hammer-head, and then slides the latter down to the left and lets the hammer come down. The sledge hammer is used for roughly trimming large irregular boulders, for loosening partly dislodged rocks, etc. The crowbar serves various uses as a lever, very much the same as we would employ it. I do not think however that it is a native tool, but was probably introduced by the foreigners.

It has been recorded that the Romans made use of the expansive force of burned lime with water to fracture large stones. Heating stones and then pouring quantities of water upon them is another primitive procedure. We do not know whether either method was used by the Chinese. Lime might have been used in this manner, to judge from the rôle it played in the early Chinese experiments to find explosive mixtures for warfare. We are only too apt to lose sight of the fact that primitive people accomplished wonderful feats by patient mass labor and simple mechanical means. In observing ruins of old temples and pagodas I have often seen slabs of stone which have their edges curiously embattled, and furnish a clue how they have been cut from the solid rock. The procedure was to cut along a straight line rectangular holes about $1\frac{1}{2}$ inches long, 1 inch wide and about 2 inches deep, with the distance between the holes about $2\frac{1}{2}$ inches. Very likely the universal, very ancient method of quarrying with plugs and feather was employed to fracture the rock. In this process two wedges are put into the holes and a third one is driven in between them. The workingman tapping one after the other of the wedges in the row will finally fracture the rock along a line passing from hole to hole. Slabs are thus pried from the solid rock with edges lined at intervals of about $2\frac{1}{2}$ inches with rectangular incisions. After such slabs, sometimes of enormous size, have been dressed, and the quarrying marks obliterated, we stand and wonder how the Chinese with their primitive methods were ever able to quarry them, and only when ruins reveal their hidden faces can we guess at their methods.

FIG. 19. ROCK SPLITTING STEEL WEDGES WITH QUARRYMAN'S HAMMER AND CHISELS.

I still wish to call attention to the bamboo tube used for taking water from the blast-hole. The same principle is made use of in an instrument known in Europe and called thief-tube. A metal tube, usually with a handle on top is employed to draw liquids from a barrel by inserting it through the bung and closing the upper hole with the thumb whereupon the tube filled with the liquid can be withdrawn. The Chinese go still a step farther in applying such a tube for withdrawing sediments from their kongs (earthen jars) stored with rain water. For this purpose a bamboo tube is kept about the premises, $3\frac{1}{2}$ feet long, $2\frac{1}{2}$ inches in diameter, and closed at the upper end, but with a small hole about 3/16 inch wide on the side near the closed end. This tube is pushed into the kong with the forefinger tightly pressed over the little hole until the open end is in contact with the sediment at the bottom. Now the finger is taken off the little hole, the imprisoned air escapes and the slimy sediment is syphoned into the tube. When the tube is filled the little hole on top is closed once more and the tube withdrawn from the kong. This done, the little hole is opened again and the contents of the tube is let run out. In this way the sediment can be completely removed without much trouble, and without disturbing the clear liquid above it.

I was told that in the Laushan, a mountain group northeast of Tsingtao, the breaking of granite into slabs for building purposes is carried on in primitive fashion with wooden wedges, driven into chiselled holes, wooden wedges which with water poured on them expand and break the stone. This may have been the case years ago, but since building stone for a populous city has been taken from the Laushan during the last three decades the methods of procuring the stone have changed. I spent some days in the Laushan and found that instead of the wooden wedges as I had been told, steel wedges are used. First there is a row of square holes made with pointed chisels, like the two in Fig. 19, and then the steel wedges are driven into the holes, until the stone fractures along the line of the holes. The same picture shows three of the wedges and the hammer used by the stone worker. Powder for blasting is not used at all, in these parts.

FIG. 20. QUARRYMAN'S SLEDGE.

For trimming stones, breaking off of projecting edges, breaking thinner slabs in two, a sledge hammer, as is shown in Fig. 20, is used by quarrymen, with an unusually thin handle for the size and weight of the head. This sledge hammer is wielded with enormous force, by taking the end of the handle with both hands and swinging the hammer in a large circle backward and up in the air, so as to let it come down upon the stone. The hole in the hammer is conical and the flexible handle sticks with its thicker end in the head and can only get the faster wedged into place by being used. The length of the sledge hammer is about 30 inches. Figs. 19 and 20 were taken in the Laushan Mountains near Tsingtao in Shantung.

IRON WORKING IN CHINA

The singular fact that in China casting iron has preceded the full development of forging iron is a surprising phenomenon. In a way it seems quite logical that when taking up iron as a substitute for bronze it might have been assumed that, being a metal, the best way to shape it was to cast it. In overcoming the technical difficulty of generating sufficiently high heat, a valuable aid may have been the superior box-bellows, whose construction is exceedingly simple and effect surprisingly powerful. We have certain proof that the casting of iron was already highly developed in the first few centuries of our era. Products of cast iron are far more in evidence than those produced by forging, which led some modern writers on China to speak disparagingly of Chinese attempts in forging iron. Economy restricted the use of either iron or steel and only closer observation reveals that the Chinese attained considerable skill in producing edged tools, and wrought iron. If we examine closely some of the trades in which their implements are employed we must perforce acknowledge that their skill is by no means contemptible.

Glass became known to the Chinese in the 5th century A.D., and it was manipulated in the same manner as hard stone. A bottle for instance was not blown but worked cold out of a solid lump. A hole

FIG. 21. BLACKSMITH SHOP.

was drilled and this being laterally enlarged, decorations were cut on the outside. Chinese drills readily perforate cast iron which scarcely yields to a file. The western world stands astonished at Chinese products of the carver's art in precious stones, notably jade, which is harder than steel. Tropical woods of exceeding hardness which cannot be planed are fashioned into furniture and patiently carved to show the most intricate ornaments. At the bottom of all these things are simple little tools, conceived by clever minds and executed by skillful hands with forge and hammer.

Localization of trades and lack of easy communication are also factors apt to give rise to the impression that certain of the trades are not at all or but poorly developed in China. We glean from Chinese writers that in the first few centuries of our era the iron industry and trade were in the hands of the people of Liang, then a district in Western China. Taiyuan Fu, (now the capital city of Shansi province), used to be famed for its cutlery, and even Marco Polo, usually reticent on such details, remarks that it was "a place of great trade and great industry, for here they manufacture a large quantity of the most necessary equipment for the army of the emperor." Down to the middle of the last century there was in that city an imperial factory of artillery, matchlocks, and similar implements. In the Chow Ritual, dating from pre-Christian times a statement occurs, that "Cheng swords, Sung axes, Lu knives, Wu and Yueh two-edged swords could not be made equally good when the materials were removed and manufactured at a distance from the place of their production." The fame of Chinese iron spread early abroad and Pliny tells us that the best iron upon the Roman market was the one procured from the Seres, undoubtedly the Chinese who also supplied the old world with silk.

BLACKSMITH SHOP

Fig. 21, photographed near Kuling, Kiangsi province, gives a view of a Chinese blacksmith shop. The hearth is built up roughly of bricks and clay, with no hood over it for the smoke. On top is the place for the charcoal fire and beside it the bellows, with a clay pipe, not seen, leading therefrom into the fire. The wooden bellows is smeared with clay to protect it from the fire. On top of the hearth are lying various tongs and tools; the cast iron kettle near the fire has to do duty for work and for cooking the meals. In the latter case an iron tripod is put over the fire or sometimes a chain or iron hook fastened to a rafter above the hearth holds the cooking pot directly over the fire. Shoes are lying on the hearth for drying and a rain hat is pressed into service to keep the wind from the fire. The quenching water in an earthenware bowl stands over the bellows. In front of the hearth are the stumps of old trees, rammed into the ground, each one supporting an anvil. The stump nearest the beholder has a peculiar staple driven in its side. The oblong slot receives the unhandled lever of the blacksmith shears shown in Fig. 25. The blacksmith can assert great strength on the handled lever and yet have one hand free to hold the piece to be cut. The old fashioned tobacco-smoker's water pipe, standing beside the cloth-shoes is also quite necessary for good work. After great exertion a few whiffs are always welcome. In the foreground there can also be seen several large-handled hammers. A rack on the wall contains a few pieces of finished ware, ready for sale, besides some odds and ends.

The Chinese blacksmith is capable of making almost anything of iron, from a tiny nail to a large anchor. He forges, welds, brazes, carbonizes iron into steel, furnishes iron tools with steel cutting edges. His most efficient implement is his bellows which gives with slight effort an abundance of air. For raw material he relies nowadays very much upon the import of foreign iron. In some districts where native iron ore is found and reduced to iron, the blacksmith buys small pieces of pig-iron and decarbonizes it on his forge to produce wrought iron.

According to local demand or preponderance of certain industries some blacksmiths confine their activities to the making of a certain line of utensils and tools. So we find at places where building of native watercraft prevails an anchorsmith, in the porcelain center King Teh Chen, the makers of the iron tools for paring the porcelain on the potter's wheel, in Lung Chuan, Chekiang, for hundreds of years past, swordsmiths, who make excellent steel or iron blades. The cutlers of Wuhu make scissors, pincers, thimbles, razors, shears, scalpels, etc.

The trade of the blacksmith seems the most important in the economic life of the Chinese. First of all he makes the tools for a great variety of tradespeople, in fact they are almost all indebted to him for one or the other of their tools. For agricultural pursuits he makes hoes, shovels, rakes, teeth for harrows, cleavers and cutters, knives, spades, plow shares, trimmings for mills, scythes, wheelbarrow tires, etc., for kitchen use cleavers, tongs, forks, shovels, firewood hooks, singeing irons for meat, stove grates, and the household at large is also greatly indebted to his efforts, when he furnishes nails, bolts, hasps and staples, locks and keys, hinges, door-knockers and rings, candlesticks, lampholders, lantern-frames and handles, rat-traps, awls, scissors, pincers, pliers, packing needles, scale-hooks, knives, files, handstoves, covers, etc.

The pictures of the blacksmith shop and the shears were taken in Sha Ho, at the foot of the Kuling mountains.

Fig. 22 shows a typical specimen of a Chinese blacksmith's anvil. It is cast of iron in one piece. There are iron founders who engage only in the making of anvils. They produce a high grade casting perhaps more akin to cast steel than iron or else they have a method of surface hardening, a kind of cementation process. Many of the anvils I have looked at stand up very well under the heavy blows they receive, much better than ordinary cast iron would, to my judgment. In principle they resemble ours. There is a certain central horizontal top-surface for most of the work, with flat-topped projections set below it on two opposite sides which would correspond to the beak in our anvils. I noticed some Chinese anvils in Shanghai with a hardy hole, but this seems to be foreign modification. In the country I never saw it except in the kit of a traveling tinker. A separate arrangement serves for holding a hardy or

Fig. 22. Blacksmith's Anvil.

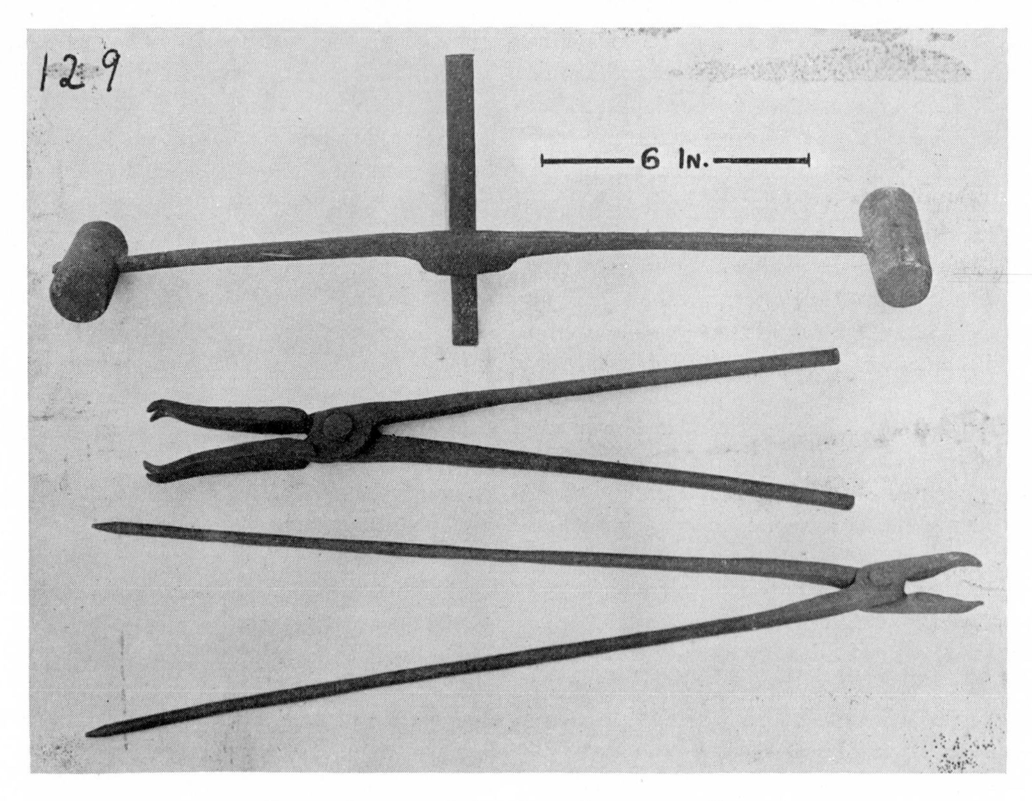

FIG. 23. BLACKSMITH'S IRON-SCALE SCRAPER AND TONGS.

fuller. A stout post is rammed into the ground, about three inches square and extending about two feet above the ground. Near the top a ring is fastened to hold the fuller or hardy.

The anvil is mounted upon a tree trunk, which is set into the mud floor of the smithy. The height from ground to the top face of the anvil is about 26 inches. The top point of the wooden support has usually a chiselled-out recess into which fits the square bottom surface of the anvil, and the latter is further secured by iron spikes driven close to its perpendicular side faces into the wood. The anvil as shown on the picture would present the same view if turned around to show the opposite side. Either projection on the side forms one continuous surface with one vertical sideface of the anvil. The top face is square with sides 5 inches long. The height to the surface of the projections is 4 inches, to the middle part 5½ inches. The extreme length is 13 inches. The surface of the projections is square with sides extending outward 4 inches. Very often the stamp of the anvil maker is shown on one of the perpendicular sides in raised characters.

The photograph was taken in the Native City, Shanghai.

BLACKSMITH'S TOOLS

Of the tools used by the blacksmith I have only been able to get pictures of a few, but of these one is very characteristic. It is the scraper shown in Fig. 23 on top, resembling a spoke shave. A wrought iron rod or blade-holder has wooden handles on both pointed ends, which pierce the wood and are clinched where they emerge. The thickened part in the middle of the rod has a rectangular slot to insert the narrow steel blade, which is held in place with an iron wedge. In the picture the shorter extending part of the steel blade has at its end the cutting edge. This is formed by a bevel with an angle of about 60 degrees. The steel blade is 6½ inches long, ⅝ inch wide and ⅛ inch thick. To manipulate this instrument it is taken by the handles and pushed away from the body. The article to be scraped is held on a low bench with a wooden clamp which is tightened by a wedge. Sometimes articles are held down by a rope which is kept stretched by the foot, resembling the way a cobbler holds down the shoe he is working on. These contrivances, as substitutes for a vise, are very important and are not only confined to the blacksmith shop, but are the *sine qua non* of many other trades. Most forged articles, with larger surfaces, are freed from

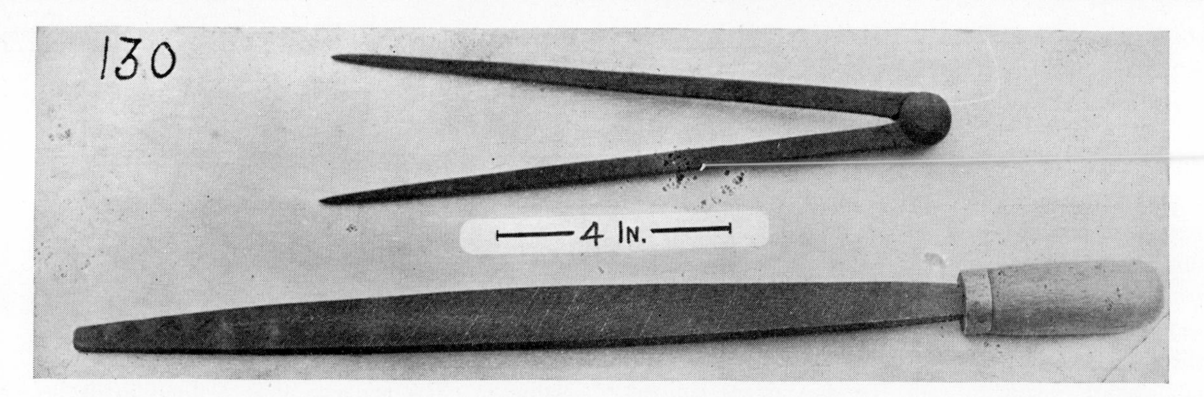

FIG. 24. BLACKSMITH'S FILE AND COMPASSES.

scale and made smooth with this scraper. The whole length of the blade holder from handle to handle is 20 inches. Its horizontal width in the middle is one inch, and its vertical thickness ½ inch. The length of the wooden handles is 3½ inches and their diameter 1¼ inches.

Fig. 23 (middle and lower) shows also blacksmith's tongs, two of the many he uses. They are wrought of iron and generally resemble ours. The longer one is 20 inches long and the other 16 inches. These tongs differ among themselves only in the form of the jaws. Some are flat, others long and pointed. In some one jaw is convex and the other concave to fit into the convex part. In short they are formed to hold all manner of shapes which need holding in the fire of the hearth. The photograph was taken in the Native City of Shanghai.

Files are also used in the blacksmith shop. They are usually rather long and heavy, and have tangs on both ends. One receives the wooden handle and the other a wooden end piece, not here shown, resembling a handle, with a ferrule. But it is not used as a handle and is much longer than the handle proper. Into the bench, where this file is used, a ring-topped spike or eye-bolt has been driven, in which the wooden piece at the end of the file can slide freely. When filing, the article worked upon, is held in the left hand and the heavy file by the handle with the right hand, the other end slides back and forth in the eye-bolt and is easily handled, and exerts a helpful down-leverage. The files usually have indentations on all four sides. The ridges cross each other. That is, when making the file parallel ridges are first cut to cover the surface running from edge to edge but not forming right angles with the edges. Next the surface is covered with parallel ridges which cross the ridges previously made. The file without its guide rod, shown in Fig. 24, including handle is 21½ inches long. The guide rod when attached would make it about 16 inches longer. The file is 1 inch wide in the middle and it is ½ inch thick. The weight is considerable and without the clever supporting arrangement the file could not be handled easily. As mentioned before even surfaces are made smooth with the scraper but delicate, small and rounded forms are smoothed with this uncouth file. We hold such articles firmly in a vise and work all around them with the file. The Chinese reverse the process. The file is semi-fixed and the article to be filed is easily turned under it to be smoothed all over.

The compasses shown in Fig. 24 are used in Shanghai blacksmith shops, but it is doubtful whether

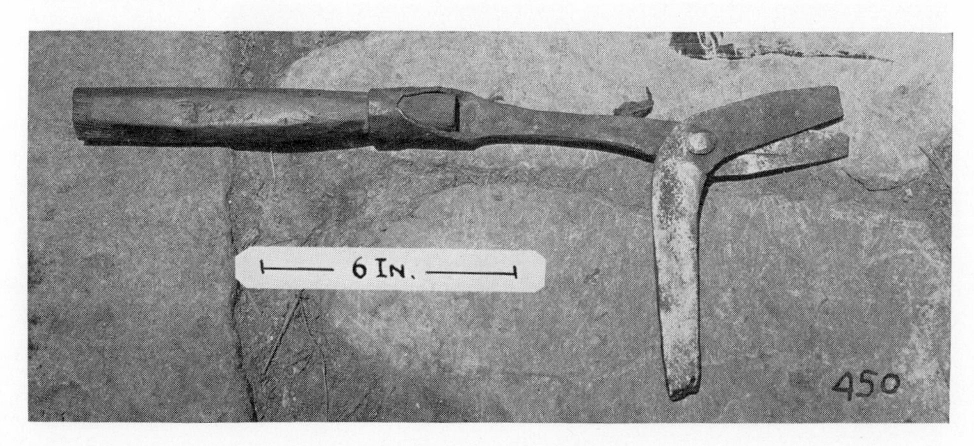

FIG. 25. BLACKSMITH'S SHEET METAL SHEARS.

the primitive artisan in the far-away village, with his innate ingenuity, would deign to use a makeshift to aid him in cutting out mathematically circular shapes. His ingenuity produces round shapes guided only by the eye, round shapes which are full of beauty and life because the vital touch has not been knocked out of them by mathematical exactitude. The country artisans are creators and not slaves of modern industrialism. It is a pleasure to see them at their work. The unfailing eye does not require measuring rods, templets, gages, calipers, or compasses. The photograph, Fig. 24 was taken in the Native City of Shanghai.

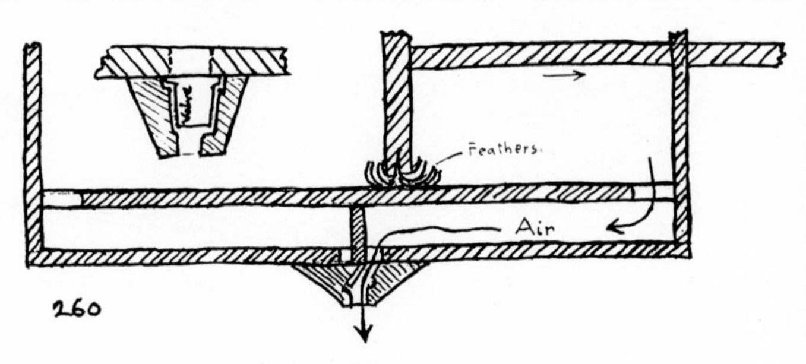

Fig. 27. Cross Section Through Chinese Box Bellows.

The sheet-metal shears, Fig. 25, is used for cutting sheet iron. The unhandled lower iron arm of the abruptly beveled, steel-edged instrument is thrust through the vertical slot in the staple seen protruding from the wooden anvil stand in the foreground of Fig. 21, whereupon the blacksmith holding the metal sheet under the staple in his left hand, pushes with his right the wooden handle of the shears in a direction away from his body. The angle of the staple-slot and bent shear-blade inserted therein compel him therefore to cut not horizontally but downward.

BOX BELLOWS

In many cases it is true that like wants in this world, have been met by like devices or in like manner by the most diverse nations or tribes. Investigating Chinese contrivances, however, we get now and then a surprise by finding that they have solved some vital problem in their own peculiar way. The box-bellows is an example of a Chinese instrument which in addition to its novelty has the merit of surpassing in efficiency any other bellows made before the advent of modern machinery.

Usually the Chinese bellows, like the one shown, is a rectangular box, divided into two compartments by a wall. This dividing wall can be moved back and forth in the box by a bracketed handle consisting of two parallel wooden rods, one fastened above the other to the dividing wall at right angles thereto, and passing thence through the end-wall of the box. On the outside these rods are united by a crosspiece, which serves as a handle for pushing and pulling. The shifting of the dividing wall changes the size of the compartments with each stroke, as one gets smaller the other becomes proportionately larger. Each end-wall of the box has an intake valve for air, one of which, a cross-slatted orifice, can be seen in Fig. 26 on the side of the box where the rods for shifting the dividing wall emerge. Inside the box and over this square orifice hangs a wooden shutter, hinged in crapaudine door hinge fashion, while, to prevent rats or mice from entering the sanctum of the bellows, the square orifice is barred, as seen in the picture, with two horizontal slats. This much explained, we can understand how air is taken in alternately at either end of the bellows by opening and closing the intake valves, opening a valve when the dividing wall is drawn away from it, and closing it when the dividing wall is pushed toward it. Consulting again Fig. 26, we see on the side of the bellows box a wooden nozzle with a round hole through which the air is forced from the bellows box. To take the air out through this nozzle a separate compartment has been formed along the inner edge of the box where the long sides of the bottom and side boards meet. This is divided in the middle by a fixed partition into two equal parts, thus forming two ducts, each with a square

Fig. 26. Chinese Box Bellows.

cross-section. At one end each duct communicates with the nozzle and at the other end with one of the large air compartments of the bellows box. The attached sketch, Fig. 27, shows a horizontal section through that part of the bellows box where the ducts run and converge into the single duct of the nozzle fastened on the outside. The edges of the sliding partition wall are made air-tight with ordinary chicken feathers, as is shown in the sketch.

Fig. 28 affords a view into the bellows box from above, after the cover was removed, and shows the feathers used to make airtight the edge of the sliding partition wall. Sometimes several folds of soft Chinese paper are inserted into a slot all around this sliding valve forming the partition wall, some hanging on one side and some on the other, when, like the feathers, they make a tight joint. Another important feature, seen only on the insert of sketch, Fig. 27, is the valve at the point where the two air ducts converge into the nozzle. This valve swings both ways so that when pushed by the draft it gives egress to the air from one side, while it closes the opening to the duct on the other side and *vice versa*. In the sketch the position of the valve in the nozzle is shown as it appears when the sliding partition wall is pulled toward the right. The air ahead of it is forced out through the duct valve and nozzle as indicated by arrows. As soon as the dividing wall is pushed in the other direction, the valve in the nozzle flies over with a characteristic click into the position indicated by dotted lines and closes that passage hole from which the air was just before blown.

Usually the bellows have an outlet nozzle only on one side, some, as the one on Fig. 26, are fitted with two, one on each side, not to be used at the same time, however. The nozzle which is to remain idle is closed against the side wall of the bellows with a long wooden slide, along the bottom outside margin of the box, as can be seen by consulting the photograph, Fig. 26. The valve in the nozzle is a thin wooden rectangle, constructed like a door, with peg-projections on top and bottom, upon which it swings, now closing one and then the other air-passage as the bellows is worked. The draft is practically continuous. The pictures were taken in San Ho, Anhwei.

Fig. 29, is added to illustrate more clearly the hinged valve, set vertically in the nozzle on the side of the bellows box. The wooden nozzle has in this

FIG. 28. CHINESE BOX BELLOWS, INSIDE VIEW.

Fig. 29. Chinese Box Bellows.

case been removed, and the blade of the valve can be seen standing in a neutral position. As the bellows is worked by alternately pushing and pulling the projecting handle the blade of the valve swings back and forth, now closing the one air passage, and then the other. The Japanese have also a box bellows. It was wrongly described to me as quite similar to the Chinese, but is designed differently on the principle of a pump. The handle pushes a piston consisting of a rectangular board with a leather valve, the skin of a fox being considered best for the purpose; the pulling of the piston opens the valve through which air is let into the chamber and upon pushing the handle the valve closes and the air is forced out through a small nozzle. The Japanese bellows is therefore only half as efficient as the Chinese one, which has practically continuous action, giving air upon pulling and pushing the handle. The bellows shown I had made in the summer of 1924 by a local carpenter in Kuling, to be sent to the Mercer Museum at Doylestown where it is now on exhibition.

USE OF SHEET METAL

Sheet metal plays a very subordinate rôle in China. The only means of its manufacture is the anvil on which it is hammered. Its use is therefore very restricted. The gates of walled cities are frequently covered with hammered iron plates which are usually not larger than 4 by 6 inches. Sheet iron is never manufactured in quantities to sell as such for further manufacture of useful articles. The coating of sheet iron with tin is not known. The reasons why the Chinese make such little use of sheet iron are several. The weightiest is probably that the art of casting iron was in very early times brought to great perfection. Another is that the use of iron has been greatly discouraged through high taxation which was at times so oppressive that people would use wooden plows and pull the weeds by hand in order to avoid the ruinous taxes placed upon iron utensils. The great skill in working copper, brass and paktong (a kind of German silver) also militated against the use of sheet iron. These metals could be cast in sheets and then hammered cold.[4]

To cut sheet metal the Chinese use shears like the one shown in Fig. 30. When using it, it is held with the right hand grasping the handle with the curved end, the other handle slides along on the surface upon which the sheet to be cut is lying. The two parts of the shears are joined together with an iron rivet without any washers between rivet-heads and the two intersecting blades which the rivet penetrates. The shears are made by a blacksmith. The whole length is 16 inches, the greatest width of blade 1 inch and its thickness 5/16 inch. The cutting edge of the blade here as in the scissors elsewhere described is formed

[4] In Europe the art of working copper and brass in the cold state was introduced in medieval times from the Orient through gypsies who therefore were given the name of Kaltschmiede (cold smiths) in Germany. (Gustav Freytag.)

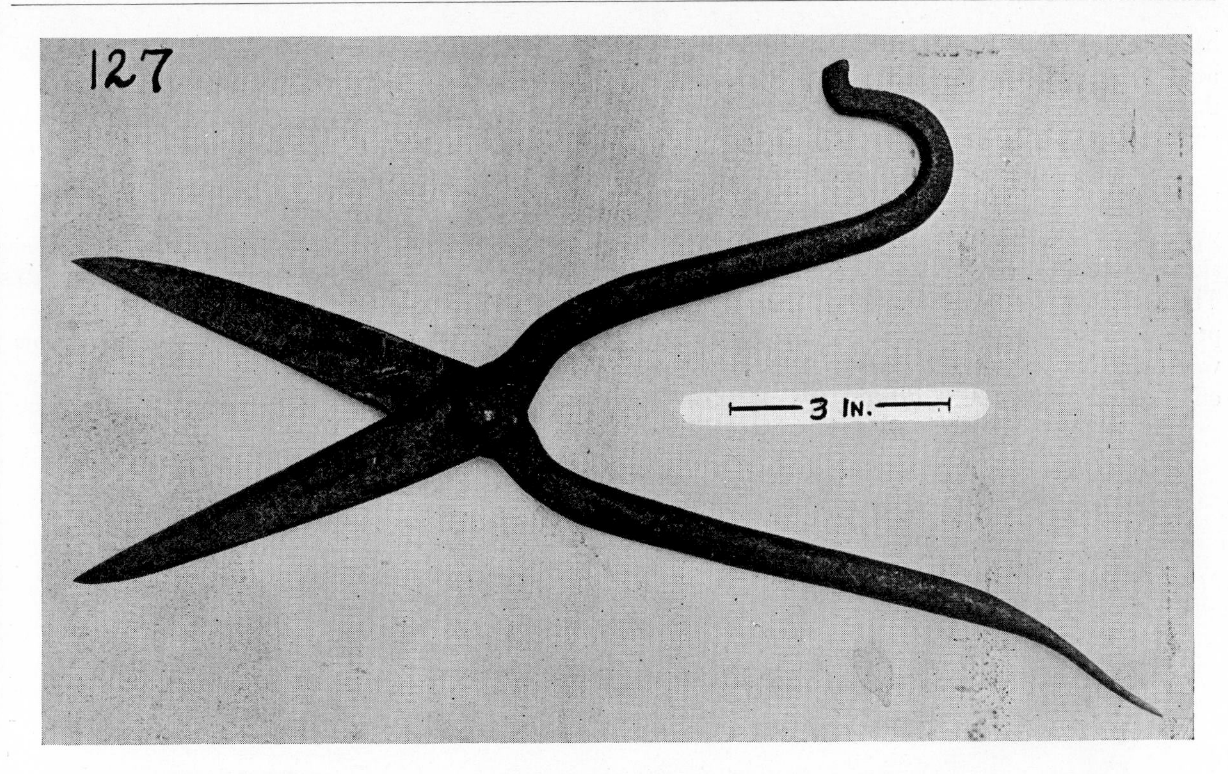

Fig. 30. Sheet Metal Shears.

by applying a bevel when forging the blade and subsequently scraping it with a peculiar scraping instrument which has been described under blacksmith tools, Fig. 23 (*A*), and finally sharpening it on a stone. The blade then does not taper from a certain thickness at the back to a sharp edge like a knife or cleaver but the thickness is pretty near the same up to the bevel. The blade is thickest near the point where the rivet passes through both parts of the scissors and only diminishes in thickness towards the points of the blades. The photograph was taken in the Native City, Shanghai.

NAIL MAKING

It has been early recognized that for forging nails it is helpful to have a pattern over which to hammer the metal to form a head. An instrument for this purpose is called in English a nail heading tool or nail-swage (German Nageleisen). The oldest example of it is probably one found with prehistoric remains of iron smelting in the Swiss Jura (information of Dr. Richard Moldenke, Watchung, N. J.). Until the era of nail-making by machinery this tool was used in Europe especially for the forging of the heads of small nails. The German type was fastened to the anvil block. In order to remove easily the finished nail from the nail hole, it contained a spring, and by giving a light tap upon this "lifter" (Lűfter) the nail was thrown out.[5]

The length of the tool, Fig. 31, is 10½ inches, the diameter of the disk on top 2¾ inches and of the top cone with its vertical orifice for holding the nail, about 1 inch. The tool in Fig. 34 is 11¼ inches long. The nail blanks shown in the same picture are 1¼ inches long, and the completed nail ¾ inch. The

[5] This information is from Johannsen, Geschichte des Eisens, Duesseldorf, 1925.

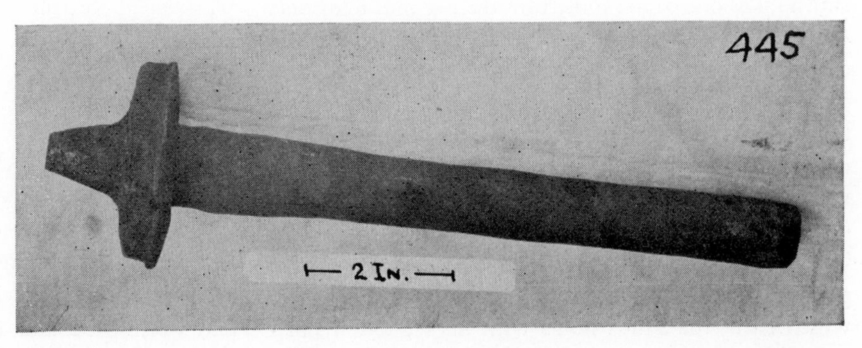

Fig. 31. Nail Making Tool.

hammer, 9½ inches long, is used for hammering the head of the nail. The finished nail drops easily from the nail-hole in the tool after striking the head of the nail sideways with a gentle blow. The conical part on top of the instrument is shaped according to the nail-head which is to be formed. A nail head pointed and with overhanging sides, as shown in Fig. 35, requires another tool top than that used for flat-headed nails. The protective disk near the top of the instrument prevents hot scales from dropping on the hand of the workman, but is primarily meant as a convenient offset on the swage to rest it firmly against the anvil when revolving the tool while hammering the nail-head.

To the nail swages shown in Figs. 31 and 34 I can add another, Fig. 32, which I saw used in Shangtung. There are nailsmiths who make nothing else but nails. The smith sits on a low stool and has an anvil standing before him on the ground. A helper keeps the fire going with the bellows and watches a few iron rods which with their ends lie in the fire. The smith takes one of the rods from the fire and hammers the red hot end to a point and then lays it over the cutting edge of a hardy, extending from the anvil, and gives a blow with the hammer which almost severs the pointed end from the metal rod. The pointed end he sticks now into the hole at one end of the nail swage and breaks it off from the rod by bending it over into a direction parallel with the nail swage. The metal rod he then puts back into the fire. The pointed nail blank sticks in the hole of the swage which latter the smith holds with his left hand horizontally with the nail end upon the anvil. With his right hand he hammers the head of the nail over the steel nozzle which extends from the swage. There is no danger of the formed nail sticking fast in the hole of the swage. As the metal cools under the blows of the hammer it apparently contracts and the finished nail is thrown out with an abrupt upward jerk of the swage. A nailsmith makes about five to six hundred nails a day. The length of the swage, a solid iron bar with a steel nozzle inserted at the end, is 10 inches. The nozzle has a diameter of ¾ of an inch. Below the surface the hole in it is squared to conform to the square shank of the nail. For larger nails there are swages with larger nozzles. The swage here shown was procured in Kiaochow, and photographed in Tsingtao.

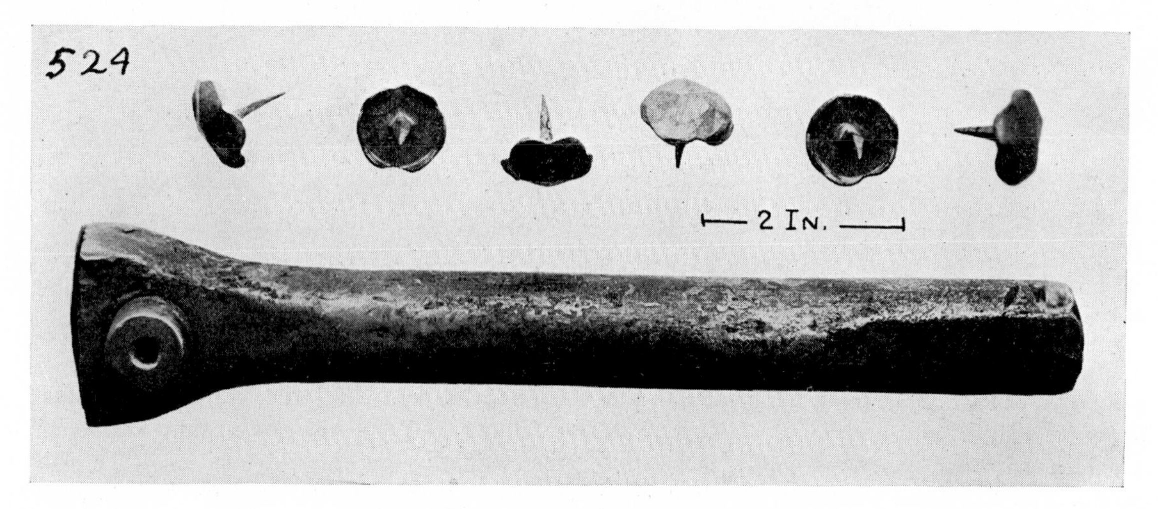

Fig. 32. Bore or Nail Swage and Hob Nails.

Fig. 33 shows an assembly of Chinese nails. (*A*) is used in shipbuilding to fasten the board-sheathing to the inside partitions. The straight point is driven into the board, quite close to the partition and then the bent right-angled point is driven into the wood of the partition. (*B*) is more of a clamp than a nail and used when sawing boards to prop the log to its support. (*C*) and (*D*) illustrate an unusual mode of making nails without a heading tool. A double-pointed spike is hammered out on the anvil and then is flattened in its center with a hammer. By bending it back and forth the spike is easily broken in half and furnishes two nails. When using these the hitting of the hammer bends the flattened, sidespread part over to form a sort of head, as is indicated on (*D*), a nail which had been used and extracted from its place in the wood.

(*E*) are hob-nails for Chinese shoes made with a heading tool.

(*F*) shows the short, Chinese bamboo pegs, hand-cut with a knife, used to fasten the skin upon drum tops. A hole is first made through the tough skin with a brad-awl and then the bamboo nail is easily driven into the soft wood. The bamboo nails are seen lying on a section of the drum top.

(*G*) is a wrought iron nail for fastening the iron tire to the wheel of a Chinese wheelbarrow. A cross-section of the tire would show a groove which protects the nail head narrowed to enter it.

(*H*) shows two coffin nails recovered from old graves on the shore of the Poyang Lake near Nankang-Fu, Kiangsi.

All the specimens are now in the Mercer Museum, representing nails in use today, and were procured in Kiangsi province by the author.

Fig. 35 shows various hob-nails for shoes, and two broad-headed nails with two nail blanks used in making these, which latter resemble the Anglo-American scupper nail used for nailing down leather in the 18th century.

A thick, solid-headed hob-nail, not shown here, procured in Kuling, has on the flat top regular indentations, very reminiscent of the hatched stamped pattern on the head of modern, European machine made wire nails. It may have been made recently in this way to resemble imported foreign nails, or merely to afford a better grip on the ground when once put on the rain-shoes of the Chinese. At any rate if the blacksmith should ask me why foreign nails have that lozenge pattern I could not satisfactorily answer the question. As children, who are ever inquisitive, we made up our mind that this roughness should prevent the hammer from slipping when driving a nail, while now I am rather inclined to think that it is an incident of manufacture, a mark of the machine, helpful in forming the head of the nail and without any further significance.

Another variety of Chinese nails are small cut tacks with a brass head soldered on. A thin semi-spherical brass bowl forms the head; it is filled with solder in which is held the nail proper. They are used a good deal to fasten the cord on the top strip of Chinese roll pictures. These pictures have a wooden roller on the bottom and a wooden strip on top. Good Chinese pictures are hung on the wall only for special occasions, and for the rest of the time are put away, carefully rolled and wrapped up. The flexible picture on silk or paper is rolled around the bottom roller until the top wooden strip is reached and then tied up with the attached cord.

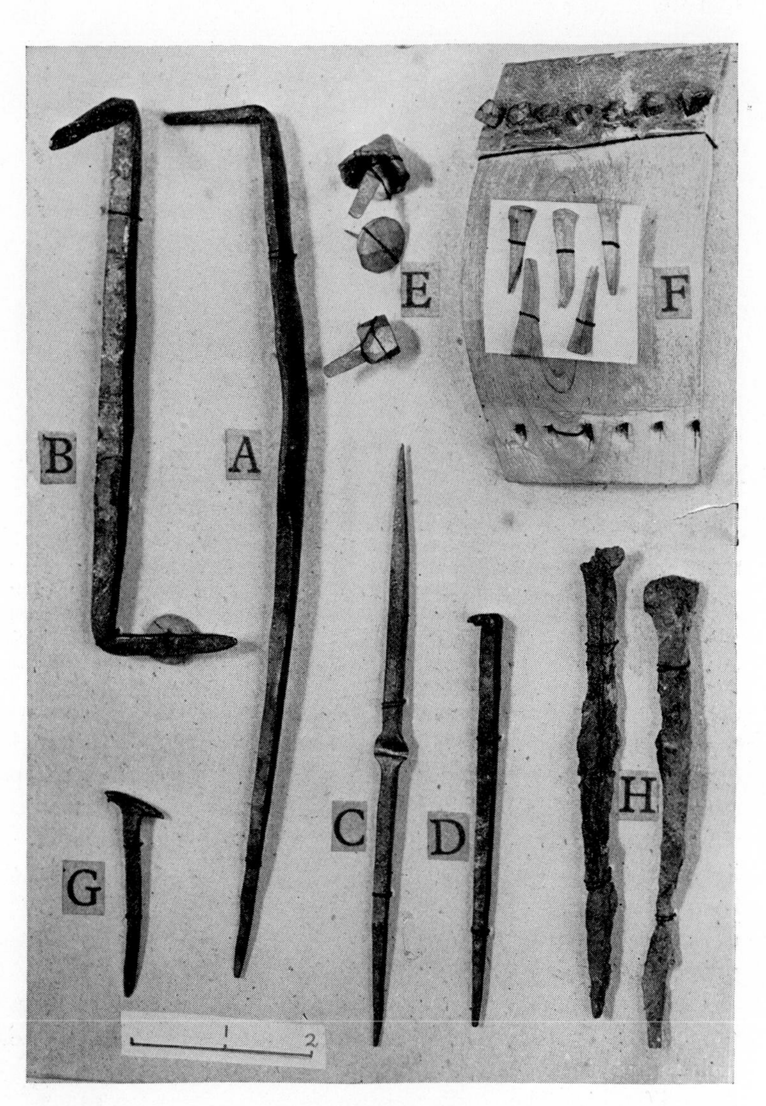

FIG. 33. CHINESE NAILS.

THE ART OF SOLDERING

What we call a soldering-iron is a tool with a pointed or wedge-shaped bit of copper, and the name interestingly indicates that in former times this bit was made of iron. The Chinese soldering-iron shown on Fig. 36 (top) is of forged iron. A wedge-shaped

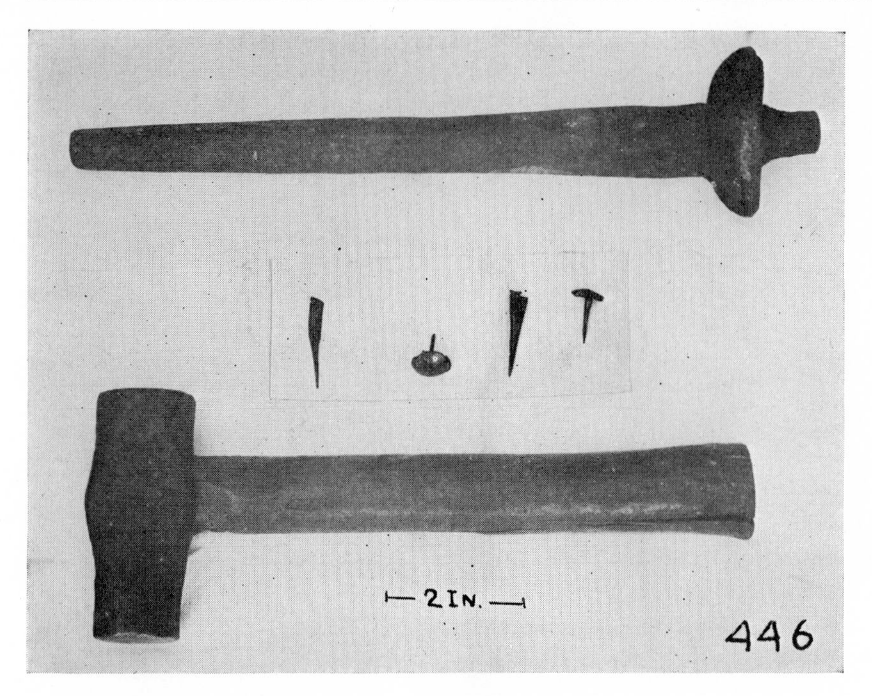

FIG. 34. CHINESE NAIL MAKING TOOL AND HAMMER. The nail making tool (top), is 11¼ inches long. The two short flat-headed nails, shown in the middle, with two of the nail blanks from which they are forged, are ¾ of an inch long. The Chinese nailer's hammer, 9½ inches long, is used for hammering the head of the nail. The finished nail drops easily from the nail making tool when striking the head of the tool sideways with a gentle blow.

raw material consists of old kerosene tins, discarded preserving tins, linings of boxes in which foreign goods have been shipped to China, and the like, but never any new tin-sheet, the manufacture of which the Chinese do not understand. The only related effort to tinning sheet iron, and an art which the Chinese practice, is the coating of copper vessels on the inside with pewter.

The process of soldering is really very old. Alyattes, King of Lydia (father of Croesus, late 7th cent. B.C.), presented to the temple of Delphi a silver vase with a beautiful stand, the work of Glaucus of Chios, famed as a statuary in metal. Pausanias described the stand as consisting of several plates of iron, adjusted one over the other in the form of steps, the last, that is, those of the summit, curving a little outwards. It had the form of a tower, large at the base, and decreasing upwards, and the pieces of which it was composed were not fastened either with nails or pins, but simply soldered together. Based on this account, Glaucus has been considered the inventor of soldering. He may have

bit, 2 inches long, 1 inch wide and ⅞ inch thick at the heavy end forms a right angle with the haft and the end of the pointed haft is driven into a wooden handle. The parts to be soldered the workman scrapes clean, and as a flux he uses resin. For more delicate work, as a substitute for the soldering-iron, a mere iron wedge is put into the charcoal fire and taken from it with a pair of tongs, when required for soldering.

Fig. 36 was photographed in a tin-smith shop in Teh An, Kiangsi. The tin-smith and his products would not deserve our consideration as he is a creation of a very recent time. But his tools are used in other trades also and therefore claim our attention. To deprecate his efforts the more, let us add, that his

FIG. 35. CHINESE NAILS AND NAIL BLANKS.

been a past master at it, but finds from earlier times show that soldering was understood long before his time. The excavations of Troy, for instance, brought to light the so-called "Treasure of Priamos" among which were golden utensils with clear indication of soldering. The articles belonged to the second city which flourished about 2500 B.C. Sir J. G. Wilkinson the explorer of Egypt, found gold and silver vases represented at Thebes, composed of plates of metal, imbricated or overlapping each other, as Pausanias described. They were part of the tribute brought from Asia to Thothmes III., who reigned in the 15th cent. B.C. Later in Pharaonic times, the Egyptians soldered with lead in coarser work or in those parts which were out of sight. Pliny, speaking of soldering with lead, points out that it cannot be made to adhere without the admixture of tin, and besides, as a flux, oil is a necessary requisite. So much for a historical background of the art of soldering, to dispose of the popular misconception that soldering, which usually has to do with cheap patchwork, is of recent origin.

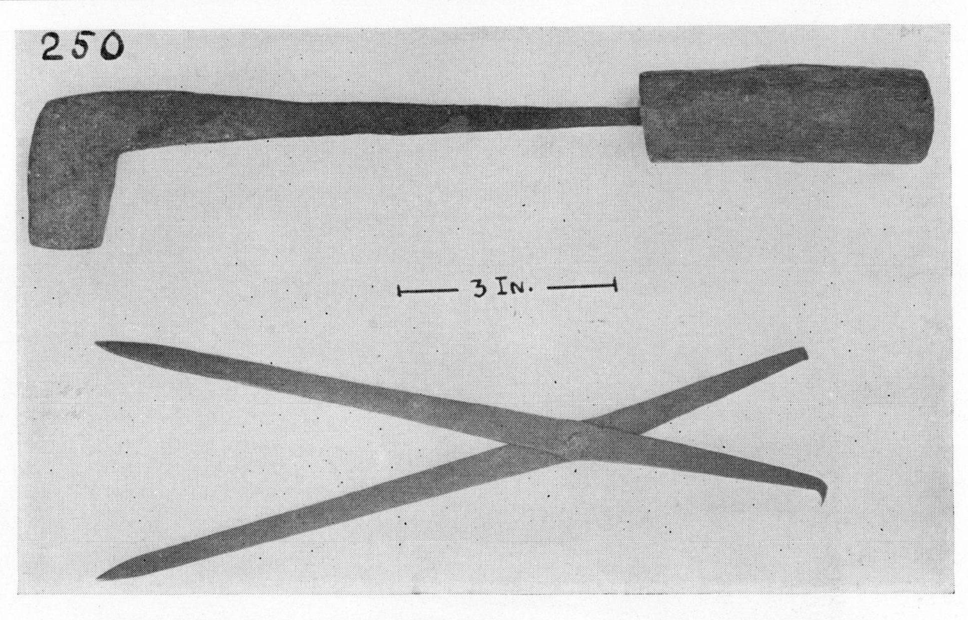

Fig. 36. Soldering-Iron and Compasses.

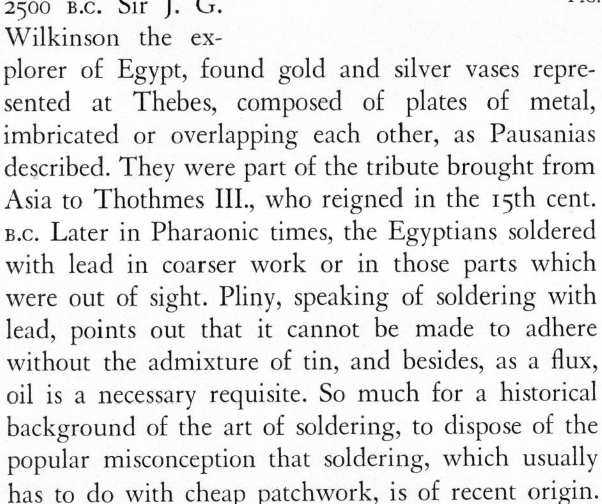

The compasses in Fig. 36 (bottom), although looking modern are Chinese and have been used since oldest times. The two legs, 1/8 inch thick and 1/2 inch wide in the middle are riveted together. The length is 10 1/2 inches. One end has a little projection for marking the inside of round shapes and measuring inside diameters.

Another feature of these compasses is that they can be used for reducing and enlarging. The shorter legs open always half the distance of the longer legs. If an article is to be made from a pattern it can with ease be made proportionately larger by using the one end of the compasses for taking off the measurements from the pattern and shaping the article according to the other end of the compasses. I have also seen such compasses among the tools of a silver-smith.

Fig. 37. Wire Drawing Tools.

WIRE DRAWING

The making of wire by means of drawing the metal through holes in a cast iron plate (or steel plate as it was done in the old world) is only a refinement or short cut in an old industry. This is probably the reason why history does not furnish us with any exact data concerning the inventor or time of introduction of this mode of

FIG. 38. WIRE DRAWING MACHINE.

manufacture. The fact that since the middle of the 14th century the wire makers of Nuremberg are no longer referred to as wire-smiths, as heretofore, but are given the name of wire-drawers, furnished the basis of the claim that wire-drawing was invented at Nuremberg in the 14th century. Of interest for our investigations (inasmuch as it points to the Orient) is a statement of Muratori in his Antiquit. Italiae, Tom. II, p. 374, which gives an account of an old manuscript of the 9th century, kept in the library of the cathedral chapter at Lucca. It refers to the drawing of gold wire, an art which probably reached Italy from the Orient, and thence was introduced into France. Theophilus, ca. 1100 A.D., mentions draw-plates for making wire as something well known. Schliemann found in the ruins of Troy various gold treasures. He submitted many of the Trojan jewels to Mr. Carlo Giuliano, the celebrated London goldsmith connoisseur of antiquities, who after careful examination, gave as his opinion that the Trojans in making the very thin gold wire employed in connection with many of the jewels, could have used only ingots of very pure gold, which they pulled through the holes of a draw-plate, and thus gradually and easily reduced to an extreme fineness. The excavations of Pompeii have brought to light a wire cable, about 12 feet long, consisting of 3 strands, each with 15 bronze wires plaited together. The Romans of the empire had already mail, knitted of iron wire.

Fig. 37 shows a Chinese outfit for wire-drawing of the most primitive form. The photograph was taken in a small market town, Chien-kiang, near Chang-shu, Kiangsi, which boasts of one solitary silversmith. The wooden bench is 23 inches long, 10 inches wide, and 7 inches high. The cast iron draw-plates are 5 inches long, ¾ inch thick in the middle, and have a greatest width of 4½ inches. The drawing pliers are 14 inches long. The draw-plates are first cast, not with perfected holes as shown, but with conical impressions which coincide with the position of each hole without passing through the metal. The wire-drawer completes the perforations with his bow-drill to suit his individual needs. The metal to be drawn is hammered to the thickness of the little finger and one end brought to a point long enough to be pushed through a hole in the draw-plate. The projecting end is then taken hold of with the pliers. The silversmith then steps on the little bench, inserts the length of wire between pliers and draw-plate into the slit seen on the front bench margin so that the wire projects up through the slit, and the plate rests flat against the underside of the bench. He now pulls with all his might the wire through the plate and up through the slit. In pulling the metal strands thus gradually through holes of successively smaller sizes, the finest wire can be drawn.

Wire-drawing is performed in more elaborate style than just described with the machine shown in Fig. 38. I saw it in Chang-shu in passing a silversmith's shop but could not get permission to photograph it until I had bought a silver chain. A sturdily built bench, 1 foot 6 inches high, 4 feet long, and 1 foot 4 inches wide, holds in mortises the windlass and the draw-plate holder, the latter an upright post with a slot and ferrule for keeping the post from splitting. The iron pliers held by the chain are 7 inches long. The mode of working is obvious. The iron chain is hooked upon a spike on the wooden drum of the windlass. The wire or metal to be reduced is again hammered small enough to pass through a hole in the draw-plate, and far enough to be taken hold of with the pliers attached to the chain. The windlass is then turned by the long iron crank arms. One arm only is shown complete, the other corresponds to this one in every respect. As soon as the wire has been drawn long enough to span the distance between plate and windless, the chain is removed and the wire is hooked upon the chain spike on the windlass drum and the performance of drawing is continued. The wire now is wound upon the windlass without further aid of chain and pliers.

Wire of gold, silver, copper and brass can be drawn by either of the methods described. The Chinese never succeeded in drawing iron wire. The iron to start with has to be highly annealed, and this has to be repeated after every two or three reductions. The Chinese do not know this, hence their inability to draw iron wire. Their only attainment in manipulating iron wire is to reduce foreign iron wire by drawing it once or twice through their draw plates. Apparently there is no distinct trade for wire-drawing. The artisans using wire in their trade draw it themselves.

Fig. 39. Iron Caster's Furnace.

IRON CASTING

Here indeed we have to do with an art which has been practiced by the Chinese long before anybody else knew much about it. In Europe the art of casting iron was gradually introduced in the latter part of the 14th century, while the most concrete example of old Chinese cast-iron I have heard of is a burial cooking-stove of the 3rd century A.D., found in a grave near Hienyang in Shensi province. The rectangular body, in the shape of a horseshoe rests on four legs, at the rounded end rises a chimney, the firing-hole is on the other side, and on the top are five cooking-holes. The dimensions are 28⅛ inches long, 16 inches wide and 13¾ inches high. It is in the possession of the Field Museum in Chicago and was procured by Dr. Berthold Laufer in China [6]). The Chinese classics furnish us data about cast iron which point to a still older use of it. For instance the Chronicles of the Hia dynasty relate that in 1877 B.C., iron was used for casting swords. The Tao Chien Lu of the 5th century A.D., is a historical record of famous swords since the time of the great Yu (about 2,200 B.C.). They were mostly of cast metal, either iron, copper or gold, also some are mentioned to have been fashioned from stone. Coins have at various times been cast of iron especially in times of political upheaval. An early example is the iron coin of Kung-sun Shu who in A.D. 25 set himself up as Emperor in what is now the Province of Szechuan.

At the present time some of the more common products of cast iron are temple bells, steelyard weights, plow-shares, charcoal stoves, caps for pestles, fire-grates, wire draw-plates, cooking-bowls, etc. The last mentioned are by far the most prominent, and foundries for casting them are to be found all over China.

Where native iron ore is obtainable this furnishes the raw material, in other places scrap iron is utilized. When a Chinese buys a new cooking-bowl he usually trades off the old broken one. In Chekiang I once visited a foundry where native iron ore was used, which according to the foundry-master is found at the foot of disintegrating mountain slopes in the shape of a coarse gray sand, probably magnetic iron sand. The sand receives a preliminary roasting in a cupola fired with charcoal. This probably is done to burn off the sulphur, the enemy of any iron ore. From this cupola the ore emerges still in granules but black as coal, and as such is ready to be smelted in a similar cupola with a blast. This latter furnace is round, about 3½ feet in diameter and about 7 feet high. Near the bottom it has a pouring spout, and on the opposite side a hole for the blast to enter. The furnace is charged with layers of charcoal, of roasted ore, scrap-iron and limestone broken into small pieces. The blast is produced by a Chinese bellows in the shape of a long cylindrical wooden tube looking like a cannon. After the heat seems high enough, a plug is withdrawn from the pouring hole, the furnace tilted, and the hot metal poured into a mold which rests on a lower level than the place where the furnace stands. The casting produced is a solid bowl-shaped mass, rough and thick and corresponds to pig-iron. These clumsy shapes are next broken up, and furnish, with charcoal and scrap-iron, the charge for a heat from which metal for good castings is poured.

The cupola for roasting which I mentioned above had about the same dimensions as the one with a blast for smelting, and stood out in the yard not under cover, perhaps for the reason that through the roasting noxious gases escaped. As far as I know iron smelting is never practiced on a large scale. It is not the Chinese method to have any business on a large scale. If at any one place there is an industry there will be so many single establishments according to the demand. For instance, Lung Chuan in Chekiang province, is famous for swords and there are all over the city perhaps half a dozen establishments making swords, each shop independent from the other, not larger than an ordinary blacksmith shop, in charge of a master with five or six helpers.

The foundries to be described, where I procured the photographs, use only scrap iron as raw material. Fig. 39, photographed in Teh An, Kiangsi, shows a tilting furnace for melting iron for castings. On a forged tripod rests a large cast iron bowl, not clearly seen here on the

[6] Pictured in the Field Museum publication 192, Anthropological Series Vol. xv, No. 2, plate II.

FIG. 40. SKETCH SHOWING AIR DUCT AND AIR INTAKE VALVE ON CYLINDRICAL BELLOWS.

FIG. 41. IRON CASTER'S FURNACE.

ground, and over this rises the furnace built up of bricks and clay. It is reinforced with iron staves and three iron hoops. The height of the furnace is 5 feet, the diameter 2½ feet. Near the bottom is the pouring-hole which is stopped up with a clay-cone-shaped plug, when the furnace is in blast. The ingress blast hole, not seen, is on the opposite side, and a clay pipe leads from it to the bellows, which is shown in the background. The clay plug, not shown, has a cavity in its base, and is prevented from dropping out of place by an iron bar which is propped against it with one end sticking in the cavity. The products of this foundry are cooking bowls of which three sizes are cast.

The cylindrical bellows shown in Figs. 39 and 41 are in principle the same as the box bellows described under Figs. 26 to 28. It is usual to find the cylindrical shape in foundries and blacksmith shops. There is never a valve in the piston head as is usual in western pumps. The intake valves for the cylindrical bellows are always in the fixed circular disk which closes each end of the cylindrical body of the bellows, and does not slide with the piston. In the rectangular bellows box a separate compartment or duct runs along the inner lower edge of the box for guiding the air to the nozzle. Such a compartment or duct is usually attached along the outside of the cylindrical bellows. It is plainly visible in Fig. 39, and made clear through the sketch, Fig. 40, attached.

Fig. 41, photographed near Tatung, Anhwei, shows another iron caster's furnace. The base is of cast iron and the furnace built on top of it of brick and clay. On top has been placed a bottomless cooking bowl as a funnel to form a convenient enlarged edge for charging the furnace with charcoal and scrap iron in proper proportion.

When the charge has been melted sufficiently for pouring, the pipe from the bellows not seen in the picture, is disconnected, and the scum covering the pouring hole is raked aside. The tilting hook, a crutch-like stick with the hook at the end, shown in Fig. 43, is hooked into a ring, not clearly shown, on the upper part of the furnace, and the furnace tilted until the metal runs from the hole into the pouring ladle held in readiness. The latter is also shown in Fig. 43. When the ladle is filled, it is covered with

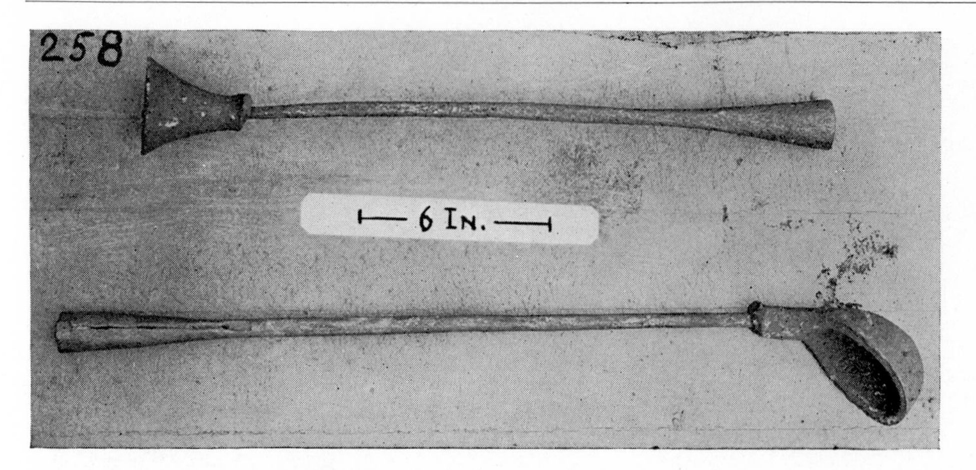

Fig. 42. Iron Caster's Finishing Tool and Ladle.

dipped into water. Then the bowl is finished and put aside for cooling. The faces of the molds after use are brushed over with water apparently full of graphite or lamp black. The water container with two compartments can be seen on the left of Fig. 47. On the wooden top cross-piece forming the handle, the brushes are hanging. The two cap-like objects set on the handle are of cast iron and used to smooth the edges of the pouring hole in the mold.

chaff-ashes and taken to the molds. When filling the mold, the covering scum on the ladle is pushed back with a piece of iron. Usually too much is poured into the mold and some of the superfluous hot metal is dipped out with the dipper shown in Fig. 42 and finally the other tool shown in Fig. 42, with the cone-shaped clay head, is pushed into the hole in the mold to finish off this exposed part of the casting. At the foundry in Tatung, ten bowls are cast at one time. As soon as they are all poured, the molds are turned over upon their sides, against straw mats, and opened, a workman takes the tongs shown in Fig. 43, scrapes over the still red hot top of the bowl with the same tongs to remove any projecting piece, turns it around, and brushes all over its inner surface with a brush

The wooden bellows in Fig. 41 (rear), formed of a hollowed tree trunk, stands rather near to the furnace and is smeared with clay for protection against the high heat. The X-shaped support which keeps the bellows in a slanting position shows this clay-protection on the part nearest to the furnace quite well. The inner workings in the hollowed tree-trunk must have become loose as they are held in place with a rope between two posts, stretched tight by a toggle. The piston is pulled back and forth by two men who are protected against the heat by a bamboo matting suspended from above. A tre-

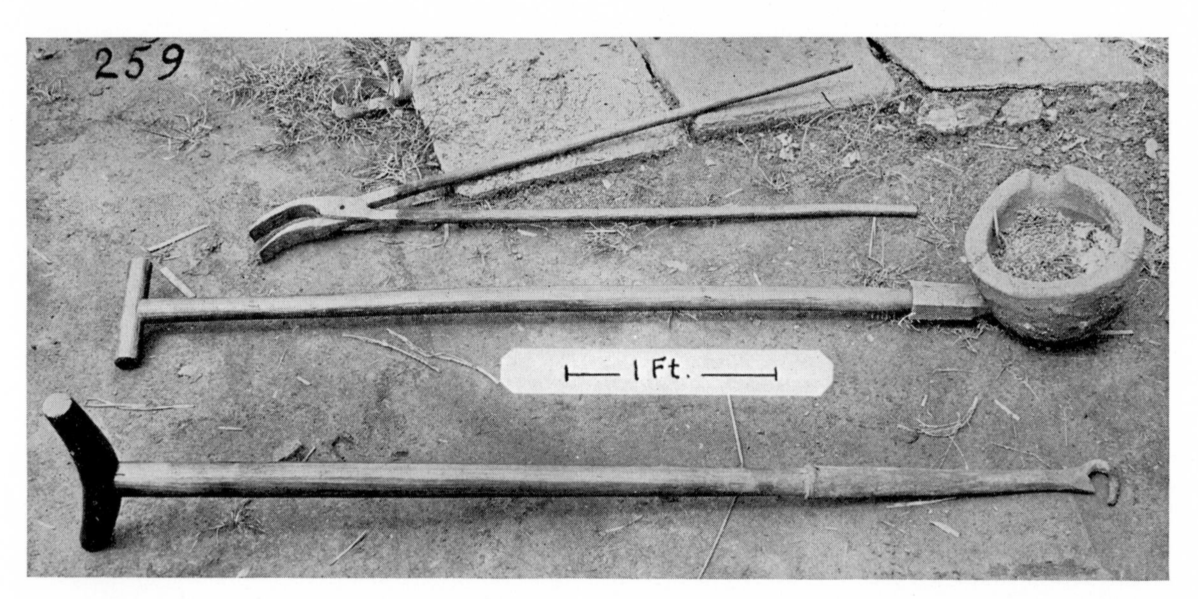

Fig. 43. Iron Caster's Tongs, Pouring Ladle and Tilting Hook. The tilting hook engages a fixed ring in the furnace top to tilt it and make the hot metal run into the pouring ladle (center). With the tongs the casting is taken from the mold.

mendous draft of air issues from the bellows with each stroke of the piston.

Fig. 44 shows the bottom-parts of a clay mold, one exhibiting the smooth convex side, the casting surface, and aside of it (on the right) one turned around and showing the concave inner side with numerous holes to diffuse the sudden heat in casting and prevent the mold from cracking. The upper mold piece which fits over the lower one is shown in Fig. 45, where we see also a pile of lower parts in the background. The projections are for handling the upper part and the large round opening on its top is the pouring hole. When the two parts of the mold are fitted together, a space is left between them corresponding to the shape of the bowl to be cast. It is wonderful how accurately the molds are formed of plastic clay with the simple aid of a templet of iron, one of which is shown in Fig. 46. One edge of the templet shows the profile of the convex part of a mold and the opposite edge the profile of the concave part. The clay forming the molds is mixed with straw, and the faces are brushed with graphite.

Fig. 44. Molds for Casting Iron Cooking Bowls.

Fig. 47 shows two molds assembled ready for pouring. The lower part is placed upon two wooden strips, imperfectly shown in the picture, and the upper half of the mold is carefully placed over it. Two other wooden strips are then laid over the top so as to leave the pouring hole unobstructed, and in order to hold together the two mold parts, the projecting four ends of the strips are fastened to each other vertically with ropes, chains and hooks as shown.

In Fig. 48 we see a finished cooking bowl. After cooling the bowls are carefully inspected, bad ones are discarded, some with minor faults such as a crack on the rim or a hole are put aside to be mended. This mending of cast iron is a process peculiarly Chinese. In Europe it was not until the advent of the Thermit process, in the latter part of the last century, that welding or mending of cast iron was ever attempted. The life of a good cooking-bowl is about 20 years, and can be prolonged by a travelling tinker, who makes it his exclusive business to mend cast-iron bowls. The important part of such mending is to have convenient means to bring a small portion of iron to the melting temperature which can be readily accomplished with the efficient Chinese box-bellows.

MENDING OF CAST IRON

We had a maltreated cast iron brazier with some pieces broken out, and called the bowl-mender to have it fixed. The day previous I saw him in town going around and collecting bowls to be fixed, so I knew he was about. He came with his outfit and a helper to work his bellows. He put the bellows down on the ground, the round cannon type, about 2½ feet long, and 7 inches in diameter. To fasten it to the ground he produced a piece of rope with a spike at each end. He laid the rope over the bellows and drove the spikes into the ground. The stove, a clay cylinder about 13 inches high and 6 inches in diameter had a hole on the side near the bottom and a metal tube served to carry the draft from the bellows to the stove. The connections were carefully smeared with clay to prevent the air from leaking out. The inner space of the stove had a diameter of about 3½ inches. To start the fire first a few pieces of burnt clay were put into the stove then some lighted straw and on this some small pieces of anthracite coal up to the rim. The bellows were worked from the start of the fire as there was no other way to get air to the bottom of the stove. Soon a brisk fire was going, after poking down

FIG. 45. MOLDS FOR CASTING IRON COOKING BOWLS. The picture gives a clear view of the clay lids (top side outward) with central pouring hole, smaller ventilating holes, and lid-handles.

the coal the man took an earthenware crucible, warmed it first on top and then put it into the stove and heaped coal all around it. Then he took some small bits of cooking-bowl fragments, put them in the crucible and gradually filled it heaping full with larger pieces. The size of the crucible was about 2 inches in diameter and 2½ inches deep. Over the whole top of the stove he then put a covering of twisted straw smeared with wet clay and over this a fragment of an iron bowl to keep the straw in its place. All the time the helper was pushing the bellows, continuing for about 15 minutes until the iron was melted in the crucible. The man stirred the metal a few times and took off some slag from the top until finally the metal was clean and ready for use. A few bowls were to be mended besides our brazier and to support these pieces three iron pins were driven into the ground and the bowl to be worked on placed upon them. The worker had in front of him a little basket of wood ashes and placed some upon a piece of felt which he held in his left hand. In his right he had a little clay spoon and took from the crucible a spoonful of the liquid iron, placed it upon the felt and pushed it from below into the hole to be mended. At the same time he pressed a short solid cylinder made of cotton cloth rolled tightly together upon the hole from the other side. In this manner the amount of liquid iron was made to completely fill out the hole and the surface became smooth from the pressure exerted from both sides. This is all there is to the mending of a small hole. In our brazier the hole was big and a piece had to be inserted which the mender took from an old bowl. He held it in place with two strips of bamboo as shown in Fig. 49, and then filled the space around it with several applications of the liquid metal until the whole surface was solid again. To my surprise the man mended also a few holes in an enameled wash basin of foreign make. Before the iron in the holes had become cool they were smeared with straw dipped into wet clay. The explanation given was that the iron sticks better in the hole. To smooth the iron in mending cooking bowls sometimes the mender rubs the still red hot iron in the hole with a piece of resin.

The observations were made at Changshu, Kiangsi.

WROUGHT IRON

Where economy restricts in a large measure the output of useful tools and utensils made of iron and steel, it is not surprising that much less is to be seen of ornamental iron work. The casual observer will see now and then in temples wrought iron stands, from a foot to several feet high, for holding incense sticks. They are usually three-legged, with a straight stem, which for ornamental purposes is interrupted by the conventionalized representation of a Chinese character. From the stem extend several arms terminating into loops for inserting incense sticks. This seemed to be the extent of my findings in wrought iron until one day, I had the good fortune to be shown, in a home of a Chinese family in Nanchang, Kiangsi, the pictures shown in Figs. 50 and 51. The frames hold wooden boards covered with light blue silk and upon this are fastened wrought iron strips which outline the pictures. The metal is wrought with great delicacy, and it is almost unbelievable that the uncouth tools of a blacksmith produced them. I was told that they were several hundred years old and came originally from Wuhu, Anhwei province. They are very much sought after and only to be found in the homes of old families.

Fig. 46. Iron Templet. Used in making clay molds for casting iron cooking bowls.

The set of four pictures in Fig. 50 represents the four fundamental callings, the faggot carrier—labor, the fisherman—trade, the peasant—agriculture, and the scholar—learning. Each of the pictures is 4 feet long and 1 foot wide.

Upon inquiry in Wuhu, Anhwei, where I could

Fig. 47. Molds and Apparatus for Casting Iron Cooking Bowls.

Fig. 48. Cast Iron Cooking Bowl.

find no signs of an industry producing this type of iron picture, I had occasion to visit a dismal shop of a blacksmith and was surprised and delighted to see on the family altar the pair of candlesticks or prickets shown in Fig. 52. The blacksmith had made them himself and showed no dislike to having them photographed. Here at least was a remnant of skill which in former times had produced the wrought iron pictures. The Chinese themselves are aware that these pictures are a product out of the ordinary, and have a legend which relates how they were made.

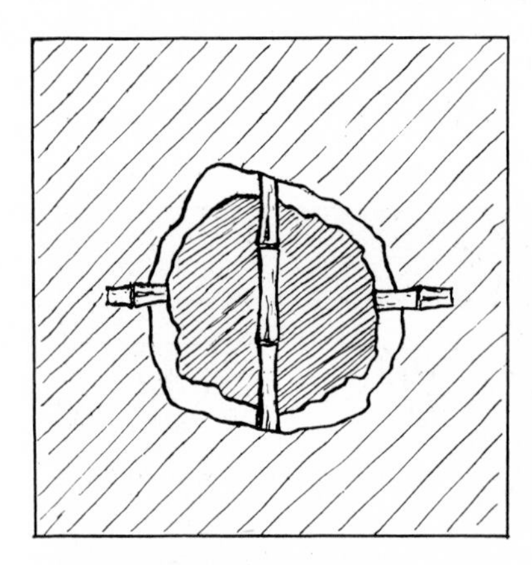

Fig. 49. Mending of Cast Iron. Sketch showing how a fragment of a cast iron is held in a hole of a cast iron brazier which is to be mended. The outer shaded surface represents the wall of the brazier in which the hole is found. Pieces of bamboo hold the mending piece in place and the space between mending piece and the edge of the hole is filled out by successive applications, one next to the other, of the liquid iron taken from the crucible. As soon as the mending piece is held fast in the hole by a few applications of the liquid cast iron (which cools as soon as applied) the bamboo strips are removed.

About two hundred years ago there lived a blacksmith in the Wuhu district who had a young apprentice named Tang Tien Che. This boy was of weak stature and being ill-fitted for the work of a blacksmith, his rough master had little patience with him, and ofttimes would mercilessly flog the poor lad who had not strength enough to do the heavy work of hammering. One day in the midst of winter, Tang Tien Che after a severe beating, grew desperate and ran away into the nearby mountains where he roamed about in the heavy snow, poorly clad, his only aim being to get farther and farther away from his cruel master. Exhausted from exposure and hunger he finally sank down under a tree. Night was approaching and notwithstanding the cold, hunger, and danger of wild animals the poor boy seemed relieved to have escaped the constant dread of bodily chastisement. From utter exhaustion he soon fell asleep. After several hours of fitful sleep he awoke, startled by approaching steps, rubbed his eyes and looked up to see an old man with a long white beard standing before him. When with kindly voice the stranger asked the boy how he came to be at such a place in the midst of night, Tang Chien Che poured forth his tale of woe. After sympathetically listening to him to the end, the old man drew forth a root and gave it to the boy with the admonition to eat it and then straightforth to return to his master who would have no further cause of complaint with him. The boy took the root and thereupon the old man disappeared. He reluctantly bit into it and as soon as he had finished eating he felt strangely refreshed, and, as he was bid, started on his return. The old man's words had inspired confidence, and he marched on without stopping. At day-break he arrived and boldly knocked at his master's door. The blacksmith opened and seeing his run-away apprentice took an iron bar to strike him down. As if imbued with supernatural strength Tang Tien Che snatched the bar from his master's hand and told him that he would show him how to work the iron as no blacksmith ever had before. Without the aid of fire, hammer or anvil, he then drew out the bar with his hands, bent it this way and that and with ease formed flowers, trees and many things beautiful to behold. This was due to the magic root which the old man of the mountain had given to Tang Tien Che, and he soon be-

FIG. 50. ORNAMENTAL IRONWORK. Wrought iron strips outlining pictures. The strips are set in frames upon a background of boards faced with light blue silk.

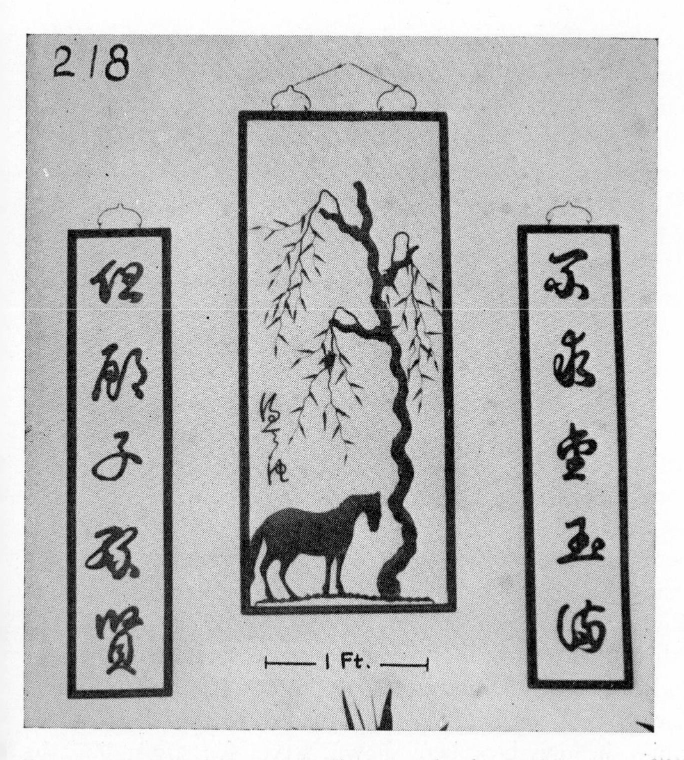

FIG. 51. ORNAMENTAL IRONWORK. Pictures made of wrought iron strips constructed and framed as in Fig. 50.

came far-famed as the best blacksmith in the land.

I have seen since some more of this unique work supposedly made by this legendary blacksmith and learned that of late such work is being reproduced in Anhwei and Peking to satisfy the demand for specimens by foreign curio-seekers.

Another interesting class of objects but rarely seen, are reinforcing door bands of wrought iron. In the western world we are acquainted with ornamental doorbands, parts of hinges, which stretch over the surface of the doors. In China where the doors invariably swing in crapaudine style, i.e., pivoted at the corners, on top and bottom, such hinges must not be expected. In King Teh Chen, the old porcelain center, I thought I had at last found a door, hinged in a Christian-like manner. Two bands emanated from the sides and passing across the surface had the ends cleft and turned outward, as sketched in Fig. 53. Upon opening the door I found that the bands were not part of hinges

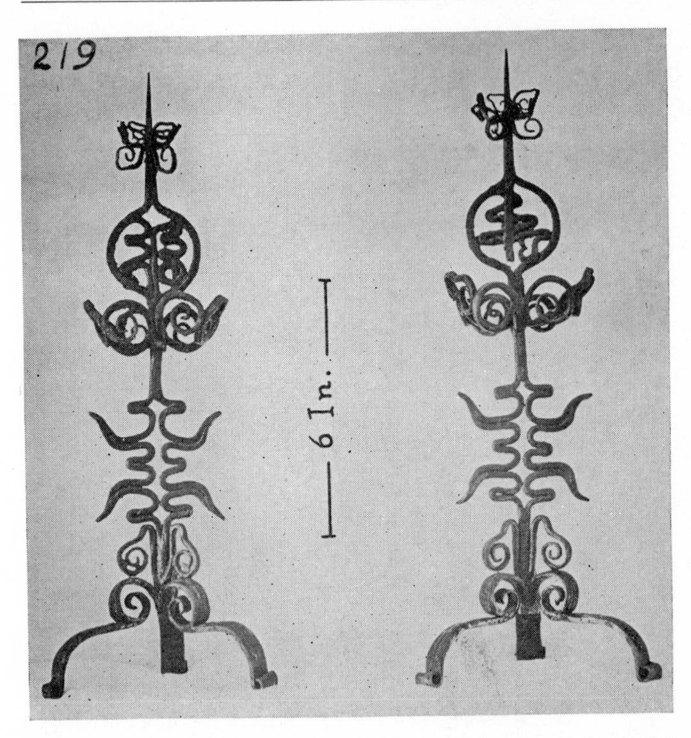

FIG. 52. ORNAMENTAL IRONWORK. Wrought iron candlesticks, photographed in Wu Hu, Anhwei province, where the art of making them is considered a rare survival of an ancient industry. They were in use on the family altar of a blacksmith who had made them.

Classed with ornamental ironwork can be also the iron rings attached to each wing of a vertically double-winged door, to draw the door shut, which in practice, however, are often used as knockers. Under each ring, but not so high up that the hanging ring can touch it, is a large-headed wrought iron nail driven into the wood. The significance of these I could not find out, much less the reason why on almost every door in Chekiang there are two such large headed nails driven in the right wing, one below the other under the iron ring. A local explanation given us was that these nails are thus placed as a reminder that politeness calls for three knocks only and not more. On the inside these nails or bolts are clinched and there is not the least evidence that they serve a useful purpose. The doors I have been speaking of represent always the main door with which the house is closed against outside contact. They are strongly built for protection and secured on the inside with a cross-beam but not with a lock. The assumption is that there always is somebody at home.

and that they curved around the inside rounded edge of the door and stopped short without being continued on the inside surface. In looking about I found that such door bands are used now and then and later in Anhwei I saw more of them, some passing from the front around to the back and extending across the opposite surface. The band from King Teh Chen, Fig. 54, was nailed to the door and the nails clinched on the inside. The arrow-shaped band from Tatung, Fig. 55, had the point turned over and driven into the wood and the band was held down by U-shaped staples, the ends of which passed through the door and were likewise clinched. On the temple door in Anking, Fig. 56, the bands encircled the wings of the door, their ends showing on the outer surface being held down by semi-circular strips.

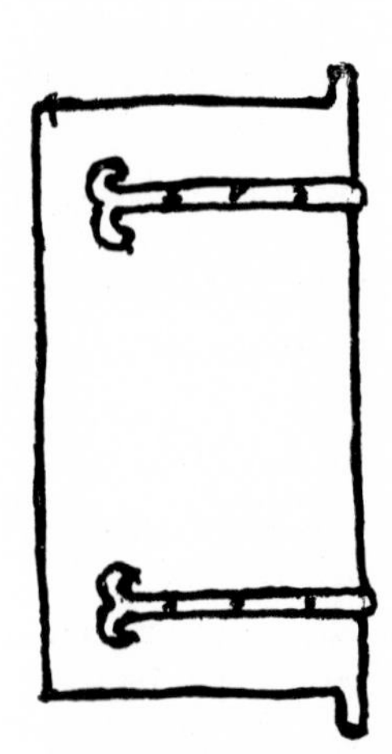

FIG. 53. DOOR FROM KING TEH CHEN, PIVOTED AT THE CORNERS, ON TOP AND BOTTOM. The ornamental doorbands are not part of hinges and stop short after curving around the inside rounded edge of the door.

ITINERANT BRASS SMITH

Prominent among the itinerant tradespeople is the brass smith or general tinker as he might more fittingly be called. His complete stock in trade he carries around with him, suspended from the two ends of his carrying pole. Fig. 57 shows his workbench and bellows combined. A similar box not here shown with drawers instead of the bellows, corresponds in weight closely to the workbench, and hangs from the other end of the carrying pole. The framework of bamboo strips nailed to the sides of the bellows box, here shown, serves for suspending the outfit from the carrying pole. The box shown is 17

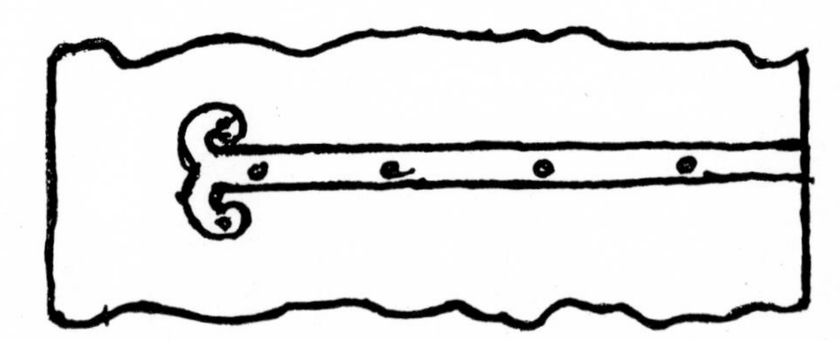

FIG. 54. ORNAMENTAL DOOR BAND FROM KING TEH CHEN. This band, a detail of Fig. 53, was nailed to the door and the nails clinched on the inside.

inches high, 10 inches wide and 25 inches long. The lower part is taken up by the bellows. Near the bottom of the opposite long side of the box, which is hidden in the photograph, is a round hole where the draft comes out. Wherever the brass smith settles

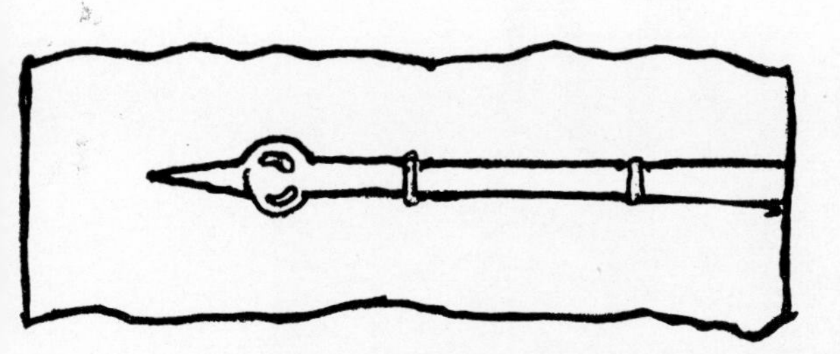

FIG. 55. ORNAMENTAL DOOR BAND FROM TATUNG, ANHWEI. The arrow-shaped door-band had the point turned at right angles and driven into the wood. The rest of the band was held down with *U* shaped staples driven into the wood, and the points extending on the inside were clinched.

down to work, he sets down his box, builds a little hearth of stones or bricks beside the draft-hole, and then is ready for work. On the top of the box is the wedge-vise, which can be raised or lowered, to serve as support for things to be filed. The typical Chinese file, described under Fig. 24, has two tangs, one for the handle and the other for a guiding rod, which slides in the eye-bolt here seen protruding from the top of the bellows-box. The vise consists of a heavy iron staple driven part way into the top of the box, and a strip of rather hard wood which is passed through it. With a wedge inserted underneath, this strip can be fixed in various positions, holding articles tightly to the bench. For fuel on the improvised hearth, charcoal is used, and for soldering a wedge-shaped piece of copper is put into the fire and taken out and held for working with a pair of tongs.

The anvil shown standing at the lower left corner of Fig. 57 is particularly interesting. I was told that the anvils used by brass smiths always have a hardy hole, namely the large square orifice here shown near the top-corner, but among the tools, I have not yet seen a hardy or fuller, for insertion into this hardy hole.

Fig. 58 shows the tools used by the brass smith. Characteristic is the scraper, a flat piece of steel, 5 inches long, 1 inch wide and 3/16 of an inch thick. The two rectangular ends have sharp edges with which the scraping is done, since at all times, instead of polishing, the metals worked upon are scraped. The four tongs are used for holding metals in the fire, and for withdrawing them from it. The hammer with a long wedge-shaped peen is well adapted for sheet-metal work.

The most interesting of the brass smith's tools is the pump drill shown in Fig. 59. The central drill rod has a square socket at the lower end for inserting a steel drill. On the other end, a lead whorl is fastened with a brass cap over it, the latter, no doubt, for ornament only. Close under the whorl is a hole piercing the rod, through which passes a leather thong. This thong is wound around the central rod and the two ends are fastened with a knot to the opposite ends of the horizontal sliding cross bar. In using this instrument the drill point is placed upon the metal to be perforated and the sliding piece is grasped with the right hand, thumb and index-finger on one side of the central drill rod and the remaining fingers upon the other side. Pushing down the sliding cross-piece uncoils the thong at the same time rotating the rod in one direction. When the thong is uncoiled the rod has sufficient momentum, thanks to the leaden whorl, to keep on turning in the same direction. The downward pressure with the hand is released at the

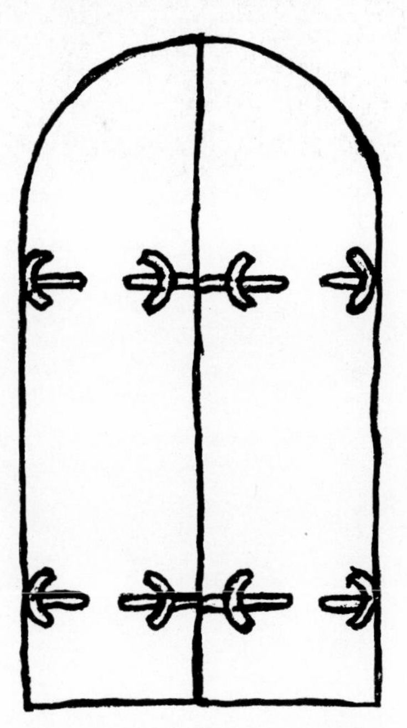

FIG. 56. DOOR BANDS ON TEMPLE DOOR IN ANKING. The bands encircle the wings of the door on the inside, and on the outside where the ends show they are held down with semi-circular strips. They are in no way connected with the hinges.

same instant that the thong is uncoiled, while the rod continuing to rotate, winds the thong around itself, but in the opposite direction, and so lifts the sliding cross bar. The force of the momentum is spent by this rewinding of the thong, and another push of the

FIG. 57. BRASS SMITH'S BOX BELLOWS, FILE, VISE AND ANVIL.

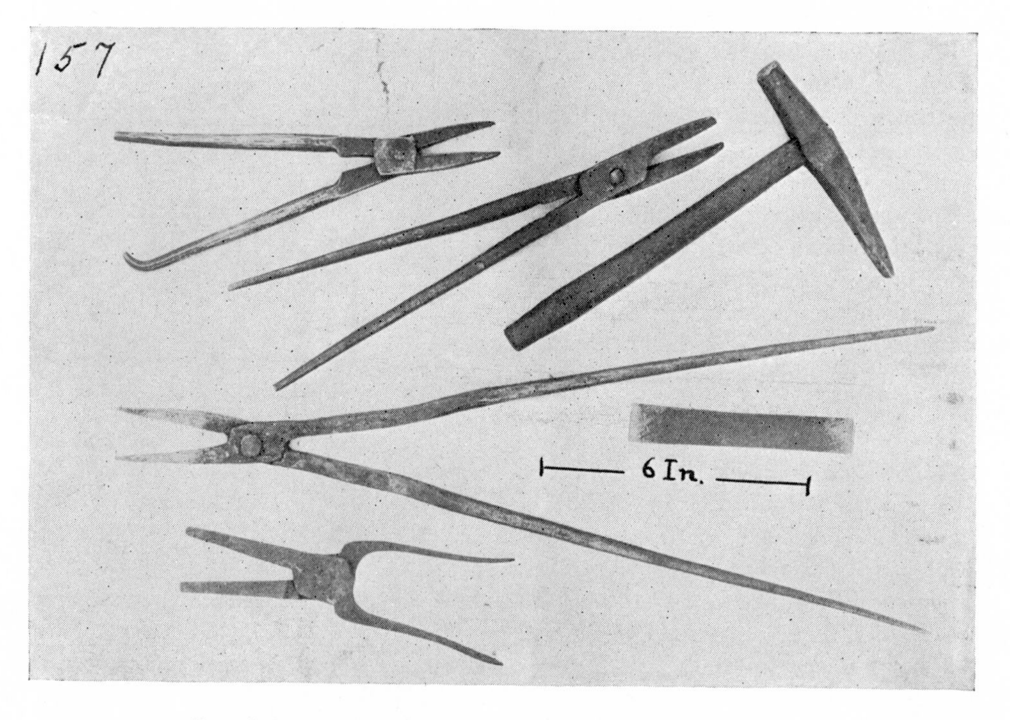

FIG. 58. BRASS SMITH'S TOOLS. Various Tongs, Hammer and Scraper.

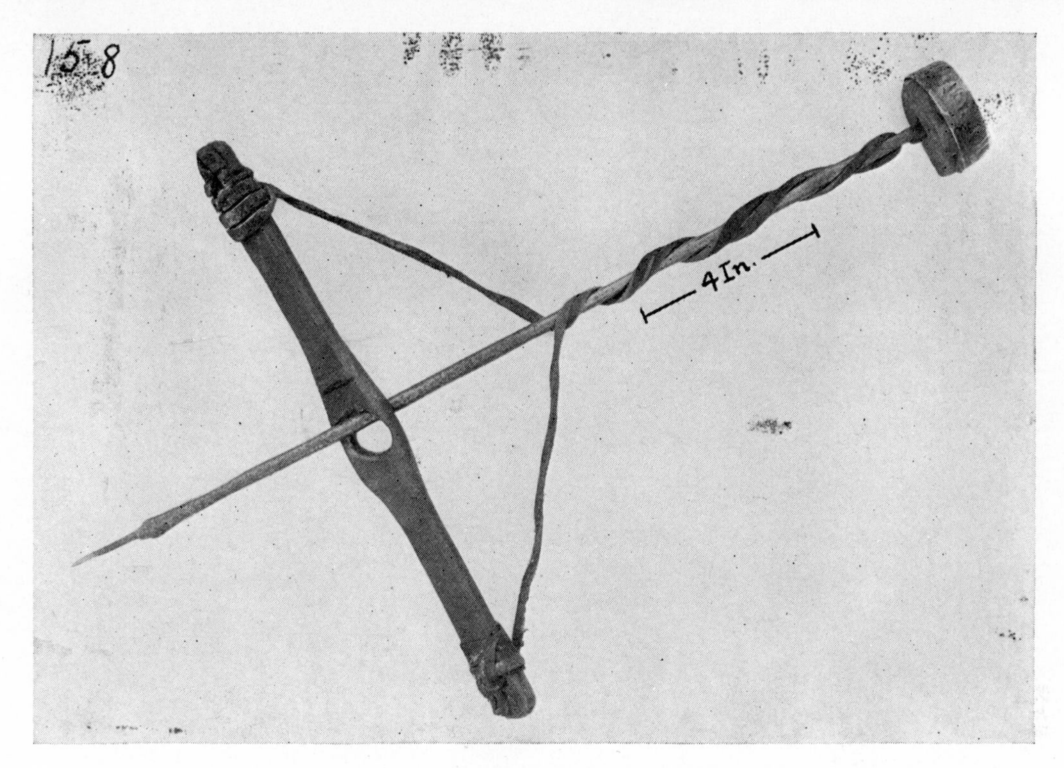

Fig. 59. Brass Smith's Pump Drill.

hand downward upon the sliding bar, which had been dragged up by the thong, sets the central rod rotating again, but this time in the opposite direction. In this manner a reciprocating motion is kept up and imparted to the steel drill. The point of the drill is shaped like the point of a blunt arrow. The brass smith makes and repairs all kinds of small wares like hinges (in those regions furniture has hinges), handles for drawers, padlocks, staples and hasps, ferrules, etc. The material he works in is mostly brass, and then tutenag or paktong (a kind of German silver), copper and silver; the latter only in repairing. The photographs were taken in Kuling, Kiangsi province.

Chapter II

TOOLS FOR PROCURING FOOD

THE sweat of the brow is daily expended by millions, and daily millions of sighs are wrung from the tormented frame of the bent and weary in the pursuit of providing food. In China nothing is more outstandingly in evidence than this toil for the daily subsistence. This chapter gives an insight into the methods of Chinese agriculture. To the supercilious they may seem primitive and sadly in need of our "superior" accomplishments brought about by modern progress and the machine age. It is hard to convince the Chinese farmer to adopt Western methods, and well it should be so. A few very practical considerations will illustrate this. In the middle-west our farmers consider a forty-acre farm too small for a single family while in Shantung province, for instance, forty acres are capable to furnish maintenance to 240 people together with 24 donkeys and 24 pigs. In China on the average one-sixth of an acre of good land is sufficient for maintaining one person while in the United States almost two acres of improved farm land is necessary to feed one chicken.

Farmers for forty centuries, the Chinese have learned not to let anything go to waste. The appalling losses sustained by our methods of garbage and sewage disposal alone through incineration and pouring into rivers, lakes and sea is inconceivable to the Chinese, and to them would mean race suicide. Wanton waste is the keynote of our methods and when its withering blight shall finally threaten to engulf our civilization, we may yet be glad to emulate the Far East for our salvation.

PLOWS

As if to emphasize its importance, one of the 214 original characters of the Chinese script *lei,* stands for plow. These characters called radicals, were the outcome of the first attempts of the Chinese, several thousand years before our era, to express themselves in writing, and one or more of these radicals were utilized in composing all of the subsequent characters evolved. The radical *lei* is not now used to designate the plow, but ancient writers tell us that this *lei* was a plow of curved wood about 4 feet long and was pushed by the plowman. The first furrow in spring was cut in those days by the emperor with this primi-

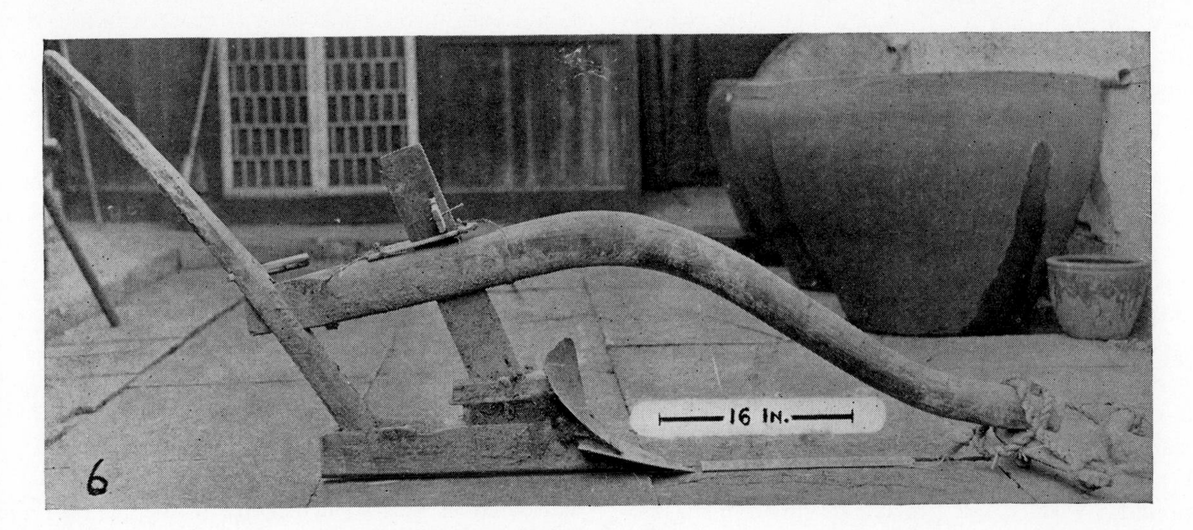

FIG. 60. CHINESE PLOW.

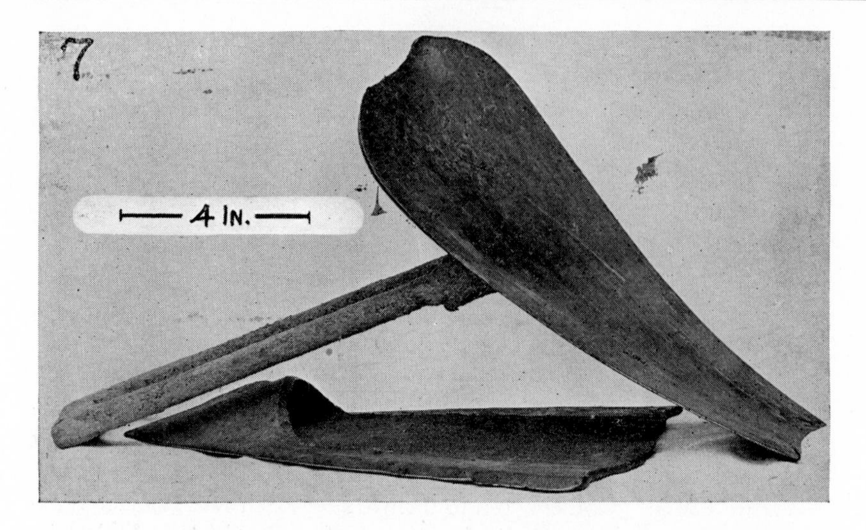

FIG. 61. MOLDBOARD AND SHARE OF A CHINESE PLOW. The cast iron Moldboard (upper specimen) is here shown, the twisted blade with its long slotted solid cast projection, by means of which it is driven down and wedged fast upon the vertical guideboard. Its purpose, as in western plows, is to throw over the furrow.
The lower specimen is the cast iron share, a slipper-shaped lanceolate point, ending in a socket, which socket is driven and wedged on the horizontal nose of the plow. The purpose of the share is to underslice the furrow.

tive plow. Thus the ancient Chinese evinced high appreciation and reverence for this, one of man's master tools. The modern Chinese name for plow is *li,* one of its elements being the radical for cattle. As the Chinese plow changed from the primitive form pushed by a man, to the one dragged by an animal, so did the Chinese character standing for the word plow.

The following observations were made and the photographs taken at Sin Tseong, a village near Ningpo, Chekiang Province.

The plow, Fig. 60, is constructed of wood. Only the share and the moldboard are of cast iron. The length from tip to tip is 7 feet 8 inches. There are two distinct parts to the plow: the body and the beam. The length of the down-curved beam is 5 feet 10 inches. At one end is inserted a wooden pin on which swings the whippletree. The other end of the otherwise round beam is squared (4 inches by $1\frac{1}{4}$ inches) to fit loosely into a rectangular slot in the single handle of the plow. The body of the plow consists of a wooden horizontal base (2 feet 4 inches long and 4 inches square) pointed at one end to fit into a socket at the tip of the share, clearly seen in Fig. 61. The single handle, and a wooden upright board (4 inches wide and $\frac{3}{4}$ inch thick) which we shall call the guideboard, are firmly mortised into the base of the plow. The main handle receives at about 17 inches from the ground a wooden side peg handle, inserted horizontally, which serves to lift up the plow when turning to cut a fresh furrow. The guideboard holds the moldboard in place. First a wooden block or sleeve, with a slot in the middle, is pushed down over the guideboard, then the loopshaped cast-iron projection of the moldboard, better seen in Fig. 61, is pushed down thereupon, and on top of this another perforated wooden block or sleeve. The latter sleeve is held in place and pressed down upon the moldboard loop, by a wooden wedge driven into a hole in the guideboard. The moldboard can be raised or lowered by putting a thicker or thinner wooden sleeve under its loop. The socket of the cast-iron share, as mentioned above, is pushed over the forward end of the horizontal wooden base of the plow under the moldboard. The wide upper end of the share rests in a slot cut across the wooden base, and is held there firmly by a wedge. The moldboard is 10 inches long and $4\frac{3}{8}$ inches wide at its widest part. The loop cast on to the moldboard is 9 inches long and $2\frac{1}{2}$ inches wide. The pointed share is 11 inches long and the wide end 7 inches across. Both moldboard and share are of cast iron. They cannot be sharpened and wear out in about two years. The upper part of the guideboard passes through a slot in the plowbeam in which it can slide freely up and down. A locking slide or wooden key, as seen in Fig. 60, holds the guideboard in place, lifting or depressing it, and with it the whole plow base, determining thus the depth of furrow to be cut by the share. This slide or key is a little top-board, 6 inches long and $\frac{3}{8}$ of an inch thick, and has its top margin cut like steps. There are three of these steps, enabling the farmer to set the guideboard and with it the base of the plow at three different heights, which result in varying depths of the furrow to be plowed. The slide once set to one of the steps, is held there by wooden pins stuck into holes in the slide on each side of the guideboard, penetrating into the slot in the guideboard. Between the bottom of this locking slide and the beam, there are two bamboo rods held together by strings on their respective ends thus embracing the guideboard. This latter contrivance is only a makeshift, and not essential; it serves as a kind of extra washer to raise the base of the plow higher than the highest step of the

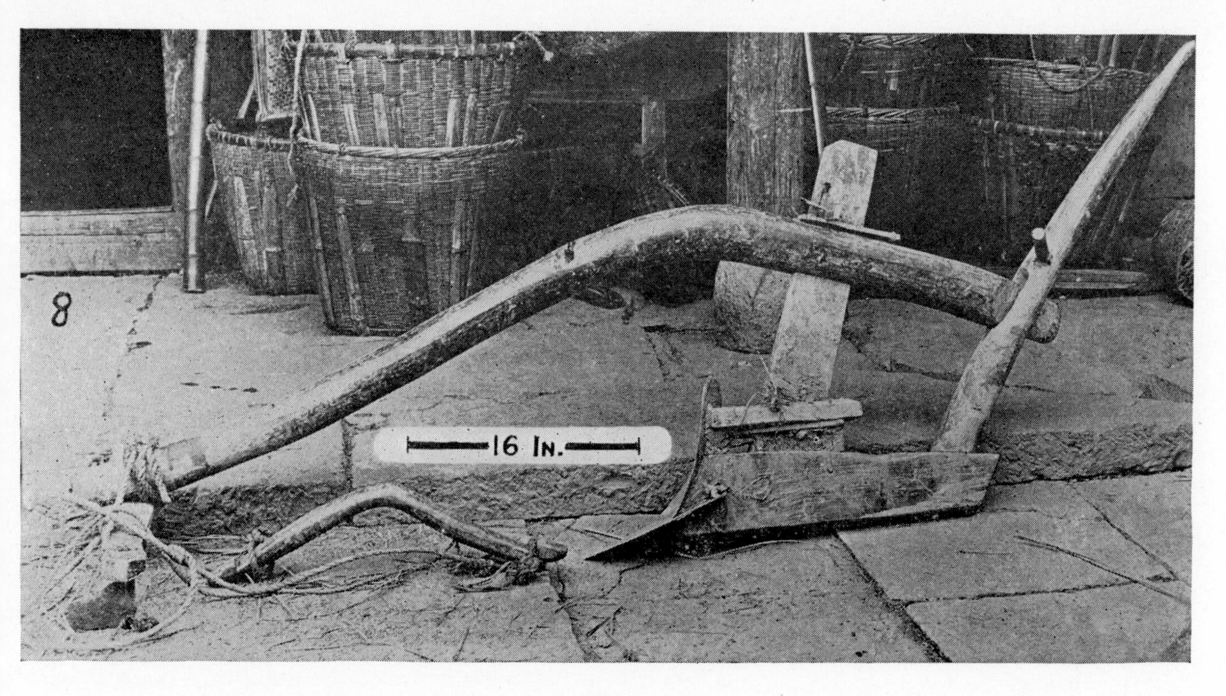

FIG. 62. CHINESE PLOW. This picture shows another plow from the opposite side and the yoke used for pulling it.

FIG. 63. MAN POWER PLOW.

locking slide will raise it. The effect of this will be very shallow plowing, more so than the original construction would allow.

The traces are attached to the whippletree and their ends to the yoke. The yoke is put upon the hump of the zebu, the draft-animal domesticated in China, which draft-animal is characterized by a fleshy protuberance between the shoulders. The yoke is shown in Fig. 62.

In plowing the farmer starts at the left-hand corner of the field, plows one furrow, the earth from which will be thrown to the right of the moldboard. After turning around at the end of the field the next furrow will be cut in the opposite direction directly adjoining the first one. It will be understood that the earth of the first furrow will then be lying directly over the new furrow to be plowed. This earth and the earth to be raised from the second furrow will then be thrown over into the first open furrow.

Fig. 64. Sketch of the Man Power Plow of Shantung. The drawing shows more clearly the details of the man-power Plow of Shantung, as described under Fig. 63.

Shantung is very much overpopulated, and poverty is therefore much in evidence among the country people. Whenever heaven is not propitious in sending the necessary rain for the crops, dire want stalks through the land, and it is heartrending to see how the people have to suffer. The poverty is reflected in the methods of agriculture, and it is, therefore, not surprising to find today a primitive plow, which for lack of draft animals has to be served by man power, one man to push and guide, and another man to pull it. Fig. 64 shows the details of this simple plow. There is a baseboard with a cast iron share at one end. Two uprights are firmly mortised into the baseboard, the rear one of which farthest from the share and bent backward, resembles the handle of one of the ancient one-handled European plows, but is not so used. Instead of grasping the upper end of this upright in his hands, as in the old western plow, the plowman leaning forward and downward, presses his shoulder against it, while his two hands grasp the two projecting ends of a cross peg-handle driven through the lower part of the curved upright. Thus in a very ingenious manner, he not only guides but pushes the plow. Into this same higher rear upright the plow beam is hinged through a slot on a wooden pin, so that its angle can be raised or lowered. Higher up to the right, the plow beam has another slot, through which passes the other shorter upright of the baseboard. The inclination of the plow beam can thereby be changed by wedging it differently, i.e., higher or lower against this shorter upright which passes through this latter slot. Thereby the plow share with the baseboard is given different angles for shallow or deep plowing. The upper open space between the two uprights is in practice usually strengthened with rope as can be dimly seen in the photograph, Fig. 63.

Another very interesting feature of the plow is what might be called the Pull-Peg. This is a wooden peg driven vertically through the plow beam close to its upper end. This enables the other plowman to drag forward the plow, when on shouldering the upheld plow beam, the peg hooks upon his shoulder as he pulls forward with all his might. The picture was taken in the Laushan Mountains, about 20 miles north from Tsingtao, here as elsewhere the Chinese have the fear of being photographed. To show the working of this plow only one Chinese could be found to pose and the author had to substitute for another.

SOWING PLOWS

The sowing plow in Europe can be traced back to the beginning of the 16th century, when an Italian by the name of Giovanni Cavallina constructed one in Bologna. Feldhaus who relates this shows a constructively inaccurate picture of a Chinese sowing plow, and remarks that probably, in simple form, sowing machines were first used in the Orient. Many inventions which we can trace back to Italy in medieval times have their origin in the Orient, and this is also the case with the sowing plow, as Feldhaus suggests.

Chinese records of the Han time relate that one Huang Fu-lung, the prefect of the Tun Huang [1] district taught the people to make a sowing plow which saved half their labor. To understand this economy we must assume that in those days the people hand-planted their wheat or grain, as is still done in Shan-

[1] Tun Huang is probably a district in the province of Kansu which in the Han time (206 B.C. to 25 A.D.) belonged to the state of Ts'in.

Fig. 65. Chinese Grain Sowing Plow.

tung by poor people who cannot afford a sowing plow. The sowing plow of the Han time is described as similar to a plow with three legs. On top was fastened a receptacle for the seed and the whole contrivance was drawn by an ox. The peasant leading the plow shook it as he walked to make the seed drop down. Afterwards a leveller or broom had to be used in order to cover the seed in the furrows.

Short as this description is, it gives a good picture of the sowing plow now in use in North China. There are two types in use, one, no doubt the original kind, with one plowshare, and another with two plowshares. The former, not here shown, when it stands unused, appears to stand on three legs, on the two thills, or shafts, and the share, while the latter, of which several pictures are here shown, rests on four, two thills and its two shares. The shaking of the plow by the handles from side to side is also an important feature now, as it was in the Han time. Fig. 65 gives a view of a modern sowing plow, entire, in a Chinese farmyard in Shantung Province. This and the other pictures were photographed in Weihsien, the field of work of the late American missionary, Frank H. Chalfant, who has made profound studies in the history of the Chinese script.[2]

There is a main upstanding handled frame with two down-pointing cast iron shares at its lower ground-penetrating end, and two handles at its upper end. The two thills or shafts extending forward at an obtuse angle from this main frame, hold between them close to the upstanding handles, a wooden bin for the seed. The pictures Fig. 65 to 69 allow a study in detail of the complicated joinery, originally without any iron parts. The seed-bin has an ante-chamber, which, instead of a bottom, has two square chutes leading downward to the shares. These are for the passage of the seed which through the chutes pass down and drop into the furrows made by the shares. The hoop of elastic wood tied with rope so as to project backward horizontally, a little above and behind the shares (see Figs. 66 and 68) has the function of closing up the furrows after the seeds have been deposited. In the Han time, as we have related above, this furrow-covering was done by hand with a broom,

[2] Conf. his "Early Chinese Writing," Memoir of the Carnegie Museum, Volume IV, Pittsburgh, 1906.

Fig. 66. Rear View of the Chinese Grain Sowing Plow Shown in Fig. 65.

as a separate job, after using the sowing plow. In order to make the seed flow evenly from the bin there is a curious arrangement which is best illustrated by the accompanying sketch, Fig. 67, in conjunction with Figs. 68 and 69.

Slide Board or Seed Gate
Seed Bin
Stone
Bamboo Rod
Passage for Seed
Chute

Fig. 67. Details of the Seed Discharging Device of the Chinese Grain Sowing Plow.

The seed-bin has a passage-way which communicates with the ante-chamber where a stone dangles. The stone is fastened to a flexible bamboo rod, and when the peasant serving the sowing plow swings the plow by means of its handles gently from side to side, the suspended stone swings and imparts a back and forth motion to the bamboo rod which half-blocks the passage for seed from the seed-bin into the side by side chute holes. The function of the rod is to retard the flow of the seed, and at the same time throw alternately a few seeds towards the left into the left chute, and then again a few to the right into the right chute, according to the rhythm of the dangling stone.

The passage-way for seed from the bin to the ante-chamber can be varied in size with the slide board or seed-gate held in place by a wedge. The top of this seed-gate with its wedge, also visible in Fig. 69, back of the forked stick which holds the pendant stone, is more fully indicated here in the sketch, Fig. 67. This seed-gate has at one end a semicircular notch and a larger one at the other end. For small seeds the gate is placed with the small notch against the communicating hole to the seed-bin, and for larger seed, as of wheat and barley, the board is reversed and wedged in place again with the larger notch against the communicating hole. The bamboo rod extends through the seed passage from the bin into the front compartment. This seed passage is a horizontal slot, the middle of which coincides with a partition separating the open tops of the two seed chutes, and as the bamboo rod half fills the slot, it follows that when the pendant stone swings the rod from side to side, the rod will interrupt the grain flow and direct it now into one now into the other of the chutes.

The sowing plow is used for wheat, barley, millet and white sorghum, but not for rice.

My father, Dr. Fritz Hommel, professor of Oriental languages at the University of Munich, Germany, furnished me some interesting sketches, Figs. 70 and 71, shown herewith, taken from representations of the middle Babylonian period, ca. 1300 B.C. We see from them that the Babylonians had already a sowing plow more than a thousand years before the Chinese introduced it, as their historians tell us.

RICE PLANTING

The rice grains are first sprouted before sowing. This is a process which takes about a week. Six catties (ca. 8 pounds) of unhulled rice are soaked in cold water for 24 hours. Then the seeds are put into a cast iron cooking bowl with water and slightly heated until the seeds get warmed. Next the sprouting tub, Fig. 72, comes into use. The bottom which has a hole about ½ inch in diameter is covered with a layer of straw on top of which six catties of rice are placed. Another layer of straw is put on, then again six catties of rice, previously soaked, and so on until the barrel is full.

FIG. 68. DETAILED REAR VIEW OF A CHINESE GRAIN SOWING PLOW. The sowing plow pictured is old, mended with iron cleats and variously reinforced with rope to hold it together. The rope which can be seen dangling down over the rounded cross bar is for attaching to the harness of the draft-animal. The main pulling force is thus applied near the shares which have to do the work of opening the furrows. The two hollow wooden box chutes are plainly seen curving downward from the seed box to the two iron shares and projecting backward just above the ground over the shares. The picture also shows the bent bamboo rod in front, close to the ground for covering the freshly planted furrows.

FIG. 69. THE SEED BOX OF A CHINESE GRAIN SOWING PLOW. The seed box is divided into two compartments. Right, a bin or hopper for receiving the seed in bulk. Left, an ante-chamber or smaller compartment for regulating the flow of seeds into the two seed chutes one of which appears at the bottom of the compartment. This regulation is effected by the dangling stone here seen which agitates a flexible stopper from chute to chute. The seeds pass from the hopper into the ante-chamber through a bottom hole in the partition board, not seen, which hole can also be graduated by shifting the wedge-fastened wooden slide here clearly seen on the upper slope of the partition board.

The barrel holds six layers of rice, altogether 36 catties, enough for planting 6 mao (6.61 mao equals one acre) of land. The barrel is now left standing in the house, well covered with straw for 24 hours. At the end of this time the first sprouts will show. Early in the morning the barrel is taken to the canal's edge, filled with water which gradually drains off through the hole in the bottom, and is then allowed to stand there the whole day long. In the evening it is filled again with water and taken back for safety's sake to the house. This procedure is continued for 4 or 5 days until the sprouts are at least an inch long. Now the seeds are taken from the barrel, layer by layer, and temporarily sowed close together in a corner of the field where they are finally to be planted. Fifteen days after sowing the little plants are advanced far enough to be transplanted in rows. A handful of plants are pulled out from the watery field, tied loosely together with straw and about sixty bundles thus formed scattered over one mao or field. Then begins the task of setting six plants together in one hole of the muddy water, each hole six inches away from the other. The peasant uses the one-legged stool, Fig. 73, to sit on when setting the plants. About 15 days after this eight piculs of manure (1 picul equals ca. 133 pounds) are applied to a field of one mao. The manure used is nightsoil. For three times after that with intervals of about five days, the peasant pushes under water whatever of the manure sticks out, so that finally only the rice plants show above the water. Until the rice gets in bloom water is always put upon the field when necessary to keep the ground under water. The rice blooms only for about three hours and then the visible development of the grain begins. From three to four weeks after blooming the rice is ready for harvesting.

Fig. 72 shows the sprouting-tub, an ordinary wooden tub with staves bound by bamboo hoops. The wooden bottom rests in a groove. The height is 13 inches exclusive of handles and the diameter on top 17 inches. The two handles are formed upon two elongated staves, 17 inches long, with a square grasp-hole through the part projecting above the other staves. A hole has been drilled through the bottom about ½ inch in diameter.

The seat board of the wooden stool, Fig. 73, is fashioned from a strip of wood, with a planed top surface, measuring 14 by 5 inches. The round leg, 1¾ inches in diameter, has been squared at the upper end and is driven into a corresponding mortise in the seat board. The height from the end of the leg to the seat is 16 inches. The information and photographs are from Sin Tseong, Chekiang Province.

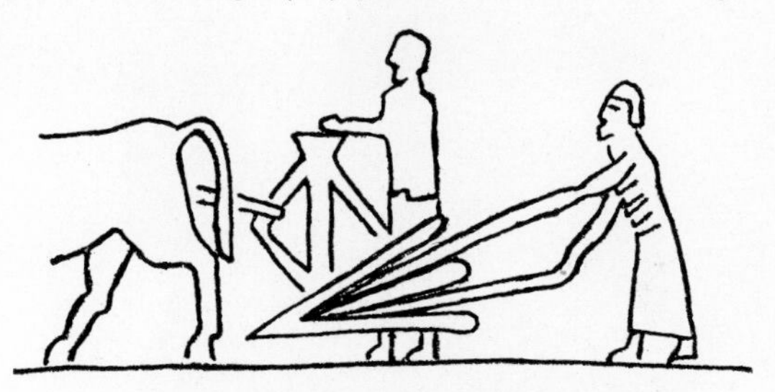

Fig. 70. Babylonian Sowing Plow.

IRRIGATION

The extensive cultivation of rice, the staple food in China is made possible by the system of canals which extend over the flat country like a spider's web and the irrigation wheels with endless chains with which the farmers flood their fields.

The fields usually are divided in plots of one mao (0.15 acre), and when contiguous to a canal or brook, have a place at the water's edge to set up the irrigation wheel, usually shaded by a tree. Fields farther away from a watercourse are supplied by ditches running from the water's edge along between the fields sometimes for quite a distance.

Fig. 74 gives the general aspect of an irrigation wheel set up at the bank of a canal. The large horizontal wheel with wooden teeth at the circumference, shown separately in Fig. 75, and here faintly seen in the background, is placed horizontally upon a wooden post extending about three feet above the ground and can revolve freely upon it. A pole with a whipple-tree is fastened to this wheel as shown in Fig. 76. The blind-folded draught animal fastened with its traces to the whipple-tree turns the wheel by walking around outside its circumference. The motion of the wheel is transferred by means of an axle-beam with two cog-wheels (see Fig. 78) to the endless chain running in the long trough, here clearly seen, extending from the water up the bank. The endless chain has 76 links with rectangular wooden blades fitting the trough. These blades as they emerge from the water carry before them an amount of water and push it up the trough to the top whence the water runs into a ditch communicating with the field to be inundated.

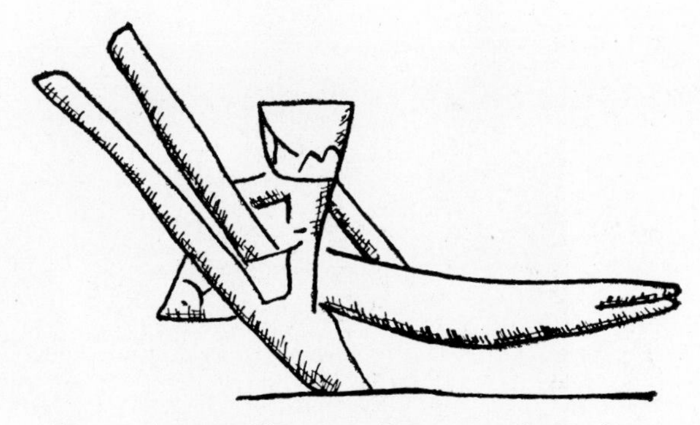

Fig 71. Another View of a Babylonian Sowing Plow.

Fig. 72. Rice Sprouting Tub.

Fig. 73. Rice Planting Stool.

Fig. 74. Animal Power Chinese Irrigation Apparatus Showing the Endless Wooden Bucket-Chain.

Details of the endless chain can be seen in Fig. 74. It is constructed entirely of wood. Each link holds a rectangular board, 10 by 3½ inches and 3/16 of an inch thick. Pushing a quantity of water before itself it is prevented from slipping on the link by a round wooden pin passing through the center of the link. The whole length of the trough is 15 feet 10 inches, the width 17 inches, and the height in the center 15 inches, at the ends 22 inches. These latter measurements show the trough to be constructed on the principles of an arch and lend it additional strength.

The end of the trough dipping into the water is held at the proper place by ropes attached to two posts stuck into the canal's muddy bottom, and frequently a basket is hung over that end to prevent foreign matter floating in the water from getting entangled with the endless chain.

The trough with 76 blades on the endless chain, is usually sufficient for the distance between the water and bank above. Most farmers have another trough, accommodating an endless chain with 100 links, stored away for times of draught, when the distance between the bank and the low level of the water cannot be spanned by the ordinary trough. In that case 24 spare links are added to the endless chain and this is then placed into the larger emergency trough.

The photographs were taken at Sin Tseong, Chekiang province.

Fig. 75. Animal Power Irrigation Apparatus, Large Power Wheel Dismounted.

The large wheel, Fig. 75, constructed entirely of hard wood has a diameter of 7 feet. The hub is held in the center by four spokes passing from rim to rim through mortises in the hub. The outside diameter of the hub is 8 inches, its length 28 inches. An axle-hole penetrating the center of the hub longitudinally is closed at its upper end (outer end as here photographed) and is 4 inches in diameter and 2 feet deep. At its inside end (lower end in action) is an iron cup in which rests the end of the pivotal post on which the wheel revolves. At the bottom opening of the hole in the hub, not here seen, and encircling the pivotal post, an iron sleeve has been inserted, 2 inches long and 4 inches in diameter to prevent the hole from wearing large. In the side-walls of the hub are four conspicuous slots, 6½ by 2 inches, one of which shows in the picture. If the wheel is left on the field over night a lock can be pushed through two of these slots, and a corresponding slot in the pivotal post. The wheel then cannot be lifted off the post.

The hub has around its top, as shown in Fig. 76 a groove to which is fastened the rope from the draught-animal's nose bolt. This keeps the animal's head inclined toward the wheel and it will consequently walk around the wheel for hours without any further guidance. On the rim of the large wheel is a wooden bracket or stop against which the whipple-tree pole, notched to fit the stop, is laid as shown in Fig. 76. To the end of this pole a notched board is fastened which just fits into the space between two spokes. Fig. 78 shows the axle beam with two cog-wheels fixed upon it which transfers the horizontal motion of the large wheel to the vertical cogs (on the left) turning the

Fig. 76. Animal Power Irrigation Apparatus, Large Power Wheel in Place.

endless chain. It has been set up on level ground for convenience in photographing. The beam measures 8 feet 10 inches, and, in the average, has a diameter of 5 inches. Where the cog-wheels have been hubbed upon it, the beam has been squared to fit their square hub holes. The bearings on each end of the beam have been turned smaller and are protected against wear by iron sleeves 2 inches long and 2¾ inches in diameter. The larger left support or bearing stand, of the beam, has a sliding board with a groove serving as a bearing. The sliding board has holes to lock it with a bamboo stick in such a position as is necessary to keep the endless chain stretched properly. The endless chain is laid around the cog-wheel shown on the left of Fig. 78, and as photographed in place in Fig. 77, this bearing-stand like its fellow on the right has a hole through which a wooden pin is driven into the ground to keep both stands tightly in place.

The animal power water-raising device, illustrated in Figs. 74 to 78 can also be set in motion by man power, with his hands. In this case the upper end of the trough has a cog-wheel the axle of which projects about a foot on each side of the cog-wheel. Two wooden crank elbows with a hole at their ends are mortised upon said axle ends and set at right angles to each other. These elbows are worked, not by the usual rigid crank handle set at right angles thereto, but by two wooden turn-sticks ending in fixed side pegs which turn loosely in holes at the crank ends so as to set the endless chain of the trough in motion. This device is worked either by one man holding a turn stick in each hand, or by two men, each with one turn stick. The manner of working is shown in Fig. 79. The picture was taken at Cha Tsuen, Chekiang.

Another way of working the irrigation apparatus is that of using foot power. This is imperfectly shown in Fig. 81, where the device is employed for pumping water from a clay pit. This mode is extensively used for agricultural purposes. The cog-wheel over which the endless chain runs is pushed upon an axle beam which is supported at both ends by two wooden sticks rammed into the ground. These wooden sticks are part of a framework, two uprights and a crosspiece, tied together with ropes, for the support of the workers who turn the contrivance with their feet. On the beam holding the cog-wheel are radial leverarms or

Fig. 77. Chinese Animal Power Irrigation Apparatus. Endless Wooden Chain Engaged on Its Wooden-Cog Wheel. The picture shows the adjustment of the cogwheel to its axle and the endless chain as described under Fig. 78.

Fig. 78. Chinese Animal Power Irrigation Apparatus. Dismounted Axle Beam with Cog-Wheels for Moving the Endless Chain

Fig. 79. Chinese Man-Power Irrigation Apparatus Worked by the Hands.

spoked foot-rests with round wooden pieces at their ends looking like mallets. There are usually two sets of four arms each, of these foot lever groups, in which the paddle-like spoke steps are set at right angles to each other, each group of spoke steps being used by one worker, who steps from one to the other of the steps and this way keeps the beam revolving. For water-raising devices with long troughs frequently three sets of these lever steps are hubbed like paddle wheels upon the beam, and three men can then with combined strength work together raising water. The way the workers hang on the poles of the framework suggests that they push the levers rather by the force of their muscles, than with the weight of their body, as might be expected. The picture was taken near Cha Tsuen, Chekiang.

Another way of getting water from the canals to the fields is by means of an arrangement in principle the same as the European "well-sweep," see Fig. 82. A wooden post about 4 feet high holds at its end a horizontal wooden pin. This post is fixed in the ground. Over this pin the long pole is laid and kept to turn about this point by another wooden pin inserted at right angles to the pole's length into the pole. One end of the pole is weighted down by a heavy stone tied to it with straw rope. To the other end a water lifting bamboo rod is tied which has at its lower end a round hole, through which the wooden bucket shown in Fig. 83 is fastened. The fastening is done by means of the framework pivoted across the open top of the bucket. The round wooden pin of this framework can be withdrawn from its two vertical holders and then pushed home again, passing through the hole in the said bamboo pole and thus enclosing the pole in the middle between its two peg-holders. In using this sweep the bamboo rod is pulled down with the bucket at its end to the water, the bucket plunged, filled and then with considerable ease lifted up, the full bucket and the counterweight at the other end of the pole about balancing each other. Thereupon the bucket is swung around to the ditch into which the water is to be poured. The bucket has on the outside two projections, hewn upon its staves, either one of which can be taken hold of as handle to conveniently tilt the bucket and empty its contents into the ditch whence it runs to the field to be inundated. The height of the bucket is 18 inches and diameter on top 13 inches. On the inside near the top rim two opposite staves have each a bulbous projection. In round holes of these latter projections turns the lower crosspiece of the framework which holds the bucket to the bamboo rod. The photograph was taken at Cha Tsuen, Chekiang.

FERTILIZING THE SOIL

The Chinese peasants use almost exclusively night-soil for manuring their fields. It is stored in large earthenware pots, similar to the ones shown in the background of Fig. 60, either standing free or sunk in the ground up to their edges. In the latter case usually privies are built over them. These, open to the public gaze, are not used by women. For the convenience of the latter, a wooden bucket with cover is kept in the house which is emptied into the free-standing earthenware pots outside the house.

The night-soil is carried to the field in wooden buckets, see Fig. 84, two of which are hung to the ends of a bamboo carrying-pole laid over the shoulder. Manure is not applied until the plants show above the ground, or water, in the case of rice. Then the dipper, Fig. 85, is filled from the bucket and a portion poured on each individual plant. When the bucket is nigh empty the peasant bends down the bamboo loop and thrusting his foot inside the bend, pulls it with his foot toward himself so as to tilt the bucket and be able to scoop out its contents completely with the dipper.

Fig. 80. Chinese Man-Power Irrigation Apparatus. This picture shows an irrigation wheel, or endless chain pump, adapted for foot power. The picture was taken near Te An, Kiangsi.

Another way to enrich the soil is to take up mud from the bottom of the canals and spread it over the field. For this purpose mud tongs are employed. Fig. 86 shows the mud basket woven from bamboo splints with its mouth-like opening and two poles crossing each other near the point where they extend through the end of the basket opposite the mouth-shaped opening. These poles, about 6 feet long, are the handles of the mud tongs. The opening and closing of the basket is done by pulling apart or pushing together the poles. The action is similar to opening or closing scissors, pliers, etc. A pivot around which the poles turn must be imagined where the poles emerge from a hole in the basket just large enough for these two poles. The ends of the poles in the basket are fastened to the jaws of the mouth-shaped opening of the basket. If now the other ends of the poles are held in close contact to each other the ends attached to the jaws will likewise be close together and consequently will be closed. If on the other hand the jaws of the basket be pulled apart, around the imaginary pivot, at the end of the basket, the ends of the poles attached to the jaws will also spread apart and thus open the basket. To take up mud the tongs are taken hold of by the poles spread apart with the jaws of the basket wide open. In this way the contrivance is pushed down into the water until the open mouth of the basket reaches the soft muddy bottom of the canal. The basket, jaws first, is pushed into the mud and then the poles, so far held apart, are pushed together which results in the closing of the basket. The basket now full of mud is pulled vertically from the water by the poles. To let the mud run out of the basket into buckets or directly on the field, the poles are spread apart thus opening the jaws and releasing the mud which drops out or if necessary, is jerked out.

Mud tongs with longer poles are used where the canals are unusually deep. The mud is deposited into buckets like the one shown in Fig. 84, or directly onto the field if it is contiguous to the canal.

HARROWS AND ROLLERS

After plowing, the field is inundated sufficiently to soften the clods, and the largest ones are broken up with the hoe. This accomplished, the harrow shown in Fig. 87, is applied. The four holes here shown in the vertical side pieces or runners of the rectangular frame, serve to fasten the traces with which the draught animal pulls the harrow. The length of these runners is 3 feet. The two horizontal wooden cross bars connecting them, which hold the teeth, are 6 feet 9 inches long, 4½ inches wide and 3½ inches thick. As is not clearly shown in the picture, the wrought iron teeth, twelve driven into one bar and eleven into the other, extend beyond the place of the rectangular frame, which results in their cutting into the ground when the harrow here shown set up on its side is pulled over the field. The staggered arrangement of the teeth ensures each tooth cutting the ground along a separate line. The teeth are flattened blades, here shown narrow edge outward, and their average dimensions are 8 inches long, 2 inches wide tapering to a blunt point, and 3/16 of an inch thick. These blade-like teeth are originally of even thickness but the cutting surface finally wears to a sharp edge giving all the appearance of having been intentionally sharpened. To the bottom of each runner a steadying blade, to keep the harrow from shifting, indistinctly seen in the picture, is stapled by means of prongs at each end which are driven into the wood to hold the blade in place. The length of these runner-blades is 8 inches, and they are slightly curved forward, the width in the middle being 1½ inches. Their thickness is 3/16 of an inch. When using the harrow the farmer stands on the frame steadying himself by holding on to the rope seen attached to the iron ring on the upper cross bar. The photograph was taken at Sin Tseong, Chekiang Province.

In the mountainous regions of the Ten Tai range in Chekiang we saw harrows used, in principle the same as the one described above, only they were much smaller, the crosspieces with the teeth being only about 5 feet long. One point of difference was that frequently all the knife-like teeth, including the runner blades, are made of fine-grained white wood which is very hard. Sometimes only the teeth on one crosspiece, the one farthest away from the draught animal, are of this hard wood. I could not identify this wood.

The harrow, Fig. 88, is different from the one shown before, inasmuch as it has handles by which to guide it and regulate the engaging of the wooden teeth into the ground. The center beam, about 5 feet long, holds the 19 wooden teeth, two of which are the

Fig. 81. Chinese Man Power Irrigation Apparatus Worked by the Feet.

prolongation of the handle bars. Two other projecting pieces, mortised into the beam at a different angle, serve for attaching the traces of the draught animal. The beam is wound along its whole length at set intervals with tightly wound bands of cord to strengthen it, and prevent the teeth from getting loose. Not a particle of metal enters into the making of this harrow.

After the application of the harrow, the field is entirely covered with water. To mix this thoroughly with the ground the field is once more plowed over, and the resulting clods are reduced with a four-

FIG. 83. BUCKET FOR A CHINESE WELL-SWEEP.

FIG. 82. CHINESE WELL SWEEP.

pronged fork attached to a wooden handle at an acute angle. The final smoothing of the field, which now looks like a huge mud puddle, is accomplished with the roller shown in Fig. 89. This consists of a wooden frame (7 feet long and 3 feet wide) which holds the roller proper i.e., a round beam equipped, as shown, with numerous knives. This wooden beam is 6 feet 9 inches long and 3¼ inches in diameter. Its ends, serving as bearings, in its revolution, are reduced to a diameter of 1¼ inches and protected against wear by iron sleeves 1½ inches in diameter. One of the bearings is longer than the other and this is pushed all the way into the hole on the right side of the frame. When in this position there is enough clearance between the other bearing and the frame, to bring this pivot directly in front of the hole in this, the left side, of the frame and push it home. Now the knifed roller beam rests with its two pivots securely in the frame, and the shifting of the roller to the right which would disengage the pivot on the left is prevented by a little wooden peg, faintly seen attached to a string, which fits into a slot on the right hand side of the frame, locking the bearing into its hole. There are seven rows of wrought iron knives stapled into the wooden roller beam. They are in the average 6 inches long and about 1½ inches wide in the middle, and one eighth of an inch thick. On each end of each blade is a tang which is driven into the wood. The arrangement of the knives is staggered and for this reason some of the seven rows have at

Fig. 84. Chinese Manure Bucket.

one end space for a shorter knife only. To carry conveniently the whole apparatus to and from the field, the knifed roller is taken from its position in the frame, and placed into notches on top of its side pieces, shown in Fig. 90.

In dragging the roller over the inundated field mud is splashed up liberally, and to protect the farmer standing upon the apparatus from the splashing a semi-circular bamboo screen is fixed between four wooden nails on the frame. Four holes in the sidepieces of the frame serve for attaching the traces for the draught animal and the rope attached to an iron ring on the top side piece, helps to steady the farmer. Two narrow wooden strips, faintly seen nailed to the outer margins of the cross bars where the farmer stands are to prevent him from sliding off into the mire. The pictures were taken at Sin Tseong, Chekiang province.

TILLING TOOLS

Three Small Hoes.—(*A*) When the rice gets ripe ditches are to be made between the plants to drain off the water as it is desirable to have a dry field when harvesting rice. For this purpose the hoe (*A*), in Fig. 91 is used. It has the characteristic concave edge which will be referred to presently under Fig. 93. When using it the hoe is held with the right hand and the rice plants are taken hold of with the left and bent to one side out of its way. The handle is 19 inches long, the metal part 11 inches long, 2¼ inches wide and 3/16 of an inch thick.

(*B*). This hoe is used for setting a kind of potato. After the potatoes are harvested in autumn some are put back into the ground and left there over the winter. In the spring each plant has from 10 to 15

Fig. 85. Chinese Manure Dipper.

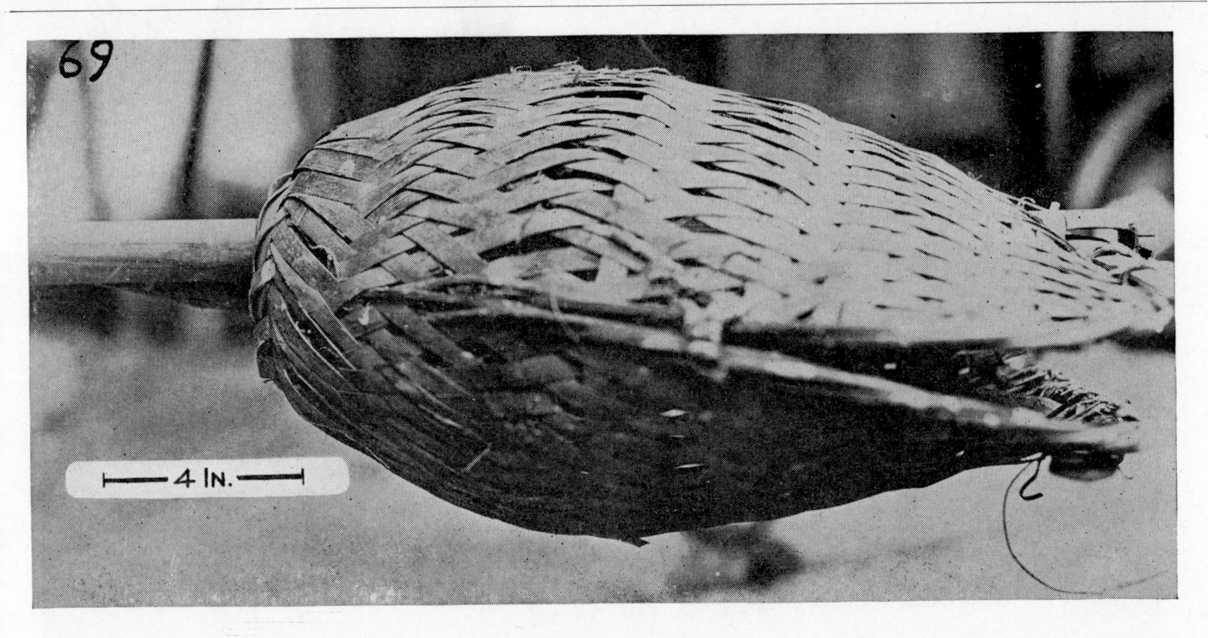

FIG. 86. CHINESE MUD TONGS.

air-roots with eyes about 2 inches from each other. These roots are cut into pieces with scissors, each piece having an eye. A hole is made with the hoe (*B*), the root put in vertically and covered up. This hoe is also used for making holes to plant maize and soy beans. The length of the metal part is 8 inches, the width 1½ inches, the handle is 14½ inches long.

(*C*). A pointed instrument, is a cross between a trowel and a hoe, and likewise used for making holes to plant seeds as of melons, pumpkins and beans. The blade from point to bend measures 7 inches, the widest width is 1½ inches. The inner broad side of the blade shown on the picture has a ridge along the middle and is ¼ of an inch at its thickest part. The handle is 12 inches long and fits into a socket sleeve 1 inch in diameter formed at the bent part of the metal. These tools are all of wrought iron and were photographed at Se Aw, Chekiang Province.

Spade.—The spade in Fig. 92 looks as if it was cast, but it is really wrought iron. The length from

FIG. 87. HARROW.

Fig. 88. Harrow with Wooden Teeth.

Fig. 89. Roller.

FIG. 90. ROLLER. The picture shows the knifed beam of the Chinese field roller displaced for transport and temporarily set into top notches on its side pieces.

the socket to the cutting edge is 19 inches. The blade itself is 11¼ inches long and 5¼ inches wide. To give strength to the blade a ridge has been left in the middle as seen on its upper side, the other under side is quite smooth. Along the ridge the blade is about ⅝ inch thick, on the edges ⅜ of an inch. The socket has solid walls and the handle, also shown in Fig. 92, is merely rammed into it. The length of the handle is 21 inches and the diameter is 1¼ inches. Its top ends in a cross-piece which has a square mortise. A corresponding tenon at the end of the handle shaft fits tightly into this mortise. It is one of the peculiarities of the Chinese that they rely on mortise and tenon joints to hold together by friction only without the aid of wedges or pins passing through the surrounding wood of a mortise and the tenon. In like manner wooden parts fitting into metal sockets are never secured by passing pins through the metal and the wood.

The spade is not used much on the field itself except for keeping in trim irrigation ditches or digging new ones, and for digging over the field along the edges which cannot be reached with the plow. Otherwise it is used for digging deep where required, as for instance, around the roots of trees in transplanting or getting out stumps.

Spades to be foot-driven require strong foot gear. The Chinese who work mostly bare-footed in their fields can not, of course, push the spade with the foot for any length of time. This is probably the explanation of the fact that the spade has never been widely adopted by the Chinese. When it is used at all, the handle has to be fitted with a crosspiece upon which that pressure can be exerted which the European peasant exerts with his well-shod foot.

Hoe.—Fig. 92 shows also the common form of hoe used in China. The handle, a pole about 5 feet long, is inserted into the eye of the hoe and held there by a wedge. The angle which the wrought iron part forms with the handle can be seen from Fig. 93. The hoe, Fig. 92, is 11¼ inches long, at the edge 3¼ inches wide. The blade is ½ inch thick near the eye and tapers toward the edge. The thickness of the metal around the eye is ⅜ of an inch. The opening of the eye is not round but 3 inches one way and 2 inches the other, allowing for a handle about 2 inches in diameter to be inserted. The edge of the blade is here straight, in Fig. 93 it is shown worn convex. In the mountains where pebbles and stones are frequently encountered the edge of this hoe will show wear sooner than in other regions where the soil is free from stones. The mountain dwellers guard against

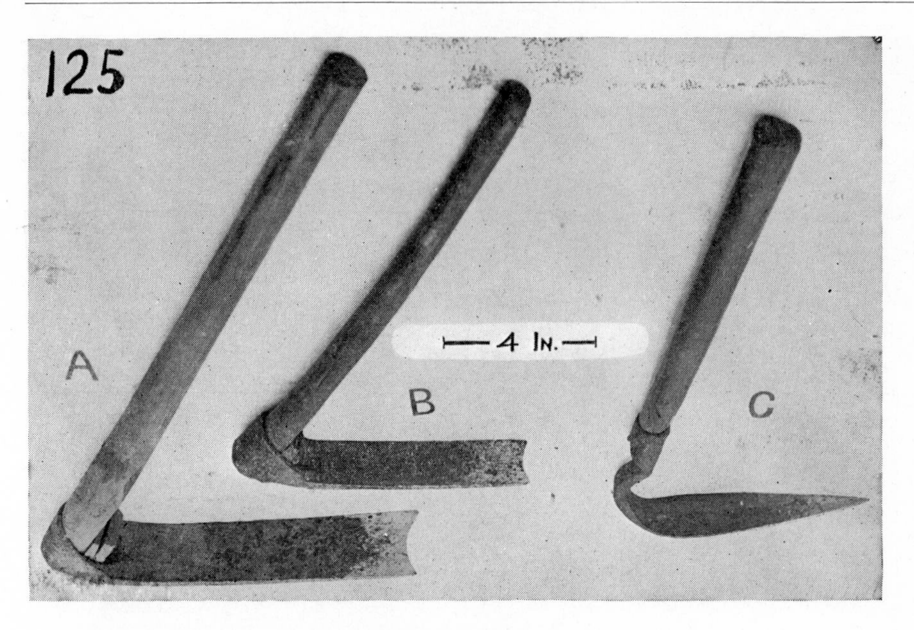

FIG. 91. THREE SMALL HOES.

this wear by making the edges of their hoes concave. It stands to reason that it takes a longer time for a concave edge to wear convex than it would for a straight one. The hoe is one of the most used implements of the farmer. After the first plowing it is used to break up big clods all over the field. Then it is used to make ridges for planting wheat or vegetables, for weeding, and for making holes beside the young plants to put in manure, etc.

Grubbing Fork.—This is likewise shown in Fig. 92, from the side upon which the handle is attached. The material is wrought iron, the two inner prongs form the loop which passes around the handle. Through holes in these two prongs passes the other metal part of the instrument whose ends form the two outer prongs. At the same time this inserted piece closes up the loop of the inner prongs thus forming the eye which holds the handle. The handle, usually a bamboo pole, as seen in Fig. 93 (left), is about 5 feet long. The length of the prongs is 9½ inches and the width of the fork 9½ inches. The prongs terminate in flat edges one inch wide.

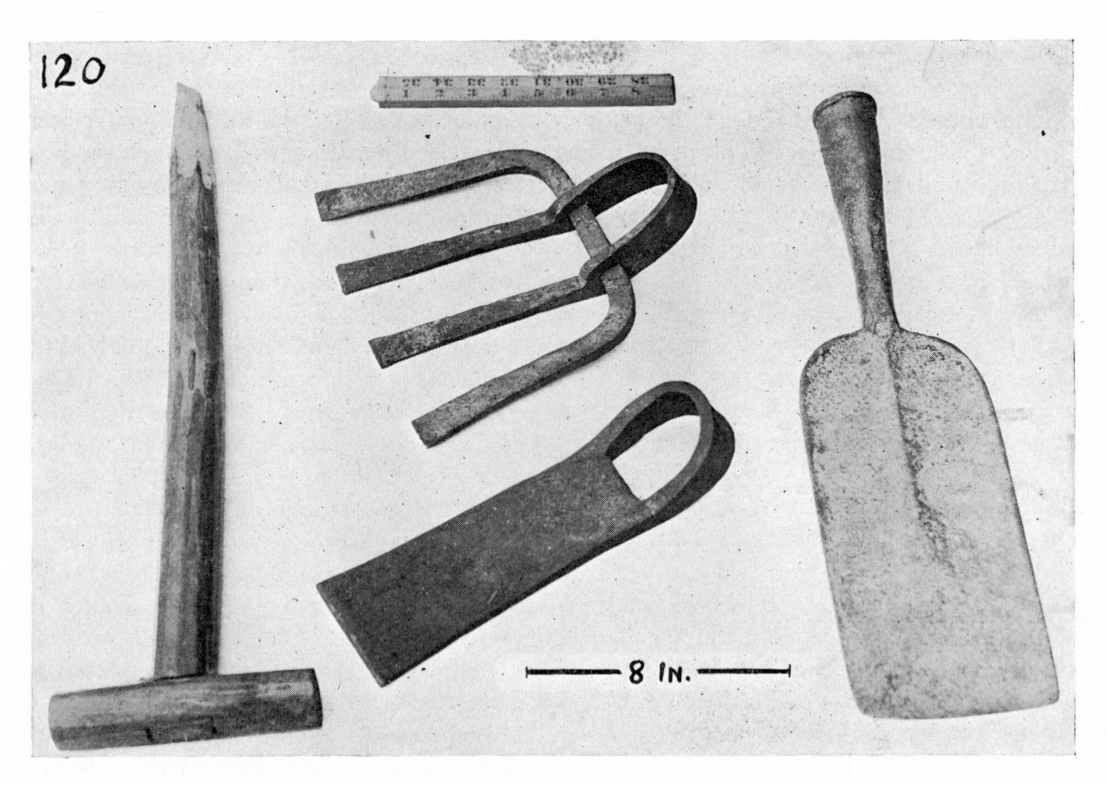

FIG. 92. CHINESE SPADE, HOE AND GRUBBING FORK.

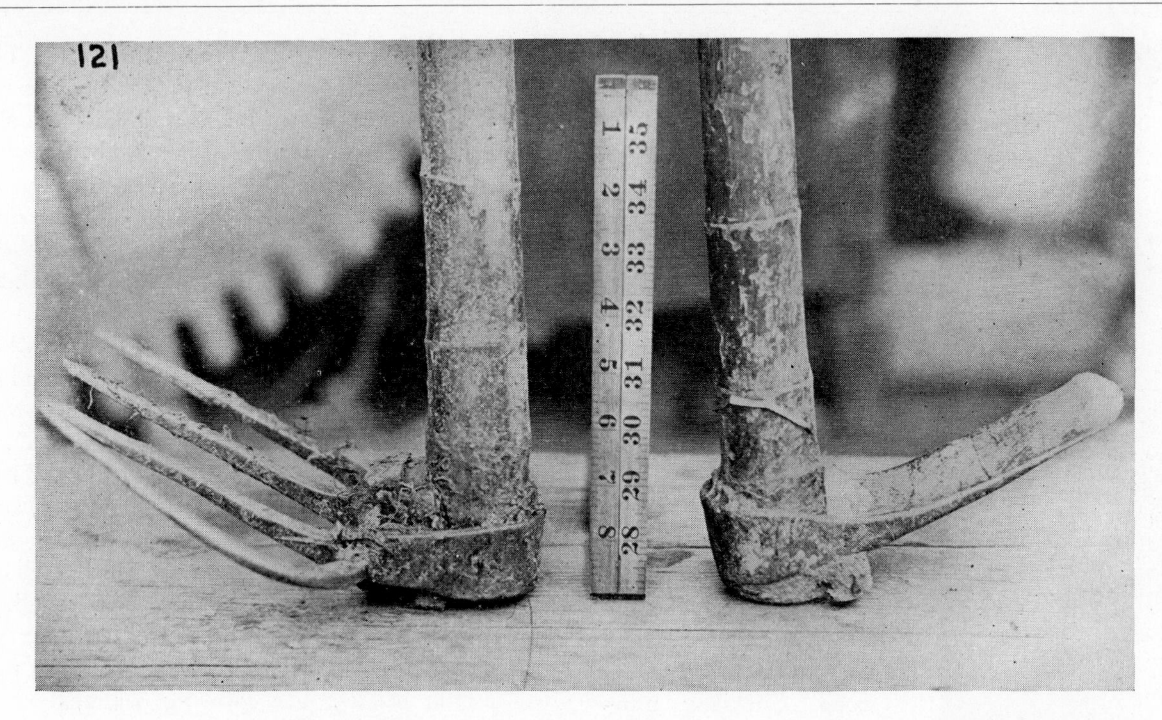

FIG. 93. CHINESE HOE AND GRUBBING FORK. Another specimen of the implements described under Fig. 92 are here shown the hoe with its blade worn convex on the stony ground. Photographed at Sin Tseong, Chekiang.

This implement is used on the field after the second plowing for smoothing the surface. Fig. 92 was taken in the Native City, Shanghai.

Two-Pronged Hoe.—We have already shown a hoe with four prongs in Figs. 92 and 93. The one shown here, in Fig. 94, with two prongs is used in a mountainous district, and is fit for deep penetration in hard soil. The length of the metal part is 11 inches, and the distance from point to point is 4 inches. The curved back which forms the socket is 3 inches wide.

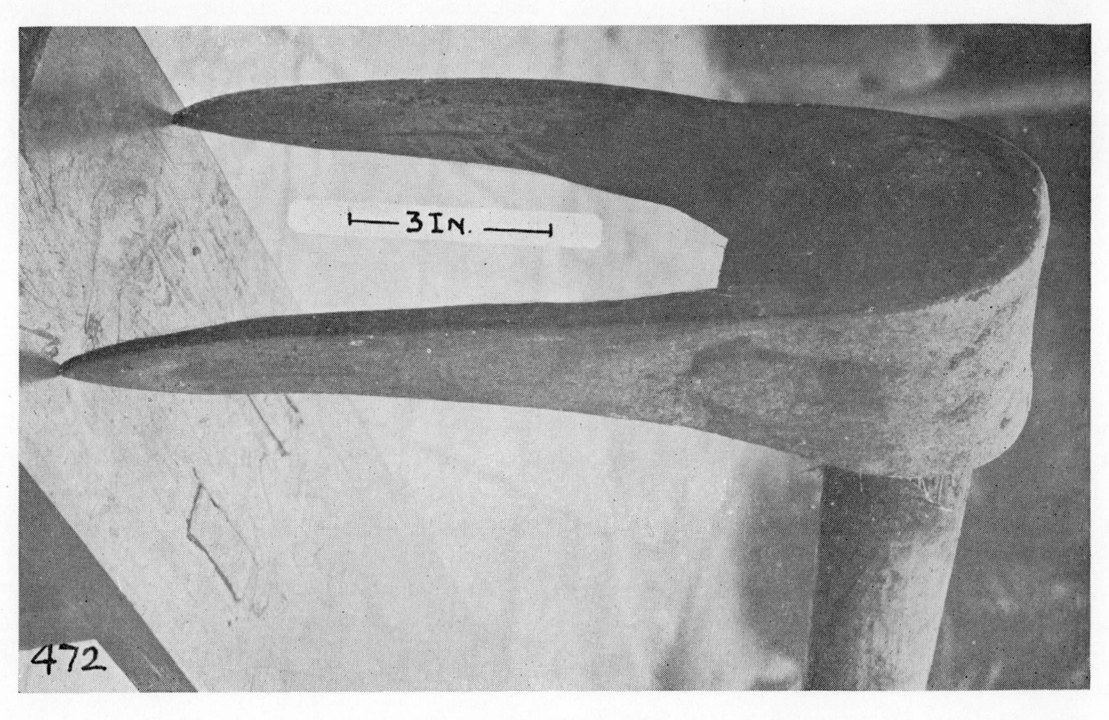

FIG. 94. TWO-PRONGED HOE.

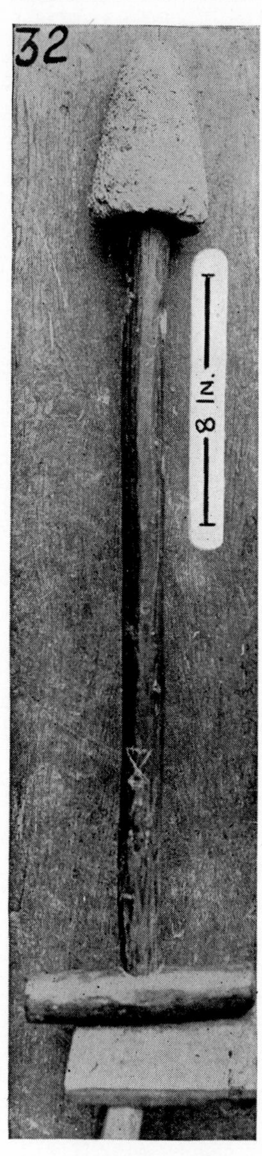

FIG. 95. DIBBLE.

A heavy iron pin riveted into place forms the socket for the handle. The wooden handle is 3 feet 8 inches long and requires stooping in handling. The photograph was taken in Kienchang, Kiangsi.

Dibble.—This instrument, a wooden handled stone cone, might just as well have been made in the stone age 3,000 years ago. It is shown in Fig. 95, and is used to make holes in the ground when planting vegetables, peas, wheat, etc. These plants were specifically mentioned upon our inquiry in Sin Tseong, Chekiang province, where we took the picture. The length of the instrument from stone tip to the end of the handle is 2 feet 8 inches. The handle is rammed into a round hole in the stone.

Wheat is very sparingly cultivated in the southern and central parts of China. From the fact that our informant mentioned it as one of the plants which are set with the aid of the dibble, we learn that wheat is not planted by sowing the grains broadcast over the field, but by putting seeds or young plants into holes made with the dibble. In planting rice, of course, the dibble is not used, as the young plants are easily pushed into the watery mud in which rice is cultivated.

In using the dibble it is pushed into freshly worked ground which of course is quite loose. Before withdrawing it, it is given a twist to prevent the dirt from sticking to the dibble and to smooth and thus keep the walls of the hole from collapsing, at least long enough for the plant for which the hole is made to be inserted.

Wrought Iron Fork.—This tool, Fig. 96, is shown more as evidence that there is such a thing in China, as a wrought iron fork, rather than to convey the impression that it is a universally used tool. The Chinese do with as few tools as possible, especially where iron is scarce, and such a fork as shown would, therefore, be considered rather a luxury than a daily necessity. We would call the tool a hay-fork, but in China the handling of hay plays a subordinate rôle. The fork is used for handling straw, of which there is plenty, as the main crop in central and southern China is rice, two or three harvests a year.

In northern China forks are made of bent wood as the following note indicates: "In the neighborhood of Lai-yang, Shantung, the insect wax tree, the *Lah-shu*, grows plentifully. The natives use the wood, which is very tough, for making a variety of articles. They begin adapting it to their purposes when young, and bend it while still growing so that it assumes any shape they please, and thus they make most excellent hay-forks, all of one piece, for purposes of husbandry; frames for the backs of mules, on which they bind the burdens; handles of large baskets, walking-sticks, and other useful articles. The growing saplings when young, are so cut, and so bound that they naturally divide into prongs and make a natural fork, both strong and useful, without subsequent cutting or nails." [3]

This account I can amplify by stating that the growing saplings are worked upon by making incisions, so as to make a fork where there was no fork, and to bind the pieces to remain in the desired position. These tied pieces are then allowed to grow for another year or two, when the forced positions have become natural, and are then cut off the stem to be used as utensils. I saw once the curved beam of a plow still growing as the limb of a tree, but tied with ropes to assume the curve. The farmer said that in a few more years the limb would be thick enough to be useful for a plow. The wrought iron fork shown was photographed on a farm 5 li from San Ho, Chekiang. The length of the wrought iron part, from the socket to the points is 14 inches, and the distance between the two points is 7½ inches.

Hand Harrow.—In some rice-growing districts the instrument shown in Fig. 97 is used. We took the photograph at Se Aw, Chekiang. In other parts of Chekiang we visited it is not used, then again in some parts of Kiangsu province people are quite familiar with it.

The wooden frame at its widest part measures 6 inches and is 12 inches long. Iron spikes extending in the average 1⅛ inches from the wood are driven

[3] From "Journeys in North China," by A. Williamson, London, 1870.

through the frame and the extending points clinched. The single handle is about 9 feet long. The end of the handle is inserted into a hole in the shortest cross-piece of the frame and then passes through a hole in a piece of wood which is mortised into the opposite end cross-piece of the frame and extends from it upward at right angles to the plane of the frame. Where the handle passes through that hole it is kept firmly in place by a wedge.

After the rice-fields have been planted in rows, always six plants in one hole, weeds growing between the plants are pulled out, thrown down and pushed under the mud by stepping on them and after this has been accomplished the hand-harrow is applied to get the muddy ground between the rice-plants smooth again. The implement is held with both hands like a rake, by the handle pole, and passed back and forth between the rice-plants.

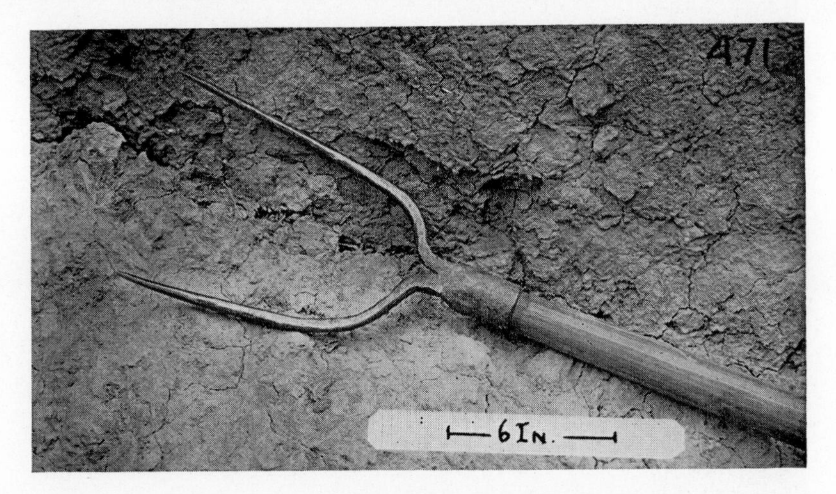

FIG. 96. WROUGHT IRON FORK.

Weed Scraper.—This tool, Fig. 98, is closely related to the hand-harrow just shown. Both are used for the same purpose, to smooth the spaces in the inundated rice-field between the plants. The weeds growing there are pushed under the water with the feet, or pulled by hand and pushed under, and then the tool shown comes into play to smooth again the ground between the rice-plants. There are various forms of this tool according to different districts. The wooden handle, a pole about 5 feet long, is split, and halfway up, at the end of the split, fitted with a ferrule to prevent the split from extending. The two forking ends thus formed of the pole are wedged into the sockets of the tool, as the picture plainly shows. The length of the iron blade along its edge is 13¼ inches. The photograph was taken at San Ho, which lies in a famous rice-producing district of Northern Anhwei.

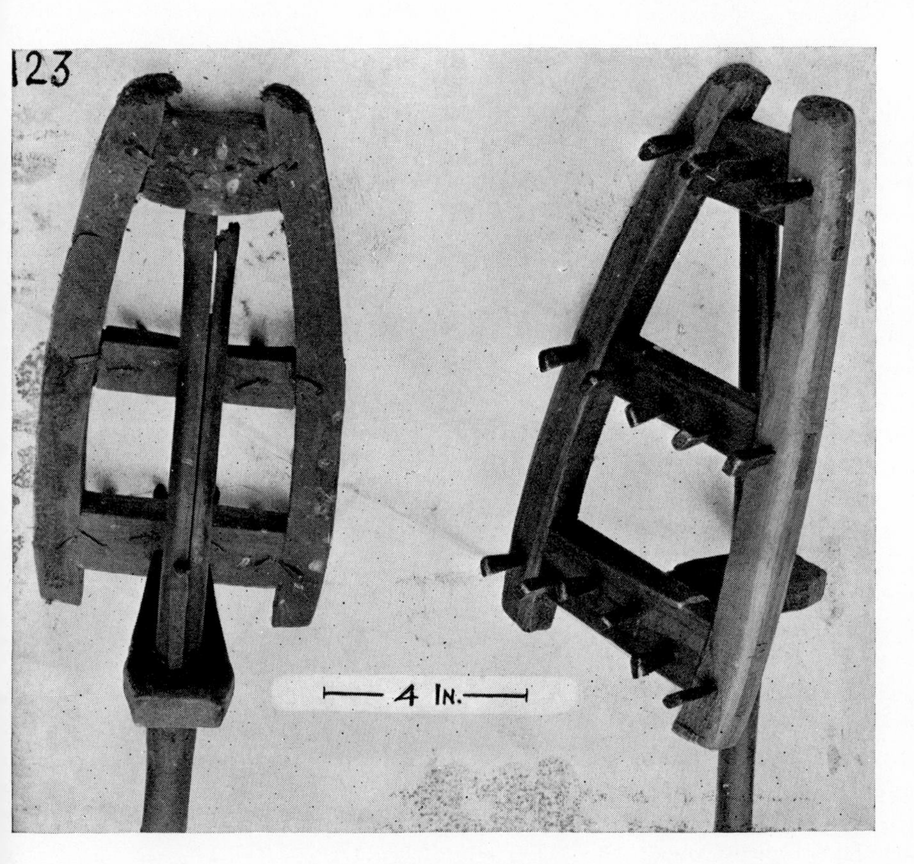

FIG. 97. CHINESE HAND-HARROW.

Weeding Hoe.—Fig. 99 shows a wrought iron weeding hoe, a modification of the ordinary hoe. The eye, manner of fastening the handle and angle

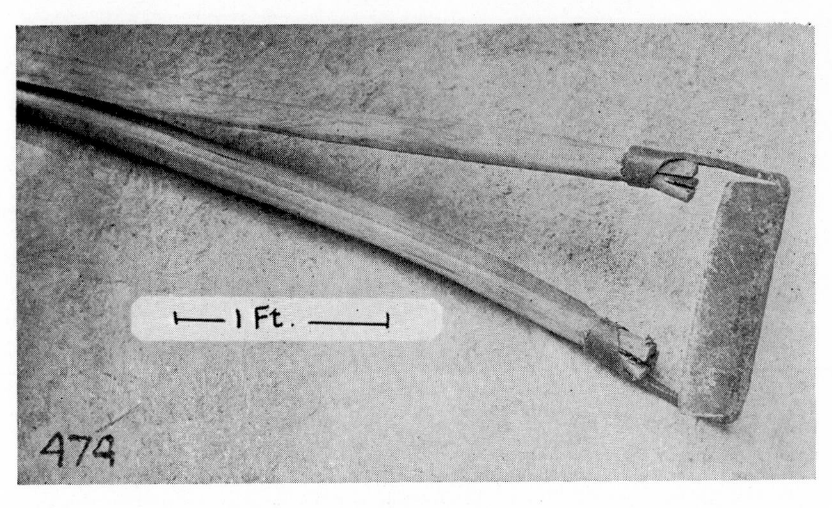

Fig. 98. Weed Scraper.

of blade with the handle is the same, only the blade is flattened out like a broad-axe and the edge is kept quite sharp. Weeds on the fields between the vegetables and other cultivated plants as wheat, cotton, indigo, etc., are cut off rather than pulled out with this hoe, by sliding the blade close to the ground with strokes toward the body of the person handling the instrument. The weeds thus cut are not gathered but left lying on the ground to dry up and perish. The handle as in most of these instruments is about 5 feet long. The distance from the edge of the blade to its eye is 4⅝ inches, the cross width of the edge from point to point on a straight line 8¼ inches. The thickness of the blade is ⅜ of an inch, tapering to the sharp edge. The photograph was taken in the Native City of Shanghai.

Chinese Rakes.—I had looked in vain for a long time for Chinese rakes, and had almost come to the conclusion that they did not exist. Here, however, they are, Figs. 100 and 101, one with iron teeth, and the other with wooden ones. I found them in extensive use finally in northern Anhui, where I took the pictures. This part of the country is given mostly to the cultivation of rice, and in connection with it the rake is used for weeding. The one with iron teeth, Fig. 100, consists of a handle ending in a wooden cross-piece with drilled holes, into which the iron teeth are driven. Their points emerging on the upper side are clinched. The rake with wooden teeth, Fig. 101, is similarly constructed, but here the inserted teeth rest in blind square mortises made with a chisel. The frame holding them is of soft wood, the teeth, however, are of a close-grained hard wood.

Bamboo Rake.—The bamboo rake, Fig. 102, photographed in Anhwei, is common to most provinces where bamboo is grown. Of late years this type has been imported to this country by enterprising Japanese and can now be bought in any hardware shop. The one we show, however, is a more primitive type and exhibits the wonderful possibilities of bamboo. The whole tool handle and prongs, is made of one piece of bamboo, with the exception of a few strips of wickerwork likewise of bamboo, which hold the prongs in their proper relative position. The stem is split to form the six prongs, and wound at the split with a withe of bamboo, to prevent further splitting, and the ends of the prongs are bent, over the fire, to form the teeth of the rake. The structure is elastic and admirably fit for raking out the straw of threshed grain. In autumn many children can always be seen, armed with such a rake and a basket, gathering up dead leaves and little branches for fire-wood.

In Shantung, where bamboo does not thrive, similar rakes and hay-forks are formed of one piece of wood, from the insect wax tree *(Ligustrum lucidum)* previously described.

Sickles.—Fig. 103 shows three sickles as used in Chekiang province. The photograph was taken at Sin Tseong, near Ningpo. (*A*) is the serrated sickle used for harvesting rice. The blade from shaft to pointed end measures on a straight line 6¼ inches, the aver-

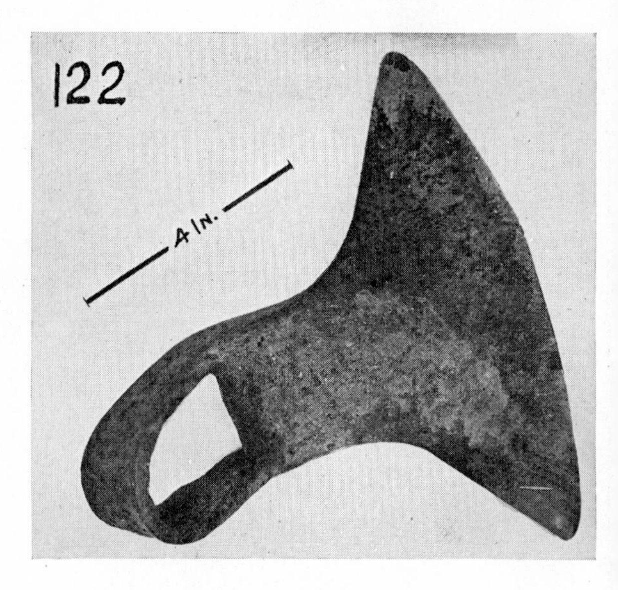

Fig. 99. Chinese Weeding Hoe.

age width is ⅞ of an inch, the thickness at the back about 1/16 of an inch. The blade at one end narrows to a tang which passes through the rudely shaped wooden handle and is clinched where it emerges. The teeth are cut into the edge with a cold chisel. The blade is made of wrought iron. (*B*) is a sickle used for cutting grass, made also of wrought iron. The length of its blade is 5 inches, its widest width 2¼ inches tapering to a point. Its thickness at the back is about ⅛ of an inch. A continuation of the blade is bent into a sleeve or socket into which the wooden handle is driven. (*C*) shows the sickle used for cutting a reed grass very much cultivated in Chekiang province for making straw hats and weaving straw mats (the warp threads of the latter are made of hemp). The blade made of wrought iron is 10 inches long and 2 inches wide. Its back is strengthened by a ridge extending generally over three quarters of the length of the blade. The socket to receive the handle is formed in the same way as in (*B*).

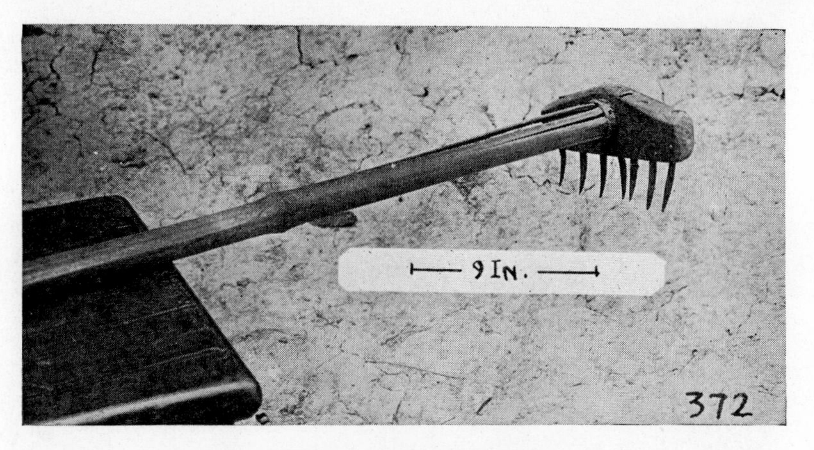

FIG. 100. CHINESE RAKE WITH IRON TEETH.

In some of the more mountainous and wooded parts of Chekiang the large sickle (*C*) is used for cutting off small branches from the trees to be used as kindling wood.

Scythe.—This is the nearest approach to a scythe which I have found. Fig. 104 shows the scythe without the handle. I add Fig. 105, not so much to show the handle, which is merely a bamboo pole, about 5 feet long, as the angle which the metal blade forms with the handle. This instrument is used to cut an herbaceous plant resembling clover which boiled like vegetables is used for human food. From the description given us of the plant and its yellow flowers it would rather seem to be an umbelliferous plant.[4]

The iron blade is wrought of one piece. At one end a sleeve or socket is formed into which to insert the handle, namely a bamboo pole. The blade has the appearance on top of a section of a double-edged sword. The thickness of the ridge in the middle of the blade is ¼ of an inch near the handle but decreases in thickness and disappears towards the end of the blade. The back side of the blade has no ridge. The blade viewed from the side, see Fig. 105, is slightly curved and its length on a straight line from sleeve to end is 12 inches.

Fig. 106 shows a peasant cutting clover with the

[4] I have found since that this plant is *"Medicago astragalus."*

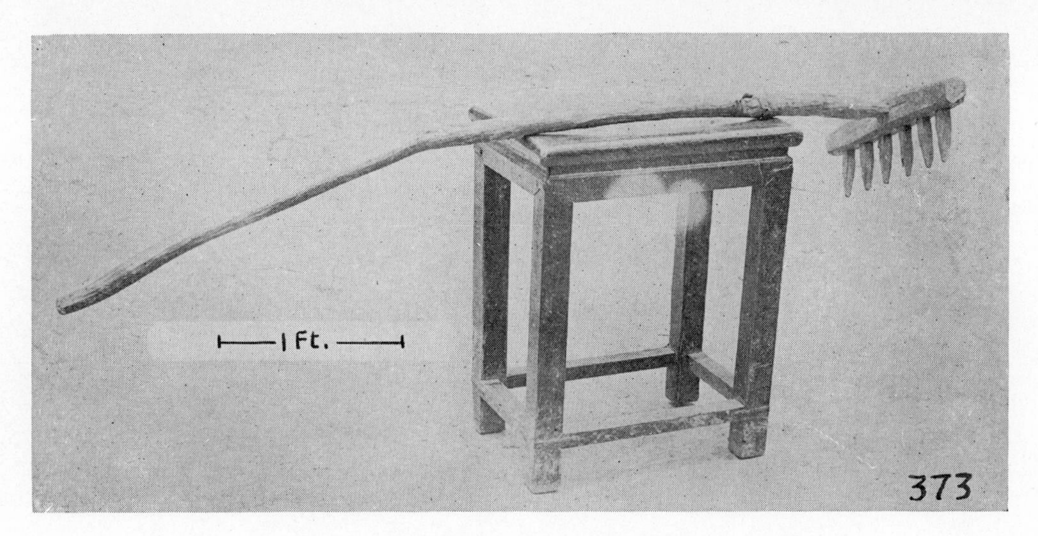

FIG. 101. CHINESE RAKE WITH WOODEN TEETH.

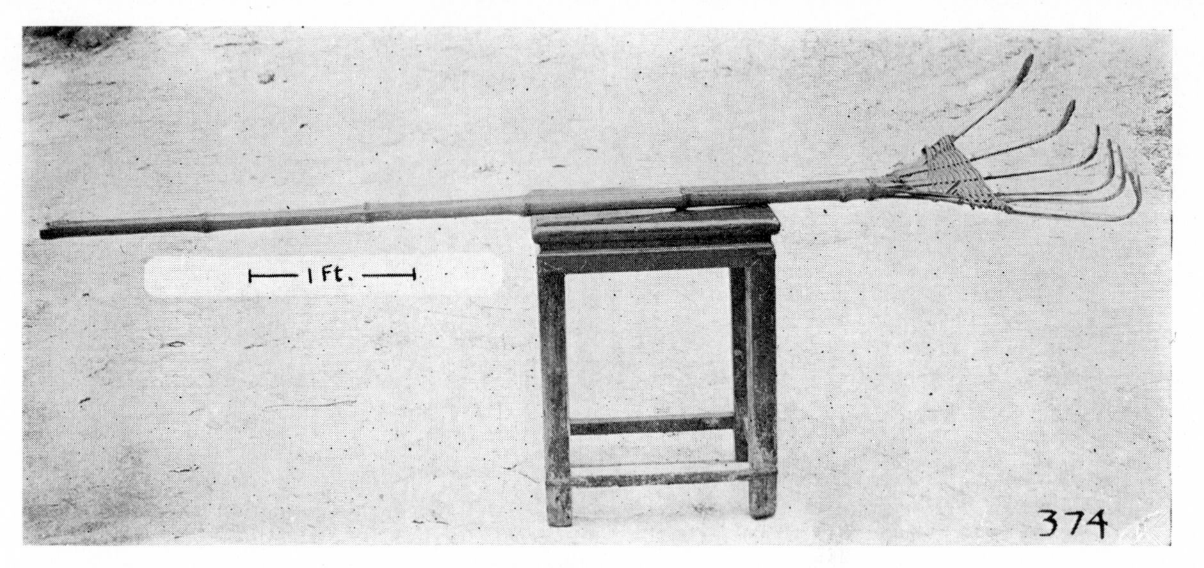

Fig. 102. Bamboo Rake.

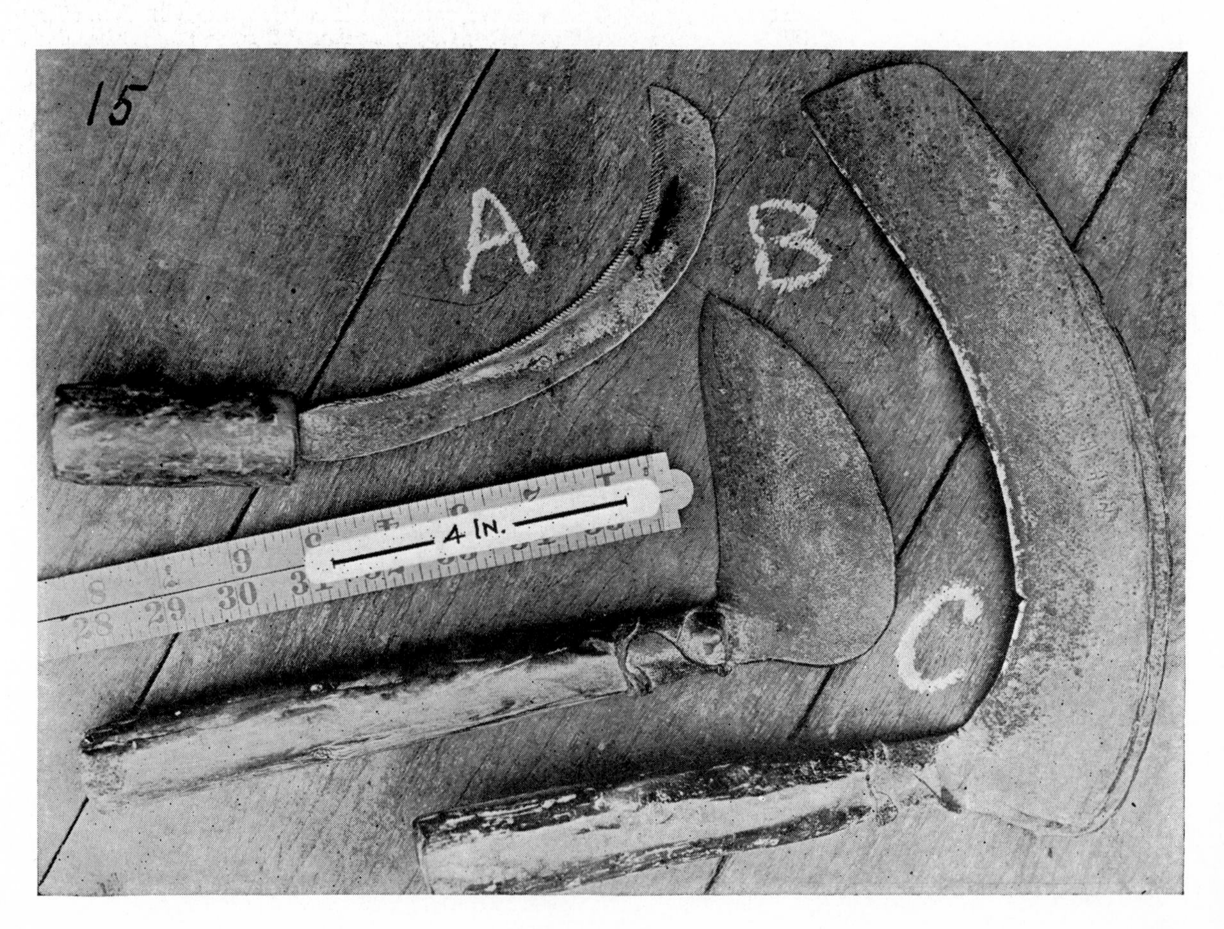

Fig. 103. Sickles.

FIG. 104. SCYTHE.

Chinese scythe. The bunch of clover cut with each stroke is carried up into the air with the blade from which it drops when the scythe is swung downward for the next thrust. The plant with yellow flowers being cut with this instrument seems to be of secondary importance. From observation in various parts of Chekiang province it appears that real red clover is also cultivated extensively for cattle-feed and reaped with this scythe. The pictures were taken at Sin Tseong, Chekiang province.

THRESHING AND WINNOWING

In the fertile regions, around Ningpo, Chekiang province, well-watered by a network of canals, of all the grains, only rice is cultivated. The fields are as a rule divided in parcels of one mou (6.61 mou is one acre). The rice is planted in rows, six plants in one hole. The reaping, done with the serrated sickle, is closely linked with the threshing. When the rice is fully ripe, ready for cutting, the farmer proceeds to the field with the sickle and the threshing-box fully equipped. Six of the individual bundles (consisting each of six individual plants) are cut and laid down on the ground. When all the rice on the whole field has been cut the threshing begins. The threshing box, Fig. 107, is put on the field and the two reapers take a sheaf (consisting of six bundles of 36 individual plants) each and hit it nine or ten times against the wooden frame, Figs. 108 and 109, in the threshing box by which action all the grains are loosened from the ears and dropped into the threshing box. The farmer is not aware that he hits the sheaves a definite number of times against the threshing box frame. When questioned the farmers would answer that they hit the sheaves until all the grains are dislodged. But actual counting revealed that some always hit the sheaves ten times, others always nine times. As the work progresses the threshing box is slid along the field until all the sheaves scattered over the field have been threshed. When the threshing box is about half full the contents are scooped out into large square baskets woven of bamboo splints.

Fig. 107 shows the fully equipped threshing box with the wooden frame, not seen, and its protecting screen for keeping the grains of rice from falling beyond the limits of the wooden box. This protecting screen is a mat woven of bamboo splints, reinforced

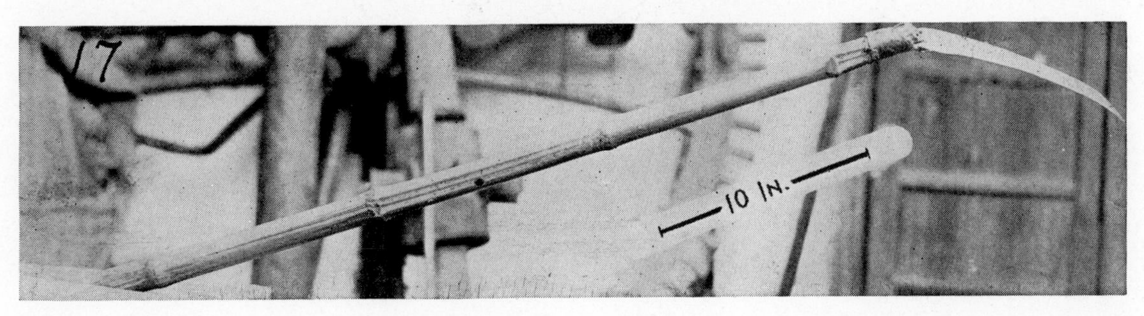

FIG. 105. SCYTHE WITH HANDLE.

Fig. 106. Scythe in Use.

pieces. The frame is of soft wood 3 inches thick, the slats and centerpiece of some kind of hard wood. The centerpiece is naturally curved. The art of bending lumber is not known. Only bamboo the Chinese know how to bend, by subjecting it to heat in an open wood-fire.

The wooden threshing box, Fig. 109, is composed of four slanting side walls and the bottom. Two of the side walls are strengthened on their outer edges by half-round ribs, through which mortises are cut to receive tenons, which are projections of the two other side walls. The upper tenons are wider and longer than the others and serve as handles for the whole box, to lift it or slide it along on the ground. To facilitate sliding there are attached two runners on the bottom of the box. These runners, one of which is seen on the front bottom margin are strips of hardwood 2 feet 6 inches by 2 inches by 1 inch. They are nailed to the bottom with bamboo nails, so that the box rests on them, the one-inch side facing the ground. The direction of the runners is at right angles to the inserted frame, and the distance between the

with vertical bamboo stays which are bound to the fabric with strips of cane. The mat which is 6 feet 6 inches wide on top and 8 feet on the bottom circumference, is inserted into the box.

The wooden slatted frame against which the sheaves are struck is shown in Fig. 108. The overall dimensions are: Length on top 3 feet 7 inches, on bottom 1 foot 9 inches. Its height is 2 feet 4 inches. The center-piece with grooves to receive the wooden slats is curved and bulges the slats forward in the center. The various parts of the frame are held together by tenon and mortise and bamboo nails driven in so as to pass through mortise and tenon. The slats are one-half of an inch thick and about 2½ inches wide, pointed at both ends to fit into round holes in the side

Fig. 107. Threshing Box.

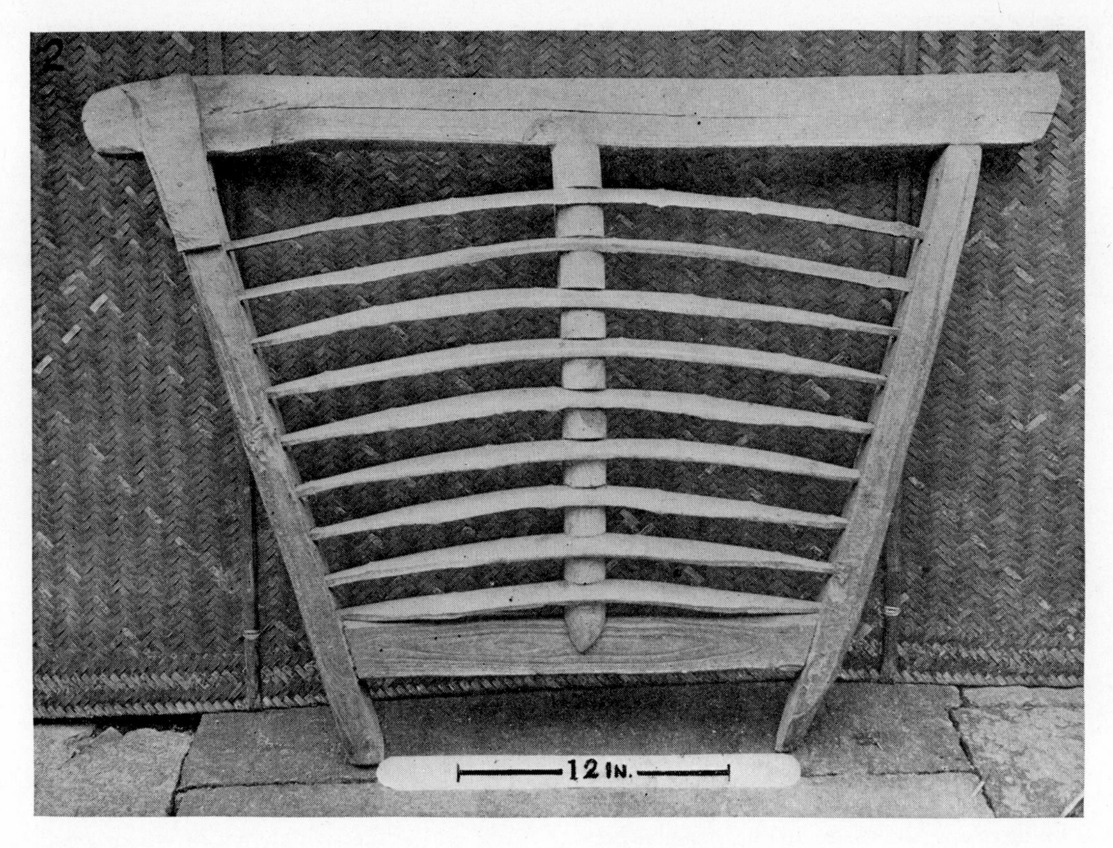

FIG. 108. CHINESE THRESHING FRAME.

strips forming the runners is 2 feet. To the side wall, showing fully as facing us, in Fig. 109, a strip of hardwood is attached, with a groove on that side which abuts against the side wall, thus forming an eye, through which passes a rope. On the opposite side is the same arrangement. To carry the box a bamboo-rod is passed through the loops of these ropes and the ends of the bamboo-rod shouldered. The box is square, measuring 3 feet 10 inches on top, 2 feet 6 inches on the bottom. Its height is 2 feet 4 inches. The thickness of the boards is 1 inch.

This is the usual mode of threshing rice. Usually the screen rests in the wooden box, in other places I saw the screen used alone, without the box, propped up upon a large bamboo mat upon which the grains collected.

For comparison I shall mention a contrivance with which the Japanese remove the rice grains from the sheaves. The heads of the sheaves are drawn through the teeth of a metal comb or hetchel held in a frame and the grains drop down in a basket standing under the frame. The same principle was made use of in a cart drawn by oxen or pushed by hand as described by Pliny, for reaping grain directly from the plants standing on the field. A similar apparatus was used by the Pennsylvania Germans in Bucks County, Pa., U. S. A., until about 1860, under the name "clover stripper." In a Swiss publication (neue Sammlung Physic.—Oeconomischer Schriften, Zurich 1732), it is related that a certain Francois Pellet and his wife, a peasant from St. Lisre (Aubonne), invented such a contrivance for the reaping of clover seed. Even if we doubt that the clover reaper was invented by these people, this account allows us to believe that the Bucks County "stripper" did not originate in America, but was brought there from Europe. In Australia a harvesting machine, called stripper, is used which strips the grain from the head of the standing sheaves in the field. Here we probably have again the same principle as made use of in the contrivance described by Pliny, and as underlying the ripple for removing the seeds from flax, broom corn, etc., or the metal comb as used in the Black Forest in Germany for gathering blackberries.

Ordinarily the threshing of rice in China is done in the manner described. There are, however, varieties of rice produced by poor soil which do not grow very high, and it would not be very effective to use that

FIG. 109. CHINESE THRESHING BOX WITHOUT THE BASKET-WORK SCREEN.

method of threshing for them. In the neighborhood of Shanghai, such rice is threshed with a flail as shown in Fig. 111. The swingle is composed of six bamboo strips, each 21 inches long and ⅝ inch square. These strips are held together by three cross braces of wood upon which the six strips are laid. Thongs of pigskin previously soaked in water and with slits in their ends are hooked over the ends of these wooden cross braces. When the thongs get dry, they contract and hold the six bamboo strips of the swingle very firmly together. The single cross brace at one end of the swingle has its wooden end extending 3½ inches, and terminates in a knob. Over this extension passes the loop of the flail handle. The handle is a bamboo rod 5 feet 5 inches long and 1 inch in diameter. Its end has been bent over to form a loop in which this wooden pin extension of the swingle cross brace turns. In flapping down the flail it is held in such a position that the surface over which stretch the pigskin thongs comes down upon the material to be threshed. The threshing is done upon the ground in the court of the house, which is usually laid with flagstones. The use of the flail around Shanghai is apparently not extensive. There was only one to be found on the farm we visited.

Our informant told us that this flail is used for poorer qualities of rice, stunted in its growth, as mentioned above, also for threshing wheat and the pods of beans after they have been dried. The picture we took at Chao Ka Too near Shanghai.

The wooden club used in washing clothes (see Fig. 280) is also employed at times in the province of Chekiang for the beating of the ripe pods of the Chinese oil-cabbage, *Brassica rapa,* to recover the seed. In other provinces this is done with a flail, but in the

FIG. 110. CHINESE THRESHING BOX IN USE. This picture shows two Chinese harvesters, threshing grain by slashing the freshly cut grain stalks upon the slatted wooden frame in the threshing box.

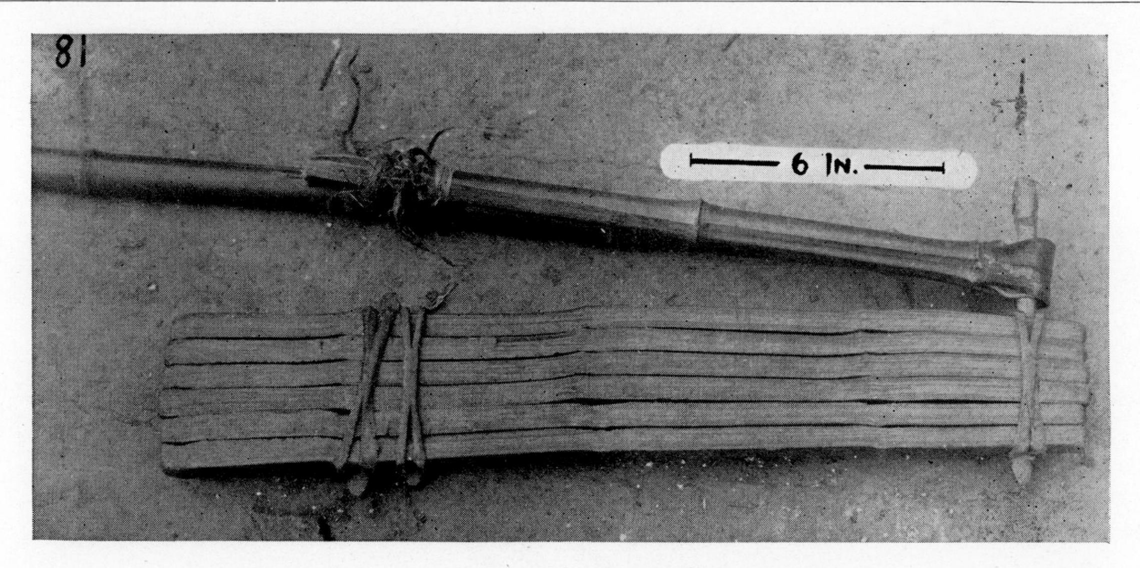

FIG. 111. CHINESE FLAIL.

parts of Chekiang which I visited the flail is not known.

When several natives are threshing together we miss the rhythm we are wont to hear when European peasants thresh with the flail. No matter how many or few Chinese swing the flail, one person will always bring down his flail after the rest have come down with theirs together. This gives a peculiar sound like a heavy impact followed by its fainter echo.

There is a word for flail in the Chinese language. It is *p'o p'a mu* and contains the elements of rhythm, scratch or dig out, and wooden implement. The word suggests the rhythmic threshing with the flail to recover the grain, and is used in the wheat regions of the north to describe an implement akin to our flail.

In Sha Ho, Kiangsi, I photographed another type of flail which is shown in Fig. 113. The handle is 5 feet 9 inches long. Eight bamboo strips rest in a mortise of a board 7¼ inches long. The bamboo strips are 25 inches long and about ½ inch wide and held apart by a rope interwoven over and between the strips as shown in the picture.

In northern Anhwei, in districts given up mainly to rice cultivation, the whole process of reaping, threshing and winnowing is usually carried out on the fields. One field about the area of a mao is cleared of the rice, rolled smooth with a stone roller (see Fig. 114), and left to the sun which bakes it as hard as

FIG. 112. CHINESE FLAIL. Another view of the same instrument shown in Fig. 111.

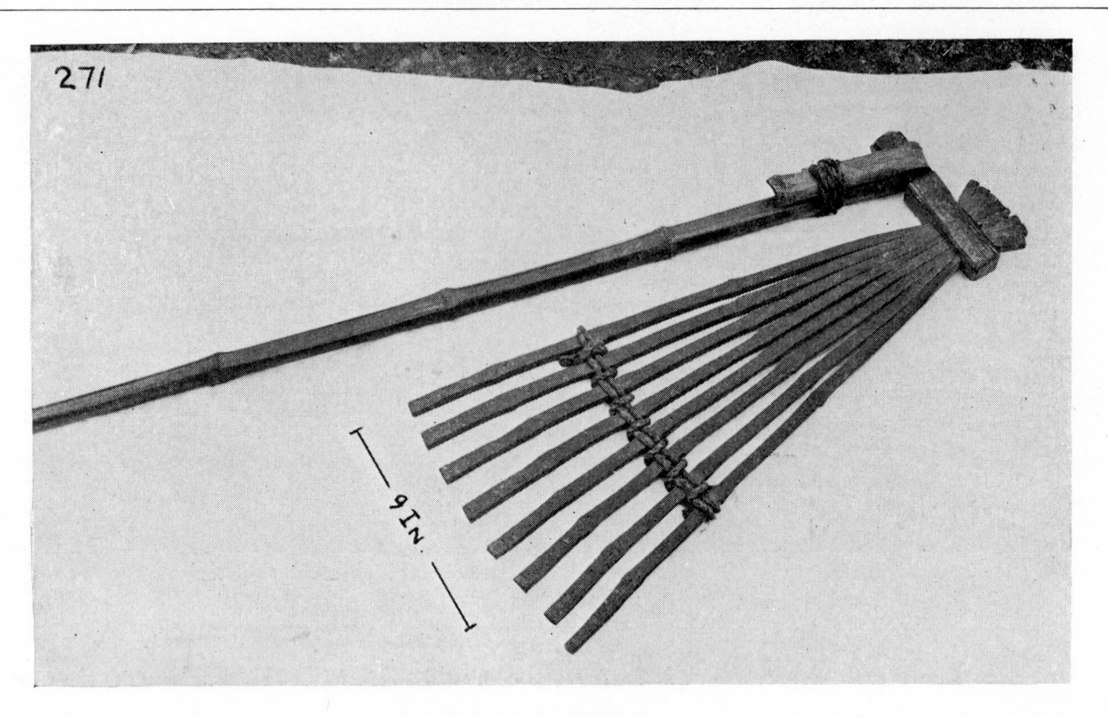

FIG. 113. CHINESE FLAIL.

sun-dried brick. The field forms thus an ideal threshing floor.

The stone roller in Fig. 114 is 25 inches long and 9¾ inches in diameter. The wooden frame surrounding the roller is 32 inches long and 18 inches wide. Two wooden pins mortised into the frame and projecting therefrom into sockets in the roller-ends, serve as an axle for the roller. They rest in 3 inch deep holes in the stone roller. The frame is held together by a twisted rope with a toggle, similar to the tightening of a saw-frame. The roller does not taper. In order to make the turning easy when dragging the roller around in circular fashion, the rope to which the animal is hitched is fastened to the frame, away from the center, as can be seen in the picture. Thus the roller has to follow a circular path. The picture was taken near Sha Ho, Kiangsi.

The sheaves are spread out and the same roller, Fig. 114, is dragged over the stalks. A zebu harnessed to the roller is shown in Fig. 115, but it must be said that the threshing floor in this picture is spread not with rice, but with the stalks of a plant yielding oil seeds. The method, however, is the same in this case as with the threshing of rice. The shape of the roller varies. The one for smoothing the field always has a smooth surface. For actual threshing the surface is often corrugated. An example is shown in Fig. 116. At times the stone roller has the shape of a tapering cylinder so that it may be easily dragged over the sheaves in a circle. Figs. 115 and 117 were taken north of Tsao Hsien, Anhwei province.

After threshing the loose sheaves are gathered up by hand and the remaining grain and chaff are thrown up into the air with winnowing shovels as shown in Fig. 117, when the wind takes away some of the chaff. For further cleaning, the grains are shaken through a riddle held up high, and again by aid of the wind the grains are separated from the remaining chaff.

The winnowing described later in Figs. 118 to 121, is done without shovels, in fact in Chekiang to which the description refers, winnowing shovels such as those we show from Anhwei are not known. We could not persuade the peasants to have the two specimens in Fig. 117 photographed while winnowing, and finally had to be content with taking these two pictures, the zebu with the roller, and the winnowing shovels.

In this district, Anhwei, we found a curious population. Their own tradition is that they are non-Chinese. The only unusual thing we noticed was that the women did not bind their feet. It was a delight to see the healthy barefoot women work in the fields, dressed in blue trousers rolled up to the knees and a white coat which reached a little below the hips. For a head-dress they wore a blue or white cloth shielding the forehead with the tied-up hair exposed.

The winnowing machine shown in Fig. 118 is

Fig. 114. Roller for Smoothing Out-Door Threshing Floor.

built up between four posts which also form the feet upon which the grain fan rests. In the body are two distinct compartments separated by a partition with a rectangular opening measuring 13 by 11 inches. One compartment, shaped inside like a drum lying on its side, contains the fan wheel with four blades mortised into a square axle. For the air intake serve two circular holes, of 11 inches diameter, cut in the sides of the fan compartment. One can be seen in Fig. 118, the other is on the opposite side corresponding to this. By turning the fan with the crank, air is blown into the other inside compartment, which is open on the left outer side, over which a bamboo-woven hood, open at the bottom, is hung up. This hood diverts the draft of air into a downward direction. On top of the grain fan rests a funnel-shaped wooden hopper which terminates at its bottom in a rectangular opening 9 inches long and 2 inches wide. The shelled grain passes from the hopper through this and a similar opening coinciding with it, in the top of the grain fan, into the path of the draft. This opening can be varied or closed by twisting a wooden strip or shutter, held immediately under the opening on each end by extensions fitting into the sidewalls of the grain fan. The very faintly seen extension on one side is prolonged beyond the sidewall (see Fig. 118) and a bamboo stick is inserted into its end at right angles. This stick can be placed upon different notches in the outer upper side of one of the fan-legs, to regulate the flow of the grain. When the stick is in a horizontal position the opening under the hopper is closed. The chute at the side of the grain fan starts from within at the left sidewall of the fan compartment, and is directly under the path of the grain flowing from the hopper. Inside and next to the left of this chute, is an opening in the bottom of the grain fan.

The hopper is first filled with the hulled rice, the fan set in motion by a man turning the crank and the grain let flow by opening the slot under the hopper. The grain passes through the current of air created by the fan, and the light chaff is blown across the inner compartment into the hood hung against the open end of the grain fan, whence it drops down into a basket under the hood. The sound, heavy grains of rice drop down in a straight line directly under the

Fig. 115. Chinese Threshing Roller.

FIG. 116. CHINESE THRESHING ROLLER OF THE CORRUGATED VARIETY SOMETIMES USED FOR THRESHING GRAIN. Here is shown a corrugated stone roller in front of a peasant dwelling. Back of the table a garment is seen fluttering in the wind. The Pisé wall in the background shows the erosion of rain splashing up against it. The two circular disks higher up on the wall are excrements of cattle which are thrown up against the wall for drying. Later on they are used for fuel. The picture was taken on a little farm about 5 li (3 li equals 1 mile) from San Ho, Anhwei.

hopper, unaffected by the current of air, into the chute from which they slide into a basket, not here shown, set on the floor, by the side of the grain fan. Smaller grains of rice and any impurities intermediate in weight between the good rice and the chaff are blown across and away from the direct line of fall, miss the chute and fall through the aforementioned hole to the left of it in the bottom of the inner compartment of the grain fan, upon a mat spread on the ground.

The height of the grain fan from the floor to the top of the hopper is 5 feet 2 inches, the length 4 feet 3 inches and the width 18 inches. The diameter of the fan wheel is 2 feet 4 inches. The square axle is reduced to round pivots at both ends, one half inch in diameter. The crank is attached to the end of one of these pivots, as shown in the photograph. The grain fan is used for winnowing the rice after threshing, after hulling and after polishing. It is constructed entirely out of wood.

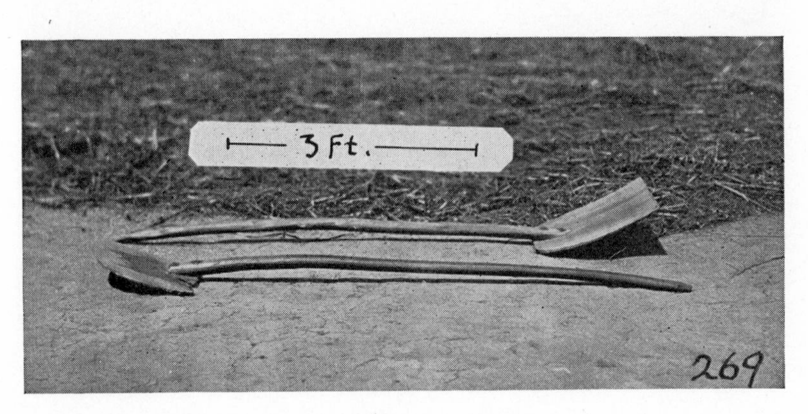

FIG. 117. WINNOWING SHOVELS.

Poor farmers, who cannot afford the luxury of the grain fan, shown in Fig. 118, separate the chaff from their hulled grain by the time-honored process of winnowing. On a windy day one man holds up with outstretched arms a riddle like the one here shown in Fig. 119, filled with grain, and shakes it by throwing the contents up in the air. The wind carries off the chaff and the grain drops straight down into a shallow basket of about 4 feet in diameter and with edges about 9 inches high. Another man scoops up some more grain from a large basket, (like the ones seen in the background of Fig. 62), with a scoop similar to the one in Fig. 120, but smaller, and fills the riddle, whenever it gets empty and the remaining bits of chaff have been blown away by the wind.

The riddle in Fig. 119 is made of split bamboo strips. For the binding around the edge strips of cane are used. The meshes are 3/16 of an inch square in the average and the diameter of the whole riddle is 21½ inches.

The grain scoop for winnowing, Fig. 120, is about the largest used on the farm. The farmers have whole sets of them of various sizes, one fitting in the other. A nest of these contains as a rule six scoops. The one shown is a foot high at the back and measures fifteen inches across the scooping edge. These scoops are made of split bamboo strips and the binding around the edges is of cane. Bamboo can not be bent more than to an angle of ninety degrees without breaking. That is why strips of cane have to be used on the edges. Thicker strips of bamboo like the ribs on the scoop in Fig. 120 are bent in the fire which softens the fibres to such an extent that bending will not break them. When cool they will keep the shape into which they have been bent. No shovels with long wooden handles are used for handling grain, the scoops described taking their place. As I stated in its place, under Fig. 117, the winnowing shovels there shown, were a surprise and only found in that particular part of Anhwei.

When winnowing threshed rice which has not yet been hulled, the procedure is somewhat different. Then a large-meshed riddle is used as pictured in Fig. 121. One man holds it up and another stepping upon a little bench, about a foot and a half high, pours into the riddle a scoopful of grain which runs through with little shaking, the bits of

FIG. 118. WINNOWING MACHINE.

FIG. 119. RIDDLE.

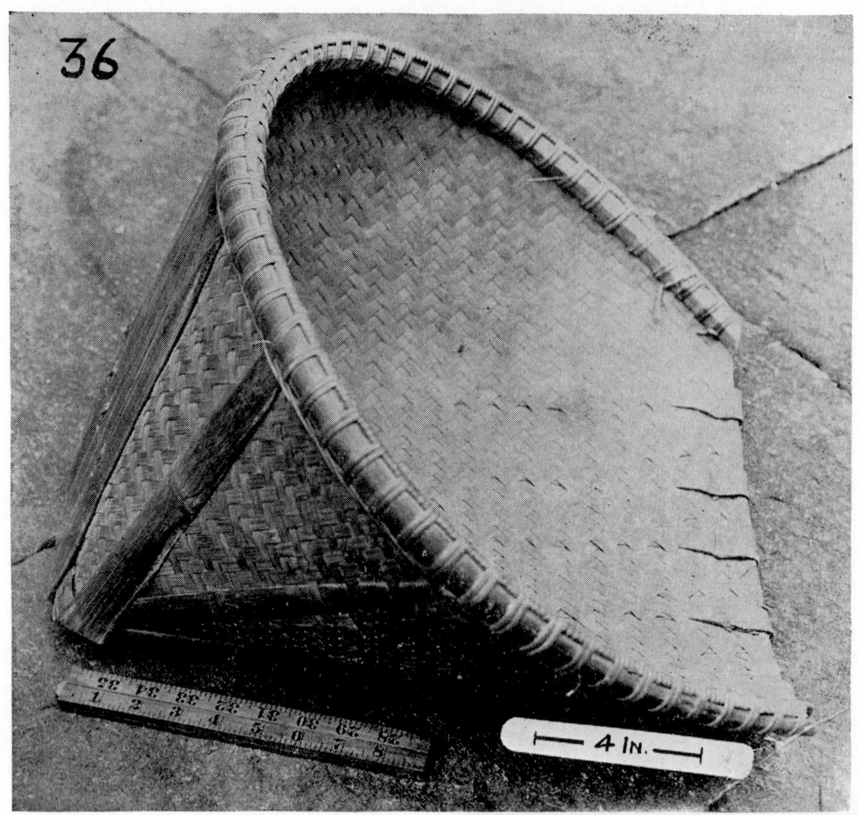

FIG. 120. GRAIN SCOOPS FOR WINNOWING.

straw staying behind. The first man must keep the riddle at a certain height in order that the swiftly running grain may have the full benefit of the wind. The meshes of this riddle are equilateral triangles, each mesh measuring about ¾ of an inch. This riddle is made entirely of split bamboo strips, and its diameter is 22 inches. The distinction between merely threshed rice and hulled rice will be made clear by descriptions of hulling rice, Figs. 143 to 150. All these photographs, pertaining to winnowing, were taken in Sin Tseong, Chekiang province.

After the grain, rice or wheat, has been harvested, threshed and winnowed it is poured upon bamboo mats laid on the ground, and spread with the spreader shown in Fig. 123. The purpose is to get the grain thoroughly dried in the sun before filling it into burlap bags, if it is to be sold, or storing it in wooden bins, if it is to be kept for home consumption. The blade of the spreader is a board of pine wood 13 inches long, 5½ inches at greatest width, and ⅝ inches thick. Crossing the grain of the blade a bottom flared groove, wider at the base than on top, like a dovetail has been cut, and the lower end of the long handle, cut to fit this groove, is driven home tightly. No glue or nails are used to hold the handle in place.

POTATOES

The Chinese cultivate various plants which can be classed under potatoes. There are several species of

FIG. 121. RIDDLE FOR WINNOWING THRESHED RICE.

taro *(Colocasia),* or yam *(Dioscorea),* and a sweet potato *(Ipomoea batatas).* Most interesting is the use of the *Solanum tuberosum,* our potato, with its claim of American ancestry, which according to G. A. Stuart, Chinese Materia Medica (Shanghai, 1911), was known and eaten by the people of the Liang dynasty which flourished from 907 to 923 A.D. At that time the tuber was called *t'u yu,* earth root. It must have fallen into disuse, for more recently it received the name *yang shu,* foreign tuber, because it had been reintroduced, at least in eastern China, by foreigners, according to some accounts by the Jesuits.

Fig. 122. Riddle for Winnowing Hulled Rice. The riddle Fig. 122 made out of bamboo and bound on the edges with strips of cane has a diameter of 21½ inches, the mesh is square, one side measuring in the average ⅛ of an inch.

In the districts between Kiukiang and Nanchang, the potato used and cultivated is a taro. Potatoes are not planted in big fields like rice or wheat, their cultivation is similar to the raising of vegetables. Small and irregular patches along the roads and dikes are allotted to them.

An unusual basket shown in Fig. 124 is used in connection with harvesting these potatoes, this implement serves two distinct purposes for carrying the potatoes home from the field and for conveniently washing them. Women usually go out and gather into the basket a supply of potatoes for a meal or two, and shouldering the load with the basket over the back, merely holding tightly to the pole, wend their way to the nearest creek or pool of water. Holding on with one hand to the pole and with the other grasping the rope attached to the contrivance, they immerse the basket in the water and

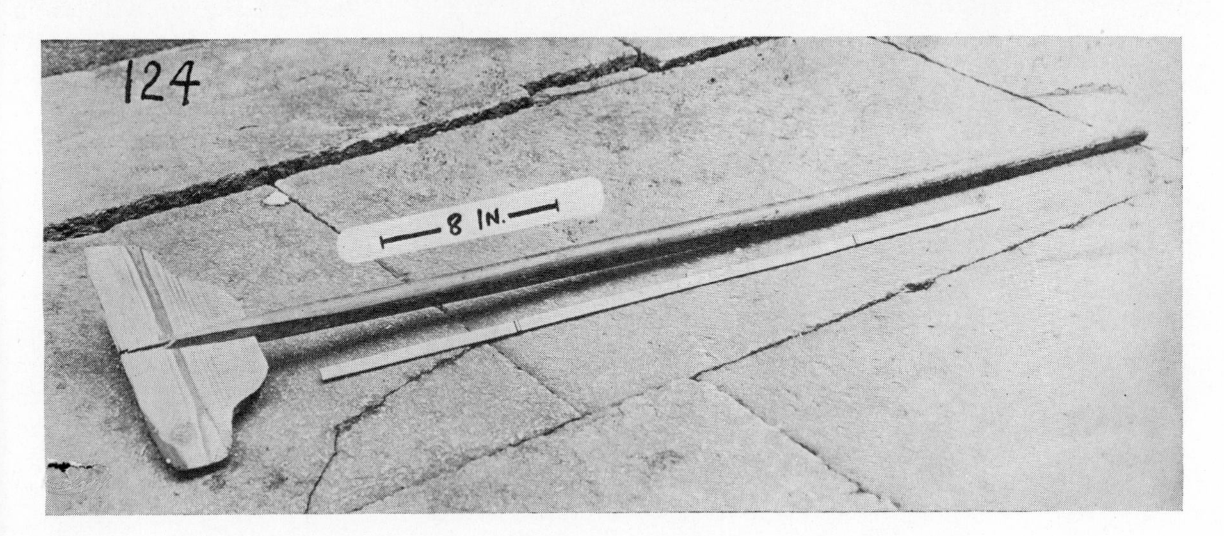

Fig. 123. Grain Spreader for Drying Grain.

Fig. 124. Potato Basket.

move it vigorously back and forth until the potatoes are freed from all dirt and perfectly clean as if scrubbed with a brush. After this the load is taken home, ready to be prepared for the family meal.

The length of the pole including the basket is 5 feet 8 inches, and the diameter of the basket is 14 inches, its length 25 inches. The pole is the stem of a pine tree, cut and smoothed, but with a number of radiating branches left projecting from one end of the pole. These branches are used as ribs and bamboo splints are woven around them to form the basket. A square opening is left at one side for inserting and withdrawing the potatoes. The photograph was taken in Sha Ho, Kiangsi Province. The basket belonged to a young peasant who served as our local guide.

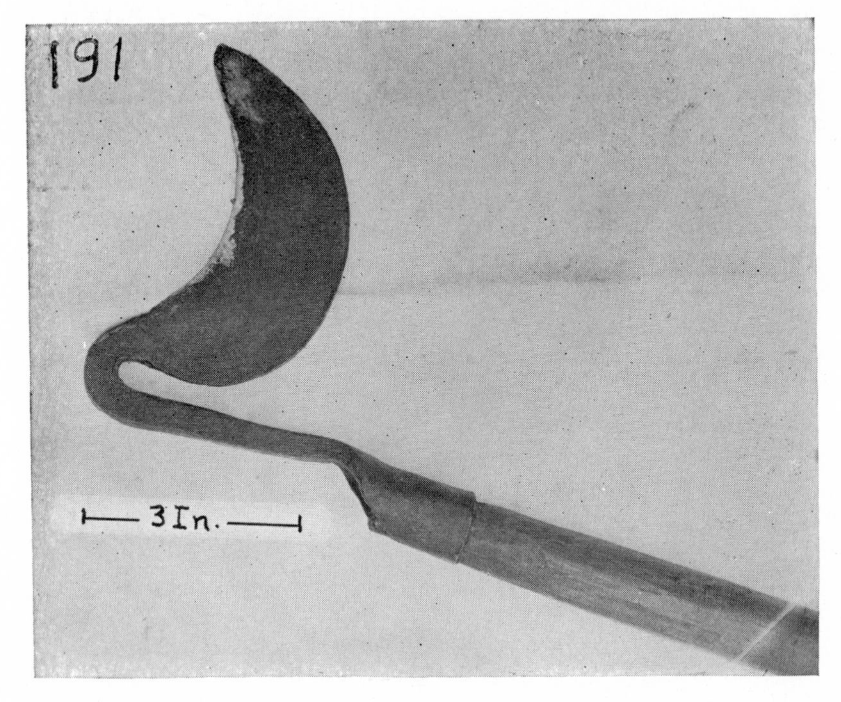

Fig. 125. Pruning Hook.

PRUNING

In Chekiang as well as in Kiangsi I saw late in autumn trees entirely devoid of foliage, but covered with white berries at the ends of every little twig. The trees stand usually alone along the roads or the banks of canals or rivers. The tree is the *Stillingia sebifera,* or tallow tree, which is quite common in Central China. The berries consist of three kernels which are coated with white vegetable tallow. Near Teh An, in Kiangsi province, I noticed peasants cutting little branches loaded with berries from the tree with the aid of the instrument shown in Fig. 125. The iron part has a concave cutting edge and is fastened with a socket upon a 14 feet long bamboo pole. The little branches are cut with an upward thrust of the pole and readily yield to the sharp edge of the instrument. The greatest width of the blade is 5¾ inches and the distance from the bend to the point of the blade is 5¼ inches.

One boy took the coiled rope in his left hand and with a sure aim threw the stone with his right hand up about 30 feet over a dry branch. He then jerked the rope, the end of which he retained in his hand, in such a way that the overhanging rope end, with the stone attached, wound around the branch it was hanging on. When next he gave one mighty pull, the

Fig. 126. Overshot Wheel of a Grist Mill.

branch broke off and came crashing down. The whole thing was done so cleverly and with such a sure hand that we stood amazed and watched the procedure for quite a while. The boy went on, and one branch after the other came down with never a miss. This procedure was new to me and my interpreter alike. I never saw it in any other part of China.

The separation of the tallow from the berries is an industry in itself and will be described elsewhere. This vegetable tallow is used extensively for making the candles seen in Buddhist temples from which candles made of animal fat are excluded. The picture was taken a few li west of Teh An in Kiangsi province.

An observation on that same excursion furnished a good example of the use of a most primitive method side by side, one might say, with a highly advanced contrivance. For the gathering of dry branches out of lofty trees, curiously enough, the pruning hook is not used. We saw boys on such an errand equipped with a long rope to the end of which a stone was tied. The dexterity with which it was handled was astonishing.

WATER MILLS

Fig. 126 shows an overshot wheel; the diameter of the wheel is about 5 feet and the diameter of the axle 6 inches. The axle rests on a cross beam and is held in place by wedges enclosing the place where it is to revolve. To lessen the wear of friction water is

Fig. 127. The Grinding Stones of a Chinese Water-Run Grist Mill.

The sluice has a gate which can be raised from the inside of the hut by using the bamboo poles, seen in the picture, Fig. 126, lying over the sluice, as levers. The water wheel axle extends farther backward into the tile-covered shed, where it revolves upon another wooden support not seen which is likewise "oiled" by a little jet of water led there from the sluice in a bamboo gutter. The axle extends somewhat beyond this second support and holds at its end a wooden wheel, about 3 feet in diameter, with wooden cogs around its circumference. These cogs engage into cogs of a similar wheel axled horizontally upon the spindle of a grist mill as shown in Fig. 127.

The spindle or axle of the top millstone, a round wooden beam, rests vertically on a horizontal bridgetree or lift beam, and thence passes up through the bedstone, or the lower of the two mill-stones here shown. The upper part of the spindle has been squared to fit into the square hole of the runner or upper millstone. To keep its position tightly on the spindle wooden wedges are driven in between the square sides of the spindle and the sides of the hole in the runner. The bridgetree can be raised and lowered to vary the distance between the stones. One end of the bridgetree rests in a vertical slot of one of the uprights of the framework supporting the bedstone. The orifice of the slot is longer than necessary to hold the bottom end of the bridgetree, and gives room for it to be raised up in the slot by driving a wedge immediately under the bridgtree. When the bridgetree is raised, the vertical spindle resting upon it together with the runner will likewise be raised, and the distance between the millstones increased. Fig. 129 shows this arrangement fairly well, also the counter-gearing which transfers the motion of the water wheel to the cogged

conducted through a small bamboo gutter, imperfectly shown white in the picture, leading from the main sluice onto the top of the part of the axle which revolves upon the cross beam. Between the wheel and the bearing of the axle a tripper or wiper is inserted for operating a trip-hammer, not seen in this picture. This wiper consists of a stout wooden piece about 4 feet long, passing through a slot in the axle. On each side it extends about 1½ feet, and when the wheel revolves raises and drops the hammer twice in one revolution. The other end of the trip-hammer is shown in Fig. 128.

wheel on the vertical mill-spindle.

The millstones in Fig. 127 have a diameter of 26 inches. The upper one has a side eye away from the spindle for pouring in the grain to be ground. The lower millstone rests immoveably upon a wooden platform and the spindle turning only the upper stone revolves vertically through it in a round hole, packed to prevent leakage of grain. The ground particles drop from the open outer rim of the stones in the act of grinding and fall upon the platform. The grain usually ground in these mills is wheat.

The trip-hammer device Fig. 128 performs the work of a pestle in polishing rice. It is similar in action to the tilting pestle described under Fig. 155. The hammer head or pestle is a solid piece of stone mortised into the wooden shaft. Its length is about 3 feet. When not in action the pestle-end is hung up to the rafter by a rope. The stone bowl with a clear opening of 20 inches in diameter is set into the ground.

The bridgetree, Fig. 129, is the horizontal log wedged into the bottom slot in the framework post in the middle foreground, and running directly backward in the picture. The spindle with the horizontal cogwheel rests vertically upon its rear end as described under Fig. 126. The millstones are penetrated by this spindle, although they seem pushed out of place and nearer the spectator than they really are.

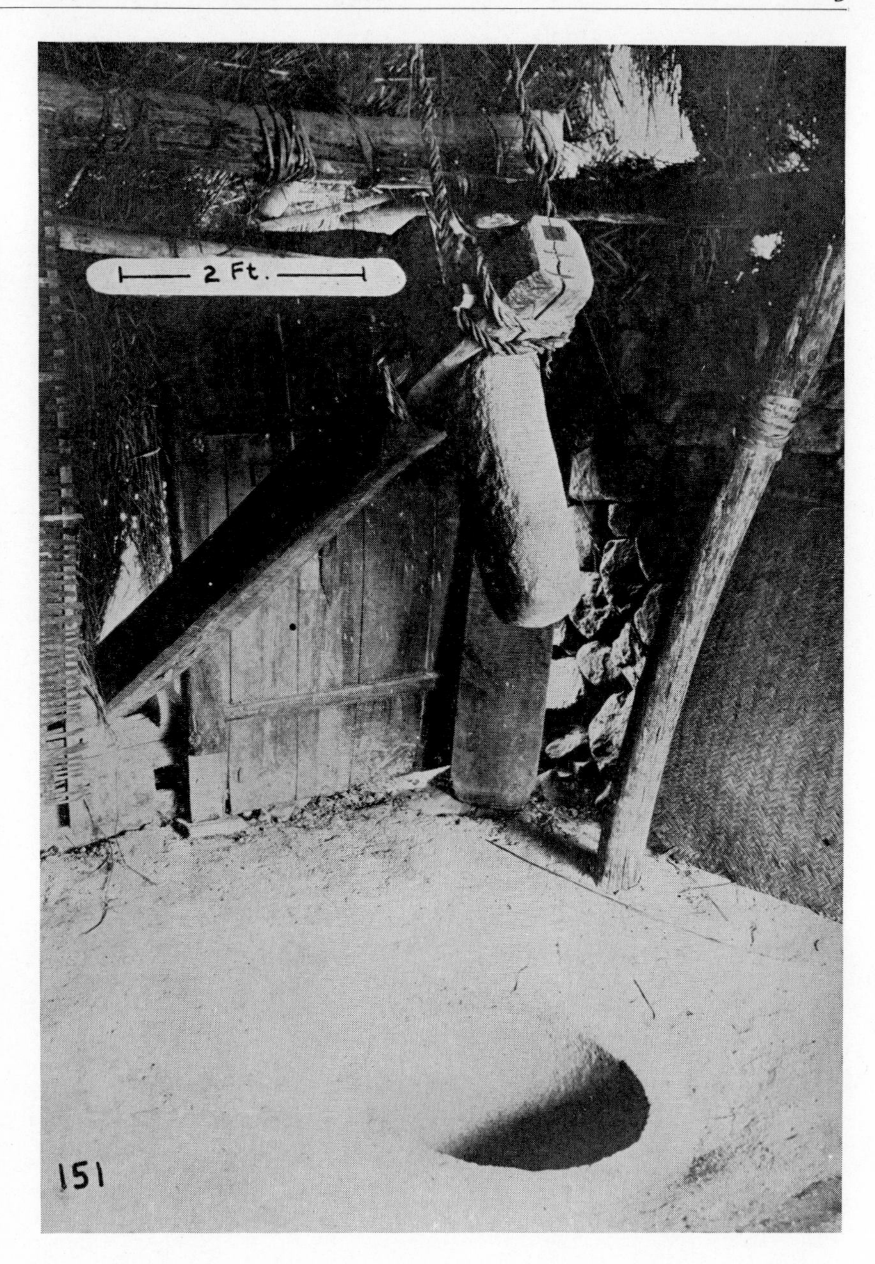

Fig. 128. Trip-Hammer Pestle for Polishing Rice, Attached to a Chinese Grist-Mill.

In one mill I saw a large wooden trough with a cradle inserted for bolting flour, rather inconveniently near the millstones. Fig. 130 shows this cradle without the trough. The trough itself is simply an oblong wooden box 2½ feet high, 3 feet wide and 7 feet long. The edges of the two long sides of this trough have notches into which the cross-arms of the cradle fit. The cross-arms are the pivots about which the cradle rocks to and fro. The framework extending upward on the right hand side of Fig. 130 is the handle for rocking the cradle. The square or rather oblong box with a cross-piece in the center for a handle, has a fabric bottom. The grist is poured into the box and by rocking the cradle, the flour is bolted.

When taking this picture in a grist-mill beyond the confines of a small village in Chekiang, I was surrounded by an unsympathetic crowd who had followed from the village. Not until I had sent back into the village for the owner to get his consent, could

Fig. 129. The Device Called Bridge Tree Which Lifts or Lowers the Upper Mill Stone (Runner) in a Chinese Grist-Mill.

I take pictures, and detailed information was withheld altogether.

In another mill, which was described to me by a missionary, a winnower, as he called it, consisting of a long sieve, was suspended by cords from the ceiling over a wooden tray, and worked in some manner by a damsel, an attachment to the millstone spindle. This information gave me the hint that perhaps the bolting device here described may have been employed in a similar manner. The position of the device close to the mill in an inconvenient corner,—inconvenient if supposed to be worked by hand—would be easily explained in that way. The upper millstone had holes around the circumference, and sticks placed therein could be made to give the bolting device an abrupt push each time they passed it.

Although the popular conception persists that the universal food of China is rice, there are vast districts where this is not the case. In northern China wheat and millet predominate, and the making of flour is well understood. Fig. 131 shows a bolting chest with a contrivance for shaking the sieve. The chest is a large wooden box with the upper half of one side open, as here seen. The open side is closed with a curtain when the flour is being bolted. In the chest hangs a wooden framed sieve, suspended by a rope from the upper framework of the chest. Rigidly connected with the sieve-frame is a shaking device or agitator, consisting of two wooden arms, parallel and close together as here seen, which project horizontally through a slot in the left side of the chest. These arms are joined together by two cross-pins near their outer ends, and between these cross-pins oscillates a wooden rod rising from a treadle arrangement resting on the floor. The treadle, a round wooden block about 30 inches long, rests on a bed of clay spread on the ground. From a mortise at the left end of this rises the wooden rod mentioned, while a foot board or rocker passes through a second mortise in the block, extending about 9 inches on either side. These extensions serve as pedals. The man working the treadle stands with one foot on each pedal, pressing down alternately first with one foot and then with the other. The vertical rod is moved to and fro between the cross-pins of the agitator and the motion is transferred to the sieve attached to the agitator inside the bolting chest. The man pedipulating the treadle holds on overhead to a horizontal strip of wood, which is suspended by two pieces of rope from the ceiling. The vertical rod in the picture has two perforations which have nothing to do with the apparatus, but mark it as having formerly been used for something else, perhaps as part of the framework of a wheelbarrow. The upper part of the clapper rod is rounded and with each tread strikes with a characteristic click against one or the other of the cross-pins in the horizontal arm of the agitator causing the abrupt shaking motion which is necessary for the process of bolting the meal in the sieve. In front of the bolting chest stands a wooden measure or receptacle with which the flour is taken from the space underneath the sieve. This space can be reached through a sliding door at the extreme right of the chest. The half-open long side face of the chest is about 30 inches high, from the ground to the railing where the open space begins. The photograph was taken in Linkiang, Kiangsi Province.

Fig. 132 gives an idea of an undershot wheel. This mill works a trip-hammer only. The wiper can be plainly seen projecting vertically between the bearing of the axle and the wheel proper. Here the bearings cannot be kept moist with a stream of water from the brook since they are on a higher level. Moist it is kept, however, by a simple and ingenious arrangement. Spiral grooves are cut around the axle starting from the center where the wheel is fastened to the axle and passing on to the bearings. When the wheel is in motion, water drips continuously from the top of the wheel upon the axle and is caught by the spiral grooves along which it runs to the bearings. This wheel is 7 feet in diameter and the axle has a diameter of 13 inches. The pictures, Figs. 126 to 130 and 132 were taken in or near Haw Be Tsz, Chekiang Province.

OIL MAKING

The oil cabbage is a plant allied to the old-world rape. The botanical name is *Brassica rapa.* In the Feng Wha district of Chekiang the seeds are planted in January. The growth is rapid and in March and April the tender leaves near the root are cut off to be eaten as vegetable. The stalk grows on, reaches a

Fig. 130. Hand Cradle for Bolting Flour Used at a Chinese Grist-Mill.

FIG. 131. BOLTING FLOUR.

height of from 2 to 3 feet and produces yellow flowers. Towards the end of April the seed pods ripen and are picked off. While still green they are slightly roasted in a cast-iron pan to get them dry and brittle, whereupon they are beaten with the wooden bat, otherwise used for beating the family wash. The seeds are thus recovered and sold to the oil miller. After rooting out the plants which are dried and used for fuel, the field is prepared for planting rice.

The oil derived from these seeds is used for culinary purposes, and before the introduction of kerosene, was the cheapest and most widely used illuminant of the Chinese.

The oil-mill to be described uses as raw material the small ovoid seed of *Brassica rapa.* The native business of expressing the oil from the seed by rather primitive methods is becoming steadily less lucrative through the lessened demand for the oil for lighting, and through the introduction of modern oil-mills and kerosene. It is therefore not surprising that the native oil-miller views with suspicion any foreigner who comes to get complete photographic records and information of his trade. At Lee Go Gao, a village near Sin Tseong, Chekiang, we visited an oil mill and were able to get but a few photographs owing to the hostile attitude of the people. I was, however, able to gather the following facts about the process.

A portion of the harvested seeds is put into a cast iron pan similar to the one in Fig. 215. This is put on the top of a square brick stove, about thirty inches high which has a depression in its clay top into which the pan fits. The fire is fed with straw, the flames do not reach the cast iron pan but strike the intervening clay top of the stove. The seeds are thus heated and dried rather than roasted, when they are ready to be put into the large circular trough of the crushing mill, Fig. 133, in which the heavy stone roller seen in the picture passes over and crushes them.

The mill for crushing the seed, Fig. 133, part of an abandoned oil-mill near Sin Tseong, is identical in construction with those in Lee Go Gao which were situated under dark sheds, unsuitable for photographing. The diameter measured from the edges of the trough is 16 feet, the opening of the trough 13 inches. The stone post in the center projects 3 feet 4 inches, and is square on top and bottom. Where the framevork revolves the central post is rounded and has a liameter of 7 inches. The roller or millstone is 5 nches thick and its diameter is 4 feet 9 inches. The axle of the roller is rigid. A square wooden pin passes hrough the center of this stone. It projects on both ides and these projections are round and turn in ioles of the framework that encloses the roller. The onstruction of the framework can be seen from the accompanying sketch, Fig. 134.

The mill stone roller in Fig. 133, in passing over and crushing the seeds presses them against the walls of the trough from which a drag or scraper, Fig. 135, crapes them off and pushes them back to the bottom of the trough.

The crosspieces of the drag or scraper, Fig. 135, esting on the trough, are 19 inches long. This drag its a trough 11 inches wide at he top. The construction of the lrag is simple, the different oarts being merely mortised together without glue. For orlinary joinery the Chinese do iot use any glue. For furniture hey use wheat flour mixed with ime, for caulking boats a mixure of wood-oil and lime.

After the seeds have been crushed sufficiently they are scooped out with wooden hovels, Fig. 136, into large baskets similar to the baskets ised for grain.

The shovels are 22 inches ong exclusive of the handle and neasure 7 inches across their gutter-shaped opening. The handle-stick, 5 feet long, is inerted in a hole in the closed nd of the shovel blade and held here by a key passing through hovel and stick. The shovel adapted to the shape of the rough of the crushing mill answers admirably its purpose vhich is to clear out the crushed eeds from the trough.

After being shovelled out of he trough the crushed seeds are nixed with straw cut into bits about an inch long. The purpose of this admixture is to bind he material together lest after pressing the oil-cakes fall apart. In Fig. 137 is shown a cylinder composed of twisted bamboo rings. A board is placed upon a table, a bamboo ring laid on this and a layer of straw put into the ring. On top of this, powdered seeds are placed and rammed in to fill the ring. Then another ring is laid on top and the same operation repeated. The result finally is a cylinder made up of bamboo rings filled with layers of powdered seed separated each from the other by layers of straw.

The cylinder, Fig. 137, is thus made up of individual rings twisted together from strips of bamboo. The outside diameter of such a ring is 15¼ inches and the thickness ½ inch.

The press, Fig. 138, consists of a trough hewn from a log or rather two logs pinned together. The trough

Fig 132. Undershot Water Wheel of a Chinese Rice Polishing Mill.

FIG. 133. OIL-MILL.

is open on top and has a slot in the bottom parallel to its length. The cylinder, a tube-like basket open at the top and bottom composed of over fifty bamboo rings filled with powdered seed, is laid longitudinally on its side against one end of the log trough and immediately over the slot. A wooden block, (not clearly seen), to resist pressure is placed against the other end of the cylinder so as to cover its entire opening. The remaining space is packed with three rows of smaller wooden blocks like those seen lying in front of the press in Fig. 138. Wooden wedges bound on top with an iron ring, are then driven in between some of the smaller

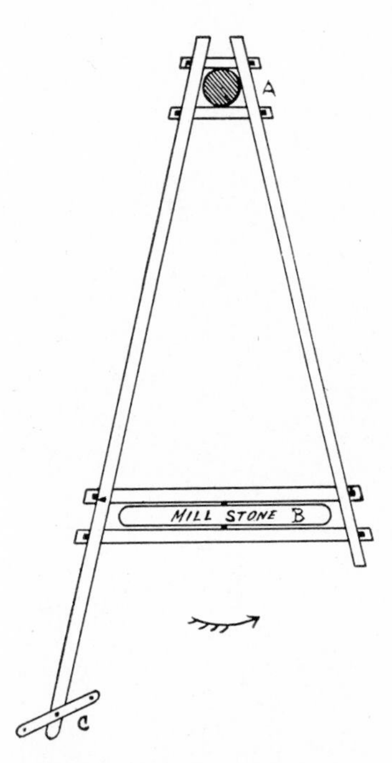

FIG. 134. SKETCH SHOWING THE CONSTRUCTION OF THE FRAMEWORK OF AN OIL-MILL (*A*) is the central post, (*B*) the Mill Stone, and (*C*) the Swingle Tree for the draught animal.

FIG. 135. TROUGH SCRAPER OF A CHINESE OIL-MILL.

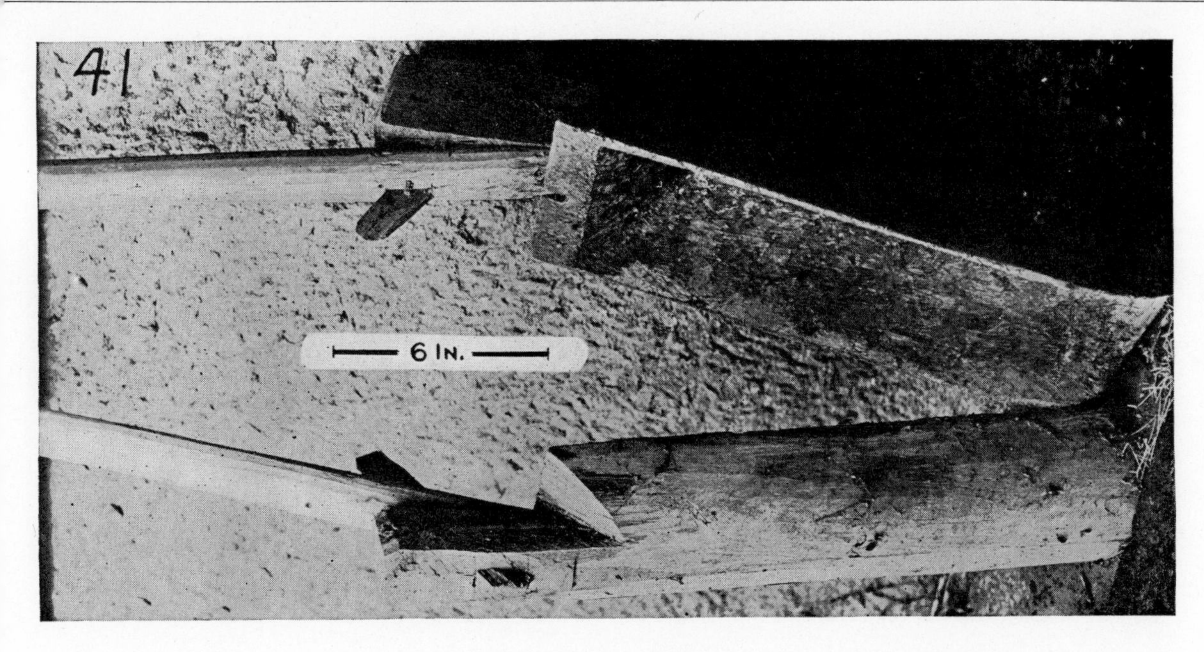

FIG. 136. TWO WOODEN SHOVELS FOR CLEARING THE SEED-TROUGHS IN A CHINESE OIL-MILL.

wooden blocks with a large hammer. As the oil oozes out and the pressure slackens other wedges are pounded in to restore the pressure. This hammer seen lying on top of the press deserves more than passing notice. It is a stone hammer and well illustrates the desperate conservatism of the Chinese, who have not modified this instrument in this particular trade for perhaps thousands of years. The flexible bamboo rings in the cylinder are thus compressed with wooden wedges driven home by the stone hammer, and the oil oozes out and through the slot in the bottom of the log, runs into a gutter under the press, and thence into a cistern in front of the press. One of the stone hammers is clearly shown in Fig. 138, and a wedge, 27 inches long, in Fig. 139. The material in the press is left under pressure for 24 hours.

Fig. 139 gives a detail view of a press in action. The last wedge inserted is not driven home. After twenty-four hours the pressure is removed and then a workman hits one of the other wedges a heavy blow whereupon the one sticking out a little is loosened. The oil cakes formed in the bamboo rings are pushed out of the confining rings and stacked up awaiting their removal for export to foreign countries where they are used for cattle feed or as fertilizer.

The press shown in Fig. 139 is packed with the bamboo cylinders containing the seeds, and the wedges are driven home. On the left of the picture the ends of two wedges can be seen extending below the body of the press. Two hollowed-out tree trunks are keyed together with large wooden pins, and form the body of the press. The length of the press is 12 feet. Fig. 133 was photographed near Sin Tseong and Figs. 135 to 139 at Lee Go Gao, a village also not far from Sin Tseong, Chekiang Province.

In Kiangsi the process of pressing oil is similar, only the press used is quite different. I was able to

FIG. 137. CYLINDER OR BASKET FOR HOLDING THE CRUSHED SEEDS UNDER PRESSURE IN A CHINESE OIL PRESS.

FIG. 138. CHINESE OIL PRESS. Seen lying on top is a stone hammer with wooden handle for driving wedges.

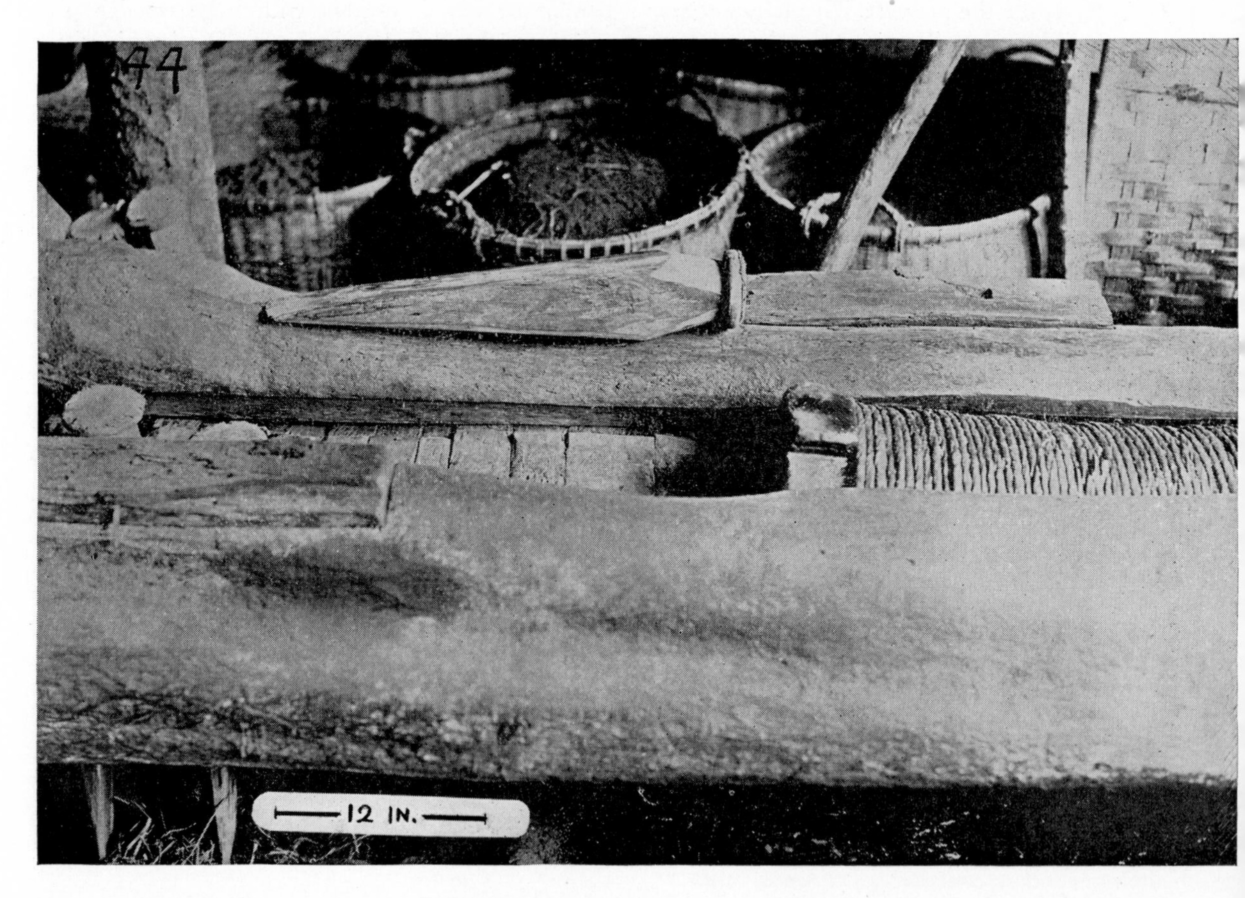

FIG. 139. CHINESE OIL PRESS IN ACTION.

FIG. 140. OIL MILL PRESS.

get a few pictures illustrating the working. In Chekiang the wedges are driven down into the press vertically with stone hammers. In Kiangsi they are driven in sideways, not with hammers, but with an iron-shod swinging beam a sort of battering ram. Fig. 140 shows a typical press of Kiangsi. It consists of the hollowed trunk of a tree with a long slot opening on the side and passing clear through the trunk. The rings to receive the powdered seed are of wrought iron, and a set of them is shown in front of the press. To fill a ring it is laid upon the ground and straw placed over it in such a way that the ends of the straw extend radially all around the ring. The powdered and usually steamed seeds are then poured into the ring from a container which holds a set measure. These containers are wooden forms in the shape of the frustrum of a cone. In Fig. 142, three of them can be seen standing in a row in the foreground. The workman compresses the oil-bearing seed with his feet in one of the iron rings and folds over it the overhanging straw thus forming a round package encircled by the iron ring, but about twice as thick as the width of the ring. The filled rings are inserted sideways into the press through the open slot and then set up vertically like wheels face to face inside the large central trough. After a number of these rings are in place the remaining space in the central log orifice is filled with wooden blocks, inserted horizontally through the side slot, and then wooden wedges are driven sideways in between the blocks to compress the powdered seed.

Fig. 142 shows another such press with the wedges driven home. The inner oil trough of the press has along its base, directly under the ringed seed-holding disks, a hole, from which the expressed oil drips into a receptacle standing under the press. The pictures were taken at three different oil mills, in the neighborhood of Teh An, Kiangsi; Fig. 141, at Chang-shu, Kiangsi.

HAND MILLS

The type of mill illustrated in Fig. 143, is used by farmers who have no draught animals to turn the animal power mill. It is used also as a convenient means of hulling small quantities of rice at home thus saving the trouble of resorting to the large hulling mill with the draught animal.

The mill is put upon a stand with four legs. One

FIG. 141. SWING-POLE FOR DRIVING THE WEDGES IN A CHINESE OIL PRESS. The driving of the wedges is done with a heavy pole here seen suspended at a slant by a rope from a framework with four props. Several men take hold of this pole and holding it in a horizontal position swing it against the wedges. The end of the swing-pole giving the impact is shod with an iron ferrule.

pair of legs is higher than the other pair and the height of the stand is therefore 9½ inches at one side while on the other it is 8 inches. The top of the stand looks like the letter H. The length is 22½ inches and the width 19 inches. Instead of millstones wooden disks are employed. These are laid upon the stand against the projecting tenons of the two shorter legs of the stand. The inclination of the disks owing to the different size of the legs is further heightened by placing a rolled-up burlap bag under one side of the lower disk. These disks are composed of sections of pinetrees arranged in a circle. Bamboo strips are then wound around the circumference of this circle like hoops around barrels. The interstices between the round sections of the pinetrees are filled out with pinewood cut to fit the spaces. In the middle of each disk a hexagonal space is left. The lower disk has a diameter of 25 inches and its height is 5 inches. The hexagonal hole in the lower disk (14½ inches diameter from corner to corner) is covered with a tightly fitting lid of wood about one inch thick. Through the center of this board lid passes a wooden pin 2 inches in diameter tapering toward the top to 1½ inches diameter. The other end of this pin below the board above mentioned, is held at the bottom of the lower disk by a wooden strip measuring 15 inches by 3 inches by 1 inch, inserted across the hexagonal bottom opening. The round projecting center pin, cut square at the bottom end, is wedged into a square hole in this strip, the ends of which strip are cut like dovetail tenons fitting tightly into corresponding mortises in the bottom block of the disk. The solid top surface of the disk is covered with radial grooves. The upper disk has the same dimensions, but the radial grooves are on the bottom side. Its top surface is smooth, and the hexagonal hole is left open. Another wooden crosspiece, 24 inches by 4 inches by 1 inch, passes diametrically across the whole top of the upper disk to which it is held by wooden nails. Through a hole 1¼ inches in diameter, in the center of this cross-strip, passes the wooden center pin of the lower disk, upon which the upper disk revolves. At each end, this wooden top cross-strip has a round hole ¾ inch in diameter into one of which the iron bottom pin of the turning pole $\frac{1}{2}$ inch in thickness is inserted. The turning pole is suspended from three bamboo poles tied tightly together on top. If the mill is used indoors, the turning pole is suspended from the ceiling. The turning pole works horizontally and as we can see in the Fig. 143, it has at one end a wooden crosspiece as a handle. Into the opposite end a vertical piece is mortised projecting downward. At the lower end an iron pin is inserted extending therefrom about $2\frac{1}{2}$ inches. To reinforce this end an iron ferrule is pushed over it.

To vary the distance between the two disks in grinding, a short wooden strip is laid over the top of the center pin which projects about $\frac{1}{4}$ inch above the hole in the wooden crosspiece passing over the upper disk. As shown in Fig. 143, this little strip is fastened with cords on either end to the crosspiece. This simple arrangement, crosspiece with cords, is the means of setting and varying the distance between the two grinding disks. The cords are tightened in such a way that the upper disk is raised a sufficient distance from the lower disk. To insure ease in turning, the wooden cross-strip, 5 inches by $1\frac{1}{2}$ inches by $\frac{3}{4}$ inch, has a wrought iron nail with a large head driven into it at the point of contact with the center pin. Thus the upper disk really rests on the head of this nail, whose head measures $\frac{1}{2}$ inch across, and projects about $\frac{3}{8}$ of an inch from the wood.

The mode of handling is obvious. A mat woven from bamboo splints is laid upon the floor and the mill placed on it. The unhulled rice is scooped into the hexagonal opening of the upper disk with a wooden hand shovel (shown leaning against the stand of the mill in Figs. 143 and 144).

The man operating this mill stands in front of it and takes hold with both hands of the cross handle of the turning pole, (Fig. 145) so that each hand rests near the rope from which the pole is suspended. The down-turned elbow of the pole with the iron pin is heavy enough to prevent it from jumping out of the pivothole on the cross-strip of the upper disk.

The Chinese turn any turnable contrivance in the opposite direction to the movement of the hands of a clock. The rice between the wooden disks of the mill is freed from the hulls and, working toward the edges of the disks, drops down together with the hulls

Fig. 142. Chinese Oil Press with the Wedges Driven Home.

FIG. 143. HAND RICE-HULLING MILL.

upon the bamboo mat upon the floor. The edges between the grooves of the disks wear flat in about a year's time and then the carpenter is called to cut deeper grooves with a half-round wood chisel. The photographs were taken in Sin Tseong, Chekiang Province.

The type of mill shown in Fig. 146 is extremely interesting. We have seen that the disks of the mill previously described are of wood, but here they are of clay with inserted strips of bamboo and wood. The diameter of the disks is 18½ inches. The height of the lower is 6½ inches, of the upper 4½ inches, and both are surrounded by basket work. The lower disk rests firmly in a wooden tub, which is 28 inches in diameter, and 8 inches high from the trestle. Clear through the middle of the upper disk, in a direction parallel to its plane, runs a wooden strip 3 feet 1 inch long, 2¾ inches wide, and 1¾ inches thick. At each end of this strip is a round hole, i. e., two holes per strip, either of which may receive the turning pole. In the center of the strip is a blind hole or round socket into which fits the round central pin seen protruding upward from the lower disk. The upper

FIG. 144. WOODEN GRINDING DISKS OF THE CHINESE HAND RICE-HULLING MILL. The disks are here shown detached to give a view of axle and grinding surface.

disk has a square feeding hole lined with boards, each side measuring $5\frac{3}{4}$ inches. The above mentioned wooden crosspiece, which passes through the upper disk has on one side where it emerges from the disk a small wooden slat in a mortise, which dips into the hollow space of the tub and when the upper disk revolves pushes the hulled rice to a hole in the bottom of the tub through which it drops into a basket placed immediately under that hole. The central pin seen in the lower disk is wedged into place and the distance between the disks can be varied by loosening the wedges and thereby raising or lowering it. The mode of manipulating this mill is essentially the same as previously described, conf. Figs. 143 to 145. This type of mill is common throughout Kiangsi province and was photographed in Sha Ho. Chinese records relate that an implement made of bamboo and plastered over with mud was used for hulling rice from grain already in the Chow dynasty (1122 to 255 B.C.) and we are probably correct in assuming that it was similar to the mill we have described.

FIG. 145. TURNING POLE OF THE HAND RICE-HULLING MILL. The motion of the turning pole can be likened to the connecting-rod attached to the piston of a steam engine. Two strokes, one forward and one backward, are required for one complete revolution of the disk.

In the old city of Fuchow, Kiangsi province, I had the opportunity to see the manufacture of the disks of this unique rice-hulling mill. Fig. 147 shows a lower disk, the so-called bed stone, in course of manufacture. The wicker form is filled with freshly dug loam beaten down like the walls in Pisé masonry. Wooden pieces about $1\frac{1}{2}$ inches long with the grain, 2 inches wide across the grain and 3/32 inch thick, are hammered at intervals of about $\frac{1}{4}$ inch down into the mass. More loam is put upon the surface and beaten down with a wooden chisel which fits between the spaced top edges of the wooden pieces, until the latter thus forming radial teeth, extend slightly from the beaten mass. The upper revolving disk has the greater wear and here the inserted teeth are of oak wood, while in the bed-stone they are of bamboo. The pieces of oak wood have been subjected to smoke for hardening and better preservation. The life of these hulling mills is not long. The Chinese expect them to last for the hulling of 40 piculs (40 times 133 1/3 lbs.) of rice. Labor being cheap it is not costly to have a quern rebuilt, filled with fresh loam and studded with new pieces of wood and bamboo. Dust of the loam which necessarily wears off is easily removed from the rice with the chaff.

The Chinese are careful to make the distinction between bamboo and wood. Bamboo is botanically a grass, although in appearance a tall tree with branches and leaves.

ANIMAL POWER MILLS

In almost every village in the rice-growing districts of Chekiang province there is a rice-hulling mill, the

Fig. 146. Hand Rice-Hulling Mill with Grinding Disks Made of Clay.

property of the community. It is contained in a square hut, with one or two sides bricked up, and the others furnished with slots to let in the daylight and air. Every farmer owning a draught animal can use it, the others have to be content to use their hand mill.

In the center is a platform like a flat cone built up of slabs of hewn stone, and around this runs a trough also of stone. Built up over its edge, is a wooden rim held together by bamboo strips like the hoops of a barrel. The diameter from rim to rim is 9 feet. The height from the ground to top of the rim is 21 inches. In the center is a pivotal wooden post wedged into the platform on which the wooden turning frame of the mill turns, (see Fig. 149). The height of the center post from its point of insertion into the stone base is 2 feet and 4 inches and diameter 3½ inches.

The construction of the frame work holding the millstone and hopper can be seen from the accompanying sketch, Fig. 150. The hopper is hung up on the main beam of the frame work. The pivotal center post fits into a socket in the upper end of the curved beam which is pinned to the main beam. The millstone is a stone cylinder 23 inches in diameter and is 16 inches wide. It revolves on two short rigid steel pins protruding from the framework which encircles it. On both ends of the stone cylinder in its center, an iron piece, 3½ inches square is inserted with a hole serving as a socket for the steel pivot, ¾ of an inch in diameter, which is driven into the framework so as to form an axle for the cylinder. At the end of the main beam the whipple-tree for the draught animal is fastened with a wooden pin.

In front of Fig. 149, can be seen a recess in the

Fig. 147. Clay Grinding Disk of a Chinese Rice-Hulling Mill in Process of Manufacture.

FIG. 148. MILLSTONES (GRINDING DISKS) MADE OF CLAY FOR A CHINESE RICE-HULLING MILL. Fig. 148 (right) shows an upper disk finished, while the lower needs to have the interspaces beaten with the wooden chisel. These mills are quite common in Kiangsi Province.

FIG. 149. RICE-HULLING MILL.

stone base. This is directly under the trough and serves to receive the hulled rice through two circular holes, 5 inches in diameter, in the base of the trough. A basket is inserted into this recess for the easy removal of the hulled rice.

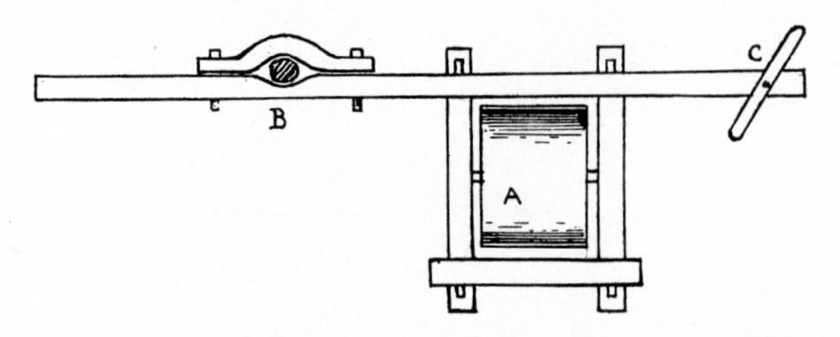

Fig. 150. Sketch Showing the Construction of the Turnstile of a Chinese Rice-Hulling Mill. (*A*) is the millstone, (*B*) the attachment to the central vertical wooden post and (*C*) the whipple-tree for the draught animal moving to the left, contrary to the motion of a clock.

The hopper constructed entirely from wood is open on top. The upper part is 16 inches square, the whole length 3 feet, and 2 inches. At the bottom is an orifice opened or closed with a slide by which the flow of the rice can be regulated. The slide once set is held tight by a wedge pushed in between it and the hopper wall.

In turning this mill the blindfolded draught animal walks around the mill with its left side toward the trough. The motion of the mill shakes the hopper sufficiently to ensure an even flow of rice onto the slanting stone platform over which the millstone passes. The hulled rice is gradually pushed into the trough by the ever increasing flow of rice from the hopper. There it is pushed along by a stone (not here seen) shaped to fit the trough, attached to the millstone-frame by a rope about 4 feet long, this stone follows the millstone around the trough. The shelled rice thus pushed along falls through the two holes in the trough into the basket below. The photograph was taken in Lung Pei Chiao, a village near Ningpo, Chekiang.

Knight's American Mechanical Dictionary defines a Chilean mill as a grinding or crushing machine in which *two* wheels revolve about a central vertical axis in a circular trough. The Chinese mills according to this definition belong to a single wheel class of their own. All the Chinese mills I have seen so far have only one wheel, or set of wheels as in Fig. 151, on one side of the central post, but never the same unit symmetrically repeated on the other side as in the Chilean mill. A chaser in metallurgical practice is defined as a rotating edge-wheel revolving at the end of a radial arm in a trough. The Chinese mills we are dealing with are such chasers rotated by animal power, and we shall, therefore, call them chaser mills.

The mill shown in Fig. 151, has two solid stone wheels revolving on a turnstile in a stone trough. Here the necessary pressure is derived rather from the

Fig. 151. Chinese Chaser Mill.

heavy superstructure of the turning frame than from the weight of the wheel. The peasant driving the draught animal sits on one of the forked horizontal beams above the wheel and thus adds his weight to

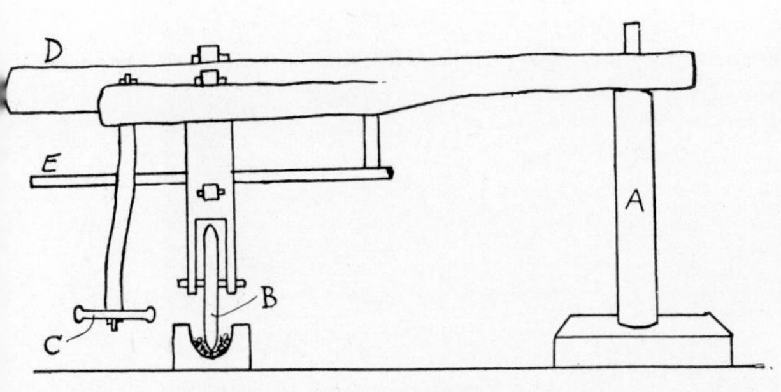

Fig. 152. Sketch Showing Structural Details of Chaser Mill. (*A*) is the turnstile, (*B*) the cast iron wheel, (*C*) the swingle-tree, (*D*) is the driver's seat (his weight adding pressure upon the wheels), and (*E*) is his foot rest.

the downward pressure. A down-reaching vertical post is mortised into each branch of the forked beam. Deeply notched to enclose the stone wheel, these posts at their lower ends engage the wooden axles of the latter. A wooden stick is tied to the frame work back of the hindermost wheel. Its end rests in the trough and stirs up the material to be rolled or crushed. The accompanying sketch, Fig. 152, shows the details of the construction. A board placed as indicated serves as foot-rest for the driver, who sits on the rear beam of the forked superstructure. The yoke is placed upon the withers of the water-buffalo, just as it would be placed on a zebu. A line for guiding the animal is attached to the nose-bolt. The peasants had run away to escape being photographed, and put the coiled guiding line upon the center post of the mill. This type of mill is much in use in the district around Kiukiang. The one photographed we saw near Teh An, Kiangsi. These mills are mainly used for hulling and polishing rice. A similar one I saw for crushing oil-seeds. The wheels of this latter were of cast iron, and the wooden trough was laid out with tile-shaped plates of cast iron. The solid wheels tapered to a narrow edge which was slightly grooved.

Another type of chaser mill, Fig. 153, we photographed near Tatung, Anhwei. The center post of stone is 2½ feet high. The stone roller has a diameter of 2 feet 2 inches, and a width of 2 feet 2 inches. The bed upon which the roller revolves is slanting and built of stone slabs. This mill is used to thresh rice. The sheaves are arranged all around the slanting platform, the roller passes over them and the dislodged grains roll down upon the adjoining level rim from which they are conveniently collected. In the background of the photograph can be seen inundated ricefields with the plants set out in regular intervals.

RICE POLISHING

After shelling the rice still retains some persistent glumes which are removed by a treatment called the

Fig. 153. Chaser Mill.

Fig. 154. Rice Polishing Mortar and Pestle Hammer.

Fig. 155. Foot Balance Pestle and Mortar for Polishing Rice.

polishing of rice. About 40 pounds of rice are placed in a large stone mortar, Fig. 154, which fills it about half full, a little water is sprinkled over the rice and a few handfulls of straw ashes mixed with it. Then the rice is pounded with a heavy stone hammer for four hours. By that time all the glumes are loosened from the grains of rice and at the same time the surface of the grains become quite white and polished. To clean the rice from the glumes and ashes, it is driven through a grain-fan or shaken in a riddle similar to the one shown in Fig. 122.

The mortar is hewn out of one piece of stone. The one shown in Fig. 154 had been broken and somewhat mended with iron cleats. The height is 19 inches and the diameter 30 inches. The thickness of its side-walls is 3 inches, its depth 12 inches.

The head of the hammer is of stone with a circular blind hole into which the wooden shaft of the hammer head has been rammed. The head from the blunt point of the stone to the end of the wooden shaft measures 12 inches. The stone where it is thickest has a diameter of 7 inches, and the wooden shaft a diameter of 5½ inches. A wooden handle 2 feet long is driven into a hole in the shaft as seen.

In the neighborhood of Canton a pestle is employed for polishing rice, instead of the stone hammer, a tapering heavy wooden piece has its larger, rounded end covered with iron. Rice is polished by the farmers in this manner for their own domestic use. Rice dealers, who buy the unpolished rice in large quantities and polish it themselves to afterwards retail it, employ a more expedient, less tiresome method. They have a board balanced on a support, as is evident from Fig. 155. Under one end of the board a pounder is fastened similar to the head of the pestle just described. The polishing mortar stands directly under the pounder. The pounding is performed by a man standing on the board astride of the support. By shifting the weight of his body alternately from one leg on the pounder side of the board to the other on the free side of the board, the board see-saws up and down and the rice gets pounded in the mortar. As occasion demands the man stirs the rice in the mortar with a long wooden staff without leaving his place on the board.

In polishing rice moist straw ashes are used as I have already related, and this may be the slower but better process. Another method is to use ground limestone. I saw primitive mills where limestone, reduced first by hammers into small fragments, is ground to powder. In a stone trough filled with these fragments a stone wheel is rolled back and forth until the limestone is pulverized. Then the powdered stone is moistened, no doubt, with a glutinous liquid, formed

Fig. 156. Chinese Quern.

FIG. 157. BOTTOM STONE OF A CHINESE QUERN.

into square cakes and sold in this shape after it is dry. The polishing with this powder undoubtedly is accomplished with more dispatch but it removes an enveloping layer upon the rice besides the glumes to remove which is the primary object of polishing. With this layer a large part of the nutritious substance of mineral composition in the rice covering is removed and our modern authorities on diet therefore recommend the use of unpolished rice. After polishing, be it with ashes or limestone, the rice is cleaned by grain-fan or riddle and the residue fed to the chickens.

The rice-polishing apparatus which is shown in Fig. 155, I observed in the country near Shanghai. The stone mortar let into the ground has a diameter of 19½ inches and is 12 inches deep. The thickness of the edge is 2 inches. The dimensions of the balance beam to which the pestle is attached are 4 feet 3 inches by 7 inches by 3 inches. The balance-beam rests on a strip of wood sunk into a groove cut into the lower side of the beam. This strip resting with each end in the top-notch of a block of stone allows the board to be tilted up and down. The pestle, a round wooden pin 3 inches thick and 12 inches long, is squared at the upper end and wedged into a corresponding mortise in the balance beam. Over the lower pestle end an iron cap is fitted, 2½ inches in diameter and 1¾ inches deep. To give more impetus to the pestle when coming down into the bowl a stone is tied to the balance beam above it as seen in the picture. When not in use the balance beam is propped up with a stick as shown, which by the way facilitates the withdrawing of the rice after the polishing has been completed. We were told that this same contrivance is used for crushing rice into flour, but in that case the operator lets the pestle come down with more force, and does not stir the rice after each stroke of the pestle as is done when polishing rice.

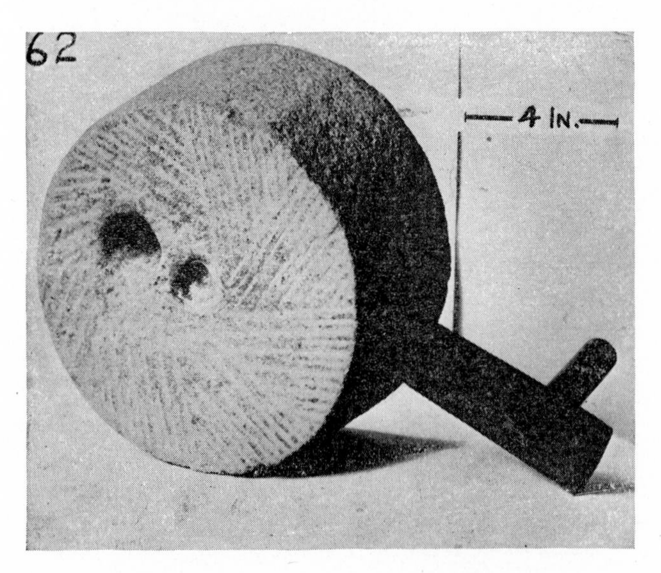

FIG. 158. UPPER STONE OF A CHINESE QUERN.

QUERNS

Whenever flour is required in the Chinese household for culinary purposes it is ground from the grain in a quern like the one shown in Fig. 156. The lower stone, shown again separately in Fig. 157, has around its circumference a trough with a spout to receive and remove the flour dropping down from the space between the two quern stones when the mill is being used. The diameter of the cutting surfaces of both groove-lined stones, is 9½ inches. The width of the trough is 2½ inches, its depth 1½ inches. The upper stone, shown again separately in Fig. 158, turns on an iron pin ⅝ of an inch in diameter and projecting ¾ of an inch from the center of the lower stone, as seen in Fig. 157. The turn-handle is the peg seen projecting upward from the horizontal strip driven sideways into the stone.

As shown in Fig. 157 the iron pin upon which the top stone turns, projects vertically upward from the top center of the lower quern stone. This iron pin, is round above the stone level. Below that where it is inserted into the lower stone, it is square, with sides ⅞ inch wide, fitting into a square hole cut into the stone and held there by alum. Alum crystals are heated and when liquid are poured into the hole around the inserted pin. Upon cooling they become hard and cement the iron pin firmly in place.

The upper stone, Fig. 158, is 5 inches high. The pivot hole in the center of its lower surface is just large enough to receive the iron pin, upon which it revolves, and has been made smooth on the inside with alum. A larger round hole between the center and rim has a diameter of 1¾ inches and passes entirely through the upper stone to feed the grain into the mill. To facilitate the grain passing between the grinding surfaces the feed-hole has been somewhat enlarged at its bottom opening as can be seen in Fig. 158. The top surface of the upper stone is cut into the form of a flat dish surrounded by a rim ⅝ inch high to hold the grain, some of which is periodically pushed into the feed-hole. This depression or dish is circular except on that side where the horizontal wooden elbow for the turnhandle, seen projecting from the stone, is socketed.

This mill was owned by my interpreter, Mr. Chang, who had it made to order by a stone mason, the usual mode of procuring one. It is turned by the handle directly grasped in the right hand.

In Kiangsi and Chekiang provinces, where I observed the use of such a quern there are two modes of grinding rice. First the grinding of rice which had been roasted in a cast iron cooking bowl. It is roasted dry without addition of any fat or oil until

Fig. 159. Chinese Quern.

Fig. 160. Quern for Wet Grinding Used in Making Bean Curd.

the grains turn slightly brown. In that state it is easily reduced to flour.

The second mode of grinding is in the wet state. The rice is soaked in water over night and then fed into the quern and a little water poured into the feed-hole each time more rice is put in. A paste-like liquid is the result of this grinding. A round-bottomed basket, like the ones used for washing rice, is partly filled with wood ashes, a cloth laid over them and the paste poured upon the cloth. The moisture is thus drained off and a dough is left in the cloth. If the quantity of dough be large the ashes are renewed several times and the paste in the cloth is kneaded with the bare feet by stepping on it. Next the dough is steamed. A sieve with large meshes, formed by bamboo strips, is placed over the cast iron bowl filled with boiling water. Over this a cloth is spread, and the dough put on top of the cloth. The dough is heated and rises. Next it is placed in a large stone mortar (see Fig. 154 for an example of one) where it is pounded. The assistant having dipped his hands in water turns the batch around after each stroke. The dough becomes very tenacious through this beating and is then ready to be rolled with the hands into long strips which are torn into smaller pieces. These are pressed into wooden molds to give them a neat shape. The result is a doughy cake which is relished by the Chinese.

The quern is primarily a household utensil. The establishment where the bean curd is made also uses this quern for grinding the beans but here a vertical pole is used for turning the stone. The handle in this case consists merely of the horizontal piece of wood stuck into the side of the stone as seen in Fig. 158, with an open hole instead of a pin at its end. Into this hole fits loosely an iron pin driven into the lower

Fig. 161. Barrel Used in Making Bean Curd.

end of the long straight turning pole. The upper end of the turning pole rests loosely in an iron ring attached to a ceiling beam right over the center of the quern. This turning devise is not essentially different from the one used by the first white settlers in Pennsylvania on their querns.

The art of baking is not well understood by the Chinese. As the foregoing shows they got as far as the dough and the raising of it by means of steam. Leaven cakes made of barley, wheat or rice are in use for the fermentation of wines. The crushed grain is mixed with water kneaded into a dough, wrapped in the leaves of the paper mulberry and hung in the open air for from five to ten days. It is curious that the seemingly obvious step of employing this leaven for the fermentation or raising of dough has never been taken. Likewise the bake-oven, so highly developed as a kiln for porcelain and pottery, is only sporadically utilized for culinary purposes. The photographs were taken at Shanghai in the Native City.

Fig. 162. Parts of the Press for Making Bean Curd.

Fig. 159, supplements the account given of the household quern. It represents a quern, with a different turning attachment, which is found in most peasants' houses in Chekiang and Kiangsi. This quern is set up for dry grinding of maize, wheat or rice. The ground meal drops into the basket below the quern trestle. The two stones are each 4½ inches high and 18 inches in diameter. The lower stone has an iron pin in the center fixed with alum. The projecting end of this pin fits into a hole of the upper stone. A funnel-shaped hole in the upper stone at some distance from the center, serves as a feed-hole for the grain. Directly across the level top of the upper stone, and projecting about 9 inches beyond it, a wooden stick is fastened with a rope, faintly seen, at both ends through holes in the top rim of the stone. This stick is perforated at its projecting end with a round hole into which the vertical wooden downturned pin, mortised into the horizontal turning stick fits. The latter is a forked branch of a tree and its construction sturdier than the T-shaped horizontal turning stick shown in Fig. 145. The cross handle of the turning stick mortised into the fork-ends (left) is held at the proper height by ropes fastened to the ceiling. The turning is done as was described under Fig. 145. The grinding surfaces of both stones are scored with grooves, divided into eight radial triangular sections which sections are so channeled that the grooves are parallel to the division lines. The grooves are cut at small intervals so as to fill each section. In this manner all the eight divisions are covered with grooves always parallel to one of the adjoining division lines. The basket has a diameter of 3 feet 9 inches and is 7 inches high. The height of the trestle is 18 inches. The pictures were taken near Shanghai, at Chao Ka Doo.

UTILIZATION OF SOY BEAN

The cultivation of the soy bean, *Glycine hispidia,* is of the utmost economic importance to the Chinese. Rice is usually considered the most prominent part of Chinese diet, but the soy bean and its products should be mentioned as scarcely less so. In the first place there is the oil which is expressed from the beans and used as food mainly by the poorer people. Its odor is not very pleasant but this is of no consequence to the Chinese people. A savoury vegetable is furnished by its sprouts, which are a common article of diet. Then there is the bean relish, prepared with salt and spices. The soy or bean sauce is an excellent condiment and seasoning medium which is in daily use in most Chinese kitchens. It is a black, easy flowing liquid with an agreeable spice flavor and if only lightly shaken in a vessel covers the sides with a bright yellowish-brown froth. Soy is exported in large quantities to India and Europe, and finds its way into many foreign condiments and table sauces of high repute. Perhaps the most extensive use of the bean is for making bean curd.

The dried beans are soaked in water over night and then ground wet in the quern shown in Fig. 160. Water is freely poured on to run down in liquid form with the ground beans into the barrel standing under the quern trestle. The barrel is shown separately in Fig. 161. A turning stick as in Fig. 159 is used on the quern. The height of the trestle is 22 inches. It is shaped like the letter T and rests on three legs. Its long arm is 3 feet long and the shorter arm mortised into it, 25 inches, both arms are 3 inches square. The lower stone is held in place on the trestle by a squared pin extending vertically upward from the trestle top and resting in a corresponding hole in the lower stone. The diameter of the stone is 13 inches.

The liquid from the beans ground with water in the quern drips down into the tub, Fig. 161, a specimen of copper's work not too common in China. There are projections inside the barrel on which the perforated disk seen on the right is made to rest. Over it a kind of cheese-cloth of native manufacture is spread through which the ground liquid mass is strained, leaving the coarse particles behind. After grinding the cloth is folded over the pulp and the water pressed out with the masher shown on the right of Fig. 163. The pulp in the cloth is once more mixed with water and pressed out a second time. The residue is fed to pigs or cattle and only the filtrate is used for making bean curd.

The barrel shown in Fig. 161 is 18 inches high and has a diameter of 20 inches. The four projections on the inside are equidistant from each other, and 11 inches from the bottom. The handles on the outside are also part of the staves. The wooden disk with four square holes is 18 inches in diameter and ½ inch thick.

The next step is to add a small amount of powdered gypsum to the filtrate and then to boil the liquid. The boiling coagulates or curdles the suspended particles in the water, while the added gypsum, it is said, aids the process of coagulation. After boiling, the liquid with the curds is poured back into the barrel. A preliminary draining off of the water, now a kind of whey, from the curds is done rather ingeniously. A round, close-meshed basket is pressed into the liquid in the barrel and the water oozes up through the meshes into the basket from which it is ladled out with a wooden dipper. This is an unexpected reversal of the process of straining which however works splendidly. The draining leaves a liquid heavily laden with curds which are ladled into a press, the parts of which are shown in Fig. 162. The two frames, one above the other, are placed upon the grooved board, at the right of Fig. 162, and a cloth is laid into the frames with its ends extending. The liquid from the barrel is then ladled into the cloth until the area enclosed by the frames is filled. The ends of the cloth are folded over the open top space upon which is placed the heavy wooden board, shown at the left in Fig. 162, which by its weight exerts an even pressure upon the curds in the cloth. The surplus water is thus pressed out and passing through the cloth runs off along the grooves in

Fig. 163. Frame for Holding the Curd, and Masher.

he bottom board shown on the right of Fig. 162. This is done in about half an hour, when the press rames can be withdrawn from the mass, now closely esembling the consistency of egg custard. To remove he frames the press board is lifted out of the top rame. The folds of the cloth are opened and another arger board is laid on the top frame. Thereupon the whole framework is turned upside down, and the

Fig. 164. Large Press for Making Bean Curd.

frames removed which leaves the coherent mass resting upon the flat board, after which the cloth is withdrawn.

To keep the square form of the released curd mass, four loose wooden strips are laid against its sides and held in place by chopsticks stuck into holes in the board. Fig. 163 shows this flat board with the chopsticks inserted to keep the four wooden strips in place. As this pudding is exposed to the air it loses its moisture and becomes sufficiently solid to be cut into smaller squares when it is ready for use. The cakes, 3 or 4 inches square are sliced into small pieces and boiled with meats or vegetables. Poorer people can be seen with their bowls of rice and a few of the bean curd cakes as a side-dish, and nothing else. The cakes can also be dried in which case they keep for a long time. To our taste bean curd at first seems insipid, as no salt enters into its making. Rice likewise is always cooked without salt, and it takes a while for a foreign palate to get used to it.

Fig. 162 shows the different parts of the simple press used in Chekiang. The bottom board is $18\frac{3}{8}$ inches square, and 1 inch thick. The surface is covered with grooves intersecting each other at right angles, to allow the water to drain off. The wooden frames are 16 inches square, $2\frac{3}{8}$ inches high, and $\frac{3}{4}$ inch thick. There are two frames to a press, they are filled level and then pressed down to about half the volume. The wooden weight-board is 14 inches square, $1\frac{1}{4}$ inches thick and strengthened by two dovetailed cross-battens. Fig. 163 shows on the right the masher, used for pressing the water from the originally wet ground beans. Its length is $10\frac{1}{4}$ inches; the head 7 inches long, $2\frac{5}{8}$ inches wide, with a rounded bottom. Its pin and handle have a diameter of $1\frac{1}{4}$ inches, the latter is $5\frac{1}{2}$ inches long. All these pictures, Figs. 160 to 163, were taken at Se Aw, Chekiang.

FIG. 165. CHINESE WINE PRESS, CONSTRUCTED LIKE THE BEAN CURD PRESS (Fig. 164). In order to better illustrate the construction of the press illustrated in Fig. 164, Fig 165 is shown, which represents a wine press of similar construction. This was photographed near Che Tsuen, Chekiang, while in action. I had to expose for a long time and the stone weight at the left kept on moving downward which unfortunately blurred that part of the picture.

The method of making bean curd thus described, I have seen practised in various places in Chekiang and Kiangsi. It is usually a household manufacture, the people making it for their own consumption.

In Kiangsi the making of bean curd is often a special industry or trade and the people buy the cakes from the dealer, who makes them in large quantities. A larger press, Fig. 164, is then used. The large bowl behind the press contains the curds. Small hemmed pieces of cotton cloth, about 6 inches square, are filled with curd, which is taken out of the bowl with a brass ladle. The cloth ends are folded over, and these bundles laid on rows upon a wooden board, five in a row, in eight rows, making altogether 40 bundles on one board. Another board is laid over these bundles; on top of this, 40 more bundles are laid, and so on until there are four layers of bundles with a board over each, when the pressure is applied, as shown in the picture.

The press was photographed at Sha Ho, Kiangsi. The beam of the press is 5 feet 6 inches long, the height of the platform 2 feet 7 inches, the width 19½ inches. The use of leverage in this press is highly interesting and quite similar to the wine press shown in Fig. 165. The horizontal beam is fixed in the framework on the left in a manner which can better be seen on the wine press, Fig. 165. The weight to pull the press beam down upon the bean curd is applied at the right of Fig. 164 through the perforated metal rod (a similarly perforated wooden rod on the wine press). This perforated rod is fastened to the horizontally hinged tray at the end of which rests a piece of iron to weigh it down. As the tray with the weight sinks down it is brought back again into its horizontal position by adjusting the perforated rod, putting it up again a few notches on the press beam.

NOTES ON BEAN CURD

Stuart (Chinese Materia Medica, Shanghai, 1911) informs us that the making of bean curd originated in the Han dynasty, during the reign of Huai Yang

Wang (A.D. 23) at Liuan. Bretschneider, however, in his "Botanicon Sinicum" (Shanghai, 1893) says that *tou fu,* bean curd, and the mode of making it are first mentioned by Liu Kan in the 2nd century B.C., but that it may have been known before that time.

The entire absence of the use of dairy products by the Chinese makes this latter conjecture appear quite plausible. The soy bean and its products supply in a measure to the Chinese diet what milk and dairy products would offer, and one could not well imagine the absence of both in our era or before without serious detriment to the welfare of the people. It was a rare instinct which led the Chinese to the utilization of the legumin or vegetable casein which the soy bean yields so abundantly. Here our food experts should take a hint and inquire why the soy-bean is only used for forage in America, while in China its products come next in importance to rice. I recall in this connection the efforts made some years ago by Mr. Hudson Maxim to interest his fellow-countrymen in this valuable food. He would buttonhole any new arrival at the Chemists' Club in New York who carelessly betrayed his ignorance of this eastern legume, deliver a lecture about the importance of the soy-bean and follow it up by sending samples, canned and in the dry, with the earnest appeal to try it and be convinced.

In my investigation I missed a point or else my informants in Chekiang omitted a part of the process, which to some authorities seems essential. It is the use of some substance to produce coagulation, just as rennet is added to milk to coagulate the casein. Stuart, quoting from the Pentsao, the great Chinese Herbal and Materia Medica, published in the 16th century, has the following:

"Wash the beans and crush them in water. Skim off what floats, and boil. Make a natron solution, or a decoction of the leaves of Shan-fan, *Symplocos prunifolia,* or use sour soy vinegar, and add to the beans. Heat all together in a caldron. Afterwards pour in a large jar in which has been placed powdered gypsum and mix well together. What will be produced is a saltish, bitterish, sour, acrid mixture, and what congeals upon the surface of the compound is to be taken out and dripped clean of the other solution. This is bean-curd."

Bretschneider explains the making of bean-curd as follows:

"The so-called 'bean-curd' is prepared by macerating the beans in water and milling them together with the water. The liquid pap is filtered. To this fluid is added gypsum, in order to coagulate the casein, and also chloride of magnesium. The coagulated casein or bean-curd is of jelly-like appearance."

From the foregoing we may conclude that the manner of making bean-curd differs in smaller details according to locality. Although there are various coagulating agents in use, the addition of powdered gypsum and subsequent boiling seems to be quite sufficient for producing coagulation.

ROPE CLUTCH PRESS

It is interesting to study in conjunction with the bean-curd press and the wine press, the Chinese rope-clutch press, although it is primarily used for pressing tobacco and in the paper making industry. Fig. 166 is the picture of a model made by a carpenter in Tsingtao and now reposing in the Mercer Museum

Fig. 166. Chinese Rope-Clutch Press.

at Doylestown. The board upon which the press rests must be considered as the ground into which the posts are rammed. The essential part is the horizontal press-beam which is pulled down upon the material with a rope and windlass. The material to be pressed rests on a support forked at one end and between this forked part a loop of the rope is hooked to a wooden pin projecting from the windlass. As the windlass is turned with the levers shown, which are alternately inserted into holes in the windlass, the rope is pulled tight and forces the press-beam downward. The way the rope is slung around the press-beam and the windlass must be scrutinized to discover that the rope has a two-fold action. It presses the beam down, and at the same time acts as a brake upon the windlass. The windlass will always remain in that position into which it has been turned by the levers. It is therefore not necessary for the one person handling the one lever to hold it until the other has newly inserted the other lever. The windlass does not fly backward and it is not necessary to have a pawl and ratchet device to prevent reverse motion. By the force of the levers the windlass is easily turned and with each turn the rope gets tighter and an immense pressure can be exerted.

The *torcular* or *torculum* of Rich (Dictionary of Roman and Greek Antiquities), also discussed by Blümner, appears to be the same press in principle as the Chinese one. Fig. 127 in Blümner, Technologie und Terminologie der Gewerbe und Künste bei Griechen und Römern, Vol. I, p. 347 (second edition, Leipzig & Berlin, 1912), shows all the elements of the Chinese press. The tackle leading upward from the press-beam seems an addition of the artist who had a preconceived idea that this should be there. The original picture, discussed by Blümner, in the Vettii House in Pompeii, does not show it. After all, the means of raising or holding the beam when the press is not in use is a secondary affair. The Chinese usually hang the beam into a loop of rope suspended from the superstructure or ceiling, or prop it with a wooden stick, or take the beam down altogether. The opinion of Blümner that the Cupids are working the levers to raise the beam is entirely erroneous. The very motion of the Cupids, working the levers with all their bodily force is exactly what the Chinese workers do when turning the windlass to tighten the rope and to pull down the press-beam. Cato Major (234-149 B.C.) describes the Roman press in detail but it appears that the clever rope arrangement which the Chinese use was not known to him.

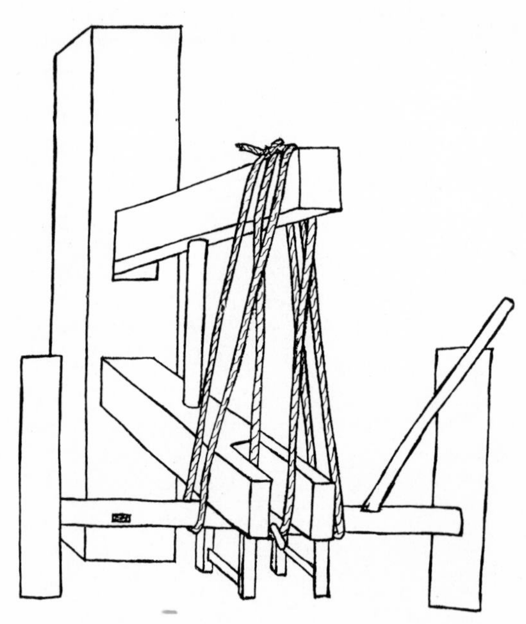

FIG. 167. CHINESE ROPE-CLUTCH PRESS.

The sketch, Fig. 167, shows a tobacco rope-clutch press which I saw in Kienchang, Kiangsi Province. It is added to show, plainer than any photograph, the unique rope arrangement. All these rope-clutch presses are made of wood except that around the windlass on each side of the lever holes there are usually iron rings applied to reinforce the wooden windlass at the point of leverage.

This is the type of press in which the once established force is *stationary*. When the material is sufficiently compressed to be able to withstand an increase of pressure, then the windlass has to be turned anew, to give the desired additional pressure. For comparison it is well to turn to Figs. 164 and 165 and observe that there we have an entirely different type of press in which not the pull of a rope, but a weight exerts *continuous* pressure. The latter principle, the loose weight, is demonstrated in China, in its most elementary form, in the making of salt-cabbage (similar to German sauerkraut): where the salted cabbage, cut in strips, ferments under pressure of a heavy stone in an earthenware jar.

There are probably no two rope-clutch presses of the type shown just alike. A superstructure is often dispensed with.

CHAFF CUTTERS

In North China where transport is carried on with carts and draft animals, almost every peasant has a mule or donkey. In addition the animals are used to

Fig. 168. Knife for Cutting Chaff.

pull wheelbarrows, turn mills, work the endless-chains of wells and to carry burdens. The feed of the draft animals is meager fare, usually only straw cut into small bits with what we call a chaff cutter. An example from Kaomi, Shantung province, is shown in Fig. 168. The whole apparatus consists of a cutting knife hinged on a horizontal wooden block. The knife here stands vertically. The horizontal base block is channelled laterally to receive the cutting knife when pushed down for cutting. The lateral channel is edged by two strips of iron, nailed on, and the slot between is just sufficiently wide for the knife-blade to enter when it is pushed down. The principle of cutting with shears or scissors is here repeated, where one sharp edge slides past another. The back of the knife is made of wrought iron with a handle socket and a perforated hinge tang, which cannot be seen in the picture, at its lower end. It has a slot in which the steel knife blade is held by friction. The knife is pushed down by the handle, turning around an iron pin, which passes through wood and tang. The edge of the blade is 27 inches long, and 6½ inches wide including the back. The length of the whole cutter with the wooden block is 44 inches. The peasants nimble and wiry use the cutter as it is shown, resting on the ground. Usually two persons handle it, one feeds the straw at right angles to the knife and the other pushes the knife.

Another chaff or straw cutter from Se Aw, Chekiang province, is shown in Fig. 169. Straw is also cut with it for mixing with clay and for use in oil mills. Clover, *Medicago astragalus,* too is cut up with this apparatus to be used for cattle feed. A horizontal fixed knife-blade, sharp side up, 12½ inches long, is driven by means of a tang at one end, into the surface of a wooden bench 3 feet 8 inches long. The other end of the blade has a round hole into which a round bamboo peg is inserted. The peg also passes through two opposite holes in the forked top of an iron spike likewise driven into the bench, so as to form a hinge for the lever knife. This hinged lever knife with wooden handle is 2 feet long. Its blade has the same dimensions as the lower knife, 2½ inches wide and 5/16 inch thick. The height of the spiked iron fork is 3¼ inches above the bench top. The height of the bench is 25½ inches. The person operating the cutter sits sideways or astride the bench.

SUGAR MAKING

The first mention of sugar in Chinese records is held to date back to the 2nd century B.C. Sugar cane is now used extensively for chewing, and this, no doubt, was the manner in which it was originally consumed. Records of the Han dynasty speak then of sugar as "stone-honey," namely the dried juice of the sugar cane, with the further explanation that it came from India. Compare in this connection our word "rock-candy." The knowledge of how to produce raw sugar by boiling the juice of the cane is said to have come to China from Turkestan or Central Asia in the Tang dynasty (620 to 907 A.D.). Marco Polo speaks of immense quantities of sugar being made in Fukien province, which supplied the demands of the Khan's

Fig. 169. Straw Cutter.

court. The refining of sugar, he further informs us, was not known to these people until some followers of the great Khan [5] from Babylonia [6] taught them to refine sugar with the ashes of certain trees, while formerly they only used to boil and skim the juice which when cold left a black paste. According to Sir Henry Yule, Marco Polo's account is curiously corroborated by the fact that in India coarse sugar is commonly called Chini, the product of China, and sugar candy or fine sugar Misri, the product of Babylon in Egypt (Misr el Antika).

Theophrastus (390-305 B.C.), and after him Pliny (23-79 A.D.) and Dioscorides (ca. 50 A.D.), mention sugar which, however, was then used only for medicine. The cultivation of the sugar cane spread from India to Southern Persia and Arabia, then to Egypt, Sicily and Southern Spain. The Arabians as early as the 9th century knew how to refine sugar, and finally in 996 A.D. refined sugar was first brought to Venice from Alexandria. The conical loaf form in which refined sugar has been produced until quite recent times in Europe is said to have first been made in Venice, while some authorities claim this shape originated in China.

Sugar cane is cultivated principally in the provinces of Kuang-tung, Fukien and Szechuan. The mode of expressing juice is primitive and wasteful. The cane is passed between two upright close-set revolving cylinders of wood or stone, and the juice, caught below in a reservoir surrounding the cylinders, is led through a bamboo pipe into the boiler. The refuse of the sugar cane, after the juice has been expressed, the so-called bagasse, is used on the spot for fuel to heat the boiler.

The picture, Fig. 170, shows a press in which the cylinders are of stone. One of the cylinders is revolved by draught animals hitched to the end of a framework seen in Fig. 171. The motion is imparted to the other stone through cogs set around its top, which engage the cogs set around the top of the first cylinder. The cogs are worked out of the solid stone. A number of them had been broken off and were replaced by wooden ones inserted into holes hewn into the cylinder.

Fig. 171 shows the whole arrangement with the long wooden shaft to which the draft-animal is

[5] Kublai Khan, 1216-1294 A.D.

[6] Old Cairo is here meant, an island in the Nile, directly south of the present Cairo, the Babylon of Egypt, a settlement established by Rameses II. in 1400 B.C., and assigned to Assyrian prisoners. Now called Masr or Misr el Antika, "Old Cairo."

hitched to set the press in motion. The tent-like structure formerly covered with straw was just being dismantled, the business of expressing the juice from the cane having been finished for the year. The photographs were taken at Kien Chang, Kiangsi, near the Fukien border.

The next step in the manufacture is to conduct the sugar juice to the boiler which rests in an excavated space in the ground. The juice runs directly from the reservoir surrounding the cylinders through a bamboo pipe into this boiler which is a huge cast iron container. It was impossible to get any more details about the process at that place. The boilers had been removed already and the gathering crowd seemed to have taken it amiss that I had taken pictures and refused any information.

To augment and make the given account somewhat clearer I add a short description of sugar refining from the Encyclopedia Sinica, (Shanghai, 1917).

"The juice from the rollers is boiled in open iron pans. While boiling, the juice is constantly stirred and all dirt removed as it comes to the surface. The boiled juice is then poured into earthenware jars with a small plugged hole in the bottom of each, and when almost full, the top is carefully closed over with earth (clay), and the plug from the bottom is removed. The jars are then placed in the open air, where they remain for from 30 to 40 days according to the weather, until the contents are quite dry. The sugar so obtained is sorted in three grades: the first or uppermost in the jar being white, the middle, green, and the lowermost brown sugar. The drippings which are merely left in the sun to dry give the black sugar.

"Sugar candy is obtained from white sugar by purifying under a boiling heat with water, a little lime, and the white of an egg. It is then poured into round wide open-mouthed jars with slips of bamboo bent about inside and allowed to cool. In cooling the sugar crystallizes in large lumps of candy over the bamboo slips and the jars are then overturned to drain off the water. The lumps are chipped with a knife into flat pieces and bleached in the sun on bamboo trays, for two or three days. The product is colorless and like rock crystal."

Fig. 170. Chinese Sugar Cane Mill.

FIG. 171. CHINESE SUGAR CANE MILL.

Mr. Bowra's account of sugar refining in his Custom Report of 1869, is quoted by Stuart in his Materia Medica. "Itinerant sugar boilers go about through the Chekiang sugar districts, carrying with them an iron cauldron and a pair of cylinders. The sugar mills are of the rudest kind, being set up in the midst of the cane plantation, and are sometimes rented out. The juice having been boiled and partly clarified is transformed into a green or black sugar of a pasty description.

"In some places a good sugar is produced by the claying process. As in the case of black sugar, the cane is ground and the juice is partly clarified, and having been boiled to a certain consistency, is transferred into earthenware vessels of a conical shape, the article being then known as *t'ang ts'ai*. These cones being inverted into empty vessels to drain, in a short time an article known as *chi ch'ih tang* is formed and partly dried in the sun. In refining moist clay is placed on the base, renewed as required, and in due course removed, when the sugar being taken free from the cone, is found to consist of three or four grades, that at the apex being course and moist, the quality in an upward direction gradually improving up to the top, which is the whitest and best."

The conical shape of the sugar loaf, with which I was familiar in my childhood days, is explained as the result of the refining process in a conical vessel.

SALT IN CHINA

In the Chinese language there is a primitive ideogram, now only used in combination, which signifies salt. In its primitive form it represents a square divided into four parts with a dot in each. It clearly denotes an earth-basin for evaporating salt. All along the sea coast of China can be seen now and then the process of evaporating sea salt in this primitive manner. The earliest Chinese records tell of salt being evaporated from sea water in the mythical times of the great Yu (ca. 2200 B.C.). At high tide square basins formed of sand are filled with salt water, (and it must be remembered that the Pacific Ocean is much more saline in composition than the Atlantic Ocean), and this salt water evaporates under the rays of a tropical sun and becomes a concentrated brine. Further evaporation is carried on in cast iron pans over a wood fire.

In the western regions of China there are salt deserts where the soil is charged with salt. Marco Polo refers to them when he describes the manufacture of salt by washing the soil in water which is afterwards boiled and allowed to crystallize.

In the south-west corner of Shansi in the Chieh Chow district is a shallow salt lake, about 18 miles long and 3 miles broad, called Lu Ts'un. To produce salt the water is evaporated in the sun. The business is carried on under government supervision and brings in a large revenue. To avoid illicit production the whole lake is surrounded by a high wall. The export of salt from this district extends to Shansi, Shensi and Honan. In the Han time, about 2000 years ago, salt was produced from this lake.

Of the greatest interest is the salt production of the province of Szechwan which is referred to as early as the Minor Han dynasty, which lasted from 221 to 263 A.D. In 347 A.D. the salt wells of Tze Liu Tsing in Szechwan some 800 feet deep are mentioned and it is also stated that natural gas was used for the evaporation of brine. The Apostolic missionary Imbert [7] was probably the first to give a detailed report of the salt production in Szechwan. According to his account there are more than ten thousand salt wells in the neighborhood of Wu Tong Chia in the Szechwan province. Every enterprising business man engages in the digging of one or two wells which cost about 1200 taels (1 tael equals 1 ounce of silver), a piece. The wells pass through rock and are from 1000 to 2000 feet deep with a diameter of 5 to 6 inches. The drilling is done in the following simple manner, a wooden tube is driven through the surface soil 3 to 4 feet deep. To steady it a heavy hewn stone with a hole large enough for the passage of the tube is set into the surface soil. For drilling, a large steel jumper or drill weighing about 300 to 400 pounds is used. The lower end is roughened with incisions and the upper end has a ring for fastening a rope which suspends the heavy drill from one end of a see-saw lever. On both sides of the other end of the lever, a platform is erected, and a lightly clad man jumps from the one platform down upon the free end of the lever and up to the other platform. At each jump, the steel drill is raised about 2 feet and then falls with great force into the hole. From time to time water is poured into the tube in order to moisten the powdered stone. The drill is fastened to a heavy rattan rope, as thick as a finger, and on it between the drill and see-saw is a wooden triangle. Each time the jumper drill ascends through the motion of the see-saw, an attendant turns the suspension rope with the triangle, so that the jumper may fall each time with a different contact of its incised cutting surface. There are two shifts of working people in 24 hours. After two inches have been dug, the jumper with all the attaching powdered dirt is pulled up, by means of a windlass, the suspension rope being wound upon a drum. The layers through which the hole passes are not always rock, but sometimes soft earth or coal in which case the drilling becomes difficult or useless, for the hole is then apt to deviate sideways. Usually, however, the holes are vertical and as smoothly polished as glass. If the connection breaks, and the jumper drill drops down, it takes from five to six months in order to crush it with the aid of a new drill, and get the old one out piecemeal. Under normal conditions, about two feet will be drilled in 24 hours, and altogether it takes at least three years before a well is finished. To raise the brine a bamboo tube about 24 feet long with a valve at the end is let down the hole on a rope. When it has arrived at the bottom a strong man grasps the rope and shakes it with his whole weight. Through the motion the valve is opened and the bamboo tube filled. Then it is raised by winding the rope around a large cylinder with the aid of from two to four oxen or buffaloes. The brine is highly concentrated and yields upon evaporation 1/5 or 1/4 part salt.

From some of these wells inflammable gas escapes. If a torch is brought to the mouth of the well, the gas ignites and throws up a flame twenty to thirty feet high. This property has been put to good account and the wells thus utilized are called fire wells. The mouth of such a well is closed with a small bamboo tube, and the gas led away as needed. At the mouth of the tube the gas may be ignited with a candle without danger of igniting the bamboo. The flame is blueish, 3 to 4 inches long by one inch in diameter. It can be extinguished by placing a piece of clay over the opening or by blowing it out. The boiling of the brine for evaporation is done with stone coal as fuel.

Near Tze Liu Tsing, forty hours from the first-named town, gas issues in sufficiently large quantities from the wells to be used for fuel in the evaporation of the brine. In one valley there are four wells originally drilled for brine. The brine gave out, and in the attempt to drill deeper a level was struck from which issued a black inflammable gas. To protect these wells from fire their mouths are surrounded with a 6 to 7 feet high wall. Surrounding this wall are four halls which contain the pans for evaporation. In August 1826 one of the wells caught fire accidentally. There was a thunderlike report and immediately the whole enclosure was a mass of flame which swayed about 2 feet above the well. Four laborers brought a heavy stone to cover up the well but it was thrown high up into the air. Nothing daunted, the Chinese found another expedient and collected a large amount of water, high up on the mountain side. This water was released all at once on the well, and the flame was extinguished.

A foot under the ground upon the four sides of

[7] "Annals de l'association del la propagation de foi," Paris, 1829.

each well a bamboo pipe is inserted into the well, to tap the gas and lead it under the evaporation pans of which altogether about 300 are in use. Each flame has its own pipe which is fitted as a burner with a 6 inch long clay pipe of one inch diameter. Other pipes are led along the walls terminating in jets above the pans to illuminate the building. The unused balance of the gas is led away outside of the buildings and burns there in three large flames about two feet high and thus regulates the pressure of the gas which is used for heating and lighting.[8]

Travel in Szechwan is for the time being (in 1928) out of the question and to make up for a personal account I feel that I cannot do better than to quote the lucid account of the salt wells at Tzu-Liu-Tsing by Alexander Hosie[9] a keen observer whose travels in Szechwan extended over the years 1882, 1883 and 1884.

"At the salt wells of Tzu-liu-ching, Szechwan, a square stone embedded in the ground has a central hole a few feet in diameter. From the hole I found issuing a hempen rope, about an inch thick, which ascending passed over a moveable pulley wheel, fixed at the top of a staging some 60 feet high, and bearing a striking resemblance to the shears at a dockyard. The rope from the pulley wheel led to another wheel, fixed nearby, a few feet above the ground. Passing over this latter wheel it entered a large shed, the floor of which was several feet underground. In the center of this shed, was an enormous horizontal bamboo wheel or drum, 12 feet in height and 60 in circumference, placed on a vertical axis, to which the rope above mentioned was attached, six feet from the ground. Now to return to the well. The other end of the rope descended from the first pulley wheel directly into the well. It was just being pulled up and after the lapse of a quarter of an hour, the top of a tube, from 9 to 10 inches in circumference, attached to the rope, made its appearance and was drawn up to within a foot of the wheel. Meantime a workman, stationed at the mouth of the well, had thrown a rope around the tube, which was composed of the stems of a number of bamboo fixed together, and as soon as its lower end appeared, he drew it to one side, and over a wooden reservoir built into the ground. Embracing the tube with his left arm, he plunged an iron rod which he held in his right hand, upward into the bottom, and raising a leather valve, which was there adjusted, allowed the contents, consisting of black dirty-looking water, to escape into the reservoir. This was the brine. The tube was again placed over the well, and descended with great rapidity, after which it was again pulled up. The drum in the shed, around which the rope coiled when pulling up the tube to raise the brine, had 4 water-buffalos harnessed to its circumference at equal distances. As the drum revolved, the rope coiled around it at a sufficient height above the ground not to impede the buffalos. For a quarter of an hour, that is, until the tube had been raised up from the well, the animals were driven around in a trot by 4 drivers, when the poor beasts, exhausted and white with froth, were unharnessed, and led back to their stable, whence a fresh relay was brought. When the animals were unharnessed and the signal given, the drum reversed with great velocity, creating a violent wind all around until the tube had again descended to the bottom of the well. Forty animals were employed at this well, and each relay raised the brine about 10 times in every 24 hours. From the chief large outside reservoir, the brine was being carried off in bamboo pipes laid down between it and smaller wooden reservoirs which received it in the evaporating sheds. On the floors of the latter, rows of brick furnaces with round openings at the top were built. On each furnace rested a round, shallow, iron pan, about 4 feet in diameter, filled with brine conducted in open bamboo pipes from the adjacent reservoirs above noted which occupy one side of each shed. Under each pan was a flame blazing from a bamboo tube coated with lime and fitted with an iron burner, while all around the pans flames burst from smaller upright tubes and lighted the sheds, for by day and night the work of evaporation goes on. The 'Fire Wells' whence the fuel is procured, are quite close to the brine well. They are carefully built over and bamboo tubes covered with lime to prevent escape, ramify from the cap covering the well mouth to the evaporating sheds. Doubtless these fire wells contain petroleum, whose vapor or gas supplies the natural fuel. The salt is of two kinds, pan or lump salt, and granular salt. The pan salt is in cakes from two to three inches in thickness, and is of the same shape and size as the evaporating pans. In preparing granular salt, bean flour is used to give it a whiter appearance. Evaporation takes from 2 to 5 days, according to the strength of the gas-flame. The pans weigh about 1600 pounds apiece and are used for about a fortnight only, when they are changed for new ones. The depth of the wells is from 700 to 2000 feet. The brine from a dirty yellow

[8] According to modern reports the surplus gas is led for many miles in bamboo tubes to the salt wells in Kia-ting-fu, where it is similarly used for heating and lighting.

[9] Alexander Hosie, "Three Years in Western China," London, 1890.

in the shallower, became a deep black in the deepest wells. Twice as much salt is evaporated from the black as from the yellow brine, the deeper the well, the stronger the solution. Salt is said to have been worked at Tzu-liu-ching as early as the Minor Han dynasty.

"The two brine wells of Pai-yen-ching are only 50 feet deep. Bamboo tubes, ropes and buffalos are here dispensed with, and small wooden buckets, with bamboo poles fixed to their sides as handles, considered sufficient for raising the brine. At one of the wells a staging was erected half way down the enlarged well hole and from it the buckets of brine were passed up to the workmen above. In the evaporating sheds, we here found a series of mud furnaces with round holes at the top, into which cone-shaped pans, manufactured from iron obtained in the neighbourhood, and varying in height from 1 to 2½ feet, were loosely fitted. When one of these conical pans has been sufficiently heated, a ladleful of the brine is poured into it, which bubbling up to the surface, sinks, leaving a saline deposit on the inside of the pan. This process is repeated until a layer, some 4 inches thick and corresponding to the shape of the pan, is formed, when the salt is removed as a hollow cone ready for market. Care must be taken to keep the bottom of the pan moist; otherwise the salt cone would crack, and be rendered unfit for the rough carriage which it experiences on the backs of pack animals. A soft coal found nearby, is the fuel used in these furnaces. At the time when Marco Polo passed through this region salt cakes, as described, were used as currency, and they, no doubt, were evaporated at these very wells."

Rock salt seems to be rare in China. It has been mentioned as occurring in the country around Whenchow, Chihli, and in the country of the Tanguts, North Eastern Tibet.[10] It never played any rôle commercially.

S. Wells Williams relates that at Chusan (off the coast of Chekiang) the sea water is so turbid that the inhabitants have to filter it first through clay before proceeding to evaporate it.

China early recognized that to tax so necessary a commodity as salt is a lucrative business. In the earliest times, before the Chow dynasty, when revenue was remitted in kind, the districts which produced salt had to supply the court and court officials with salt as tribute. The premier of the State of Ts'i (Shantung), Kuan Chung (700 to 645 B.C.) conceived the bright idea of making salt and iron a government monopoly. One after another the petty states of the time followed the example and it was due to this stimulus, that the Szechwan salt wells were discovered (330 B.C.).[11] As new dynasties came and went the monopoly was at times handled wisely to produce revenue not heavily felt by anyone, and again with such rigor that the poor people had to do without salt altogether. When the levy became too oppressive, and the murmuring of the people against it had to be taken account of, the burden was temporarily eased, only to be applied again with full vigor in subsequent financial crises. In the 8th century the great financier Liu Yen found the monopoly producing about $200,000 per annum, but through his genius it rose to $3,000,000 which equaled half the revenue of the whole country. The report of the Viceroy Ting Pao Chen of Szechwan[12] who died in 1886 throws some light on the productiveness of the salt tax in recent times. "The *likin* revenue (tax on goods in transit) derived from the salt wells at Tze-liu-tsing amounts to over a million taels (1 tael equals about 70 cents) a year. As the likin is 1/3 the cost price, the nominal official value of the salt would be over three million taels, and as the selling price is usually at least twice the cost price plus likin, the best possible nominal selling value would be Tls. 6,000,000 a year for these wells alone; the actual value may be imagined."

The latest development of the salt monopoly is that it has been pledged as security for foreign loans. This was in January 1913, and foreign reorganization, supervision and inspection have brought the so-called Salt-Gabelle to a high state of efficiency. In the last few years, however, through the inroads of the military the efficient working has been greatly handicapped.

Concerning the uses of salt there is not much to be said. The alimentary use, of course, is paramount. Rice, however, is never cooked with salt. Whether this custom arose as a measure of economy I could not find out. On the other hand meat, fish and vegetables are always served well salted. The preserving action of salt has been recognized, so that salted cabbage and fish are used in enormous quantities. An unusual use of salt is for cleansing teeth as it was formerly practiced in Japan. The brush with which it was applied was a willow stick one end of which was frayed by incisions with a knife.

[10] Les Produits de la Nature Japanaise et Chinoise par A. J. C. Geerts, Yokohama, 1878.

[11] Parker, "China," p. 223.

[12] "China Review," Vol. XI, p. 263.

Fig. 172. Well Digger's Windlass.

WATER SUPPLY

The necessity exists, of course in China as elsewhere, of digging wells to get a supply of water where all other means to procure it fail. It seems, however, to judge from the few wells to be seen that the Chinese resort to this procedure with reluctance. In cities with no other water supply, many wells can be seen distributed all over the town, and in such a case they are always public wells. It is not customary to have wells attached to private dwellings. Each separate household usually has some means of storing rain water, not sufficient, however, to be independent of a public well. Not much space is wasted for placing public wells. A square place with sides not larger than the width of the streets opens up directly from an alley and has in the center the well. A stone curb about a foot high encloses the round well and usually deep grooves are cut into the curb by the ropes sliding over it as the bucket of water is pulled up. The coolies coming for water bring their own buckets and rope with them.

The unfinished well shown in Fig. 172 is under construction. It was being dug in a mission compound in Changshu, Kiangsi. Chinese well diggers were engaged to do the work. A circular hole is dug in the ground and the sidewalls protected from caving in by bamboo wickerwork. For well-digging a short-handled hoe is used. As the work progresses, a rude derrick is erected over the hole, to receive a windlass for hoisting up the excavated material. Two wooden frames, X-shaped, are rammed into the ground and over these frames is laid a round beam which serves as windlass. At each end of the beam are mortises, in which rest firmly naturally shaped turning cranks, cut from the twisted branches of trees. The part of the beam between the supporting frames is divided into two spaces by three triangular bamboo frames. The picture does not show it, but in actual use one length of rope is coiled around the beam within one of the marked spaces, while another rope fastened to the beam within the other marked-off space extends down to the bottom of the well. At each rope-end a bucket is fastened, the one at the end of the coiled rope being above ground near the derrick, and the other tied to the uncoiled rope at the bottom of the well. After the latter has been filled with excavated earth the workmen turn the windlass. The coiled rope unwinds, lowering the empty bucket into the well and at the same time the rope attached to the filled bucket in the well is coiled around the beam of the windlass and thus the full bucket brought up to the surface. This bucket is now emptied and the bucket in the well filled. The motion of the windlass is then reversed which takes the emptied bucket down and brings up the filled one. The two different ropes coil in opposite directions around the beam and for this reason one winds around the beam while the other unwinds from it.

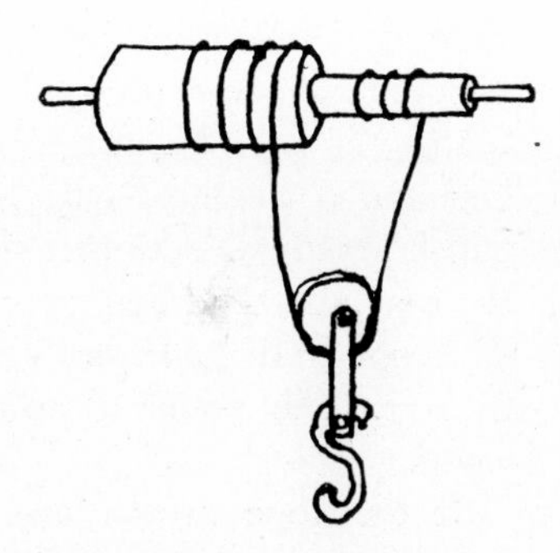

FIG. 173. DIFFERENTIAL PULLEY OR "CHINESE WINDLASS."

In old textbooks on physics, sometimes, as example of differential motion, reference is made to a so-called "Chinese Windlass," whose beam has two parts of different diameter, see sketch in Fig. 173. A rope winds upon the one part as it unwinds from the other. In this contrivance the same principle is involved as in the differential pulley with which heavy weights can be lifted with comparative ease. I have no evidence that such a contrivance is used by the Chinese. The effects of the two windlasses, the one we are dealing with, and the other so-called "Chinese Windlass" are quite dissimilar, and yet they have one principle in common, namely the unwinding of a rope from one part of the beam at the same time that another rope is wound upon another part of the same beam.

The well-digger's buckets are enclosed by a loose vertical loop of bamboo strips which pass through the holes of the handles and under the bottom of the bucket, as can be seen in Fig. 172. This produces a convenient point of attachment for fastening the rope. Under the hoist upon a board passing over the side of the well can be seen a Chinese sledge hammer. This discoid hammer-head is of cast iron, rather a heavy lump, and the handle seems disproportionately thin and flexible. In wielding this Chinese sledge-hammer either of the flat faces of the head are made to strike the object. To have the handle flexible adds to the force of the impact, and when such a hammer is swung the head seems to leap down upon the article to be struck. The Sioux tribe of North American Indians had a war club, called pogamoggan, which had such a flexible handle, and its effects must have been powerful if ever its sobriquet of *"casse-tete"* was justified. If we inspect stone club-heads, hammers and axes as they are found in various parts of the world, among the implements of peoples from the stone-age, we usually find that the holes for handle insertion are much smaller than we would make them for present day use, and these disproportionate holes warrant the conjecture that the principle of using flexible handles was common knowledge in prehistoric times.

After a Chinese well has been dug to the desired depth it is usually lined with hewn stone, built from

FIG. 174. WELL SWEEP.

Fig. 175. Undershot Water-Wheel for Raising Water.

the bottom up, and the bamboo lining, seen in the picture is removed as the masonry progresses. Shortly before reaching the top the diameter of the well is gradually reduced in diameter and finally a curb set on top.

The origin of wells is ascribed by the Chinese to their legendary ruler Huang Ti, who is said to have reigned one hundred years, from 2697 to 2597 B.C. This is of course only another way of saying that wells have been dug in China ever since the hundred families settled on the upper reaches of the Yellow River after having come nobody knows from where on the vast Asiatic continent.[13]

The well sweep shown in Fig. 174 was photographed in Nanchang, Kiangsi. It is well known in Kiangsi province. Tuan-mu Tz'u, a sage of the 6th century B.C. attests to the antiquity of the well sweep. He describes it as being made of wood, the after part heavy and the fore part light and it can raise water like a pump.

Of the construction little need be said. Between two upright posts set firmly in the ground and propped by slanting beams, the large balance-beam is pivoted. One end is weighted with a heavy stone which about balances the other end with the rope and the filled bucket at its end. The rope from beam to bucket measures 23 feet. The whole construction is of wood.

If the rope breaks and the bucket drops into the well, the Chinese peasant does the same thing as the Pennsylvania farmer did in a like predicament. He gets his grappling hook, or grapnel, an example of which is shown in Fig. 178, and lets it down the well with a rope and before long gets hold of the drowned bucket, by swinging the wrought iron grappling hook about in the water until one of its hooks or barbs engage some part of the bucket or pail.

There are three barbs on the shaft of the grapnel and on the other end a ring for fastening the rope. The whole length of the tool is 10 inches. I got this implement from the wares of a junk dealer in Nanchang, Kiangsi. The articles were spread out on the ground, in the famous second-hand alley, called Ka Ch'iao, High Bridge, named after a very low bridge nearby, which is famous for its worn pillars, against which the women rub their bellies to insure male offspring.

For irrigation purposes water-wheels similar to the wheels described in Figs. 126 to 132 are sometimes used. Fig. 175 shows an undershot wheel from Yuanchow, Kiangsi, used for raising water. This kind of wheel is rudely put together. Around its circumference, a series of bamboo tubes closed at one end

[13] While reading proof I received Herrlee Glessner Creel's book entitled "The Birth of China" just published (by Reynal & Hitchcock, New York, 1937), which revolutionizes our conceptions about early China. Mr. Creel has with unusual critical ability surveyed the whole amount of available material, comprising the finds of the most recent archæological excavations, the Shang oracle bones, the Chow bronze inscriptions, and correlated the new knowledge with a restudy of the Chinese classics. The outcome of all this, which shows the author to be an accomplished sinologist as well as paleographer, is this fascinating book which opens unexpected vistas into a field which we believed obscured forever by the dust of ages.

Fig. 176. Undershot Water-Wheel for Turning a Mill.

are fastened obliquely to the framework with bamboo withes. The tubes are submerged and filled with water and by the turning of the wheel are placed in such a position when on top that the water pours out from them into a wooden trough, whence the water is conducted through bamboo tubes into nearby fields for irrigation. These irrigation wheels are from 20 to 30 feet in diameter and are turned on the principle of an undershot wheel. As can be seen in the picture, along the circumference of the wheel boards are fixed which pushed by the running water, impart motion to the wheel. The same mill-race is utilized for a smaller undershot wheel, which furnishes the power for a trip-hammer mill in the thatched shed adjoining. There is a sluice-gate in front of each wheel. By closing or opening the sluice-gate the wheel can be stopped or set in motion.

Differing in construction and purpose from the water-raising wheel described under Fig. 175, this undershot water wheel, Fig. 176, also photographed at Yuanchow, Kiangsi, is shown in action as it works the machinery of a mill.

The question may be asked here whether the Chinese derived their knowledge of water-wheels from the west. B. Laufer in his "Chinese Pottery of the Han Dynasty" (Leyden, 1909) says that the water mill was introduced into Europe in the first century A.D., and that in Chinese writings it is first mentioned precisely at the same time, which leads him to

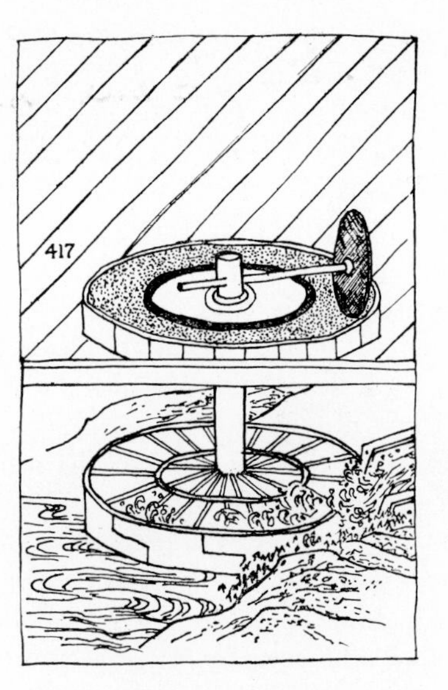

Fig. 177. Horizontal Water-Wheel Turning a Mill.

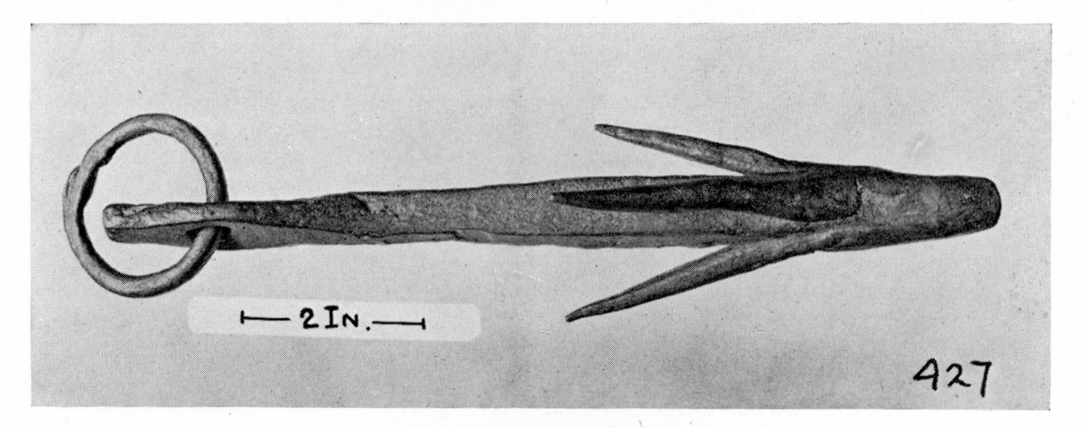

FIG. 178. GRAPPLING HOOK.

suppose that in both places its introduction was derived from the Romans. He further tells us that the first water mill was erected in Japan as late as 610 A.D. by a Korean, and in Tibet in 635 A.D.

Over and undershot wheels were known to Philon of Byzantium and described by him ca. 230 B.C., in his work on pneumatics and hydraulics. Strabo relates in his Geographica that Mithradates VI. erected ca. 88 B.C., in Asia Minor a grain mill driven by a water-wheel. Thus the earliest information about water-wheels seems to point to the East and there is as much reason to suppose that the Romans derived their knowledge of them from Asia.

The Chinese know the horizontal water-wheel. I attach a tracing showing one from a Chinese book on agriculture published in 1742 A.D. I never saw any in Central China and it seems that they were common only in Northern China. Du Halde, in his "Description of China, etc." (London, 1738), says that "Water-mills are common on most of their Rivers and are made use of in grinding the Bark of Trees to make Pastils withal. The wheel of these Mills is placed horizontally and has double Fellows about a Foot or a Foot and a half from each other; these Fellows are united by little Boards placed obliquely in such a manner, that in the upper Part they leave an Opening sufficiently large, and on the lower Part very narrow; the Water, that falls like a Sheet two Foot above these little Boards, makes the Wheel turn around pretty swiftly."

Another writer, Alexander Williamson, whose observations were confined to North China [14] gives the more probable account of the prevalence of the horizontal water-wheel. Du Halde makes it appear that it was the only kind in vogue, while Williamson, an acute observer, who actually travelled from village to village over large parts of Northern China, came across the horizontal water-wheel in an out-of-the-way mountain district and describes the novel sight as follows:

"In the pass of Ku-kwan, between Chilli and Shansi along the river Ching-shing are many mill dams and most of the corn-mills are worked by water-wheels moving in a plane; a sort of turbine wheel in fact. This form of wheel is admirably adapted to these mountain streams. A wooden spout is fixed so as to direct the stream upon the flanges at a slight angle. The shaft turns the lower of two large stones in the building; contrary to our custom [Mr. Williamson was a Scotchman]. The upper stone is fixed, being tied roughly with strong ropes to the wall. In one corner of the mill was a winnower [more likely an arrangement for bolting flour], consisting of a long sieve, suspended by cords from the ceiling over a wooden tray, and worked by a spindle; the moving power being obtained from a smaller wheel with a vertical axis, like the large one."

ABOUT CATTLE

It has often been said that the Chinese take better care of their cattle than of themselves. If a draft animal is used for turning the irrigation wheel, the Chinese build a shed to protect the beast from the rays of the sun, but if man-power is used to turn the wheel, no shelter of any sort is deemed necessary. Further illustrations of such preferential treatment are the individual cattle sheds found in many places in Kiangsi to house the zebu or water-buffalo. They are circular structures built of adobe-bricks upon a foundation of rubble or waterworn stones. The diameter is about 10 feet, the thickness of the wall 4½ inches, and the height 6 feet. An entrance is left about three feet wide. Wooden beams are laid over the open top of the circular structure, and upon these

[14] A. Williamson, "Journeys in North China," London, 1870.

is stored the farm's supply of threshed wheat and rice straw. Inside the floor is made comfortable by a spreading of dry leaves. Fig. 179 shows some of these sheds on a Chinese farm near Sha Ho, Kiangsi. In front of one stands a water-buffalo sunning himself. The overhanging straw, partly eaten away, indicates that straw is part of the diet of these animals. A magnificent camphor tree shades the farm. In other places where there is no such convenient place for storing straw it is piled around a tree and stacked high up. The cattle eat away the straw from the bottom and then one has the peculiar spectacle of trees encircled with straw rings about 4 or 5 feet above the ground, and wonders how on earth the people ever got the straw up there. When piling it radially around the tree, it is, no doubt, fastened to the tree from layer to layer in one way or another.

Fig. 180 shows one of the two stalls for zebus or water-buffalos constructed in a lean-to shed, built against the dwelling, and communicating with the latter only by a little window, not shown, on the left of Fig. 180. This window protected by vertical iron bars leads to the sleeping room of the farmer. Outside the stall, shown in the foreground of the picture, stands a wooden pail for watering the animal. The pile on the left side of the pail contains taros, a Chinese potato, which are plastered over with mud, to be kept until spring for planting.

The stall itself looks like a cage, and is formed of four uprights held in place by horizontal beams. In front there are five slats resting in holes of the horizontal beams. One of the slats can be removed by lifting it up and thus disengaging the lower end. This done the slat can be drawn out of the hole in the upper horizontal beam. The opening is then just large enough for the draught animal to pass in and out. It does not seem plausible that the animal confined in the stall could raise the slat to get out. To forestall however, any such attempt, the moveable slat has a hole directly under the upper horizontal beam to receive a bamboo pin which prevents it from being raised. The two walls of the lean-to enclosing the stall were not deemed strong enough to be freely exposed to the draught animal. They have therefore been protected with three slats each passing from corner-post to corner-post. Other slats laid over the top of the stall are covered with bamboo matting to form a surface upon which to store all kinds of implements and straw. As a bedding, straw is spread upon the bare ground which forms the floor of the stall. The photograph was taken at Sin Tseong, Chekiang Province.

In China cattle are secured and led by a rope attached to a wooden or metal bolt, which pierces the cartilaginous wall between the nostrils. By cattle we mean the zebu, the yak and the water-buffalo. Usually the bolt is made of wood or bamboo, at one

Fig. 179. Cattle Sheds. Overshadowed by a magnificent camphor tree.

FIG. 180. ZEBU STABLE.

end it has a head and at the other is somewhat bulbous so that the attached rope can not slip off. The hole in the nose is made when the animal is quite young by forcing a pointed brass pin through the cartilage and leaving the pin there until the walls of the hole have healed. The more expedient way of burning the hole seems to be unknown.

It is only the technical similarity of making a hole through living tissue which brings to mind that the beautiful way women have all over the world to adorn themselves by wearing earrings in tiny holes in the lobe of the ear calls for a similar operation. The older European way was to make the perforation with a red hot needle to prevent the hole from healing up again. But here also the Chinese have their own way of piercing the lobe with a needle threaded with a silk yarn and leaving a piece of the latter in the hole for about two weeks.

The thread is pulled back and forth daily to prevent the holes from healing up again. The earring holes, not being burned through, gradually close up again if not used for long periods. To prevent this poor girls who have no earrings push dried

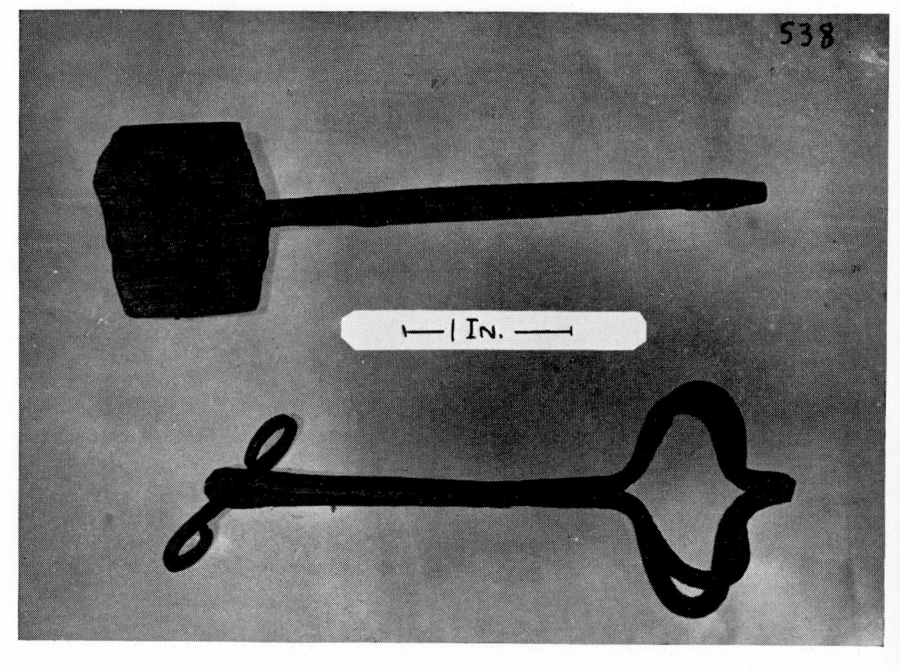

FIG. 181. NOSE BOLT FOR CATTLE.

stems of tea leaves through the holes and keep them there day and night hoping that before long a lover will come and afford them the means to replace the indecorous makeshift with ringed drops of jade or precious pearls.

In Fig. 181 (top) is shown a bamboo nose bolt which I found on a field in Changshu, Kiangsi, and a nicely wrought iron one purchased at the same place. In Germany it was customary formerly to lead bulls by a ring through the nose, but for some years now it has been prohibited, being considered a cruel procedure. Tamed bears shown at country fairs were also led about by a rope attached to a ring through the nose, as I recollect from my childhood days. I remember once seeing a ricksha coolie in Shanghai, who had a small gold ring through his nose, and was told that the man came from a rural district in Kiangsu province, where it was customary for the men to wear rings through the nose.

The upper specimen in Fig. 181 is made of bamboo. It is pushed through the hole in the nose of the cattle. The rope is tied to the almost smooth end of the bolt shaft near its end. The flat part of the other end is of course a sufficient check for keeping the bolt in place from that side. The other bolt below is of wrought iron. To put it on, one of the curled points of the cross-pin at the left end has to be bent straight and withdrawn. The bolt shaft is then pushed through the hole of the animal's nose, the pin replaced, bent into a curve and the rope attached to the curves of this pin. Cattle secured in this manner seldom get unruly, for the more they pull, the more it hurts.

In some mountainous districts of Kiangsi and Chekiang, bamboo cow-bells are used of which Fig. 182 shows a fair example. The natural section of the stem of a bamboo, about 3 inches in diameter and 6 inches long forms the sounding box. A part of the side wall has been removed to insert the wooden clappers and allow them sufficient play. The bell, although a crude affair, serves the purpose quite well; while it is not melodious, it makes enough noise to aid in the finding of strayed cattle.

The specimen shown was procured near Batu, Chekiang. While inquiring about the article from peasants belonging to an aboriginal mountain tribe, we were greeted with derision, but when they realized that we really wanted one of their cow-bells, it became at once in their eyes an article of value, and it took a lot of persuasion and a comparatively large outlay of coppers to secure one of their wooden curiosities.

FIG. 182. WOODEN COW-BELL.

TRAPS

A crossbow used as a trap is probably not found anywhere else in the world except in China. The bow is constructed of bamboo with a string of hempen rope. A little forked prop of wood, shaped like the letter Y, serves to hold the bow string when in tension. It is tied to the butt end of the crossbow with a cord attached to the two forks of the wooden prop, leaving however the extreme fork-ends free. After the bowstring has been stretched, the prop is set vertically against the bow-stock so that its two forks straddle the channelled stock just under the bowstring and hold the latter taut. Another rope attached to the single shaft of the prop (the bottom end of the letter Y) runs to three pegs seen on the side stock of the bow Fig. 183 and is held there with a toggle. As soon as this toggle is pulled off the pegs, the fork is loosened and releases its hold on the bowstring. The stock of the bow has two square holes in its under side. Two square-headed posts are driven into the ground with their ends left extending about two inches above the surface. They fit into these square holes in the bow-stock and to fasten the bow securely to the ground the stock is laid horizontally over the wooden posts and pushed down upon them. The bow is placed in such a position that it points at right angles to the path which is known to be frequented by game or wild animals. Another rope is attached to the toggle, and leads from it to the trail where it is attached to some suitable bait. When the trap is thus set, a wooden bolt, with an iron point, is laid in the grooved channel on top of the crossbow. The action must be imagined, as there is never anybody present to witness it. The animal seizes the bait, pulls at it, releases the toggle on the pegs, which in turn releases the forked prop holding back the bowstring. The bolt is shot, and if luck wills it the prey will be killed. The arrangement of fastening the toggle so that it will easily slip from the pegs when the animal pulls at the bait, must be left to conjecture. Try as I would I could not get any detailed information on this point. Even the bolts were hidden from me.

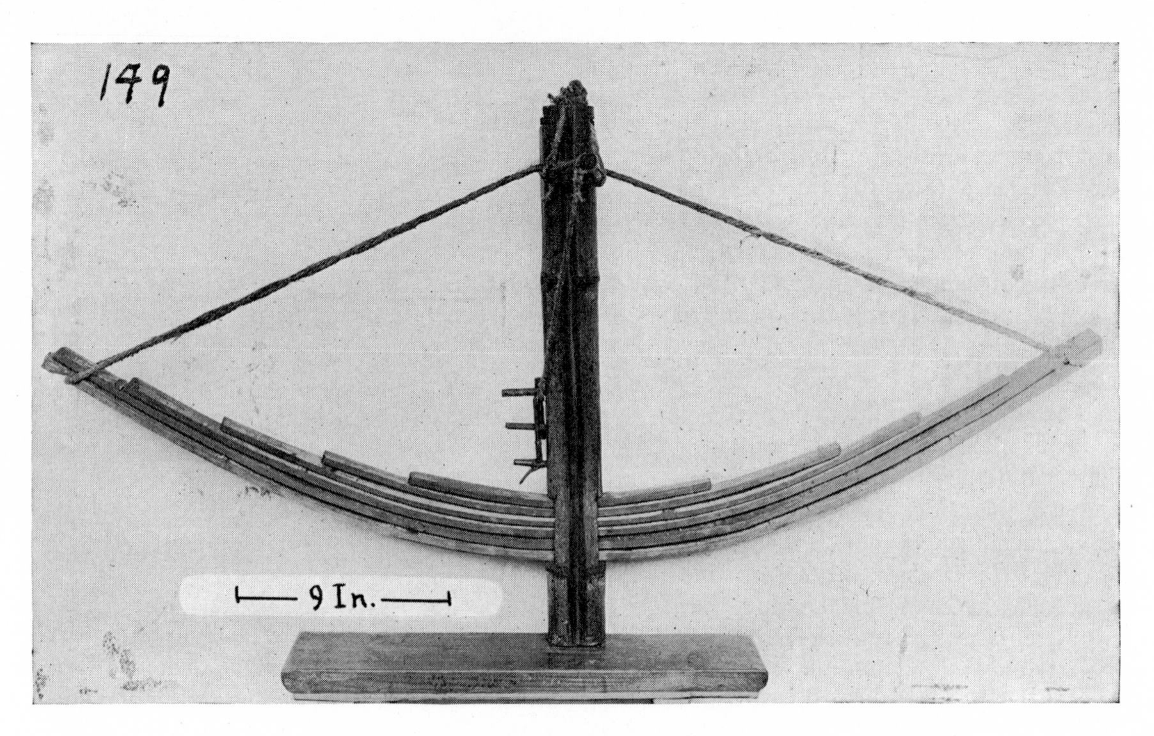

Fig. 183. Crossbow Trap.

The construction of the crossbow is simple and effective. The six-leaved spring, made of bamboo pieces, is inserted into a slot in the bamboo stock. The length of the stock, a bamboo tube, is 22 inches and its diameter 2¼ inches. The length of the spring or bow proper, is 4 feet. The crossbow here shown, was set up on a board for ease in photographing. This trap is used in the Ten Tai range in Chekiang, and the photograph was taken at Se Aw.

As children (in Munich, Germany) we had an old Swedish crossbow which had a similar spring, made up of steel leaves, but whether the Chinese ever used a crossbow constructed like this trap, for holding in the hand and shooting, I could not learn. Old Chinese stories are full of accounts of warfare with wooden bow and arrows, and the popular conception is that they were ordinary bows with strings and not cross-bows with a central stock. Botanical books mention various trees whose wood is useful for bows or arrows.

Another interesting observation is that in this crossbow the Chinese have a fully developed spring suitable for wagons and carts, but accounts of travellers in the interior, are ever full of complaints of the joltings you get when using the spring-less conveyances on poor Chinese roads.

I found in the "Hong Kong Telegraph" an intersting account in which it is stated that these traps re in constant use in Fukien province, just south of ne district where I found it. I quote in full. "Worthy f mention are the Tiger-Bows. These are extra large nd heavy (compared with ordinary crossbows), and re fastened to a framework near a path or road fre-uented by tigers or other large animals. They are set y two men and are so arranged that the moving of cord stretched across the road disengages the string nd sends the arrow on its way. The force is so great hat the shaft frequently comes out of the other side

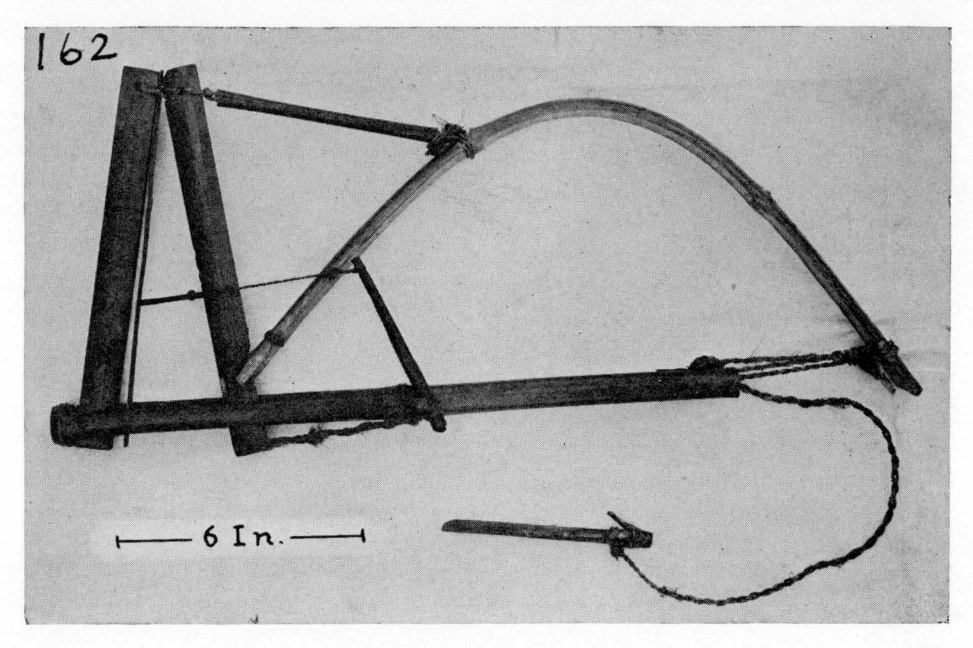

Fig. 184. Bow Trap.

f the tiger, deer or buffalo. To ensure success, the rrow is usually double-barbed and envenomed. On he mainland opposite the island of Amoy (Fukien rovince) these tiger-bows are in constant use, and nnually kill at least fifty of these huge cats."

The same source,[15] which deals with Chinese veapons, informs us that the crossbow was used in ncient times by the Chinese as a weapon and gives nteresting data on bows in general. "In archery the Chinese have long been experts, especially those of Manchuria and Szechwan. Their bows are of three ypes: the long bow, which is over 5 feet long, the hort bow, which is about 4 feet in length, and the ross-bow. The strings are made of gut, of silk, or of very strong home-made twine wrapped with fine ilk in the middle. Bows are graded according to their pull, the standard being 100 catties, about 135 pounds. To determine the pull, the bow, properly strung, is suspended from the middle and weights hung to the middle of the string, until the latter is nearly an arrow's length from the bow. Famous bowmen use bows with heavier pulls, ranging from 150 to 200 pounds, and one distinguished Chinese Robin Hood is said to have drawn a 200 catty bow (about 270 pounds). The bows vary greatly in material, construction, decoration and finish. They are made of one or several pieces of wood, and are frequently inlaid or engrossed until they are a true work of art." Ordinarily the Chinese bow is of the strength of forty to eighty catties (ca. 50 to 100 pounds), the string of silk, the arrows well-made, feathered and with iron or steel barbed points.

In the stone reliefs of the famous burial chamber of the Wu family in Shantung (dating of 147 A.D., but now dispersed) an archer is shown with a crossbow, details of which are not recognizable. Crossbow locks of bronze which fitted into the wooden shaft have frequently been excavated in various parts of China and are usually assigned to the Han dynasty (206 B.C. to 220 A.D.). There are also references to crossbows in early Chinese histories. According to the Chow Li, annals of the Chow dynasty, the crossbow was known already in the 12th century B.C., and the Historical Records of Ssu-ma Ch'ien relate that General Sun Wu in the 6th century B.C., used a division

[15] "Hong Kong Telegraph," August 17, 1892, quoted by Wer-er, "Sociology of the Chinese," London, 1910.

of crossbow archers in his army. These records indicate at least that the crossbow was known to the Chinese before the Christian era and may have been invented by them. The significance of this invention is now lost to us. It was however of tremendous importance before the advent of firearms. Its deadly certainty moved Pope Innocence II. in 1139 to forbid its use against Christians.

The acting principle in the bow trap, Fig. 184, as well as in the crossbow trap is the spring. The use of springs is not as common in China, as with us. Disregarding the modern age of progress which has enslaved us to the use of any conceivable mechanical principle, and going back to that healthier age which was transformed by machines about 1820, we find springs in many articles of every-day use; as upon wagons and carriages, mattresses and upholstered furniture, door-bells, clocks and watches, upon gunlocks, traps, shears, rattles, in the whip, etc. The Western use of the spring is everywhere apparent through its common applications. This is not the case in China. The principle is well known, as exemplified in the traps, but seldom applied. Chinese springs are mostly wooden, and of bamboo because its elasticity is most suitable. Metal springs I saw in tweezers and padlocks. Other examples of the use of a spring are the cotton-bow, its suspension from an elastic rod, the brick-makers bow for slicing clay, various traps, and of old as the most important weapon of the soldier, the bow and crossbow. The torsion spring is also known, and used in the frame saw stretched with rope and toggle.

The bow trap, Fig. 184, is set ready for action. It is not stood up vertically as here photographed, but laid down horizontally upon the ground, and the stick attached to the string here shown under the trap, driven into the ground to prevent the trap from being carried away by the trapped animal. Bait, a few grains of rice, is laid in the trapezoidal space at the lower left-hand corner of the trap, between the two upright wooden arms which act as jaws and close when the trap is sprung. The right-hand jaw, a flat bamboo strip, $9\frac{1}{4}$ inches long, $\frac{7}{8}$ inch wide and $\frac{1}{4}$ inch thick, slides in a slot of the main shaft of the trap, here shown at the bottom. One end of the bamboo bow or spring is inserted in a notch on the lower right side of this jaw and presses against it. The jaw is held open by a short cord attached to the jaw bottom kept taut by the leverage of a stick set against a peg in the main shaft of the trap. At its upper end this stick has a string attached to it which is fastened to a small pin $1\frac{5}{8}$ inches long set between the open jaws. The right end of this pin or release, rests agains the narrow edge of the moveable jaw of the trap; th other end is just barely pushed under the narrov bamboo strip running up the side of the stationar jaw. If a feeding animal touches the narrow bambo strip between the jaws, the pin is released and the tra is sprung upon the legs or body of the animal. Th whole length of the trap is 21 inches and widest widt 9 inches. This trap I found at Sha Ho, Kiangs province. It is used by peasants most frequently t catch rats.

METHODS OF FISHING

The making of fish-hooks by hand in primitiv fashion still holds its own in China. Fig. 185 show a fair assortment produced by a needle-maker in Te An. These hooks are made of foreign wire, sharpene at one end, bent into shape, and the barb is made b an incision with a chisel. The ends are usually flat tened to prevent an attached hemp string from slip ping off. Some have a loop for attaching the string The strings attached to some of the hooks shown i Fig. 185 are held firmly to the hook-shank by a stri of pewter. On the Po-shan River in Shantung a mis sionary observed fishermen using flies for bait on fin hooks in 1869.[16]

The antiquity of barbed fish-hooks is undoubted The excavations of Gezer in Palestine unearthed splendid specimen of a bronze fish-hook with a barb dating from at least 1000 B.C. Chinese records of pre Christian times speak of the use of golden hooks with silken cords for fishing lines. Also floats tied to th submerged line were used in early times made of th pith of an aquatic reed. On seeing the float sink th fisherman knew that there was a fish on the hook

The barbed fish-hook presents an interesting ques tion as to which came first, the barb on arrows an spears, or the barb on fish-hooks, and which in fluenced the adoption of the barb for the other.

A very primitive and yet efficient substitute for fish-hook is used by the Chinese around the Poyang Lake in Kiangsi province. It is a sliver of bamboo about an inch long, very elastic, the ends bent to gether to hold between them a grain of rice, and circular section of a reed pushed over the bent together ends to hold them in that position. A string is tied to the middle of the bamboo sliver which in it bent position assumes an oval shape. The manner o working can be imagined. The bent-over bamboo sliver with the rice as bait dangles in the water,

[16] A. Williamson, "Journeys in North China," London, 1870.

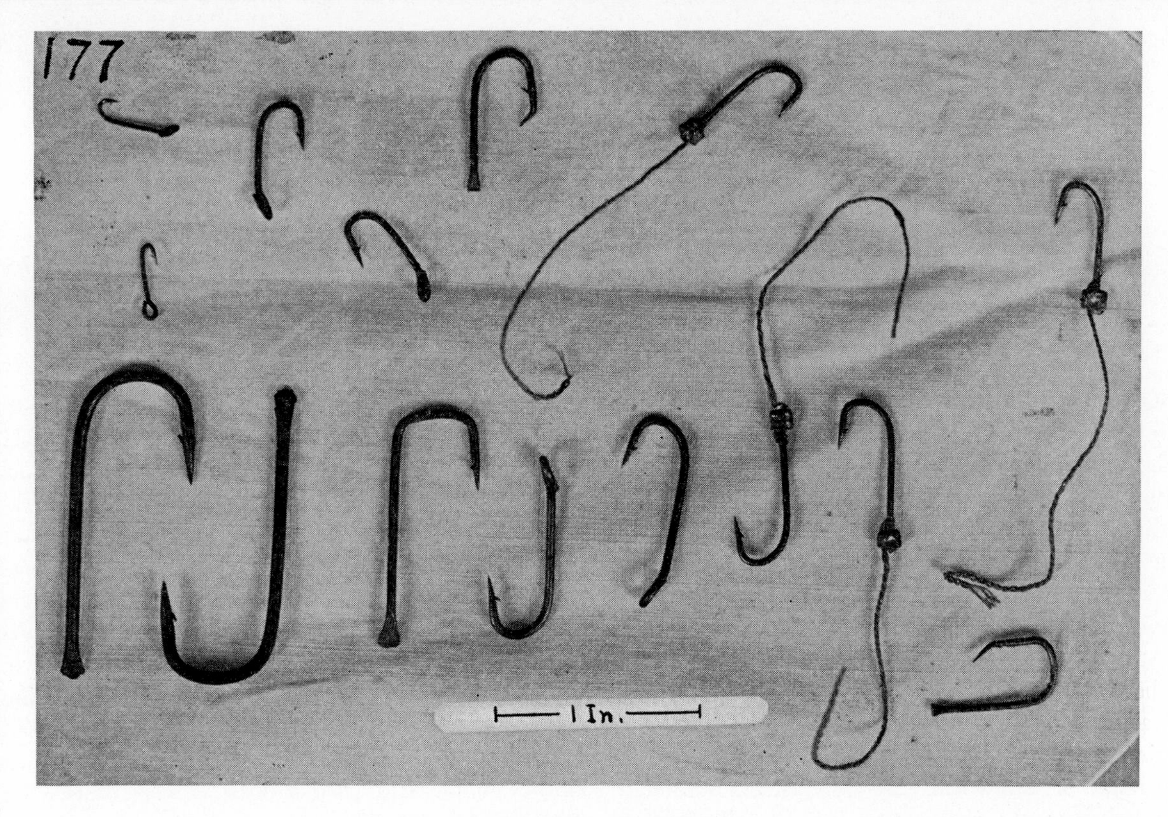

Fig. 185. Chinese Fish-Hooks.

reedy fish snaps for it. The slender reed ring is evered and the bamboo sliver straightens out in the sh's mouth, lodges in it or in the throat and the fish s caught. Usually quite a number of such fish-hooks r rather substitutions are attached to a line, which is retched out horizontally under the water. The lines re of enormous length, up to a thousand feet, and he ends are suitably anchored. At intervals of about foot the elastic bamboo hooks are tied on and after he line has been in the water all night, the catch is sually considerable.

Even at the risk of being suspected of introducing "fish-story" into this sober account of Chinese fishng methods I must call attention to a remarkable nethod where the fisherman sits calmly in his boat nd the fish jump into it of their own accord, out of nere fascination. The boat which is long and narrow as extending from the gunwale a board which eaches obliquely down into the water. The board, o be sure, has to be painted white and the moon nust shine on it. How romantic this all sounds, and et the unbelievable happens. The fish are lured by he moonlight reflected from the board, and when pproaching it get confused, jump to avoid the bstacle and land right in the boat. I was not out with the fishermen in the moonlight but I have often seen the boats in the Poyang Lake with their long side-extending boards.

We are apt to think that anything more or less mechanically complicated is the product of the Western world, and if we look at our fishing reel, nicely finished and nickel-plated, we would scarcely expect to find its prototype in China. But here it is. Fig. 186 shows one as used in conservative Kiangsi, which was ever hostile to foreign contrivances and ideas.

The rod, 5½ feet long, is made of flexible wood. An iron nail is driven through the wood at the heavier end, and serves as an axle for the reel. This reel or wheel is simply a wooden hub with six wooden spokes stuck into it equidistant from each other with notches at their ends for receiving the fishing line. From the reel the line passes through an eye-bolt fastened on the rod, and along the rod through glass rings tied at intervals to it. To the end of a line is attached a sinker of lead beneath which the snood with the hook is fastened. Fish are a wary lot and do not approach the hook if it is too obviously dangling there as an integral part of the line. The Chinese before our era learned, no doubt by experi-

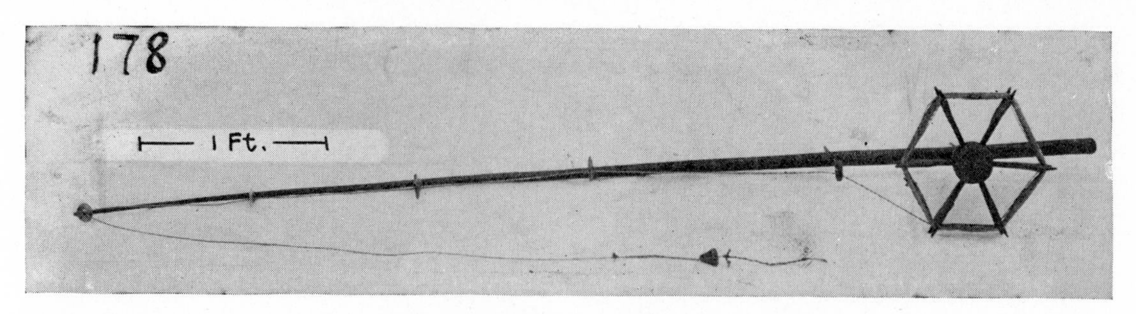

Fig. 186. Fishing Rod with Reel.

ence, that a little trickery is necessary to catch fish with hooks. For one style of fish lure, they used hooks of dazzling gold which they variegated with silver or green color, and ornamenting the line with feathers of the turquoise kingfisher, or staining it with red or green colors. Finally they used as bait cinnamon bark. The results must have justified the elaborations, although the historian keeps silence as to that.

At home we have a similar method of attaching the hook to the line. We use what is called a snood, or leader or snell, namely a short line, which is intermediate between the main fishing line and the hook. It is made of "silkworm gut," so called, a substance prepared from the contents of the silk glands of a kind of silkworm, taken when the worms are ready to spin the cocoon, and drawn out into a thread much thicker than the worm would produce. The snood is impervious to water, almost colorless, and scarcely noticeable when submerged. To the fish it severs the connection of baited hook with the line, and the result is telling.

In Southern Kiangsi, near the border of Kuangtung, the camphor trees are full of worms or caterpillars which at the time for spinning their cocoons descend from the trees. The Chinese collect them then and squeeze out the substance, ready for spinning, into a thread about 1½ feet long. These threads are laid in vinegar and then finally sold to Japanese dealers who tell the inquisitive natives, they are used in aeroplane construction. I suspect that this story is only a blind, and that these threads are the so-called "silkworm gut" which are finally sold in America and Europe as the snoods for fishing lines.

The Chinese around the Poyang Lake, Kiangsi province, have a saying that there are ninety-nine methods of catching fish, and when you ask, as you should, why there aren't a hundred, they will tell you that if there were, no fish would be left in the Poyang Lake. There are indeed many ways of catching fish practiced by the Chinese and this bit of native wit, clothes in pleasant garb a boast of cleverness, combined with common sense, which stops at utter extermination of so valuable a food product.

The instrument shown in Fig. 187 is used for catching a species of slender river fish. It is furnished with a handle, a straight stick about 4 feet long. The fisherman stands in the clear, shallow water of the stream, holding the stick vertically with both hands. The metal part is submerged, the points of the prongs being near the bottom of the stream. He stands there motionless and when a fish happens to pass directly under his instrument he swiftly darts it down and pins the fish to the bottom. With his hand he easily takes hold of his prey and puts it in his basket. His helpers often agitate the water up- or down-stream to drive the fish in the proper direction. The length of the iron instrument is 8½ inches. The prongs are four-cornered, the edges are quite sharp, and the points bent outward. I procured the specimen, Fig. 187, in Kien Chang, Kiangsi.

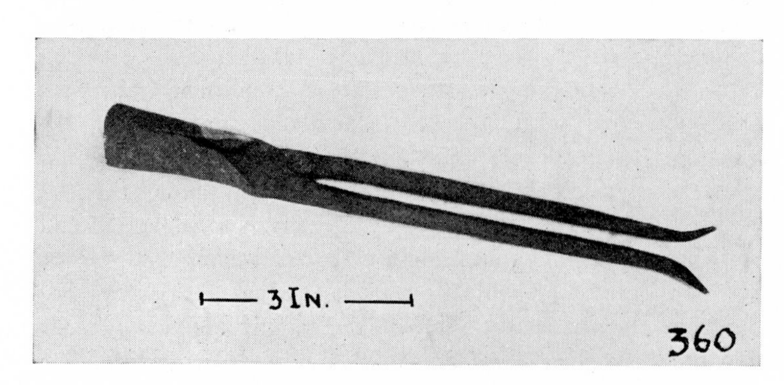

Fig. 187. Fishing Prong.

At Nankang on the Poyang Lake, I photographed Fig. 188, which shows an iron basket or cresset used as a torch. For night fishing the fishermen go out on the river in a boat, and one man holds this torch, mounted on an iron holder, as here shown, socketed on a long stick, over the water. It is a well known fact, which has not escaped the Chinese, that fish are attracted by light. Fishing with nets is considerably aided thereby, as I was informed by the Chinese. The height of the basket with the bail is 8 inches, the diameter of the opening 5 inches. The length of the iron holder with its socket is 7 inches. The fuel consists of bits of resinous pine wood.

Fishing in rice-fields is another method peculiar to the Chinese. Early in spring the peasants fasten in the water near the banks of rivers bundles of tall grasses, and the fish resort to these for spawning. These bundles burdened with the spawn are then taken to inundated rice-fields. After a few months the fish have grown to sufficient size to afford profitable fishing. For this the peasant wades about the field and with a bamboo stick disturbs the water. As soon as he spies a fish he comes down on it with a wicker hood which has a small opening on top. Through this opening he reaches into the hood and gets hold of the entrapped fish. The hood is a round basket, woven of bamboo splints, without bottom and with the small opening above noted, on top.

Fig. 188. Fisherman's Cresset.

Not only fish, but also eels are artificially bred and caught in rice-fields. The baskets shown in Fig. 189 serve to keep the eels alive and confined until a sufficient number have been caught to justify a trip to the market for disposal. The eel-baskets, here photographed upside down, are inserted with their

Fig. 189. Eel Cages or Baskets to Keep Alive Captured Eels.

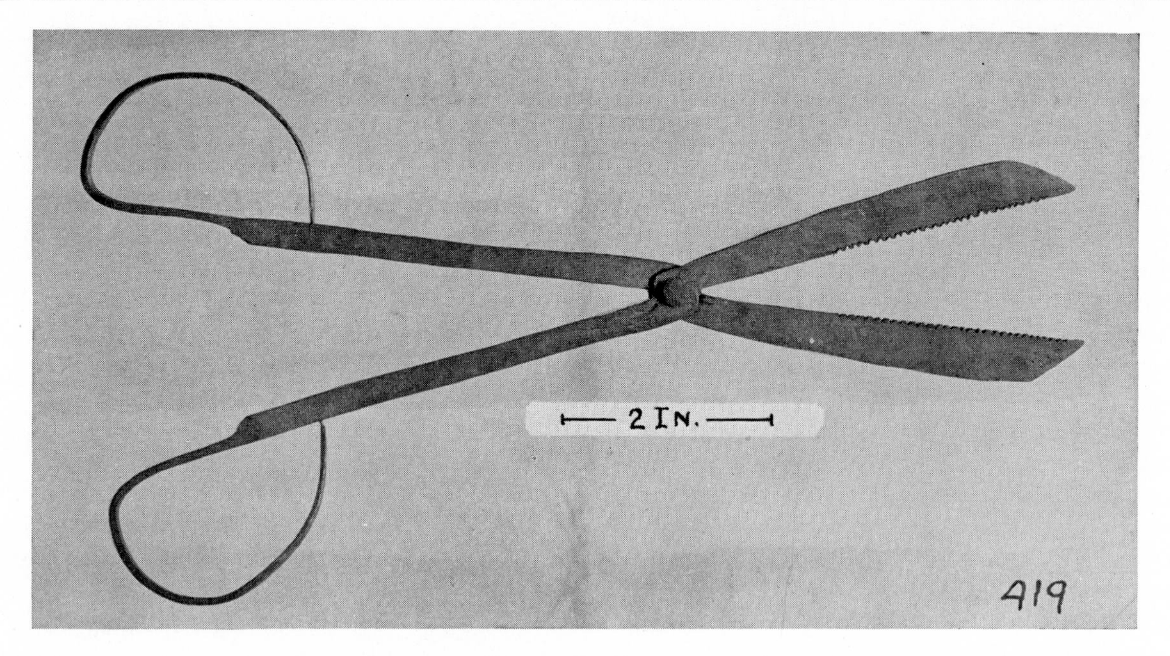

Fig. 190. Eel-Tongs.

closed rounded bottom downward into the flooded rice-field with the open funnel-shaped top extending above the water. The largest of the baskets, which are here shown upside down, is about 3 feet tall. Chinese eel-traps, which we would call "eel-pots," are of similar shape, perhaps more elongated, and fitted with a removable cover at the rear pointed end. The entrance opening is more properly an internal funnel, inasmuch as bamboo splints extend a distance into the hollow of the basket. The eel can very easily enter, sliding past these splints, which however with their flexible close-set points bar his retreat. These eel-traps are laid on their side into the water, and the entrapped eel is removed through the rear end.

The fishing tool shown in Fig. 190, is a pair of eel-tongs used to catch slippery eels, which the Chinese frequently raise in the inundated rice-fields. They are made of wrought iron. The two members of the tongs are joined together with a rivet-pin as a pivot. The length of the tongs is about 10 inches. We watched a blacksmith one rainy day making this tool in Wantsai, Kiangsi. He was sitting on a low stool under a mat-roofing held up by four posts. He had an anvil before him on the ground and the hearth, a small earthenware bowl connected with the bellows by a pipe, beside him. His products are only small wares and he can well make them sitting down. Eel-tongs he can produce at the rate of about 20 a day. When closing

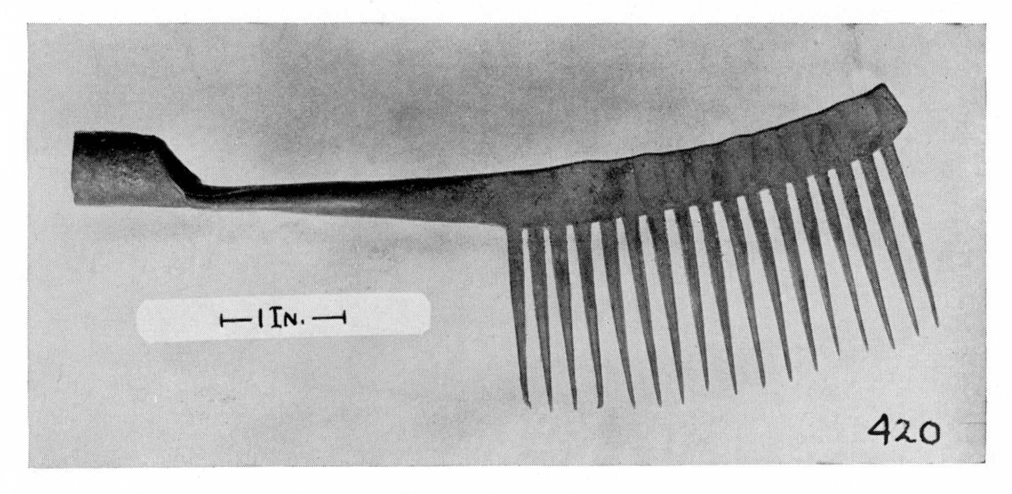

Fig. 191. Fishing Comb.

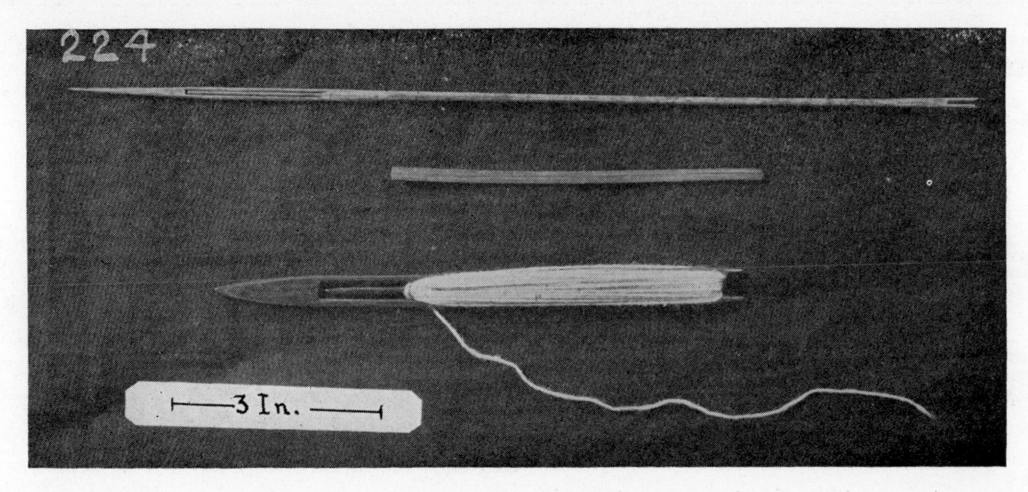

FIG. 192. NETTING NEEDLE.

op he takes bellows, anvil, hearth and all his tools
ome with him.

Another tool for fishing, also the production of the
me blacksmith who made the eel-tongs, is shown
Fig. 191, and looks like a comb. It works on the
inciple of the trident, the fisherman's implement
nce olden times, and for want of a better name we
ight call it a polydent. A wooden handle long
ough to afford a grip for both hands, one above the
her, is stuck into the socket, and the patient fisher-
an squatting motionless in a clear shallow stream
olds the tool, teeth downward directly over the
ater. When an unsuspecting fish comes along he
cks down upon it so that the sharp teeth penetrate
back. The length of the polydent is $6\frac{1}{2}$ inches and
e teeth are $1\frac{1}{2}$ inches long. The back of the comb-
ce instrument is formed of a metal band folded
er, and the separately made spikes are laid into the
ld, heated, hammered and thus welded into place.

NET MAKING

A large part of fishing is done with the aid of
ts and we must therefore say a few words about
aking them. Fig. 192 shows a typical Chinese net-
g needle, made of bamboo and wound with hemp
read. There is also shown a longer netting needle
ithout thread, and a short mesh stick. The shorter
tting needle is $7\frac{1}{2}$ inches long, the long one $12\frac{3}{4}$
ches. The mesh-stick is a smooth piece of bamboo
ce a knife, one longitudinal edge thick and rounded,
d the other thin but not really sharp.

Netting is a simple performance, easier done than
plained. The Chinese employ a wooden frame or
ck, Fig. 194, onto which the meshes are fastened
hen starting a net. The rack is hung with the upper
bar wherever it is convenient in a horizontal position. Netting is performed from left to right in such fashion that after one row of meshes is finished the rack is reversed and another row started. New meshes are formed over the so-called mesh-stick. This is held with the edge downward in the left hand, thumb in front and the index finger behind. The thread coming from the knot previously formed is laid around the stick from front to back, whereupon a simple or overhand knot is formed behind the stick in some mysterious manner but not yet drawn tight. Then the thread is carried through the V-shaped loop hanging loosely from the upper row, and finally pushed through the overhand knot and pulled upward, which draws the knot taut. The accompanying sketch, Fig. 193, it is hoped, will aid in comprehending this description. To get meshes of uniform size the Chinese rely entirely on their eyesight. In Europe, on the other hand, it is customary to have a round mesh-stick which determines the size of the meshes. When the thread is laid around the European mesh-stick, and the knot tied, the size of the new formed mesh equals the circumference of the mesh-stick. To form large meshes in Europe a stick with a correspondingly large diameter has to be used. The Chinese, however, in forming large or small meshes, use one and the same mesh-stick. The size of the meshes is determined by the distance at which the stick is held from the upper row of meshes. The netting needle holds the supply of thread, usually hemp. The other

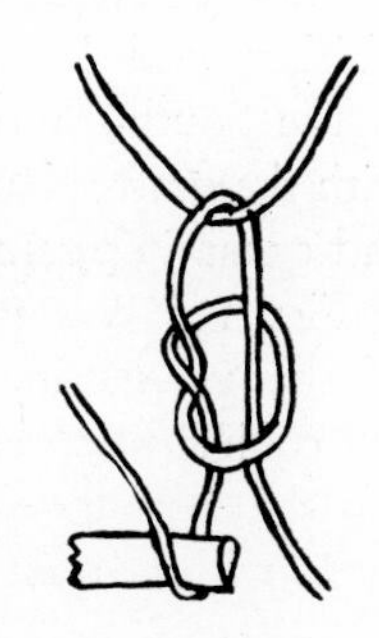

FIG. 193. FORMING A MESH IN NETTING.

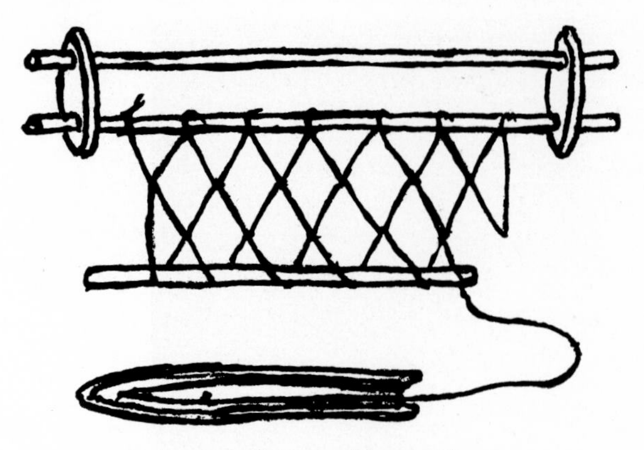

Fig. 194. Rack for Making Nets.

sketch, Fig. 194, gives an idea of the construction of the rack used in connection with net-making. Only the lower of the parallel rods is used to hang on meshes when starting a net. The variety of nets is very great in China. One kind, formed like a cone is much in vogue. It is started with a few meshes and to each row a new mesh or accrue is added.

About the history of net-making little can be said. It is closely allied to one of the master wants of mankind, the procuring of food. Its distribution is universal and its origin lost in prehistoric times. From the Eskimo of Greenland, where hair from whales' whiskers and sinews of seals furnish the twine, down to the South-sea tribes, travellers upon first contact with the natives have found nets employed for fishing and ensnaring game and fowl.

Fig. 192 was photographed in Kuling, Kiangsi. The longer netting needle is used with silk for making conical nets. The Chinese have a way of preserving the hempen nets from rotting by impregnating them with a mixture of pig's blood and oil. I procured the netting needles in Kiangsi, but they are typical for many other parts of China.

HANDLING OF MEAT

In the Chinese kitchen there is no meat-safe or icebox, in which to keep perishable foods. The supplies for the three meals of a day are usually bought early in the morning, and meats and fish are attached to the prongs of fork-hooks shown in Fig. 195, which are hung with the ringed end to a peg on a ceiling rafter, or high up on the door or window jamb so as to be out of reach of stray dogs, which will find their way into the kitchen only too often. These hooks are made of wrought iron and are 20 inches long, their thickness is ¼ of an inch. The prongs have sharp points which are readily pushed through meat or fish. Other foods such as vegetables and fruit are hung up to the ceiling in baskets, which as a rule are those in which the supplies are brought from the market or dealer. The Chinese do not trust the dealer and always take their own steelyard along when they go marketing, to be sure that they get the right measure weighed with honest scales. Many Chinese dealers, one must know, have two sets of scales, one for buying and another for selling.

In Canton and in Chekiang Province the straight-edged cleaver, Fig. 196, can be found in every kitchen and the peculiar thing about it is that this is the only cutting instrument used in the house except the firewood cutter. In Shanghai a cleaver with a curved edge is used but of that later.

The dimensions of this cleaver blade, exclusive of the unseen tang which terminates in the handle is 8 inches by 3 inches, the thickness at the back was

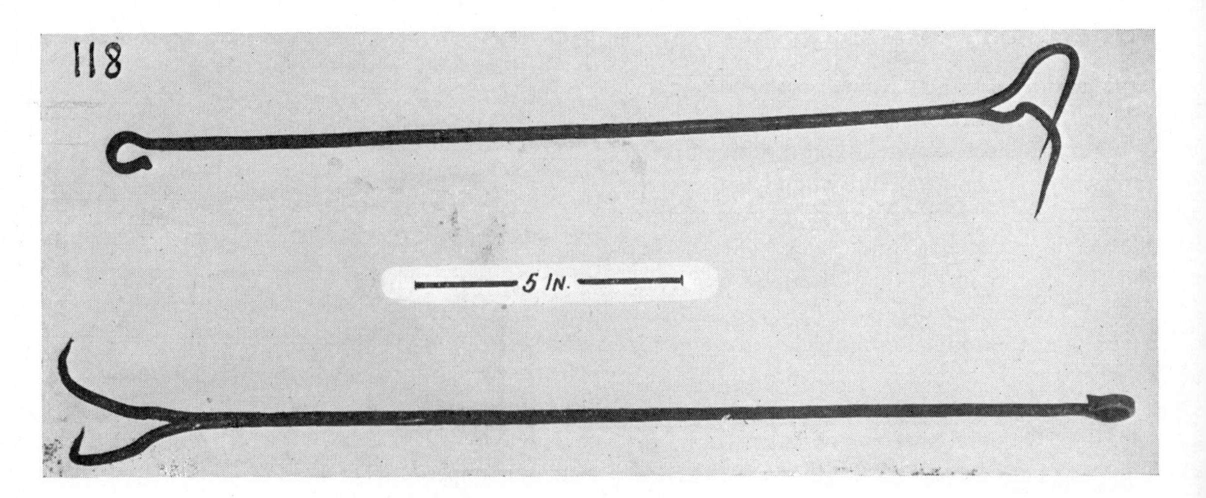

Fig. 195. Meat Hooks.

Fig. 196. Kitchen and Butcher's Cleaver with Straight Edge.

originally 3/16 of an inch, but this has been widened through hammering on it. The blade tapers from the back to a sharp edge on the cutting side. The tang goes entirely through the length of the wooden handle upon the end of which it is clinched. Between the blade and handle is an iron ferrule.

The Chinese are very parsimonious when it comes to iron or steel. I never saw iron nails used for instance, in any implement, furniture or construction, truly Chinese. They love to join things together as has been said by tenon and mortise, dovetailing, or with wooden nails. The maker of this cleaver, made in Canton, as the stamp on the blade reveals, did not feel like wasting too much steel on the blade. He made the latter therefore of wrought iron, and welded a steel edge onto it. Similar economy I saw practiced on hatchets. This specimen of a cleaver was the property of my interpreter, himself a Cantonese, who bought it from a Cantonese dealer. The photograph was taken at Shanghai, in the Native City, Kiangsi province.

In and around Shanghai, also in parts of Chekiang province, a cleaver with a curved edge is more common, like the one shown in Fig. 197. The length from its steel point to the end of the handle is 14 inches. The greatest width of the blade is 3½ inches, its thickness at the back 3/16 of an inch, the length of the blade along the back to the iron ferrule of the handle 9½ inches. The tang, a continuation of the blade, passes through the wooden handle and is clinched where it emerges.

Realizing that all the food served at Chinese meals must be reduced in the kitchen before serving, into such morsels as can easily be taken up with the chopsticks, one will understand that the chopping block, Fig. 198, is of vital necessity in the Chinese kitchen. When hashing meat the cook places the flesh upon the chopping block, and hacks into it alternately with the two cleavers, holding one in each hand.

In butcher shops they have a section of a tree trunk for a chopping block standing upon the floor. This block is 3 or 4 feet in diameter, and when they chop meat they have four people standing around it each with two cleavers, chopping away at a great rate. The photographs were taken in the Native City of Shanghai.

This specimen, a section of a cypress tree, is three inches thick and at its widest diameter twelve inches. Wood of the "soap tree," I was told, is the most desirable material for such blocks. The soap tree

Fig. 197. Kitchen and Butcher's Cleaver with Curved Blade.

FIG. 198. FOOD CHOPPING BLOCK.

meant is probably a tree better known under the name of Soapberry Tree, *Sapindus saponaria,* a native of tropical regions. This tree gets its name from the fact that it bears as fruit a nut whose outer rind or covering contains a principle, saponin, which lathers in water, and is on that account useful as a substitute for soap. The information was obtained and the photograph taken at Shanghai, in the Native City, Kiangsu province.

Fig. 199 shows a sight one can see all over China. I refer to the various pieces of meat and fowl hung upon a south wall to dry in the sun. I always thought it curious that the Chinese should not have appreciated the use of smoke for preserving meat. Sun-dried meat is hung on the rafters, sometimes for a long time until used, and here it frequently gets unintentionally some smoke-curing, especially in houses without a chimney, where the smoke from the stove rises up to the rafters and oozes out slowly through crevices and chinks in the roof, or through a single small opening left purposely for a smoke-hole. Chimneys in this latitude (Central China) are extremely rare. Workshops like the blacksmith's don't have them, and the only other place where there is need for them is the kitchen. We saw many houses in the country where the smoke was oozing out of various cracks in the roof, between the roofing tiles, with never a suggestion of a chimney. The ceiling and the walls of the kitchen are covered with soot. Meats are hung up against the ceiling in the kitchen, and while they are not getting smoked that way in our sense, they are exposed nevertheless to the preserving influence of the smoke. In general, however, deliberate smoke-curing does not seem to be known to the Chinese. An exception I must note from Hunan province. A missionary told me that in Changsha, the capital of Hunan, fish are cured with smoke. A large earthenware water jar or kang (in the background of Fig. 60 can be seen several) is filled with some chaff, and the fish tied to a pole are suspended over the jar. The whole is surrounded with bamboo matting and the chaff ignited. As little air is admitted it smolders, sending forth a dense smoke which cures the fish. On the border of Kiangsi and Hunan, I was served some excellent smoke-cured ham by a Chinese family and was told that the practice of curing was Chinese. It certainly was a singular case, and I suspect the result of missionary influence. Ordinarily the Chinese have ham prepared quite in their own way. The hind leg of a pig is soaked in brine and gets then a fearful beating until it is quite flattened out. Air-drying does the rest and the result is a deliciously tasting ham.

In the picture, Fig. 199, there are in view, for drying, a few pieces of pork, three ducks, two pig's stomachs, and a pair of rain shoes. Domestic animals are pretty well trained in China. The cat sleeping peacefully in the midst of this array of meat knows full well that it would not take long for her skin to be hung up to dry, if she dared to touch any of the meat out on the wall. With the stick leaning against the wall the meats are hung up and taken from the nails on the wall. The top of the stick is a forked piece of iron with a smaller hook on each prong. In order to hang a piece of meat on the wall the string fastened to it is passed over both of the smaller hooks on the prongs and the horizontal stretch of the string between the two hooks is then easily laid over a nail in the wall when the stick is withdrawn. The picture, Fig. 199, was taken in Changshu, Kiangsi. The wire stretched across the window opening is foreign and probably meant to keep birds out of the house, chickens included.

FIG. 199. FORK WITH HOOKED PRONGS FOR THE DRYING OF MEAT.

CHARCOAL STOVES AND THEIR MANUFACTURE

The charcoal stove, Fig. 200, is made of red, unglazed clay, and fire-baked. It is simply a pot with a square hole cut into its side to be used as a door for the draft and extraction of ashes. Inside the pot, half its height, a sieve-like earthen disk is inserted, see Fig. 201, and fixed there permanently to serve as a grate to hold the charcoal. The cooking utensil is put on the open top of the pot and made to rest on the three knobs here seen forming part of the top rim. The space between the top level of the knobs and the rim, ensures the necessary ventilation for the fire. It is customary to assist the ventilation by swinging a palm-leaf fan rapidly to and fro in front of the draft hole of the stove. Ordinarily this stove is an auxiliary arrangement in the kitchen to cook anything quickly, or else to cook things for which there is no place on the larger built-up stove. Poorer people, however, lacking the latter, use these smaller portable stoves altogether.

Fig. 200 shows a full view of the stove and Fig. 201 a view of its perforated grate. The height, including the knobs, is 8¼ inches. The thickness of the grate is ½ inch. The wall of the stove is ½ inch thick at the bottom and gradually increases in thickness to 1¼ inches at the rim. These stoves are made in various sizes, from about 4 inches top diameter to about 2 feet; their height varies, of course, in proportion. The information and photographs were obtained at Shanghai, in the Native City, Kiangsu province.

Charcoal is extensively used in the Chinese household for braziers, foot-warmers, hand-warmers, for table-stoves, used in winter to keep the food warm, and for tea-kettles, etc., hence the necessity for tongs to handle live charcoal.

The tongs, Fig. 202, are made of wrought iron. The length is 19 inches. Unusual is the way in which the two arms are held together. One arm of the tongs has a slot through which the other arm passes. The most obvious way to hold the parts together would be by a pin riveted through a hole in the two arms thus crossed, but the Chinese don't waste a rivet on this. They drill a hole through the enclosed arm where it passes through the slot, and then indent with a round punch the metal of the other arm on both sides directly over the hole. The round indentations result in bulges on the inside which fit into the

FIG. 200. CHARCOAL COOKING STOVE.

bottom and placed into the sun to dry. The dimensions of such a cake are 2 inches high, 2¼ inches in diameter at one end, and 2 inches at the other. The photograph was taken at Shanghai in the Native City.

Chang-shu, Kiangsi, is a center for making charcoal cooking stoves, similar to the one shown in Fig. 200. A suitable kind of clay is found there in large quantities which fact gave rise to the industry.

On the right-hand side of Fig. 203 can be seen a pit which is used for storing clay. Lumps of it are taken out to be used directly in a mold for shaping the body of the stove. Fig. 203 shows a number of such molds, those on the extreme left standing individually on the ground contain each a shell of a stove, left standing there to dry in the air. To form a shell the mold made of baked clay is put on the wheel, Fig. 204, and is sprinkled on the inside lightly with ashes from rice chaff and a lump of clay is thrown into it. The potter holds the mold with the left hand and shapes the clay with the right hand; the wheel is not turned all the way around, but only about a quarter of a revolution at a time. Cracked

drilled hole, and thus a pivot is formed, upon which the two arms of the charcoal tongs turn.

Besides the ordinary charcoal, pressed cakes of powdered charcoal are used which burn much slower. These are used where moderate heat for a long time is desired as for instance under tea-kettles. To make these cakes the charcoal is sprinkled with the glutinous water, in which rice has been boiled, and reduced to powder in a stone mortar, similar to the one used for polishing rice. The method of crushing the charcoal is similar to that described on page 101. A board balanced on a support like a see-saw has a stone pestle fastened under one of its ends. A man stands on the board straddling the center of balance and by shifting his weight, pounds the pestle upon the charcoal in the mortar. A long wooden stick, which he holds in his hand, serves to turn the mass in the mortar once in a while to get it evenly reduced to powder. The powdered mass, still moist, is then filled into an iron mold, round and tapering, open on top and bottom, for which a piece of iron, having the same diameter as the large opening in the mold, serves as a pestle. The finished charcoal cake is then pushed out of the mold from the

FIG. 201. CHARCOAL COOKING STOVE (TOP VIEW).

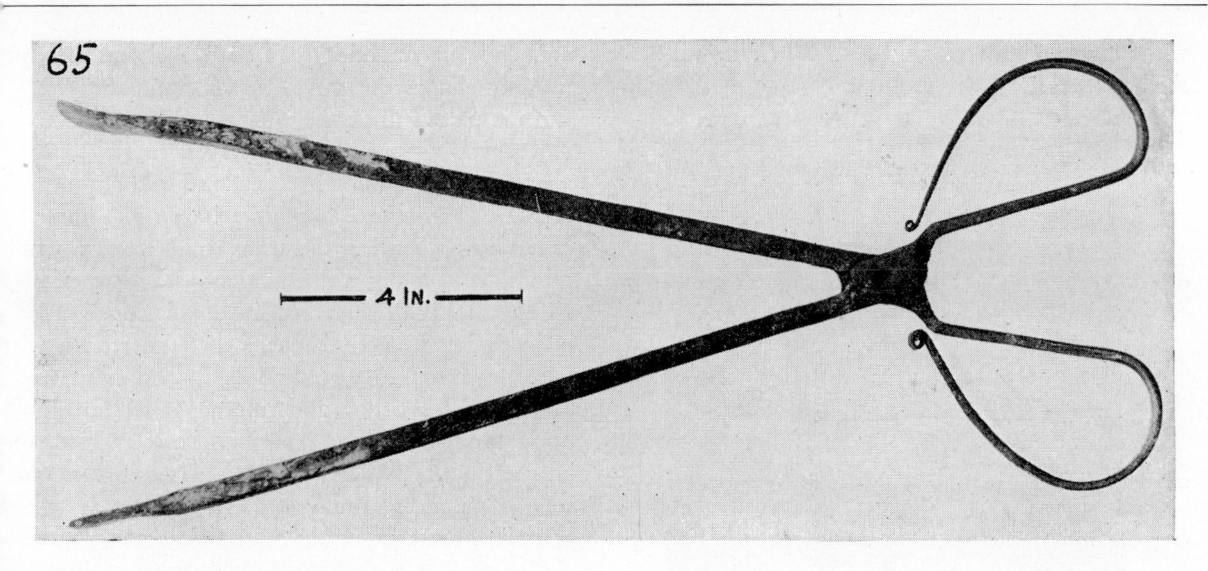

Fig. 202. Charcoal Tongs.

molds are reinforced with bamboo hoops like the one shown standing on the wheel. The plastic clay shell in the mold when finished shrinks through drying and can easily be withdrawn. The next step is to finish the shell detached from the mold. It is placed upon the wheel, the wheel set spinning and the outside of the shell made smooth with a wet rag. Its top is trimmed with the knife shown in Fig. 205. On the inside of the shell about half way down, a ledge is left by the potter when originally forming the shell, and onto this a round perforated clay disk, the grate, is laid and fastened down with wet clay. The top rim of the shell is cut out with the same knife so as to form three projections, as shown in Fig. 208, and the draft-hole is cut in the side of the shell.

The wheel in Fig. 204 has a smooth top platform

Fig. 203. Manufacture of Charcoal Stoves.

without projections of any sort. When forming the shell of the stove the mold is placed in the center and, as we have said, turned occasionally as the pott roughly shapes the stove. In finishing, the semi-dı stove is placed upon the wheel, and heavy as it is, will stay where put without clay-pasting to fasten i and only then is the wheel made to spin around. Th height of the wheel is 2 feet 3 inches. The base is stone disk (often a discarded mill stone), with central post upon which the wooden disk revolve

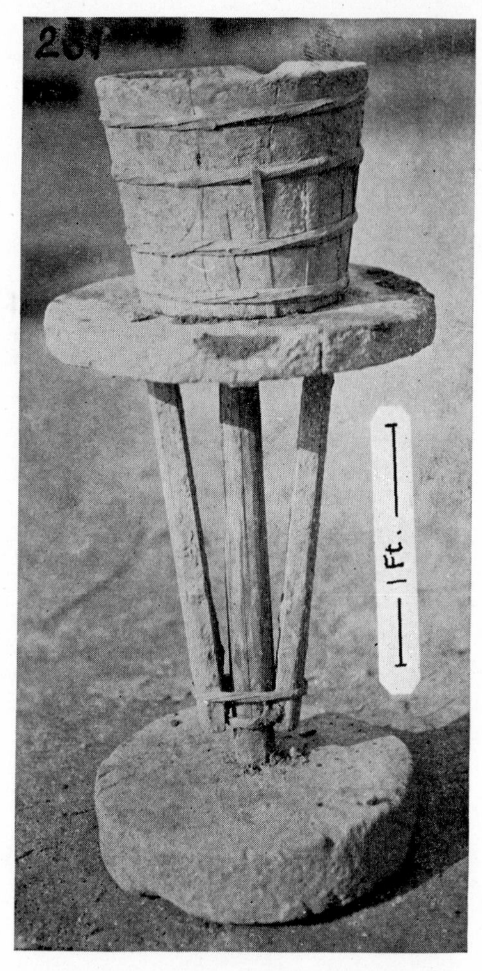

FIG. 204. POTTER'S WHEEL OF THE CLAY STOVE MAKER.

The knife in Fig. 205 is double-edged and ı inches long. It often happens that the artisan whe asked for a tool to have it photographed disappears i the back of his shop and rummages for an old di carded one. The photograph might cast a vicious spe on the one he has in daily use. Thus in this case was given an old knife without a handle for photo graphing. Better be on the safe side the potter though

The maker, not ashamed of his product, impresse his "chop" or trademark on each stove with a woode block which bears in raised letters some Chines characters. It is held against the side of the stove an given a tap with the knife. Both block and knife ar photographed in Fig. 205. The block on its uppe side shows considerable wear from being hit with th knife.

Fig. 206 shows a number of finished stoves lyin in the sun for final drying before being burned. Th perforated disks or grates when made, are placed fo drying upon conical clay forms as can be seen in th same picture. These forms serve also as molds fo making the disks. The holes are made with a bras tube, 7½ inches long, shown in Fig. 207. A piece o wood, also shown at the bottom of the picture, fit into the brass tube and with it the wet clay plug, cu from the disk, is pushed out.

FIG. 205. STOVE MAKER'S CLAY KNIFE (LOWER) AND CHOP OR TRADEMARK CLAY STAMP (UPPER).

Fig. 206. Drying Charcoal Stoves.

The stove shown at the right in Fig. 208 is fitted with a loose cover in which there is only a small circular opening. At the left is a finished stove with its cover removed, while the right one with its cover is otherwise not quite finished. The draft hole faintly seen below, has been cut with a knife, leaving a rectangular clay plug which still remains in place. This type of stove is employed by jewellers for melting precious metals. Box bellows of course have to be used in connection with it to produce the necessary draft. On account of the high heat which is attained in this stove it is fitted permanently upon a clay disk which prevents the heat from passing downward and injuring the surface upon which the stove is made to stand, such as a wooden bench or table.

DISTILLING

Chinese stills, as we discovered in our travels, are nearly always housed in dark sheds or corners which precluded taking photographs. We succeeded in getting the pictures (Figs. 211 and 212) in Linkiang, Kiangsi, showing two essential

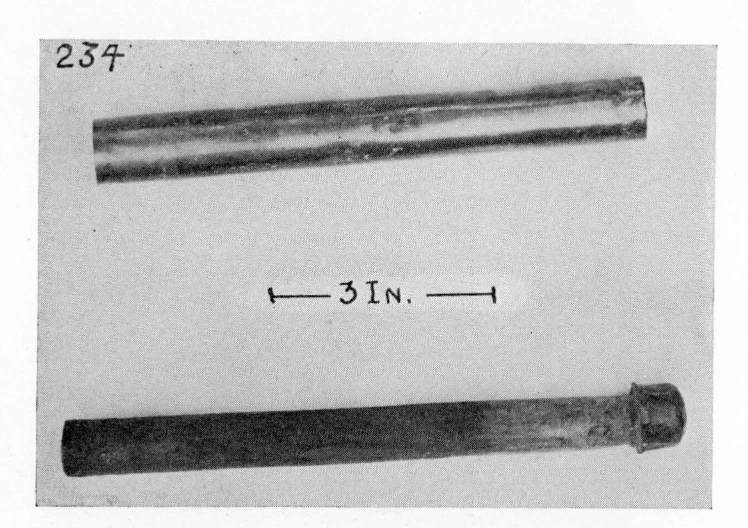

Fig. 207. Stove-Maker's Hole-Cutting Tool. This device as noted under Fig. 206 consists of a brass tube 7½ inches long, shown at the top of the picture and a wooden plug fitting therein which serves to push the clay out of the tube when the latter has been thrust through the clay disk to make the perforations or draft holes necessary for the use of the disk as a grate.

Fig. 208. Charcoal Melting Stoves.

parts of the Chinese still, but it was not until later on an excursion in the neighborhood of Tung Cheng, Anhwei, that we ran unexpectedly across a still planted in the open under a tree, and we were happy to be allowed to take the picture, Fig. 209. The adjoined sketch, Fig. 210 (Lower), shows a cross-section of the still. The fireplace or firebox is formed by a circular stone wall smeared with clay. Upon this rests the boiler, a cast iron bowl. Over the bowl is placed a barrel-shaped wooden hood, without top or bottom, around the upper edge of which is laid a tube-like ring, of sewn cloth filled with sand to serve as a gasket. The lower edge of the hood is luted with clay to make it air-tight. A shallow pewter catch-basin, 10 inches in diameter, with an open top, and terminating in a long pipe, is set obliquely, into the wooden barrel-shaped hood, the pipe passing through a hole in the side of the hood. This catch-basin with its pipe, measuring 32 inches over all, is shown upside down in Fig. 212. The basin is held suspended by means of three strings fastened equidistant from each other on its rim. To the ends of these strings are fastened stones or pieces of wood, two of which are here faintly seen, and these are laid over the upper edge of the wooden hood and thus keep the pewter catch-basin, with its drain pipe, suspended in the center of the hood. The next step in building up the still is to put on top of the wooden hood the pewter cooling kettle which is shown upside down in Fig. 211. It is 21 inches high and 24 inches in diameter across its opening. When in use it hangs rounded part downward immediately over the pewter catch-

Fig. 209. Chinese Still.

basin. This cooling kettle is filled with cold water, and has on its upper rim two projecting handles (here seen) for conveniently lifting it. One of these handles is a hollow pipe and serves as overflow. The kettle in Fig. 209 has this overflow pipe on the hidden side of the still, and in that picture only part of the bamboo gutter can be seen into which the water from the invisible overflow pipe discharges. The process of distilling can now be understood. The cast iron bowl previously mentioned as set upon the fire, under the lower part of the hood, contains the mash consisting of fermented glutinous rice. A wood fire heats the mash and steam rises, strikes the cool bottom of the pewter cooling kettle, condenses, and aided by drip channels grooving the kettle's bottom, runs down its sides, and drops into the catch-basin suspended under the kettle. From the catch-basin, the distillate runs through the oblique catch-basin pipe into an earthenware wine-jar placed conveniently beside the still. The water in the pewter cooling kettle is kept cool in its lower zone close to its bottom by a simple arrangement. As the sketch Fig. 210 shows, a pewter funnel is thrust into the kettle, the bowl-shaped part touching the concave bottom of the kettle. Above the cooling kettle a shallow wooden tub rests on a wooden frame. From this tub a wooden pipe leads down into the pipe of the funnel and from time to time water is allowed to run down from the tub above by removing a wooden stopper from the wooden pipe. The cooling water running down into the funnel strikes the bottom of the cooling-kettle and thus chilling it aids condensation within the still. The cooling kettle is kept filled with water up to the overflow and as cold water is allowed to flow in from the tub above, the warmed top water runs off through the overflow. The process of distilling is very efficient, the distillate runs in a continuous trickle from the still. Rectification is not practiced. A handful of cinnamon bark and dried orange peel is placed in the jar into which the liquor runs. This imparts a pleasant flavor to the spirit which is really only what we would call low-wine.

The Mongols employ a similar still, Fig. 210 (upper), in which a liquor is distilled called arrihae, from airak which is soured mare's milk. Instead of the catch-basin with the pipe, they merely suspend a small basin in the barrel-shaped hood, for collecting the condensate which drops down in very much the same way from a round-bottomed kettle filled with cold water. The airak itself, mother of arrihae, is slightly intoxicating, and is a favored drink among the Mongols. The name arrack, which we give to a strong distilled liquor from the East, seems to be related to this Mongolian word.

It would be fruitful to investigate the etymology of these Mongolian words further and establish their relationship to the Arabic *araq* which means sweat, or the condensate which deposits in drops like beads of sweat in the process of distillation. A Chinese name of one of the products of distillation is *A-la-chi,* clearly a transliteration of the Arabic *araq* [17]).

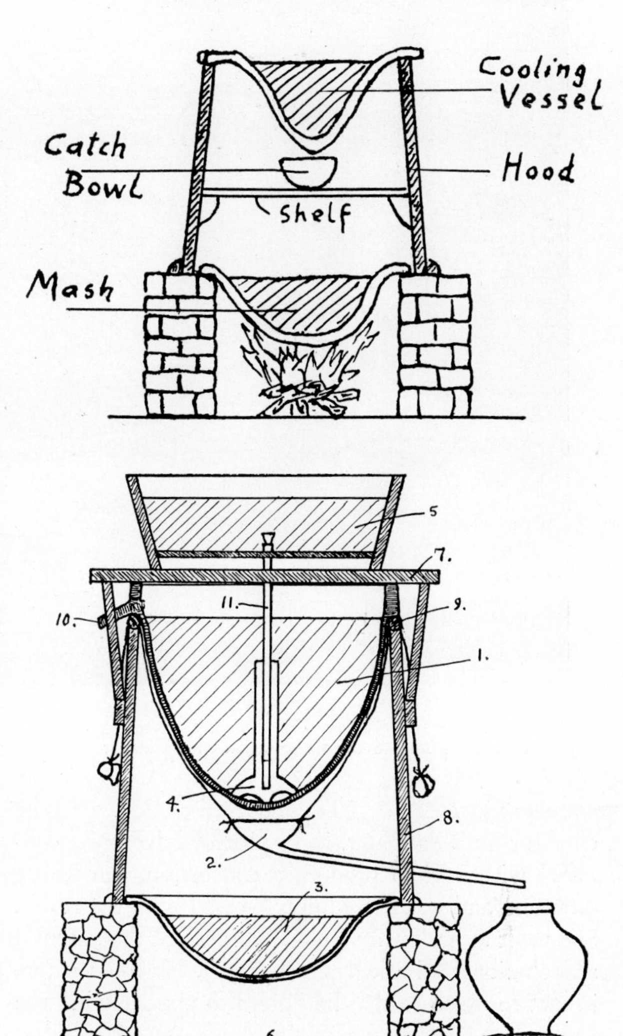

Fig. 210. (Upper) Mongolian Still. (Lower) Chinese Still. (1) Condensing or cooling vessel. (2) Pewter catch basin with conveyer pipe. (3) Cast iron bowl with mash. (4) Pewter funnel. (5) Shallow wooden tub. (6) Fire box. (7) Wooden frame supporting shallow tub. (8) Barrel-shaped hood. (9) Gasket of sewn cloth, filled with sand. (10) Overflow pipe. (11) Wooden pipe with wooden stopper for letting cold water run down into the condensing vessel.

According to a Chinese legend the art of making

[17] G. A. Stuart, "Chinese Materia Medica," Shanghai, 1911. p. 419.

Fig. 211. Cooling Kettle Used in a Chinese Liquor Still. The pewter cooling kettle kept full of cold water to condense on its outer surface the rising steam in a Chinese still, is here shown out of place and for better inspection upside down.

wine was invented by I-Ti, who lived ca. 2200 B.C. The emperor Yu's daughter, in a spirit of adventure, connived with I-Ti to produce a concoction, something different, and was exceedingly pleased with the result. She went to her father, quite confident of the parental approbation, and asked him to try it. He liked it too, in fact so much so that he started to ponder what the effect might be for coming generations if everybody should get to like it as he did. It was probably under the effect of the ensuing headache that the emperor banished I-Ti from the country as a reward for his invention. The secret of making wine, however, was out and wine making has flourished ever since.

Chinese wine is called *chiu,* and the analysis of the sign denoting it gives us better proof of the high antiquity of this alcoholic beverage. Among the ancient simple signs of the Chinese script, the 214 radicals which enter into the composition of the many thousands of Chinese characters, is the one called *chiu,* which even in its modern modified form can be recognized as a pictograph showing an amphora or winejar. To translate *"chiu"* by "wine" is misleading, as we understand by wine the prod-

Fig. 212. Catch Basin in a Chinese Liquor Still. This device, made of pewter, with its long spout used to drain off the distilled liquor in a Chinese still, briefly explained under Fig. 209, is here shown separately, taken out of the still, and placed upside down for better inspection.

ıct of grapes. Grapes have scarcely ever been used by he Chinese for making wine, and then only in a few ocalities where they were introduced by early ravellers from Irania. The translation "rice-wine" is better as it brings out the metaphorical meaning of wine as merely an alcoholic beverage with the definite statement of its source. To treat the whole subject under the heading of "Spirits," as Stuart does in his Chinese Materia Medica, is also misleading and his account, though giving valuable information, is not free from confusion. For brevity's sake we shall retain the word wine in our discourse and ask the reader to bear in mind its broadest sense of alcoholic beverage.

The studying of the processes involved brings clearness into the subject. The intrepid Scotchman, Alexander Williamson, who in the sixties of the last century went from village to village in northeastern China to sell Bibles to the natives was a keen observer and noted in Shantung the cultivation of a glutinous kind of millet which was used for food, "but more especially for preparing a kind of beer called *huang chiu* (yellow wine)." To call it a kind of beer shows that he observed its manufacture and found that it was a fermented grain liquor, which he could not very well call wine or spirits.

The original Chinese brew was a fermented beverage of millet or rice, the same for the making of which I-Ti had to leave his country. To make it, malt and yeast were needed and we find mention of it in a simile introduced in the Shu Ching, Book of History (24th to 8th century B.C.), where it says: "Be to me as the yeast and the malt in making sweet wine." The straining of the liquor from the lees, another important feature of the making of fermented grain liquor, is also vouched for in oldest times by the reference to it in the Shih Ching, Book of Odes (23rd century to beginning of 6th century B.C.), which disclosed that the wine was separated from the lees by pouring it over a filter bed of herbs or through a basket with a rough (woven) bottom. The fermenting of the mash is also hinted at in the Shuo Wen (ca. 100 A.D.) in which it is said that wine was made of soured cooking rice and if it was not spoiled the wine would not be sweet.

In making a fermented grain liquor we start out with the grain, be it millet or rice, which represents the starch. The grain or starch is soaked in water of which it takes up about 50 percent of its own weight. This water solution of the starch is a preparatory step in changing the starch into sugar. Two other requisites for this change are the proper temperature of the solution, from 30° to 50° C., and the presence in the solution of a kind of "watchman," without which the change from starch to sugar would not take place. This "watchman," a chemical compound called enzyms, has a curious function, it aids by its mere presence, the breaking up of the starch particles into sugar particles; chemically expressed, it acts as a catalyst. The enzyms are produced by sprouting and malting grain, and to make sure that this important compound is present in the starch solution, the grain is first malted or at least some malt is added. Not much malt is required to produce the enzyms. With these conditions fulfilled: water-dissolved starch, the presence of enzyms and the proper temperature, the starch changes rapidly into sugar. The next step is fermentation with the aid of yeast which changes the sugar solution into an alcoholic liquid. The yeast acts on the sugar and breaks it up into alcohol and carbon dioxide, a gas which rises from the liquid and escapes into the air. The temperature must also be of the proper degree. When the process of fermentation is completed no more gas rises and the liquid is ready to be strained or separated from the residue by pouring off or decantation.

These in short are the principles underlying all the alcoholic beverages of antiquity which were made of grain, principles which persisted down into medieval times. The alcoholic beverages into the manufacture of which grain did not enter, and where the initial process of changing starch into sugar was therefore eliminated, forms a subdivision. In these the manufacture started out with sugar-bearing substances such as honey or ripe fruit, especially grapes. Typical examples are the mead of the old Germanic races and grape-wines.

The grape was introduced into China in the 2nd century B.C., by Chang Ch'ien who had learned the art of making wine in Irania. In China, however, alcoholic grain liquors were the beverages mainly used, until the art of distilling or separating the alcohol from the watery solution was introduced. Chinese tradition says that it was in the Yuan (Mongol) dynasty (1280-1367 A.D.), and it would appear that the Mongolian conquerors from the northwest were responsible for the introduction of the art of distilling into China.

With this event a new era in the history of beverages in China started and only since that time is it permissible to speak of spirits, the product of distillation. The Chinese in general have retained the old name *chiu* for the new product and this explains the fact that writers on China when they speak of beverages have usually not clearly distinguished the two types, the fermented grain liquor, and spirits.

The history of distilling alcohol is still in the controversial stage but the investigation has narrowed down to the views of two great scholars. Hermann Diels[18] says that ca. 1300 A.D. alcohol begins to be distilled more and more, probably after an ancient recipe. The recipe he has in mind is found in Way's MS. of the Mappae clavicula of ca. 1150 A.D., a compilation which drew from older Greek and Byzantine sources. Edmund O. von Lippmann[19] is more positive and says that alcohol is an invention of the Occident, probably made as late as the 11th century, possibly in Italy.

The still as such is much older than its use for the distilling of alcohol and there are sufficient data extant to follow its development around the regions of the Mediterranean, from the beginning of the Christian era. Maria, the Jewess, a renowned alchemist of Egypt (1st century A.D.), gives the first detailed information, stressing the fact that a pipe leads away from the cover of the still and lets the condensate drip into a receptacle standing beside the still. Zosimos, also of Egypt, writing ca. 300 A.D., speaks of distilled water. The cooling of the cover, to aid condensation, is still primitive and done with a sponge dipped in cold water. Synesios, in the 4th century A.D., described the still in its more advanced form: a tripod holds the receptacle, the vapors rise up into a helmet of glass or metal, formed like a human head or a woman's breast, condense on its upper surface and flow off through an oblique pipe. Thus the development of the still went on and the apparatus received its distinct form with the cucurbit for holding the liquid, the head or alembic for condensing the vapors and the beak which delivers the distillate. When alcohol was finally made there was already an efficient apparatus for its manufacture. The beak or oblique pipe, a part of the alembic or head, is a distinctive feature throughout the whole development and a still without it can hardly be considered a part of this Mediterranean development.

Let us recall the description given of the Chinese still and the more primitive Mongolian still. The similarity between these is so close, the Chinese still merely modified by a pipe extending from the catch-basin, that we clearly recognize in the Mongolian still the prototype. This, however, is distinctly different from the Mediterranean type and cannot by any stretch of the imagination be explained as related to or derived from it. My conclusion is that the Mon-

[18] "Antike Technik," Leipzig & Berlin, 1924. "Die Entdeckung des Alkohols," Abh. der Berliner Akademie, 1913, phil.-hist. Kl. 3.

[19] "Entstehung & Ausbreitung der Alchemie," Berlin, 1919.

FIG. 213. ALCOHOL STOVE AND WINE CONTAINER.

golian still which was used solely for distilling alcohol is a distinct development of inner Asia and that it may be closely linked with the invention of alcohol. Traders who first observed it may have imparted their knowledge to the Occident and it seems also plausible that there the more efficient Mediterranean still was pressed into service for making alcohol, instead of using the more primitive type which survives to this day in Mongolia.

CHINESE ALCOHOL STOVE

It is the custom in China to drink all beverages hot. Bitter experience has probably taught the people to adhere strictly to this custom and avoid, especially in the tropical summers, all kinds of infection conveyed in unboiled water. The same principle of taking tea infusions or plain water hot, has also been extended to Chinese wines be they fermented or distilled beverages. In the latter case this is, of course, misplaced prophylaxis, for wines and spirits do not convey any noxious bacteria. One interesting effect of heated wine is that it rises much quicker to the head and that the Chinese feels when he has enough before he really becomes intoxicated. Drunkenness is a rare occurrence in China. In northern China much distilled wine made from millet or sorghum is consumed. It is very strong, almost pure alcohol, and the head of a household usually takes some with his two main meals a day. At each meal a child or servant is sent to the shop to have the container filled. Fig. 213 shows on the left the container for the liquor, a little vase 4 inches high holding about 5 fluid ounces. In order to heat the liquor at the table the spirit lamp or alcohol stove at the right in Fig. 213 is employed. A circular open bowl with a wide rim surmounted by three knobs for the container to stand upon is perforated through the sides, by two round air holes opposite each other. Inside of the bowl stands a small immovable cup, and into this a little of the liquor is poured and ignited, and then the container put on top to be heated. Both the spirit lamp and wine container are made of coarse porcelain and glazed with a brownish black lustre. The Chinese call this alcohol stove *sheng hsien lu,* which means fairy stove. The specimen photographed was procured in Kiauchow,

Fig. 214. Kitchen Stove—Rear View.

FIG. 215. KITCHEN STOVE—FRONT VIEW.

Shantung province. In this province the alcohol stove is quite common among the peasants and was surely not introduced from abroad. It is, of course not older than the introduction of distilling. We have said above that according to Chinese tradition the art of distilling was introduced during the Yuan (Mongol) dynasty, 1280-1367 A.D., which may not mean more than that it came to China through Mongolia, possibly even earlier. Another interesting fact is that a second name for Chinese spirits, especially in the south, is *samshu,* which means thrice burned, and that the annals of a Chinese commissioner of customs who wrote in the beginning of the 13th century about the Arabian trade relations mentions *samshu* as an article of export [20] taken in exchange by the traders who brought goods from Arabia.

KITCHEN STOVE

Chinese kitchens are small, dark and sooty and it is almost impossible to take a picture of the kitchen stove. The latter is in principle a square support built of four brick walls about four feet high to hold the cast iron cooking bowl. The wall with the firing hole is raised up a few feet higher, as a protecting wall or screen, to keep the smoke and soot from the cooking platform. It is clear then that it takes at least two persons in a Chinese household to cook a meal. One stands in front of the platform facing the stove top with the cooking bowl and does the cooking. The other sits in front of the firing hole, facing the raised wall, the protecting screen, and attends to the fire. Usually a woman supplies the fuel and a man cooks. The woman, a superannuated member of the household, or a half-grown slave-girl or servant, sits low in front of the firing hole and listens to the shouted commands of the cook on the other side in regard to the firing.

I saw once in the monastery of Guo Ling, near Feng Hua, Chekiang province, a more elaborate cooking stove, showing the same principle, and was able to take two pictures, Figs. 214 and 215, giving the rear view and front view, respectively. Starting

[20] F. Hirth, Chinesische Studien, Műnchen & Leipzig, 1890.

in our description with Fig. 214, we see two firing holes and in the center a recess for the oil-lamp. The small niche at the right is a place for flint and steel. The little stove on the left with a wooden hood over the cast iron bowl is built on to the large stove and is used for cooking when only a few people are to be provided for, while the large double stoves, of which there are several in the monastery, are employed for pilgrims who at certain times come by the hundreds. The fuel for these stoves is brushwood. There is usually no chimney provided for, and the smoke continuously emerges from the firing hole, as can be seen from the discoloration of the wall above it.

Fig. 215 gives the front view, or cooking platform of a double stove with two cooking bowls. The higher wall at the back has, at the extreme left, a niche for the oil cruse, and the niche in the center contains a tablet with the picture of the kitchen-god who presides over the culinary affairs of the household. All during the year incense is burned before the image of the kitchen-god at the time of the full moon and new moon, the 15th and the 1st day of the Chinese months respectively. Finally at the end of the year when the kitchen-god repairs on high to report of the doings of the family during the year, the conscience-stricken are wont to smear the idol's mouth with honey, hoping that its report may sound sweet to the avenging gods. The cast iron cooking bowls set into the stove top are covered with wooden lids. At the left stands a wooden container for taking the boiled rice to the table and nearby a piggin for providing water needed in cooking.

The first impulse to use fire for preparing food was more likely a measure of economy than the desire to make the food more easily digestible. When primitive man had with very inadequate weapons procured a huge quarry to feed upon, the problem must have arisen how to preserve the leavings for several succeeding meals. The first suggestion may have come through observation of the drying of food stuffs by the rays of the sun, which no doubt preceded the application of artificial heat and led to it. But once in the possession of the art of using fire for cooking, no matter how it was derived, it was bound to improve step by step, and as far as the Chinese are concerned, we find, at the time of the Han dynasty (206 B.C. to 20 A.D.), perfectly developed cooking stoves with firing hole at one end, openings for pots on the top and at the other end a well defined circular sleeve extending upward for smoke egress. The knowledge of these ancient stoves has been derived from pottery and cast iron specimens which have been recovered from graves of the Han dynasty. At present the Chinese do not have any large movable stoves for kitchen use, which in the least resemble these early diminutive grave-finds. The modern kitchen stove, as we have explained is stationary.

It is an archaeological problem how to explain the fact that the Chinese were acquainted with the principle of the chimney two thousand years ago and used it, while now there is scarcely a chimney to be found in southern and central China. After giving it much thought I have come to the conclusion that the Chinese dispense with chimneys for economy's sake. The scarcity of fuel which became more and more acute in the course of centuries must have induced the people to abandon the comfort of chimneys to make the scant fuel go farther.

PROCURING FUEL

In the Chinese household cooking is done mostly with wood. Fire-wood is retailed in the cities, in pieces about 3 feet long, and has to be reduced into convenient pieces to fit the stove. This is done with the cleaver shown in Fig. 216. The most striking feature is the projection at the end of the instrument which serves as a protection for the cutting edge of the

FIG. 216. FIRE-WOOD CLEAVER.

cleaver. Chopping the fire-wood into small pieces is done by the women who crouch down with bent knees to do it. In place of a chopping block, they utilize the ground, the door-sill of stone or wood, the paving of the yard or street, it matters not, the cutting edge is foolproof. As children we often thought what an ideal chopping block a stone floor was. With all our might we finally got the hatchet through the chunk of wood, but it did not stop there. Nothing kept the edge from the stone, sparks would fly and the Italian knife-grinder would charge double rate for putting back an edge in the place of the dents. But in China women and children handle with impunity this cleaver with the big projection, guardian of the cutting edge.[21] A wooden stick, about 12 inches long, is driven into the socket of the cleaver for a handle. The cleaver itself is of iron forged in one piece, and measures from end to end, 13¼ inches. At the back it is ⅜ inch thick, and the projection at the end is 3⅛ inches long and ⅜ inch thick throughout. The photograph was taken in the Native City, Shanghai.

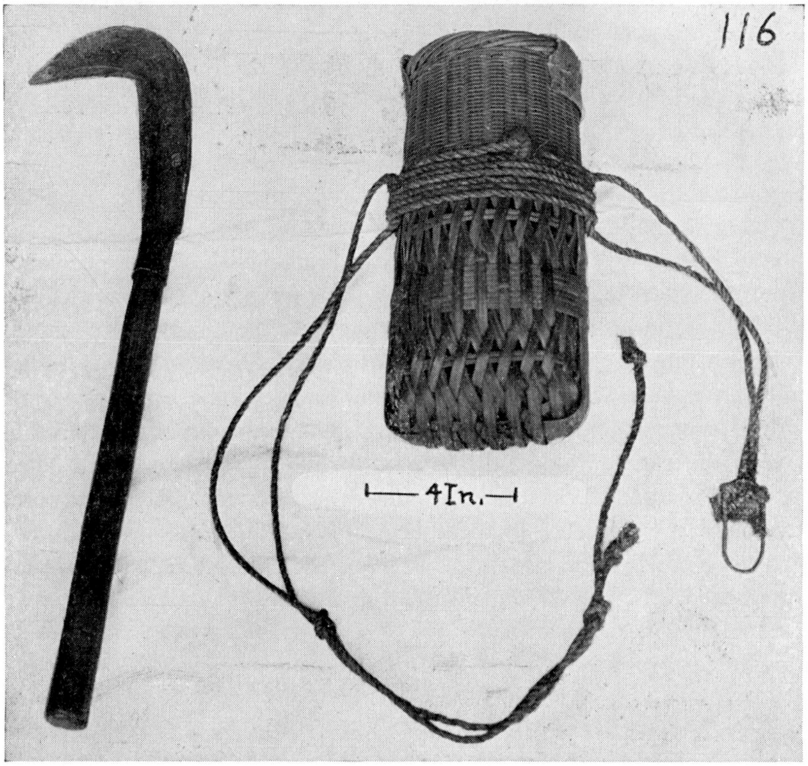

Where hundreds of millions of people cook their meals with fire-wood the forests cannot look very flourishing. In the Ten Tai range in Chekiang this is quite evident, the slopes everywhere are covered with brushwood only, and where lighter trees have escaped, they are denuded of their branches almost up to the top. Everywhere peasants and young boys from about ten years on are seen engaged in climbing the mountains in search of fire-wood. Besides farming their main pursuit is dealing in fire-wood. To cut branches of the trees, or fell young trees, they are equipped with a hooked cleaver, shown in Fig. 217. The basket shown is tied with its attached cord around the wood-cutter's waist so it hangs on his back and the hook is put in the basket. In this way the boys climb trees, reach for the hook, and cut off the branches. When two large bundles have been gathered, they tie the cut twigs together and push the pointed ends of a carrying pole, about four feet long, into each bundle, take up the pole in the middle upon their shoulders and carry their load home.

116

4In.

Fig. 217. Kindling-Wood Hook.

The whole length of the hook, from end to end including the handle, is 20 inches. The length of the curved part is 5 inches. The iron part is forged in one piece with a socket for inserting the wooden handle. The curved back of the hook is ½ inch thick, and tapers to a sharp cutting edge. The basket, woven of bamboo strips is 11 inches long, 5½ inches wide and 3 inches thick. The picture was taken at Se Aw in Chekiang province.

COOKING

Fig. 218 shows a Chinese cooking bowl, so often referred to in these pages. It is made of cast iron of excellent quality, and used for boiling rice, frying, stewing, and steaming food. The diameter on top is 16 inches and the height 5½ inches. It is thickest at the bottom where it is ⅛ of an inch thick, tapering to a thickness of 1/16 of an inch at the edges. The

[21] In a Vergil edition of Strassburg, 1502, illustrated by Grűninger, a peasant is shown handling such a cleaver to cut wood. A table-knife with a projection to prevent cutting into the tablecloth can plainly be seen in a picture in the "Hortus deliciarum" of Herrad von Landsperg, dating from the 12th century.

FIG. 218. COOKING BOWL.

sizes of these bowls range from about one foot in diameter to five feet. The largest sizes are used in places like a Buddhist monastery. The Chinese kitchen stove is fed with wood, straw, chaff or argol, and the flames strike directly against the bottom of the cooking bowl which fits into a hole in the top of the stove.

A necessary adjunct to the cooking bowl is the little brass shovel or ladle, Fig. 219, which is used for putting food into the bowl and withdrawing it, and for stirring and turning food while being boiled or fried in the bowl. Its length without the handle is 5½ inches, and its width 4 inches. A socket on one end receives the wooden handle, 6½ inches long and about 1 inch thick.

Often when boiling things in the cooking bowl, a bamboo screen (see Fig. 229) is laid over it, the edges resting on the inside wall without touching the food underneath. A porcelain dish with some additional food is then placed on top of this screen, and the whole bowl covered with the wooden hood shown in Fig. 220. This is an interesting economic feature. While food is boiling in the bowl, the steam rising from it is confined under the hood and utilized to heat or cook other food. The hood is shaped like an inverted tub, and the opening measures 13½ inches in diameter, and the top 12 inches, the height not including the handle on top is six inches. The staves are on the average ¾ of an inch thick likewise the wooden top disk. The wooden handle is either nailed to the top, as in this case, or it is dovetailed into a bottom-flared groove in the cover. The staves are held together by bamboo dowels and a hoop encircles them, made of twisted bamboo strips. The material of this hood is pine-wood, lacquered red-brown with a heat-resisting native lacquer. The pictures, Figs. 218 to 220, were taken at Shanghai, in the Native City, Kiangsu province.

The pot holder, Fig. 221, is a contrivance for placing a side-handled pot upon the burning embers and withdrawing it therefrom. A stick handle, 20½ inches long, is mortised into a wooden cross strip 4 inches long and 1½ inches square. Into this are mortised two wooden pins, 2¼ inches long and ½ inch thick, here seen projecting from the cross strip. The holder is applied as shown in Fig. 221. The pot is made of brass, 7 inches high and 6 inches in diameter. The picture was taken at Sha Ho, Kiangsi.

The Chinese cook most of their food in the cast

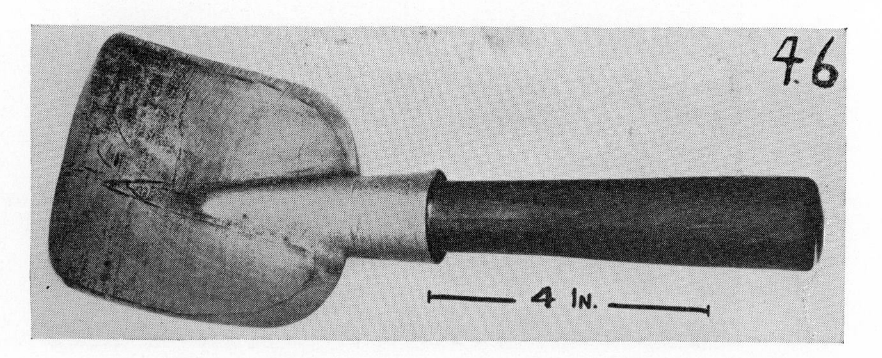

FIG. 219. COOKING LADLE.

FIG. 220. WOODEN COVER FOR A COOKING BOWL.

to our taste for the want of salt. Meats, fish, soups and sauces are on the contrary highly seasoned, and red and green peppers are always a part of the country people's meagre fare.

Botanical authorities assert that the Chinese had in classical times neither white nor black pepper (*Piper nigrum*), nor the peppers of the *Capsicum* family (Chillies), and that the Chinese pepper of old (Hua tsiao) is the fruit of a *Zanthoxylon,* of which more than a dozen species are known in China.

The pepper shaker is a round bamboo box with a lid turned on a reciprocating (i.e. fore and aft action) lathe. Lid and box are topped and bottomed by the natural joints of the bamboo. The ground pepper is introduced into the box and is shaken out through a small hole (at the side of its lower end) which can be closed with a slide. In Fig. 222, two pepper shakers are shown, one with the hole open and the other with the slide pushed over it. The specimens were procured in Nanchang, Kiangsi province.

At Chinese feasts each guest has at his place, for his personal use, a small shallow dish filled with soybean sauce in which to dip pieces of meat *ad libitum*. For dipping pieces of Chinese ham, similarly, a little dish with vinegar is furnished at times.

In the Japanese kitchen a rasping instrument is used for grating various substances. I have seen it used for grating the "daikon," a kind of radish and the root of ginger. Fig. 223 shows the usual form of the instrument. It is a flat piece of tinned copper. Both surfaces are indented in rows with coarse projections made by a triangular pointed punch. The punch is applied slantingly and the rough projections point then in the direction of the punched slant. The rows are made

iron bowl. But stewing pork is frequently done in a brass pot such as is shown in Fig. 221. The pork is cut into square pieces, in such a way that in each piece there is meat, fat and part of the skin. The stewing takes hours. With the lid upon the pot, all the flavor is preserved and the meat tasty, even the skin, and pig-skin at that, becomes tender.

As in all rice-producing countries, pepper is used very extensively in China. White pepper is most in favor, and almost the whole output of the Straits Settlements is exported to China. The pepper shaker, shown in Fig. 222, is used only in the kitchen. The Chinese don't season their food after it is served, and consequently there is neither salt-cellar, caster or cruet-stand on the table. The Chinese have altogether peculiar ideas about seasoning. Rice is boiled and served without addition of salt, and so are various vegetables. Bean curd, somewhat resembling egg custard in consistence, is highly nutritious but insipid

FIG. 221. POT HOLDER.

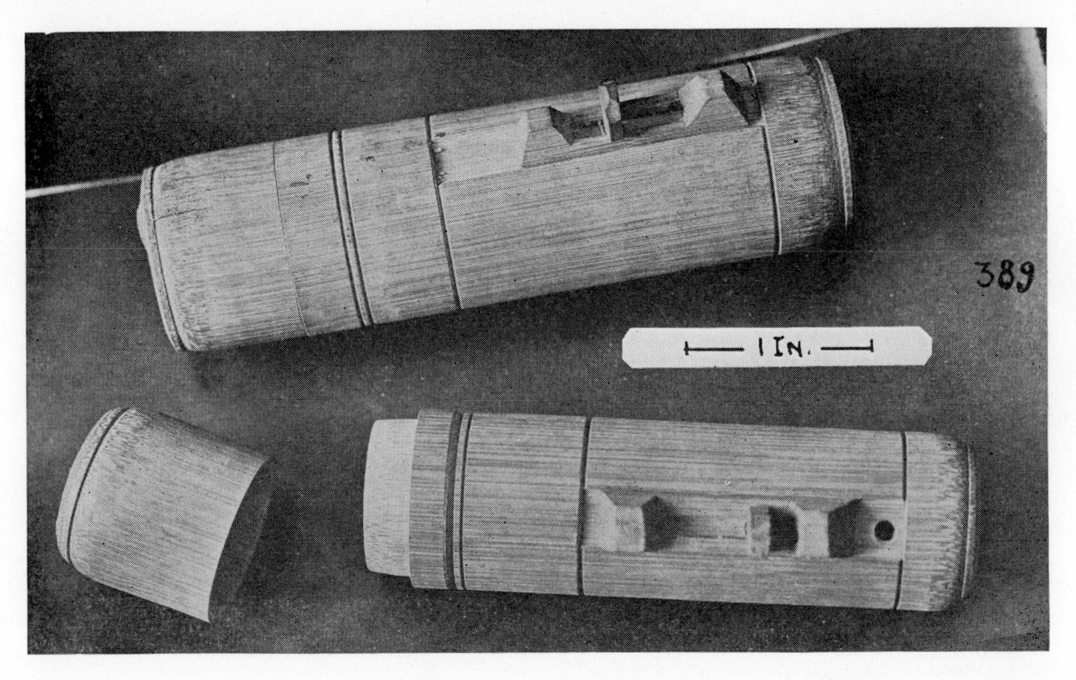

FIG. 222. PEPPER SHAKERS.

in such a manner that some have the projections pointing toward the handle and others in the opposite direction. The instrument is held by the handle with the left hand in a downward slanting position over a dish and with the right hand the article to be grated is passed over the surface. On both sides the thin edges are bent up to form rims for guiding the grated material as it slides down into the dish. The whole length of the instrument is 8¼ inches. It was photographed in Nagasaki.

I have seen the same instrument made of unglazed porcelain and it answered quite well if used for grating soft material for which it was intended. It must be understood, that both graters, the metal and the porcelain one, have no holes penetrating the grater, the points of abrasion simply rise from the surface. The action is that of a rasp.

A porcelain dish with similar rows of toothed projections is shown in Fig. 224. It serves the same culinary purposes as the instrument described under Fig. 223. The edge of the rim is upturned and shaped to form a spout for pouring out the semiliquid grat-

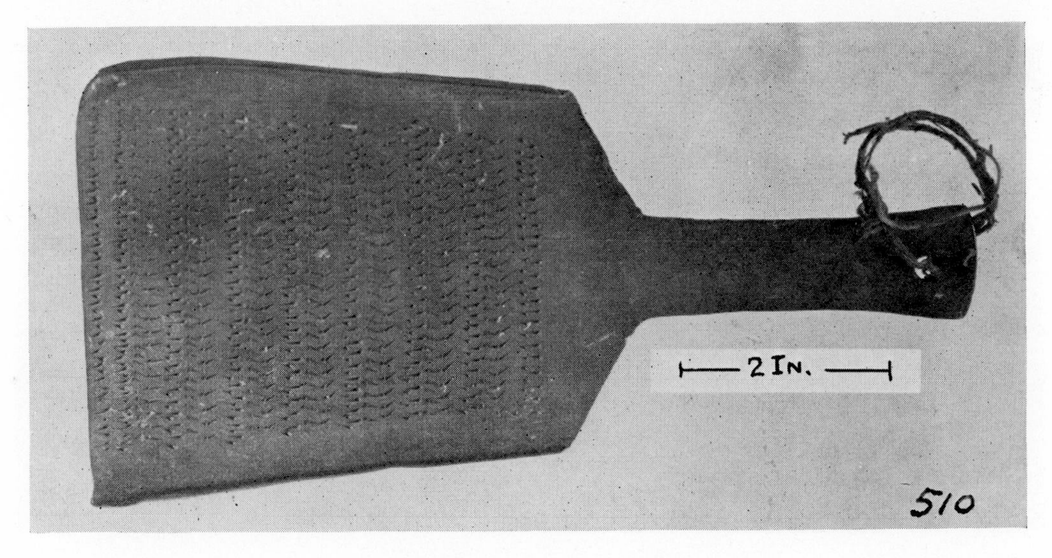

FIG. 223. JAPANESE GRATING INSTRUMENT.

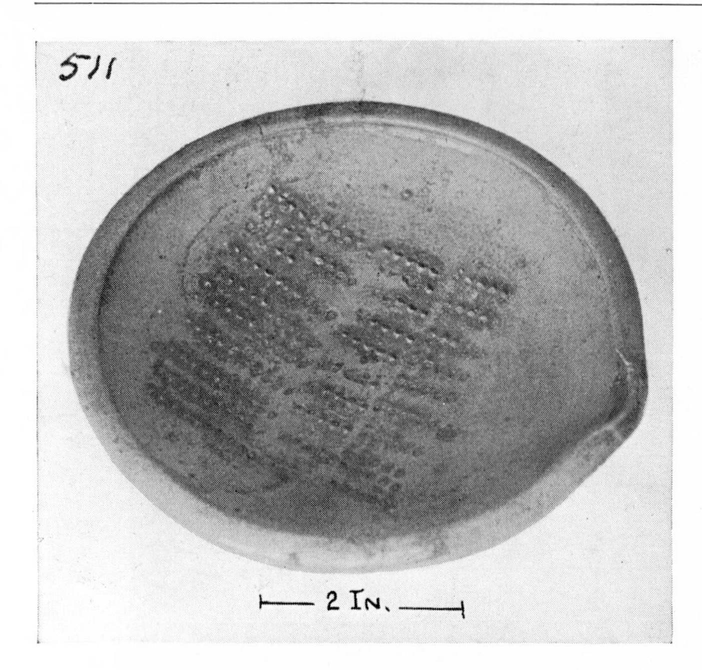

FIG. 224. JAPANESE CULINARY GRATER OF PORCELAIN.

ings of succulent roots. The diameter of the bowl is 5¾ inches and the height 1⅛ inches. The photograph was taken at Nagasaki. This Japanese grating bowl reminds one of the Roman clay bowls with inserted flint chips found among the remnants of Roman frontier forts in Germany,[22] many of which have been excavated at various places.

It is said that the Roman soldiers carried such bowls with them and grated wheat mixed with water in them and in this manner got a dough at once fit for baking without the tedious intermediate step of making flour.

The sieve shown in Fig. 225 is used in Chinese kitchens for straining. The framework is made of bamboo splints stitched together with strips of cane. The tightly stretched fabric is coarse grass-cloth made of the unbleached fibres of the ramie (*Boehmeria nivea*). The smaller unfinished sieve on the right, shows the overlapping ends of the fabric, which will be cut off to complete the process of its manufacture. The diameter of the sieves is 16 and 12½ inches respectively.

The steaming-trays in Fig. 226 are used for baking Chinese meat patties. The patties are made of a circular piece of wheat dough. Minced meat is placed upon them and the edges are then folded upwards and crimped together. Into each tray a circular piece of wet cotton cloth is placed, and upon this the patties. One tray is put upon the other, and finally upon the uppermost one the cover, shown in the picture leaning against the trays. The whole stack of trays is then placed upon the cooking bowl filled with water, and this brought to boiling. The steam percolates through the trays and cooks the patties the dough becoming light and fluffy.

Both photographs, the kitchen sieves and the steaming-trays, were taken at the workshop of a bamboo worker who manufactures sieves and trays, outside the East Gate of Lingkiang, Kiangsi province.

In Fig. 227 a cake mold is shown, which reposes now in the Mercer Museum, in Doylestown, Pa. I

[22] "Die Technik des Altertums" by Albert Neuburger, Leipzig, 1920, Fig. 148, and description on page 93.

FIG. 225. KITCHEN SIEVE.

FIG. 226. KITCHEN STEAMING-TRAYS.

saw it in use while walking along a busy thoroughfare in Lung Chuan, Chekiang. A street cake-vender, who had set up shop directly on the pavement against a house was busily engaged in forming little cakes with his mold. Aside of him stood a little charcoal stove with a pan of oil on it, in which the cakes had to be fried and then were ready for sale.

The mold is a composite contrivance. The essential parts are first a flat base-board of camphor wood, nine inches long, five inches wide and half an inch thick, and then hinged thereto another board of the same thickness but otherwise only about half the size of the base-board. This hinged board can be made to swing between two lugs rising from the sides of the base-board as pivots, and as shown in Fig. 227 is seen lying over the left half of the base-board. The hinged board has in its center a scalloped hole, 2¼ inches in diameter, and through it can be seen the carved design of a flower on the surface of the base-board. By swinging the perforated board over to the right, the hole will fit over the design of a Chinese character carved on that side of the base-board.

FIG. 227. CAKE MOLD.

The forming of cakes is easily done by pressing some dough into the scalloped recess of the hinged board as it rests over the flower design in the base-board (the position shown in Fig. 227) and then lifting the hinged board to push from it the flat cake with the imprint of the flower design on its one side. To get a cake with the other design the cake-vender merely has to swing the hinged board over to the right side and push his dough into the recess over the

FIG. 228. CHICKEN FEEDER.

design on that side of the base-board. One might think that the cakes made in this mold are stamped with a design on both sides. This is not the case. The convenience of this composite mold is that with it now a cake can be made with one design, and then another with another design by simply using one or the other half of the mold. One ornament represents a flower, probably *Hibiscus Rosa-Sinensis,* which the Chinese are very fond of picturing, and the other the conventionalized Chinese character *Hsi,* meaning Joy, Gladness.

When I wanted to buy the hinged cake mold I introduced a serious problem into the simple, even-flowing, cake-baking existence of its owner. There were a few pennies to be made, and yet it would stop the flourishing business of making cakes until a new mold was procured. I understood the perplexity and graciously agreed to wait a few days, until a new mold could be made, and then obtained it for a just consideration.

For feeding a litter of pigs, very wisely a long narrow trough is used, so that each pig gets a chance at feeding. If this precaution were not taken and the food presented in a round basin or dish the most forward of the litter would try to "hog" it all. Similar tendencies are inherent in chickens, and to assure communistic feeding, namely equal opportunities in the pursuit of the grain proffered, a feeder, as shown in Fig. 228, is usually employed by the householder who keeps chickens, and they are legion. The feeder is simply what in England would be called a piggin, a wooden vessel, with one stave extending upward for a handle. What transforms the piggin into a feeder is the row of gothic windows, fourteen in all, cut around the whole extent of the wooden wall. It is great fun to watch the chickens crowd around at feeding time, each hunting a window to pick through. Sometimes this feeder has a wooden lid with a notch for the handle extending on the one side, and a second notch for a short stave extension on the other, which is to keep the lid from sliding off. The goose-head handle extends over the center of the tub, and in this manner affords an easy and steady grip. The staves are bound with hoops of bamboo which material is eminently fitted for such use. The dimensions of the feeder are 16 inches in diameter on top and a height from the bottom to the upper rim of 16 inches. It was photographed at Tao Yao, Chekiang province.

The raising of chickens is for meat and eggs. Fish, pork or chicken are the dishes accompanying the vegetables and rice at a Chinese gentleman's table, and at the poorest farm, even though only once in a great while, one of the chickens has to do duty at table to interrupt the monotonous fare of rice and salt-cabbage.

KITCHEN UTENSILS

Fig. 229 acquaints us with some utensils which are found in almost every Chinese kitchen. From left to right the first article is a bamboo screen which is used in the cast iron bowl for the process of steaming food. While the rice is being cooked in the bowl, as we explained under Fig. 220, this screen is placed directly over the rice, but not in contact with it, and porcelain bowls with other food to be steamed or merely heated or kept warm, are placed on the screen and the whole covered with the wooden hood. The screen is made of bamboo and has a diameter of 21 inches.

The next object is a basket used for washing rice preparatory to cooking it. The dry rice is placed in it, and wherever a stream or pool of water is near at hand the Chinese women can be seen at the water's edge filling the basket with water, stirring the rice with their hands and lifting the basket up to let the water drain off through the meshes of the basket. At first a liquid like milk runs off and the dipping, stirring and draining is repeated about four or five times until the water loses its milky appearance, I was going to say until the water gets clear, but checked myself in time. The waters around Chinese villages and habitations are rarely clear, and often it seemed to me that the rice might be more wholesome if it remained unwashed. The milkiness referred to, is due to traces of powdered limestone or wood ashes which had become mixed with the rice when polishing it. The basket woven of bamboo splints, is 16 inches in diameter, and 4 inches high.

Next in the picture are two dippers. The semispherical one is made of pine wood, the handle and bowl being in one piece. The inside diameter is 8¾ inches, the thickness varies, being about 1 inch more or less, and the height 4 inches. It is used for dipping water out of the water *kong* (an earthenware storage tank for rain water) in the yard, when larger quantities are needed. The smaller dipper is used in the kitchen to take water from a smaller *kong* which is usually found standing near the kitchen stove. The body of this dipper is a section of a bamboo tree and its bottom is formed by one of the natural joints which divide the hollow stem of bamboos into different sections. On the side of this cylinder a dovetail mortise has been cut and the handle, fashioned to fit it, inserted. The height of the cylinder is 5½ inches and the diameter 4 inches. The bamboo handle is 13½ inches long.

The last article to be described is a slicer for turnips, seen in the picture lying in front of the screen and basket. A board 21¼ inches long, 3 inches wide and ⅝ inch thick has in its middle a rectangular hole and over this hole is fastened, with little native made brass nails, a strip of sheet brass. In the manner of repoussé work long grooves have been hammered into the sheet and one end of each of these grooves cut open. These narrow openings with sharp adges form the knives. When sliding the turnip over these knives with pressure, lengthwise with the board, narrow slices are cut which pass through the holes in the metal and then through the hole in the board. The knife edges, I was assured, keep sharp indefinitely, and this, no doubt is due to the brass sheet having been hardened by thorough hammering. The picture was taken in Sha Ho, Kiangsi province.

Fig. 229. Kitchen Utensils.

TABLEWARE

The most universally known fact about the Chinese is that they use chopsticks to convey food to their mouths. We are apt to look down upon this as a crude method, but should remember that the general use of the fork in Europe does not date back farther than the late 16th century, before which our ancestors used only knives and their fingers, while the Chinese have been using chopsticks for several thousand years.

Chopsticks are two slender rods of wood, bone, ivory or silver which are dexterously manipulated to pick up morsels of food. They are held in the right hand between the thumb and the fingers with only the little finger idle. The one is held stationary resting in the crotch between the lower part of the thumb

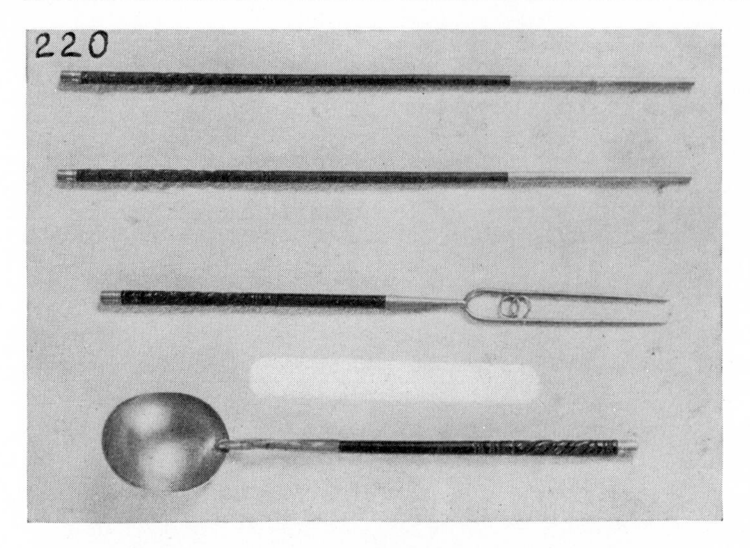

Fig. 230. Chopsticks, Table Fork and Eating Spoon.

and index-finger and is steadied with the tip of the extended ring-finger. Above it the other chopstick is pressed by the tip of the thumb against the upper parts of index and middle-fingers and through the motion of these made to move, so that the tip of the chopstick approaches the tip of the other when attempting to pick up pieces of food. Ordinarily the Chinese use at their meals no tableware except chopsticks and a porcelain spoon. Placed on the table the spoon rests on the flat bottom of its bowl. The short handle slants upward and is never heavy enough to upset the spoon. The spoon is used for eating soup or sauces out of a common bowl placed in the middle of the table.

The set of tableware shown in Fig. 230 is of the better grade, and even if not typical for the whole of China, highly interesting as it contains a fork. This set was bought in Peking, and I was told that in the northern part of China it is customary to have these four pieces for each guest as table-ware at festive gatherings. The chopsticks are of bone dyed red, tipped with a silver cap at one end, and a long silver sleeve at the other, which latter comes in contact with the food. At large banquets, when you have to reach to the center of the table where the food is standing, very aften ivory chopsticks as long as 12 inches are used. The pair shown in the picture is 9½ inches long, a comfortable size for every day use. The handle of the fork as well as that of the spoon is of red-dyed bone, nicely turned. The metal part is of silver. The fork is two-pronged and the slender prongs hold between them two ornamental rings soldered into place. The bowl of the spoon is soldered into a slot in the curved stem. The length of the fork is 8¼ inches, and of the spoon 7⅝ inches. The fork is used solely for taking up confections or sweetmeats. At home some stylishly gotten up boxes of candies with a variety of candied fruits and the like are often furnished with a similar two-pronged fork and it may well be that the idea of doing this came from the Orient.

The sporadic use of a table fork in Italy is vouched for in the 11th century and the Italian Gabrotus Martius, when in 1470, the guest of Matthias Corvinus, king of Hungary, was surprised that at the court of his host the table fork was unknown. Rules about table manners of the end of the 15th century indicate clearly that table forks were then not in general use in Europe. The advice is given to reach for a piece of meat only with three fingers and not leave the hand unduly long in the bowl. Another point of good behaviour was not to wipe the nose with the same hand which you use for taking a piece of meat.[23]

The expert use of chopsticks prevalent among the Chinese seems to me quite as much an evidence of refinement and culture as the use of the fork among western civilizations. It is a more natural and less dangerous method of eating; more natural because the chopsticks are but convenient and more sanitary extensions of the fingers: less dangerous because the mouth and tongue are not exposed to the sharp prongs of a fork (or the blade of a knife such as most of our ancestors used well down into the 19th century). The knife is never used at the Chinese table. The food is cut into small bits in the kitchen and can be taken up easily and gracefully with the chopsticks. The only objection to the use of chopsticks is the concomitant of serving the food for all in one dish and the dipping of all the chopsticks into it. But the same objection could be made to forks under similar circumstances.

Early European forks were always two-pronged similar to Chinese forks. A Chinese general writing about his country says:[24] "Chinese tables are provided, besides the celebrated ivory chopsticks, with porcelain spoons and silver forks, and it is quite easy to do justice to the feast without the use of one's fingers."

It is not so well known that the Chinese alway

[23] Feldhaus, "Technik," etc., Leipzig & Berlin, 1914.

[24] "Le Theatre des Chinois," General Tchung-Ki-Tong, Paris 1886.

se a spoon in addition to the chopsticks. As ıentioned above, it is usually made of porce-ıin, rarely of metal, like the one shown in Fig. 30. In the historical records of the After Han)ynasty (25 to 220 A.D.) mention is made of a :t of lacquered spoons and chopsticks, and later, ıough before the Sung dynasty, which com-ıenced in 960 A.D., the account notes as royal ifts a spoon and chopsticks of rhinoceros horn, nd another spoon and chopstick set made of *utchuk*, a costly incense wood. These data are clear indication that the combined use of hopsticks and spoon is of great antiquity. Early uropean spoons are quite similar to the Chi-ese spoon shown. The bowl is broadly elliptic ather than ovate, the handle of equal thickness ıroughout and not flattened at the end.

The use of chopsticks is confined to China, orea and Japan. The nomadic Mongols carry n their belts a case with a knife and chopsticks. lore discriminating travellers, Mongols and hinese alike, in those northern parts, carry a ase containing chopsticks, fork, spoon, knife nd a metal wine cup. In another case which I aw, there was a silver band added to the out-t, about 8 inches long and ¼ inch wide, thin nd flexible, which apparently served as a ıngue scraper.

Tongue scrapers are quite common in China and re used in the morning toilet. They are generally ıade of horn. The Chinese are not the only people othered with fur on the tongue. My grandfather 1813-1892) in Germany used habitually a tongue :raper. Apparently it was then the custom to use ıem, a fashion which in recent years seems to have ied out.

The national drink of the Chinese is tea or, to be ıore exact, hot tea. At work and at rest the Chinese ıust have a cup of tea now and then. If a guest omes, hot tea is offered. Even when you go into ıops which deal in higher grades of merchandise, n apprentice is sure to be at hand, with a cup of hot :a, to lubricate the powers of bargaining. Under ıese circumstances the economic instinct of the hinese has found means to keep the tea in the ettle hot for many hours at a time. A predecessor of ıe modern thermos bottle of the West, a closely voven basket or wooden container, is snuggly packed with raw cotton, the teapot set into it so that only the spout extends, and a circular wad of cotton put on top, so that the teapot is protected on all sides against rapid radiation of the heat. The cover of the basket or wooden container is placed over this wad.

FIG. 231. TEAPOT WARMER.

Fig. 231 shows a lacquered wooden teapot warmer, in shape it resembles a small barrel, excluding the handles it is 9 inches high and the diameter across the cover is 11 inches. Two of the staves, opposite each other, are extended to form handles. In these ex-tensions are holes into which fits a horizontal wooden cross bar to keep the cover tightly pressed down. By sliding this wooden strip as far as it will go towards the right, it disengages from the hole on the left, and can be withdrawn to remove the cover and get at the teapot for refilling. The teapot itself is made of pewter. For pouring tea the warmer is tilted, and the tea runs out from the spout, here seen protruding from the slot in the (top front) rim of the warmer. The photograph was taken in Sha Ho, Kiangsi province.

Chapter III

TOOLS FOR MAKING CLOTHING

THE beginning of clothing takes us back to the very cradle of mankind. Spinning of fibres into yarn and weaving are among the outstanding inventions man became blessed with, and yet we know nothing about their origin. Neolithic finds in China show pottery with textile imprints, but so do similar finds in practically all the investigated cultural areas all over the world. About one thing we are certain, that China has given to the world the knowledge of using silk for weaving. There is an extensive literature covering all its aspects, and we have therefore not gone into this.

Cotton garments were worn by imperial maids in attendance at court as early as 246 B.C. Originally the Chinese received cotton goods as tribute from other nations and it was held in greater esteem than silk. The cultivation of cotton does not seem to have begun until the Sung dynasty (960-1280 A.D.). For a time the opposition of silk rearers and hemp growers was so persistent, that cotton did not come into general favor until the Yuan dynasty (1280-1367 A.D.).

COTTON GINNING AND BOWING

The most primitive method of separating the cotton seeds from the boll is pulling them out by hand. It is still practiced in China by poor people who buy the raw cotton in small quantities for immediate home use. Ordinarily, however, a contrivance has been in common use until very recently which consists of two rollers which revolve in contact in opposite directions. The raw cotton is fed in between the rollers, passing through like a ribbon and the seeds remain behind. This primitive machine is fast being replaced by a modern foot-driven cotton-gin, which does the work more rapidly and is much preferred even though the fibres are much torn and the yarn produced is not as strong.

The primitive cotton-gin is either fixed firmly upon a three-legged stand, or tied to a bench, as shown in Fig. 232. It consists of a frame made of two uprights mortised into a wooden base-plate, and held together on top by a horizontal crosspiece.

FIG. 232. COTTON-GIN.

The uprights have two bearing holes each for insertion of the rollers. The lower roller is of hard wood, 1⅜ inches in diameter and 24 inches long. At the protruding end a wooden crank is inserted. The roller is kept from sliding out of position by wooden wedges which passing horizontally through the uprights, fit into circular grooves crosscut into the roller, where it rests in the bearings. Above the wooden roller and in contact with it, rests a wrought iron roller ⅝ of an inch in diameter and 17 inches long. It is turned with a treadle attached to a wooden shaft whose ends are weighted with wooden blocks. This weighted shaft serves as a sort of fly wheel to keep the motion constant. The shaft is mounted, through a hole in its center, upon the projecting squared end of the iron roller, and is held in position by a wooden wedge. A wooden turnpeg projects at right angles from the flyer-shaft below the roller and a string with a loop resting loosely in a groove of the turn-peg leads to a bamboo stick which completes the construction of the treadle. The bamboo treadle-stick, as I learned afterwards, should extend in the opposite direction under the bench. Its end rests loosely upon the ground. The whole contrivance was set up for us by an old peasant woman in her small yard and my ignorance of this most primitive cotton-gin prevented me from correcting the position of the bamboo stick. Previously I had seen only the type permanently fixed upon a wooden stand, which, however is the same in principle as can be seen from Fig. 233. The length of the flyer-shaft is 3 feet, the wooden mallet-shaped ends have dimensions of 7¾ by 3 by 2½ inches. The height of the frame as it rests on the bench is 15 inches, the width 12 inches. The length of the bamboo treadle stick is 4 feet and 7 inches. The frame below the wooden roller is stiffened by a wooden board pegged onto it with treenails.

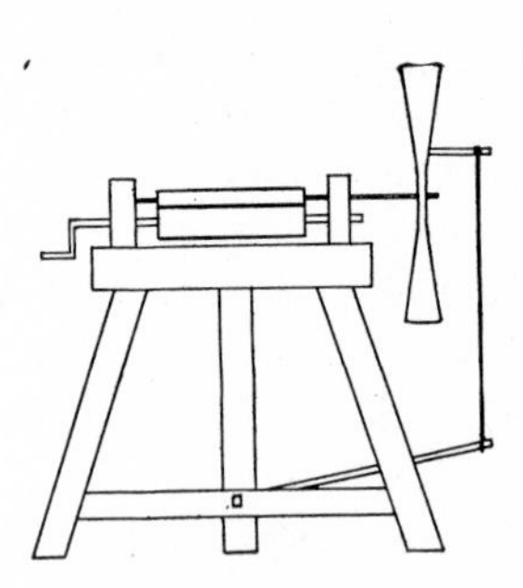

Fig. 233. Cotton-Gin Upon Permanent Stand. Sketched after a gin which I saw once in front of a poor hut, in Pootung, Kiangsu.

Women usually operate this cotton-gin, and as Chinese women wear trousers, the operator sits on the bench astride, turns the crank in one direction with her right hand and the treadle and fly-shaft in the opposite direction with her left foot, and feeds the cotton to the rollers with her left hand. That one roller should be of iron, and the other of wood does not seem to have any significance for the process, beyond the fact, that experience probably taught them that a wooden rod would not be of sufficient strength to hold the flyer-shaft which in revolving exerts quite a strain upon its axle. For a long time I had been on the lookout for this primitive cotton-gin with rollers usually the people knew about, but none were to be found, until I was directed by a little boy to the house of a poor woman, a few lis west of Sha Ho, near Kiukiang, Kiangsi province.

A description of a cotton-gin of the Sung Dynasty is extant, see sketch Fig. 234, according to which a wooden square held two pillars, each about 1 foot 5 inches high, the pillars being connected on top with a wooden crosspiece. Each pillar was pierced for an axle, but the other end rested in a socket which did not penetrate the pillar. Each of the opposite ends of the axles was fitted with a crank. This contrivance, it would seem, was served by three people, two turning the cranks, and the third feeding the raw cotton.

In Italy a ginning machine was used, probably an adaptation of the "churka" of India, which is in principle the same as the Chinese contrivance. The Italians learned the cultivation of cotton from India and call their ginning machine "*Manganello*." That sounds suspiciously like mangle and the question arises did the Italian *manganello* form the pattern for the mangle used by washer-women to smooth clothing? To mangle means to lacerate, that which the ginning machine actually does, tearing the fibres of the raw cotton apart and leaving the seed behind. The name then of the clothes mangle seems a misnomer, but suggestive of the origin of that contrivance as an adaptation of the *manganello* of the Italians to other purposes, namely the smoothing of clothes.

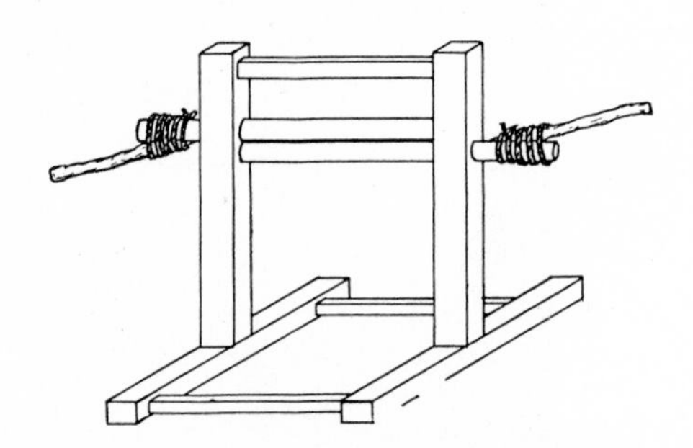

Fig. 234. Cotton-Gin of the Sung Dynasty. The sketch shows the reconstruction of a cotton-gin of the Sung Dynasty (960-1280 A.D.), drawn after a contemporaneous description. The height of the uprights is 1 ft. 5 inches.

Fig. 235 shows another view of a cotton-gin, in principle the same as the one described. This specimen saw and photographed in Kien Chang, Kiangsi. The treadle stick is here shown in the proper position. The height of the bench is 21½ inches. The frame of the gin is 15 inches wide and 11 inches high, the diameter of the wooden roller 1¾ inches and of the wrought iron roller ⅝ of an inch. The length of the fly-rod with its mallet-shaped ends is 2 feet 10 inches.

That these primitive, slow-working cotton-gins still persist is due to the occasional demands of small households, who could not afford a more expensive contrivance. A secondary reason may be that this simple gin does not tear the fibres as much as faster working gins do.

Fig. 235. Cotton-Gin.

Whatever the use to which the cotton is to be put after ginning, the various fibres have to be extricated from each other and put into some semblance of order; this is done by bowing. The requisites for this process are a bow and a hammer or pin for striking the string of the bow to make it vibrate. Fig. 236 shows the simplest form of a bow as it is used in the country by the peasants. It consists of a wooden rod 5 feet long and 1½ inches in diameter to which is fixed at one end by means of two dowels, a flat wooden board. This board is 3½ inches long where it rests against the rod, 3 inches wide and 1 inch thick. The rod tapers off at that end (at the right in the picture), to correspond with the thickness of the board. Near the other end (on the left), from a mortise in the rod extends another board 8 by 4 by ⅜ inches. On its outer edge this latter board fits into a mortised cross-strip of wood about an inch thick. Its function is not unlike that of the bridge on a violin. A piece of tightly stretched catgut passes over the two projections on the rod. One end is fastened to the loop of a rope attached to the large end of the rod and the other is wound around its top.

The method of handling the cotton bow is illustrated in Fig. 237. The operator sits on a low stool (shown separately in Fig. 238) holding the bow with the left hand directly over the ginned cotton, which is spread out upon a mat on the ground. The middle of the bow is tied to a string leading to an elastic bamboo rod, 7 feet long and at its thickest end ½ an inch thick. The lower end of this rod as shown in the picture rests in a framed support attached to the stool on which the operator sits. The catgut held immediately over the cotton is struck in rapid succession with a wooden pin 7½ inches long and 2 inches in thickest diameter, which is shown in Fig. 236 and in Fig. 240, and kept thus in vibration. The vibration is communicated to the fibres of the cotton which are disentangled and align themselves in such a way that the cotton becomes a loose fluffy mass suitable for the

Fig. 236. Cotton Bow.

Fig. 237. Operator Holding Cotton Bow.

wadding of bedspreads, padding of clothing and for twisting into rovings for spinning.

The old man in Fig. 237 is an elderly woman and we had to act quickly to take her picture, before she had a chance to think the matter over and come to other conclusions. She was only posing for our benefit, and there was no spread mat upon the ground, nor any ginned cotton upon the mat, as there should have been.

The stool, Fig. 238 with its back-frame forming the support of the bamboo rod is 18 inches high. The seat-board is 18 inches long, $11\frac{1}{2}$ inches wide at one end, 9 inches at the other end, and $1\frac{1}{2}$ inches thick. The seat is rather low, its upper surface being only 4 inches from the ground. The lower end of the flexible pole, whose purpose is to lessen the strain on the operator's hand by suspending the heavy bow over the work, is here seen set vertically through two holes in the back frame of the stool.

Fig. 239 shows a cotton bow, as used by professional cotton bowers in Shanghai, with a more elaborate bridge which makes it more efficient for constant handling. The length of this bow is 5 feet 7 inches. Its striking pin, shown separately in Fig. 240, is 10 inches long and in largest diameter $2\frac{3}{4}$ inches. The modified bridge of the professional cotton bow needs some detailed description. The explanation I got about this modification was that it helps to make the catgut vibrate more easily and efficiently. I affix a sketch, Fig. 242, which shows the details of this bridge with a bamboo tube to support the catgut. The bamboo tube is held in place by a strip of pigskin. Between the wood and the bamboo tube is a folded piece of paper to keep the bamboo tube from sliding out of place. The lower end of the pigskin strap which is about one inch wide, is inserted in a groove in the wood and kept from sliding out by a round wooden plug. This is made clear by the sketch, Fig. 243. The other end of the pigskin is attached to a piece of string which passes to the rod of the bow and is kept stretched by a toggle-stick. The end of the catgut is knotted over a wad of cotton and the string attached to the base of the rod is looped over this knot and holds the catgut firmly against the bridge. The catgut passes over the pigskin of the bridge to the end-board of the rod. This end-board is protected by a strip of leather which prevents the catgut from cutting a groove into the wood. Over this end-board the catgut passes to the end of the rod, then down the rod about 16 inches to a projecting bamboo nail. Starting with this nail the catgut is wound around the pole first in large spirals and then in close ones under the last of which the end of the catgut is tucked. When the catgut is struck with the pin the groove under the glandiform head catches the catgut and by stretching and quickly releasing it imparts to it the vibration. The bow it is held sideways as can be seen in Fig. 241, in spite of the unfortunate background. The photographs, Figs. 239-241 were taken in the Native City of Shanghai, and Figs. 236-238 in Chao Ka Too, a village near Shanghai, Kiangsu province.

Chinese records of the Sung dynasty (960-1280 A.D.)

mention bows strung with sheepgut, and another cotton bow strung with a cowgut cord wound closely with string. In some parts of China instead of gut, waxed silk strings as in musical instruments or strong twine are used.

SPINNING

Spinning done without a spinning wheel is not uncommon in China. Passing by the miserable straw-huts of poor people, one can frequently see the Chinese women standing at the door spinning with a spindle a few yards of sewing yarn. Such a primitive spindle is shown in Fig. 244. A piece of wood about 4½ inches long and 1½ inches thick, with a small forked tree-branch cut to form a hook, or with a bent iron nail is all that is required. The height of the whole contrivance shown in the picture, is 2¾ inches.

In using this spindle, the yarn is started by rolling the fibres between the fingers, or upon the upper part of the leg, then the twist thus fashioned is fastened to the hook of the spindle. The spindle hangs free and is set spinning by taking the hook between thumb and forefinger of the right hand and giving it a twirl. The material, be it silk, hemp or cotton roving, is then fed into the twirling twist and when the spun yarn gets so long that the spindle almost touches the ground, the spinner winds it upon the base of the spindle, passes the end up under the barb of the hook and resumes spinning. The spinners sit or stand when using the spindle. In Se Aw, Chekiang province, where this picture was taken, this type of spindle with a square whorl is used only for silk, but around Shanghai I saw it used for cotton and hemp spinning. The block-base which serves as a whorl is most frequently rectangular, but in other parts of China I have also seen round whorls.

Fig. 239. The Cotton Bow of a Professional Bower.

Throughout Kiangsu province, the itinerant cobblers on the street spin their own hemp yarn with spindles as pictured in Fig. 245. A bone from the hind-leg of a zebu forms the whorl in the center of which a hole is drilled to receive an iron hook or a barbed bamboo stick. A thread started by rolling hemp fibres between hand and thigh is wound upon the bone whorl and then a few times around the shaft of the hook. No knot or loop is necessary to secure the hemp to the barb or hook. Winding it around the stem twice and then letting the spindle dangle is sufficient, as is evident from the sketch, Fig. 246. The cobbler then grasps the free end of the twist of yarn which now suspends the spindle, the bone is spun around and while the spindle thus spins, hemp is fed to the twisted yarn end held in the hand. After a convenient stretch of yarn has been spun, it is wound around the bone so as to distribute it equally on both

Fig. 238. Cotton Bower's Stool.

sides of the central stem. The spindle with the iron hook is 7 inches long and 3⅝ inches high, the other with the bamboo stem is 7¼ inches long and 3⅝ inches high. The former I procured in Wuhu and the latter in San Ho, Anhwei, where the peasants use this type of a spindle. I found no bone spindles in Kiangsi province.

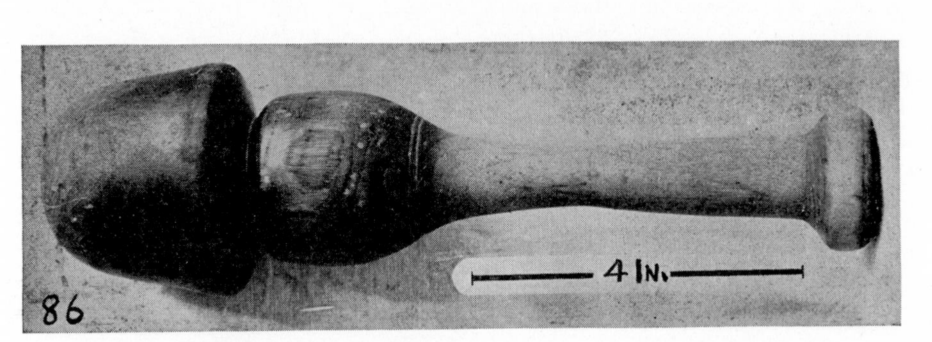

FIG. 240. STRIKING PIN OF A PROFESSIONAL COTTON BOWER. This striking pin belongs to the cotton bow of a professional cotton bower, shown in Fig. 239, and was photographed with the bow in the Native City of Shanghai.

It was only through descriptions found in an old Chinese encyclopedia of the 16th century A.D., that I learned of the use of the distaff in connection with spinning of floss silk. Floss silk is made of the loose short silk fibres surrounding the cocoon and is considered much inferior to the long silk reeled from the outer layers of the cocoon. The translator of the passage[1] informs us that the process of spinning described refers to the time of Absolute Monarchy in China, 221 B.C. to 221 A.D. I quote: "The way to make a 'nien mien chou,' axle or roller for twisting floss silk, was as follows: A small roller was made of wood or stone, a small axle about a foot in length being fixed to it. The floss silk was then first hung to a crotch, and the crotch held in the left hand whilst with the right the silk was guided on to the roller, which being suspended in the air, the floss silk was twisted into a thread, and then wound around the axle. After this it could be used on the warping cylinder as silk thread. It would be used by women and girls, taking the place of their skilled labor in weaving and spinning." The translator, not happily translating the technical terms, means of course by "axle or roller" the spindle, by "a small roller" the whorl, and by "crotch" a sort of distaff.

[1] E. T. C. Werner, "Sociology of the Chinese," London, 1910.

In Linkiang, once a flourishing city, which never recovered from the ravages wrought by the Taipings, situated on the old road which led from Canton northward through Kwangtung and Kiangsi provinces to Kiukiang, a part of the old overland route to Peking, I found the distaff pictured in Fig. 247. I happened to walk into the shop of a candlemaker, a place hardly to be thought of in connection with spinning, and discovered on each of the several work-benches one of these distaffs with raw silk hooked upon it sticking in a slot. At these benches workers sat engaged in making wicks for candles. The method employed is as follows: The pith of a rush is wound around a stiff kind of straw or sedge and when in

FIG. 241. PROFESSIONAL COTTON BOW SUSPENDED FROM A BODY POLE. Here the flexible suspending pole is not set into the framework of a stool, as in Fig. 238, but fastened upon the back of the worker, in this case an apprentice boy, who posed for the picture. The operator spreads the cotton upon a low table, not here shown, and holds the bow with the left hand.

winding, the end of a piece of rush is reached, it is tied down with a piece of silk fibre which the worker pulls from the distaff. The distaff, a forked stick, with the silk wound about the prongs, and a few pieces of rush-pith wick lying beside it, is shown in Fig. 247. I took the picture scarcely expecting to get anything at all, as the light conditions were very poor. The length of the distaff is 13 inches, its largest width 1½ inches, and average thickness ¼ of an inch. It is fashioned out of one piece of wood.

The high antiquity of the distaff is best attested to by quoting from Schliemann, the excavator of the ruins of Homer's Troy. The destruction of Troy by the Greeks took place in 1184 B.C. according to the calculations of the Alexandrine scholar Eratosthenes.

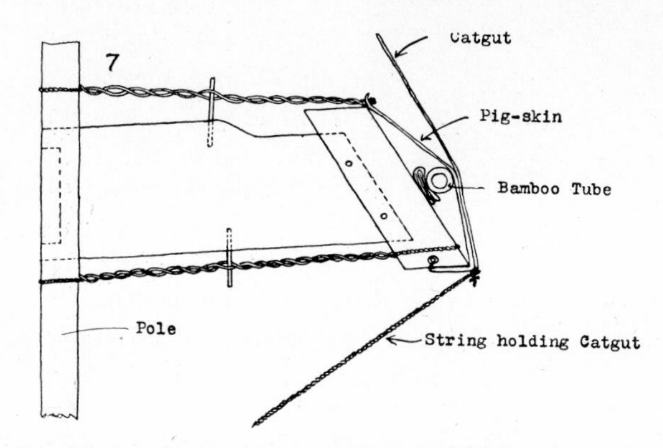

FIG. 242. DETAIL OF BRIDGE SHOWING BAMBOO TUBE FOR INTENSIFYING VIBRATIONS OF COTTON BOW.

The results of the excavations point rather to an older age.

"One of the most curious objects ever found in my excavations is undoubtedly a distaff, 11 inches long, around which is wound lengthwise a large quantity of woolen thread, as black as coal, evidently from being charred. I discovered it in the royal mansion at a depth of 28 feet below the surface."[2]

HEMP SPINNING WHEEL

The observations about the hemp spinning wheel, Fig. 248, were made in Sa Sai Dung Gao, (Thirteen Arch Bridge Village), Chekiang province. For the warp of straw mats a single strand yarn is used which is spun on the wheel here shown. The materials used are the unhackled fibres of hemp. My informants insisted that it was flax but they described it as a plant over 5 feet high with angular stems, white flowers and little round seeds. Further inquiry revealed that the Chinese have one and the same word to denote flax and hemp. The hemp plant when ripe is pulled up with the root and then dried in the sun. After it has been thoroughly dried out, the stem is broken close to the root, when, because the core adheres to the root, the stem rips open along its whole length. The material is not retted, as is the practice in Europe.

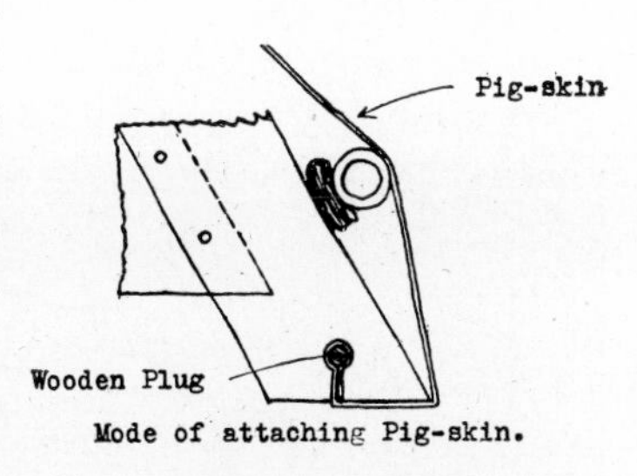

FIG. 243. DETAILS OF BRIDGE ON PROFESSIONAL COTTON BOW.

The spinning wheel is very simple, a stand with an axle, and a reel revolving it. The stand consists of three legs joined together with four braces by tenon and mortise. Two of the legs are 1 foot 2 inches long, 2¼ inches wide, and 1½ inches thick. The third leg extending upward, is made longer to hold the axle for the reel. It is a naturally curved stick 2 feet 8 inches long, 2 inches wide, and 3 inches thick, tapering to smaller dimensions toward the top. About 3½ inches from the top of this curved leg, is a hole which holds the axle rigidly in place by means of wooden wedges. The axle on the spinning wheel shown in Fig. 248 is made of a very hard wood (we saw others made of iron), squared where it fits into the hole of the leg. Where the crossed arms of the reel revolve on

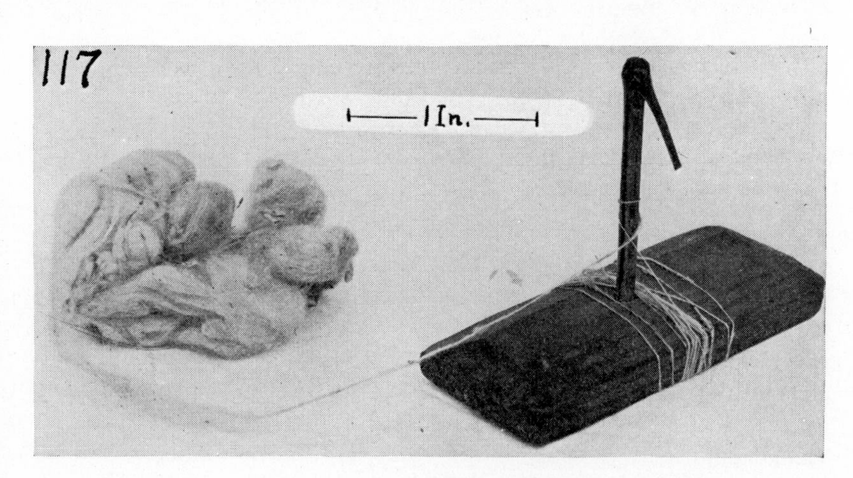

FIG. 244. SPINDLE.

[2] H. Schliemann, "Ilios," London, 1880, p. 327. Later investigations brought out that this find belonged to the second city which had flourished between the 3rd and 2nd millennium B.C.

it, it is perfectly round, and ⅜ of an inch in diameter. The whole length of the axle is 1 foot 2½ inches. In mounting the reel upon the axle the right-hand cross is slipped over the axle first, then a hollow wooden cylinder, interposed between the two crosses of the

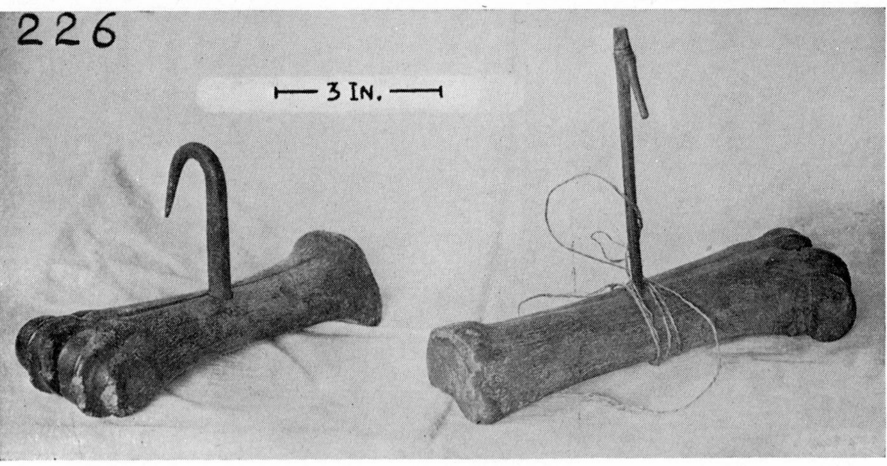

Fig. 245. Spindles.

reel, and finally the left-hand cross. The wooden cylinder which rests loosely on the axle between the cross arms of the reel, is pushed up on the axle until it touches the right-hand cross arm, and is wedged tight to the axle by inserting splinters of wood. The reel can now revolve freely on the axle and is prevented from slipping off by the wooden cylinder thus wedged to the axle. The axle bearings in the cross arms are lubricated with peanut oil. The reel itself is a simple affair, two crosses formed of wooden strips 12 inches long, connected by four wooden longitudinal braces 9 inches long. The crosses each have in the center a hole, one half inch in diameter which serves as bearing for the axle. The method of working the wheel is described under the next picture, Fig. 249.

First the spinner starts a yarn by twisting the fibres together between hand and thigh, then this yarn is tied to one of the wooden braces connecting the crosses of the reel. The other end of the yarn, scarcely visible in the picture, is held in the left hand of the spinner, see Fig. 249, and by simply moving the left hand with the yarn in a circle the yarn causes the reel to revolve, which naturally twists the yarn. As soon as the yarn is as long as the spinner can make it without leaving her sitting position, she changes the angle of the yarn to the reel in such a manner that it will no longer twist (spin) but be wound onto the reel which is still revolving. When the spun part of the yarn is thus disposed of, the angle of the yarn is changed again to its former position by hooking the end of the wound yarn to one of the radial cross-arms of the reel, whereupon the circular motion of the hand is resumed to keep the reel revolving, and new fibres are fed to the yarn as before. The fibres are used dry without moistening of any kind.

The same kind of wheel I have seen in Shanghai, only larger, for spinning the strands of rope out of palm-tree fibres. It is worked by a man standing in front of it, who walks backward as he feeds the fibres to the strand. A quite similar mode of rope making with a stationary wheel, in front of which the ropemaker sits, is shown in a woodcut in a German translation, published at Basel in 1493, of a French work which a Chevalier de la Tour produced ca. 1370 for the instruction of his daughters. A copy of this picture is given in Volume II of "Schaffende Arbeit und Bildende Kunst" by Paul Brandt (Leipzig 1928), Fig. 208, with the legend "Aus dem Ritter vom Turm. Basel 1493."

"Flax, *Linum sativum,* L., was unknown to the ancient Chinese. It is nowadays cultivated in the

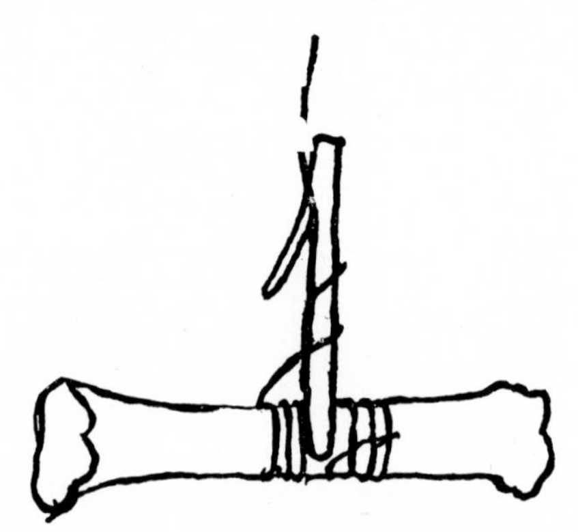

Fig. 246. Sketch Showing Mode of Attaching Yarn to Hook of Spindle.

mountains of North China (probably also in other parts of the empire) and in Southern Mongolia, but only for the oil of the seeds, not for its fibres. The Chinese call it *hu ma* (foreign hemp). The great Chinese Herbal and Materia Medica published in the

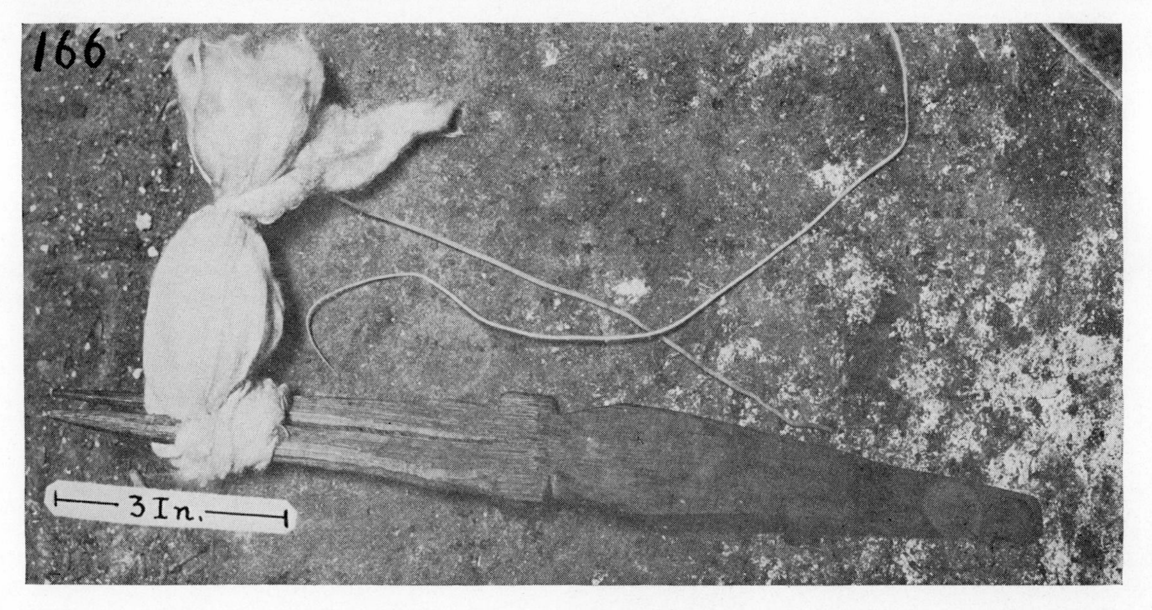

FIG. 247. DISTAFF.

16th century by Li Shi-Chen does not speak of it. Its introduction must be of more recent date." [3]

The spinning wheel just described, Fig. 248, for spinning hemp fibres, is quite common in districts given over to the manufacture of straw and rush mats, where large quantities of hemp yarn are needed for warp. For domestic purposes, especially for the sewing of soles for cloth-shoes, which is usually a home industry, the twisting of hemp yarn is done without any wheel merely by twisting the fibres together upon the thigh. Apparently the cotton spinning wheel, which is found in every rural home, does not lend itself to spinning the coarser fibres of hemp, and if no hemp spinning wheel is present, resort has to be taken to the time-honored method of twisting the fibres with the palm of the hand upon the thigh. The operation as I saw it, many, many times, is about as follows:

A bundle of fibres, dry as they are, is laid beside the sitting spinner. She selects the fibres judiciously, so as to get a yarn of even thickness. To begin with, a few fibres are taken by their ends with the left hand and held tightly. The fibres are then laid upon the thigh of the right leg and the palm of the right hand is passed with pressure over them in a direction towards the knee. Still leaving the right hand upon the fibres the hold with the left hand is released, whereupon the fibres so twisted will coil around themselves. The process is continued, and as the spinner comes to the end of the fibres, new ones have to be fed in, until the yarn is as long as desired. To understand this principle clearly, take an ordinary one-ply cotton string, double it and take hold of the looped end with thumb and forefinger of the left hand. Lay the loose ends over your leg and twist each around its own axis by pressing down upon them with the palm of the right hand, and moving it toward the knee. Keep your right hand upon the twisted ends, and release your hold upon the looped end between the fingers of your left hand, and you will see how the released end will coil to form a two ply string. Itinerant cobblers on the street, and sometimes women in the country (I don't forget the one in Kien Chang, Kiangsi, who would not sell me the beautiful green glazed tile of the Ming dynasty, as it fitted her thigh so snugly), place a roofing tile upon their thighs, and twist the yarn upon this, others to save their clothing, roll up their trousers and twist the fibres upon the bare leg.

The use of a roofing tile to cover the thigh as a base for twisting fibres reminds one of the *"epinetron"* or *"onos"* of the old Greeks, the longitudinal half of an earthen pipe which fitted the thigh for the same purpose.

SPINNING WHEELS

The type of spinning wheel shown in Fig. 250 is extensively used in Chekiang Province. I also saw it used in the neighborhood of Shanghai, Kiangsu province. A simple framework holds the wheel proper. The wheel consists of an axle 2¼ inches in diameter in the middle, reduced to 1½ inches diameter at both ends where the axle rests in holes of the framework.

[3] "Botanicon Sinicum," Part II, by E. Bretschneider, Shanghai, 1893.

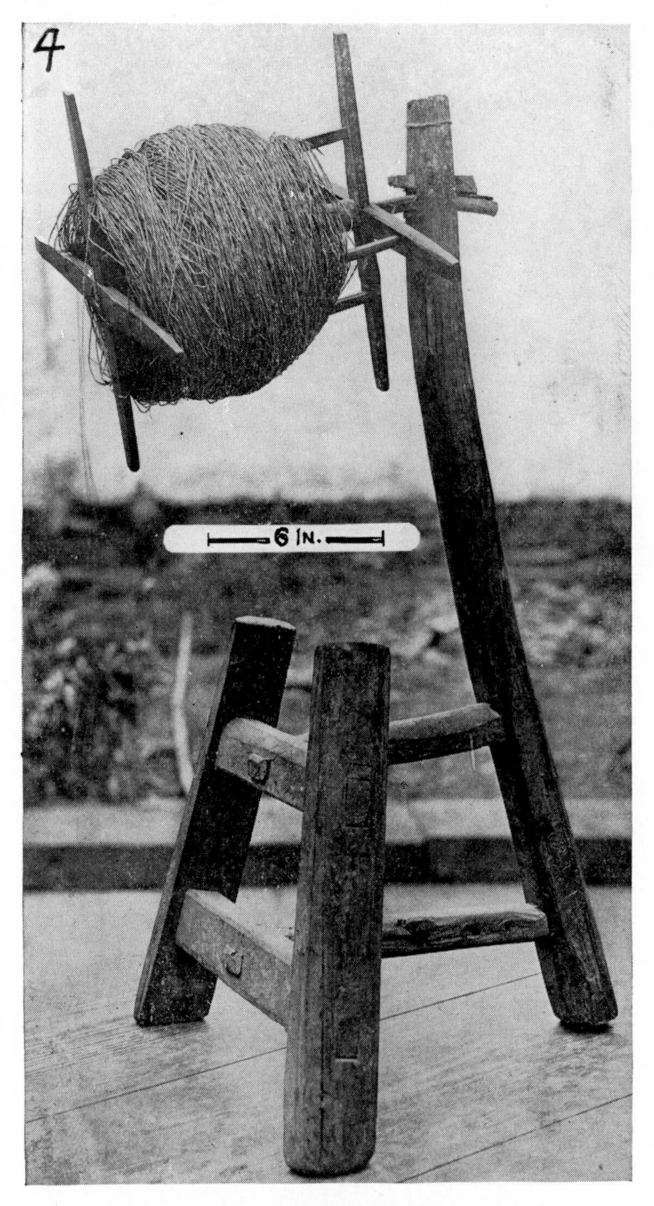

FIG. 248. HEMP SPINNING WHEEL.

The whole length of the axle is 17 inches. One end which extends beyond the hole in the framework is squared and receives the crank for turning the wheel, very imperfectly seen in the picture, because it is photographed parallel to the axle. There are two sets of 8 spokes each, formed by bamboo rods, 3 feet 3 inches long, pushed through two sets of holes at either end of the axle. The ends of the spokes are connected in zigzag with strings, the strings always running from one spoke of the one set, to the one nearest of the other set. Over these strings, which form an elastic resting place, runs the line which sets the spindle in motion.

The spinner sits upon a low stool about a foot high in front of the wheel and turns with the right hand the wooden crank, which is mounted upon the projecting axle of the wheel. The spindle is not set horizontally but points downward at an angle. In winding, the yarn is held at right angles to the spindle. If the spindle were set horizontally the spinner would have to lift the arm up straight into the air to do the winding. When spinning the yarn the left hand is held at the same height as the position of the pointed end of the spindle and moved away from it in a horizontal direction. The cord which transfers the motion from the wheel to the spindle, runs over some bee's wax on the spindle, the purpose of which is the same as when the cobbler draws his thread over wax to stiffen it. The cord thus waxed also imparts some of its wax to the cross-strings on the wheel over which it runs. Without wax, cord and strings would soon wear through. A turning stick such as was used on the primitive occidental spinning wheel would of course be of no avail for this type of wheel.

Fig. 251, shows the spindle of the apparatus at closer range. Its position and adjustment on bamboo leaf-bearings are much more clearly seen. The spindle, made of steel, is 11¼ inches long, ⅛ of an inch thick, and ends in a sharp point. It is kept in place by tough twisted leaves of the bamboo shoot resembling the husks of American sweet corn. The twisted leaves bent into loops serve as axle bearings for the spindle. The ends of the twists pass through holes in the upright base-block and are held in place by wooden wedges. A wooden sleeve or pipe, 2 inches long and ¼ of an inch thick, fits tightly over the spindle between the bearings, tight enough to revolve with the spindle. On this sleeve some bee's wax in smeared, and over it runs the cord which transmits the motion from the wheel to the spindle. The bent wooden twig, tied tightly with a strip of cloth to the framework beneath, apparently serves to prevent the cord from wabbling back and forth following the zigzag direction of the strings on the circumference of the wheel. We saw some spinning wheels which did not have this steadying device.

Before starting to spin a loose tube or spool-sleeve, called a cop-tube, must be thrust upon the projecting spindle, upon which the freshly finished yarn may be wound as fast as it is spun. For this purpose a bamboo leaf is rolled over the projecting part of the spindle, or a kind of straw is pushed upon it and a piece of yarn, taken from the bundle hanging on the frame of the spinning wheel, is wound upon this cop-tube to hold it tight. The loose end of this yarn is then led to the point of the spindle so as to act as starting yarn in the spinning process. It is held so as to form an angle of about 120 degrees with the spindle. In doing this the yarn will no longer be wound upon the spindle, but will turn around its own axis. Then the cotton rovings, not here shown, are fed into this twisting yarn and as the roving gradually disappears the yarn gets longer and longer. The spinner sits in front of the wheel, turns it with her right hand, and feeds the rovings with the left into the lengthening yarn until the spun product gets as long as the arm can reach. Then the new yarn thus twisted or spun is held at right angles to the spindle and wound upon it, over the cop-tube above mentioned. The process is repeated until the yarn upon the spindle is of sufficient bulk, when the cop-tube is pulled off of the spindle, and put aside to await the next operation in the chain which begins with the loose cotton and ends with the woven fabric. It should be mentioned that the spinning wheel stands upon the ground when in use, and not as here shown on stools where it was placed for convenience in photographing. The height from the floor to the center of the wheel axle is 2 feet.

The previously prepared fluffy rovings are rolled between the hands from the bowed cotton, to a length of about 12 inches and a diameter of about an inch. They are placed in a basket, not here shown, beside the spinner. The photographs were taken in Sin Tseong, Chekiang province.

In Kiangsu province, in and around Shanghai, a spinning wheel is used with which three yarns can be spun simultaneously. Fig. 252 shows this wheel in action and it will be noticed that the spinner holds three rovings with the left hand between thumb and fore-finger, the yarns resulting from the rovings then pass between fore-finger and middle-finger, between middle-finger and ring-finger, between ring-finger and little finger respectively. They are next guided through the same fingers respectively of the right

Fig. 249. Hemp Spinning Wheel.

Fig. 250. Cotton Spinning Wheel.

hand, whence they pass to the ends of the three spindles. The spinner holds in the right hand between thumb and fore-finger a wooden stick about 1½ feet long and ¼ of an inch thick. This stick comes into play when the yarns have been spun as long as the left arm can conveniently be stretched out, away from the spindles. Then the spinner withdraws the fingers of her right hand from the yarns and pushes the yarns with the stick towards the right side of her body until the yarns form with the spindles approximately a right angle, when the yarns cease to twist (spin) and begin to wind around the spindles. The wheel is kept in motion by pushing with the feet up and down the treadle board, which is supported on a pivot near its one end, while the other pointed end rests loosely in a hole on one of the spokes of the wheel.

The construction of this compound spinning wheel is shown more clearly in Fig. 253. The stand is a wooden structure which holds wheel, treadle board and spindle holder. At its highest part it measures 33 inches from the ground. Its widest breadth at the bottom is 26 inches. The back and front uprights of the supporting frame are sketched separately in Fig. 254. A round wooden axle, 12 inches long and 1 inch in diameter, serves for the support of the wheel. The wheel is pushed upon the axle and kept from sliding off by a bamboo pin in a hole on the axle end. The wheel measures 26 inches in diameter. The eight spokes of the wheel are formed by four wooden strips. The thickest one has two holes equidistant from the center, either of which can be used to receive the end of the treadle board. The other pieces, forming the remaining six spokes, are mortised across the thickest strip, and held in their relative positions by the bamboo axle which passes through the center of all the wooden pieces forming the spokes. Upon the end of each spoke a wooden block is mounted, 3 inches long, 1½ inches wide, and ¾ of an inch thick. In either end of the block, a groove has been cut, each of which receives a bamboo hoop which forms part of the circumference of the wheel. Between the blocks attached to the spokes blocks of the same dimensions are inserted. These latter are not mounted upon the ends of spokes but are inserted between the bamboo hoops and have no further support. These transverse pieces, 24 altogether, serve as a surface for the belt to pass over, which transmits the motion from the wheel to the spindle.

The treadle board, pointed and rounded at one end, is 3 feet long, 3 inches wide and 1½ inches thick. On the under side about 9 inches from the blunt end away from the wheel, there is a conical hole about ¾ of an inch deep, into which fits the pivot (see the diagram on the right of Fig. 254), set in the block or upright, seen on the outer end of the stand. The setting in motion of the wheel will now be easily understood. The left foot of the spinner rests on the treadle board outside the pivot and the right foot on the treadle board between the pivot and the wheel, as shown in Fig. 252. By alternately pushing the board first with one and then with the other foot the board sways up and down and imparts the motion to the wheel.

Fig. 255 gives a detail view of the spindle holder with the three spindles. It consists of two wooden boards held at the proper distance from each other by two heavy square pins. These are mortised tightly into the board passing through the heavier back board of the spindle holder, and extending beyond it for about two inches. The ends of one of these pins can be seen extending beyond the rear board. That of the near pin is hidden from view. The long central pin with the knob at one end fits tightly in the square holes of each board but can easily be removed. To attach the spindle holder to the rear upright of the stand, above the wheel, the two short pin extensions are made to rest upon shoulders, (see sketch, Fig. 254) formed by the projection of a wooden strip mortised through the same upright, which holds the wheel. Finally to keep the spindle holder firmly in place the large central pin, running through the square holes in the center of the two boards of the spindle holder is forced into a corresponding hole in the upright where it is held tight with a wedge.

The spindles, 13 inches long, are turned out of a very hard wood and have at their thickest part a diameter of ⅜ of an inch. They are inserted into holes in the heavier board. To lubricate the bearings a square bit of cloth, soaked with oil, is placed over the holes and the spindle ends are pushed through the cloth. Where the spindles rest in the open grooves in the thinner board, they have been turned to a smaller diameter to correspond with the grooves. A sort of bearing made out of bamboo is inserted into the grooves, and a tightly fitting bamboo sleeve is fitted over that part of the spindle over which the belt passes, that is between the two boards of the spindle holder. The protruding ends of two crude sticks locked between the crosspieces of the spindle holder under the spindles keep the belt from sliding off the spindles. When the spindles are wound full the yarn is wound off into hanks. For some reason no cop-tubes are used for this spinning wheel. Cop-tubes, either a leaf wound around the spindle or a straw pushed over it, are used for the one-spindle wheel so as not to interrupt the work of the spinner who without tubes would have to unreel the yarn from the spindle before continuing. Why the cop-tubes were not used with the three-spindle wheels I could not find out. Even a child can take the full cop-tube, and holding it loosely in the hand, or sticking it into his shoe reel the yarn off into hanks on a hank reel like one shown in Fig. 262. The photographs were taken at Chao Ka Too, near Shanghai.

TWISTING

It is well to remember that a yarn technically speaking is a single filament spun from raw fibres, and that a thread is composed of two or more yarns

Fig. 251. Spindle and Spindle Bearings of a Cotton Spinning Wheel.

twisted together. In order to twist two or more single yarns into one compound thread, two distinct processes are necessary. First the yarns must be laid side by side throughout their entire length, second, the parallel yarns must be stretched out and then twisted together.

For the first step two Chinese devices are shown in Fig. 256, the reel stand with three hanks of single spun cotton yarn on bamboo reels set one above the other and the spool reel. The object of the two devices is not to twist, but simply to bring together side by side, in lengths of about 200 yards (i.e., the total hank length) three thin spun cotton yarns.

The reel stand is 4 feet 10 inches high and the vertical posts have notches which serve as bearings for the reels. The reels, 19 inches in diameter, are made up of bamboo strips, as can be seen by inspection, the ends of their radial arms are connected with strings, and over these strings the hanks are wound or placed.

The apparatus on the right of Fig. 256, the spool reel, shown separately again in Fig. 258, consists of a vertical frame with a small wooden reel or spool axled upon it, secured with wedges to the end of a bench. This spool reel, which is made to revolve continuously in a very unique and ingenious manner, to be described presently, is set up near the reel stand, with its axle at right angles to the axles of the three larger reels on the stand. Its purpose is to draw off the three yarns from the reel stand and for convenience in subsequent handling wind them up into sets consisting each of three untwisted parallel yarns. In doing this the workman brings together the ends of the three reel stand yarns and ties them thus, to one of the arms of the spool reel.

Fig. 257 shows the spool reel removed from its axle and frame. It is constructed entirely of bamboo. The diameter is 6 inches and the length 8 inches. The Chinese are masters in wooden joinery without the aid of glue, it must however not be forgotten that they have in the climate a helpful ally. The excessive humidity in summer and winter never lets the wood get dry enough to produce those shrinkage phenomena with which we are so familiar in our furniture. The two star-shaped pieces held at the proper distance from each other by strips stuck into the points of the stars compose the whole spindle.

Fig. 252. Compound (Three Spindle) Cotton Spinning Wheel.

FIG. 253. FRAMEWORK SHOWING THE CONSTRUCTION OF A COMPOUND (THREE SPINDLE) COTTON SPINNING WHEEL.

The reel when wound full must continually be removed from its axle and replaced by an empty duplicate. It does not revolve around its axle, but turns with it being easily pushed upon the axle and as easily pulled off. The axle holes are round and the axle, rounded to fit them, is held tight by friction only.

A close view of the spool reel is given in Fig. 258. The reel consists of a wooden frame made of two upright pieces which are connected by two cross pieces wedged over the end of a bench. The larger upright piece is 2 feet long, 2½ inches wide and 1½ inches thick. It has a slot in its upper part 10 inches long, ¾ inch wide and 1½ inches deep. In the other upright at the same height as the lower point of the slot in the larger upright there is a round bearing hole 1 inch deep. The wooden axle or driving rod, 22 inches long and ⅝ of an inch in diameter, rests loosely with its left end in the bearing-hole of the smaller upright. To set the driving rod going the leather strap attached to the larger upright comes into play. This strap suspended from the top of the slot in the left upright hangs straight down to the back side of the axle and then curls loosely around the axle between strap and upright. A small pull-stick, as a handle, is tied with a string to the strap end.

The workman does not sit astride the bench but across it with his back toward the viewer of the picture and his right hand close to the pull-stick. He faces the reel stand, Fig. 256 (left), brings together the three yarns from the three reels on the reel stand, ties them close together to one of the arms of the spool reel, Fig. 258, and holds them together loosely in his left hand so that they turn a right angled corner, flow forward to be wound upon the spool reel at right angles to its axle. When now with his right hand he pulls the pull-stick the flexible strap gripping the axle not only causes the axle to revolve but lifts it high in the slot until the man stops pulling, when the strap relaxes its hold and the axle drops back to the slot-bottom, pulling back the strap at the same time to its former position. In the course of the process the axle with the spool reel upon it has been continuously revolving, and the spool reel has been gathering and

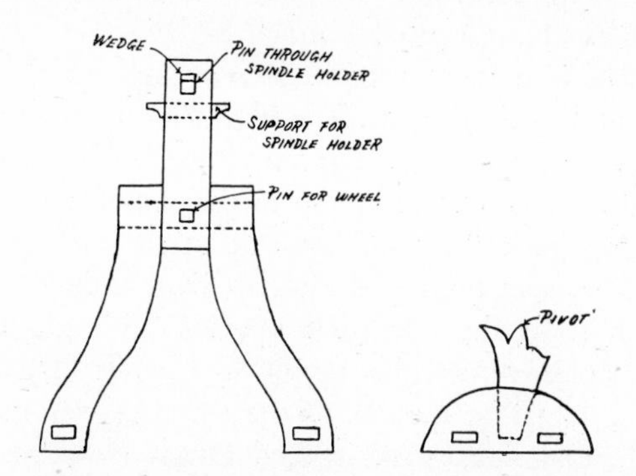

FIG. 254. DETAIL OF FRAMEWORK FOR COMPOUND (THREE SPINDLE) COTTON SPINNING WHEEL.

winding the three untwisted yarns directed upon it from the workman's left hand. Repeated strap pulls increase the momentum of the spool reel to a high speed.

FIG. 255. SPINDLE HOLDER OF A THREE-SPINDLE COTTON SPINNING WHEEL. One spindle is removed and shown lying on the stool.

This interesting reeling machine produces circular motion of high speed simply by pulling a cord or strap of leather laid around the axle of the reel. Testing it I found that with one pull the reel wound twelve feet of cotton thread, which would correspond to about 15 revolutions per pull. Once the machine is in full swing, the speed is much higher.

There is a relationship between this reeling machine and a Chinese toy. The player holds two sticks, one in each hand, connected by a cord. This cord is placed around a reel-like top in the same manner as the strap passing around the axle of the reeling machine. To spin the top the player with a short sharp motion jerks the one stick upward with his right hand, holding the other firmly in his left. This imparts a whirling motion to the top engaged in the string. The right stick is then lowered and jerked upward again and so on until the speed of the whirling top becomes tremendous. The top at great speed gives forth an uncanny whizzing sound. If the cord should break at top speed the top flies off at an angle, and pity the person it hits.

When the winding process is finished the second step, i.e., that of twisting the three parallel yarns into three-strand threads begins.

To accomplish this three full reels are set so as to revolve on three vertical pivots on a stand like that shown at the left of Fig. 259, just back of the hank reel which partly obscures it. The workman then seizes the ends of the three untwisted yarn groups on the three reels and carries them forward inserting them between the bamboo separating-loops on top of the high twisting frame seen at the right in Fig. 259. He next walks onward still holding the three yarn groups in his hand, and stretches them like telegraph wires the whole length of the alley, 100 yards. To prevent the yarn from sagging he passes over a series of wooden crosspieces fixed upon 5 foot sticks driven into the ground about twenty yards apart. At the end of the alley stands a pole, in the present case it was a telegraph pole to which, five feet from the ground, a horizontal strip of wood about three feet long has been nailed and upon this strip three empty spools have been set or axled upon nails passing through their holes. Over these spools the man now guides the yarn groups and walks back to the starting point, laying the yarn groups on the supports as before. When he gets back to the twisting-stand which is the first support and the only one movable shown to the right in Fig. 259, he stops and proceeds to cut the outgoing three yarn groups between the twisting stand and the reels and attaches these likewise to spindles.

In Fig. 259 the three lower groups are not yet furnished with spindles but are temporarily tied to the lower bar of the reel stand. This illustrates again the difficulty of obtaining pictures in China. We wanted to photograph the operator with the yarns in his hand as he passed them over the twisting-stand in order to attach the spindles. Unfortunately he refused to be photographed and we were forced to fasten the yarns to the reel stand to prevent them from sagging. The hank reel is not in operation in this picture. Fig. 260 shows the twisting-stand with the spindles as they should be, i.e., six brass-whorled spindles suspended over the twisting-frame, one at each end of each yarn group. Now finally the actual twisting can begin. The cotton twister takes hold of the two boards shown in Fig. 261 by their handles, places the rod of the spindle suspended on the extreme left of the stand between the leather-lined surfaces of the boards, and pushes the boards rapidly in opposite directions and thus making the spindle spin around at a lively rate. Then he starts the next spindle spinning and so on one after another until they are all going. He watches the motion carefully and whenever the spindles slacken in their speed he imparts a new impetus to them with his boards. As the threads twist tighter and tighter they get shorter and the spindles approach gradually the horizontal top bar of the stand. To lower them again so as to keep them effectively spinning, the workman now takes the stand and moves it about a foot farther up the alley. After having kept up the twisting for about ten or fifteen minutes, and having through the successive forward moves of the stand progressed up the alley about twenty feet, the twisting of the yarns into three-ply threads, each now somewhat less than 200 yards long, has been accomplished. Then they can be wound into hanks and replaced by another set of untwisted yarn groups. In doing this the three spindles on the left of

Fig. 256. Reel Stand and Hank Reels for Spooling Cotton Threads.

Fig. 257. Spool Reel Unmounted.

the stand are detached and the loose ends tied to the ends of the untwisted strings on the reels. The other three spindles on the right of the stand are also detached from the twisted threads which are led to a large reel, like the one in Fig. 262, which we shall call a hank reel, upon which they are to be wound in three separate hanks. The handle of the hank reel is now turned and the three twisted three-ply threads are wound onto it, dragging the three untwisted yarn groups into place over the supports the whole length of the alley and return. The turning of the reel is kept up until the knots uniting the twisted threads with the untwisted yarns come back from their trip up and down the alley. Then the whole process starts over again, the ends of the untwisted yarn groups are fastened to the spindles and the twisting can be resumed.

Fig. 261 shows three of the spindles used in the twisting process. They are about 4½ inches long. A brass knob, one inch in diameter, serving as a whorl, is cast around a steel pin. The pin has a notch near the end to keep the filaments fastened to it from slipping off. The two leather-faced twisting boards, with which the thread maker causes the brass spindles to revolve are shown at the bottom of the picture. The brush-shaped boards are fashioned out of one piece of teak wood and their lower surface is covered with leather which is held in place by two wooden nails at each end. The length is 10½ inches, the thickness of the board exclusive of the handle ⅜ of an inch. It is 2 inches wide at one end and 1½ inches at the other. The holes in the handles serve no purpose we were told, they may have been made by one of the workman to tie the boards together when not in use. The leather surface is smeared over with thick bean oil, the sediment of the freshly expressed oil of the *Glycine Hispida,* the Chinese soy bean.

As we have said we meant in Fig. 259 to show the cotton twister at work using his brush-shaped boards to set the spindles going, but our purpose and point of view did not appeal to him. So we took the picture without him. The twisting process we "staged" in our garden, and the reader has to imagine the cotton twister standing in front of the wooden frame shown in Fig. 260, with the brush-shaped boards in his hands keeping the suspended spindles spinning around at top speed.

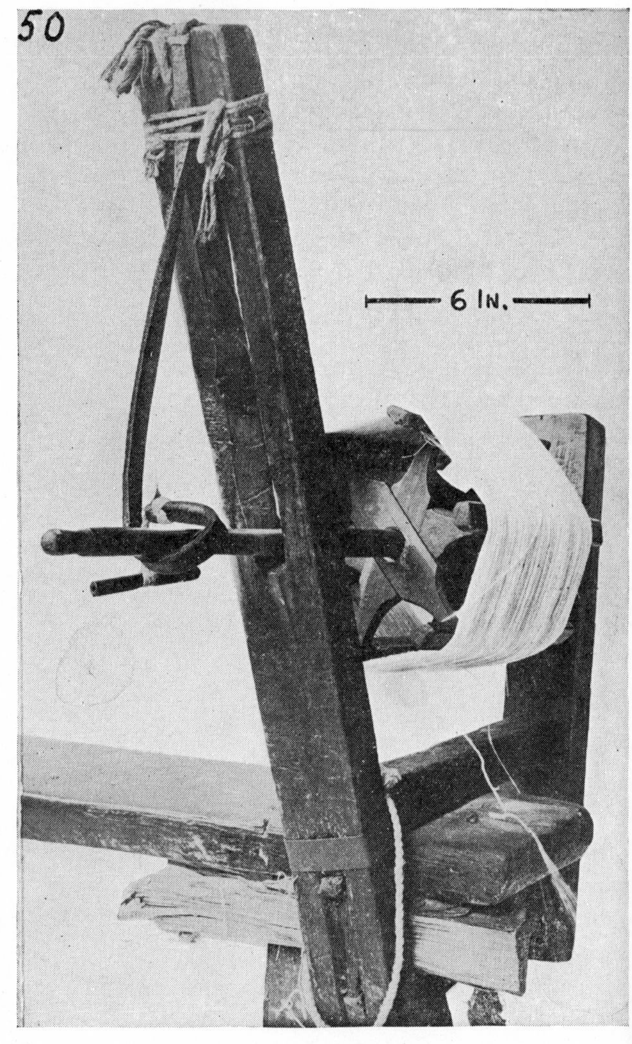

Fig. 258. Spool Reel for Spooling Cotton Thread.

Fig. 262 gives a view of the crank-turned hank reel. It is quite a substantial, well-built affair compared with the other parts of the outfit. The height of the stand is 22 inches, its width 15 inches. On top of the uprights are slots in which rests the wheel with its iron bearing-rods at each end of the wooden axle. One of the rods is bent to form a crank for turning the wheel. The diameter of the wheel is 19 inches.

Fig. 259. Cotton Thread Twisting.

The whole apparatus, Figs. 256 to 262, can also be used for twisting silk, but in that case smaller spindles are used, about 3½ inches long with a brass whorl ¾ inch in diameter. The photographs were taken in the native city of Shanghai, Kiangsu province.

The Chinese names given me for these different implements are mostly vaguely descriptive and not at all specific or scientific terms which would be worth recording. Of interest, however, is the name for the brush-shaped board called *chang pan,* meaning palm board, denoting that boards are used for imparting motion to the spindle instead of the palms of the hands, as in primitive spinning without a wheel.

WEAVING

Fig. 263 gives a picture of a type of loom, shown again in Fig. 264 from the opposite side, found extensively all over China, in the homes of the peasants, who weave their own goods from homespun yarn as our forefathers did. The construction follows very closely the European hand loom. There is the warp-beam over which the loose parallel strings of the warp are wound. Parallel to the warp-beam, bamboo rods are placed between the layers to keep the warp yarns in their proper relative positions. The warp is then guided downward, glides under a horizontal beam and passes thence to the front part of the loom. Just after the warp emerges from under the horizontal beam there is a wooden rod inserted which divides the warp into two layers, in such a way that one yarn passes under it and the next over it, for the whole width of the warp.

The harness is a rather complex affair consisting of a see-saw arrangement overhead, four cords extending down to the heddles, the heddles themselves and underneath two treadles connected by cords to the bottom of the heddles. The heddles are a system of vertical strings with a loop in the center. The warp passes through their loops. One heddle moves the even numbered yarns and the other the odd numbered ones. By pressing upon one of the treadles with the foot the one heddle is raised and the other lowered causing the two separate layers of the warp to cross

FIG. 260. TWISTING STAND FOR TWISTING COTTON THREAD.

of the warp-yarns it is fastened at each end to a bamboo rod which is seen in Figs. 263 and 264, passing to a movable frame at the back of the loom. Beyond the heddles and the reed, i.e., after passing them, the warp changes its character by the process of weaving, i.e., the interlaced crossing of one row of yarns upon another, and passes as the web or woven fabric to a wooden cylinder at the front end of the loom, around which it is wound. It is kept tight by a wooden stick, seen in Fig. 264, which rests in a hole in the beam on the right side of the loom. This wooden stick serves as a lever, with it the fabric is stretched taut when the stick is braced against one of several pegs set in the inner side of the long horizontal wooden base beam of the loom frame. Another contrivance must be mentioned which keeps the fabric stretched widthwise so that it can be wound evenly. It is called a temple and can be seen in Fig. 263, lying on the fabric in its proper position. Each rod has each other like jaws which open and shut thus forming the so called "sheds" for the passage of the shuttle. A similar "shed" is formed by pressing the second treadle, the action being, of course, exactly the reverse of the first. This type of weaving, i.e., where the weft crosses the warp alternately, is the simplest form.

Next comes the reed, namely two horizontal bars one above the warp the other below held in their relative position, about four inches one above the other, by very thin, smooth, parallel bamboo slips, close set like the teeth of a comb. Each of the warp yarns passes through one of the spaces between these bamboo slips. The reed is suspended from two ropes passing to the superstructure of the loom, and to keep it at right angles to the direction

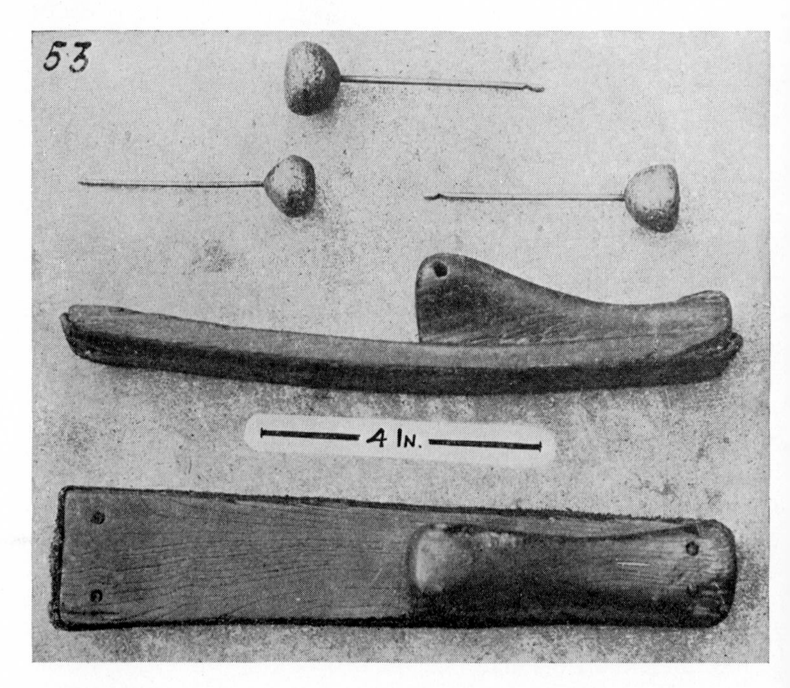

FIG. 261. SPINDLES FOR TWISTING COTTON THREAD AND TWISTING BOARDS.

two pin-points at one end and these are pushed into the opposite selvages of the fabric. In the center of each rod is a hole and on each side of the hole three wooden pegs. One of the pegs of the lower rod is fitted into the hole in the upper rod, the peg selected depending upon the width of the fabric. The pin-ends are kept as nearly opposite as possible. The rods cross each other and are kept from sliding from their relative position by a string tied to both rods at one end. For a narrower or wider fabric this stretcher can be shortened or lengthened by selecting another peg of the lower rod and fitting it into the hole of the upper. The rods are, of course, interchangeable.

With the essential features of the low-warp loom in mind, the process of weaving can be better understood. One of the two treadles is pushed down with the foot, and this pulls down one of the heddles to which it is attached, and at the same time lifts up the other heddle by means of the sea-saw gear fastened to the upper structure of the loom, the combined arrangement being called the harness. The reed is kept close to the heddles by the backward pull of the connecting framework at the rear of the loom, and between the reed and the already woven fabric a shed is opened through which the weaver throws the shuttle bearing the weft yarn. The weaver, usually a woman, sits upon the board in front of the wound fabric, catches the shuttle as it emerges from the other end of the shed, holds it and by grasping the upper horizontal bar of the reed at its center pulls it toward the woven cloth, in order to drive home the cross yarn of the weft just left by the shuttle. Then the reed, let go, falls back against the heddles, and the weaver pushes down the other treadle which, by again lifting one heddle and depressing its fellow, opens the other, alternate shed. Thereupon she throws the shuttle through the shed again, catching it at the other end. In this manner, by throwing the shuttle back and forth, the fabric is woven, and, at intervals, wound upon the beam in front, but not before a like amount of loose warp yarns has been released from the warp-beam at the further end of the loom.

The warp-beam is turned by four arms radiating at right angles from each of its ends, and is kept from turning by a wooden horizontal stop-bar set against the radiating arms. This bar is inserted in the slots of the cross-bars mortised into the two upright side posts of the loom. These cross-bars are extensions of the bar in which the ends of the warp-beam revolve. Fig. 263, which by the way is not the same loom as the one shown in Fig. 264, represents a somewhat different arrangement for holding the warp-beam by its radiating arms. The horizontal bar rests on separate wooden props mortised into the uprights of the loom. Looking at this picture it might confuse the careful student to see that the radiating arms are not in contact with this bar as according to the description they ought to be. In this loom to keep the warp tight a wooden lever resting in a slot of the farther upright intercepts one radial arm before the bar is reached. This is an exceptional feature, more or less a makeshift, not usually seen on these looms.

FIG. 262. HANK REEL FOR WINDING UP FRESHLY TWISTED COTTON THREAD.

The two looms, Figs. 263 and 264, were photographed in Chekiang province, 264 at Cha Tsuen, and 263 at Se Aw.

The shuttle for the low-warp loom is shown in Fig. 265. It is carved of wood and both ends are bound by a strip of brass. The boat-shaped cavity contains the bobbin from which the yarn unwinds. The bobbin is formed of a hollow bamboo tube which easily revolves upon a thin flexible bamboo rod, the ends of which are bent to be inserted into holes at each end of the shuttle cavity. The yarn from the bobbin passes through either one of two holes in the sidewalls of the cavity. The whole length of the shuttle is 9¾ inches.

In order to pass the yarn from the spool through the hole in the side wall of the shuttle, it is laid across the hole from the inside and pulled through with a sharp sucking motion of the lips. This was formerly also practiced in Europe and called "shuttle kissing."

The loom with two heddles is suitable only for plain weaving, the simplest of the three fundamental weaving processes. Twills can be woven on it by increasing the heddles, and I have seen such looms, used by professional weavers. These very often have an additional feature, the fly-shuttle, apparently a foreign introduction. The fly-shuttle, an automatic arrangement for throwing back and forth the shuttle was patented to John Kay of Bury, a manufacturing borough in Lancashire, England (English patent No. 542 of 26th May, 1733).

Sometimes two shuttles are used for weaving striped or checkered goods. The shuttle with the colored yarn is alternated as required with the shuttle containing the plain yarn. When either of the shuttles is at rest it is placed in such a way that its yarn runs along the selvage parallel to the warp yarn. By passing the shuttle in use over the idle yarn the latter is incorporated into selvage.

The memory of the high-warp loom has not yet passed out of Europe, and if I am informed correctly such looms are still used in Scandinavian countries for tapestry.[4] In China such a loom is used for making rush-matting. Fig. 266 shows a specimen from Chekiang which I photographed at Sin Tseang, near Ningpo. The warp is stretched out vertically between the two horizontal beams of the rectangular frame.

FIG. 263. CHINESE LOW-WARP LOOM.

[4] In Worsaae, Afbildninger fra det K. Museum for Nortiske Oldsager, Copenhagen, 1854, a picture is given of an upright loom as used then on the island of Faroe.

The perforated board suspended from the upper beam takes the place of the heddles. The word "heald," vaguely described in the dictionary as harness-shaft, is probably the name of such a board. At any rate our forefathers in the 18th century were well acquainted with this perforated board which was part of their old ribbon loom and they surely must have had a name for it, to distinguish it from the composite string arrangement of heddles. This Chinese "heald," as I shall call it, has a row of parallel grooves, incising but not penetrating the board. At the deepest part of each groove is a hole which passes entirely through the thickness of the board. The space between the grooves is also bored with a hole which comes out in a corresponding groove on the other side. If the board is reversed, we have the same aspect, every space with a hole is followed by a perforated groove.

Fig. 264. Chinese Low-Warp Loom.

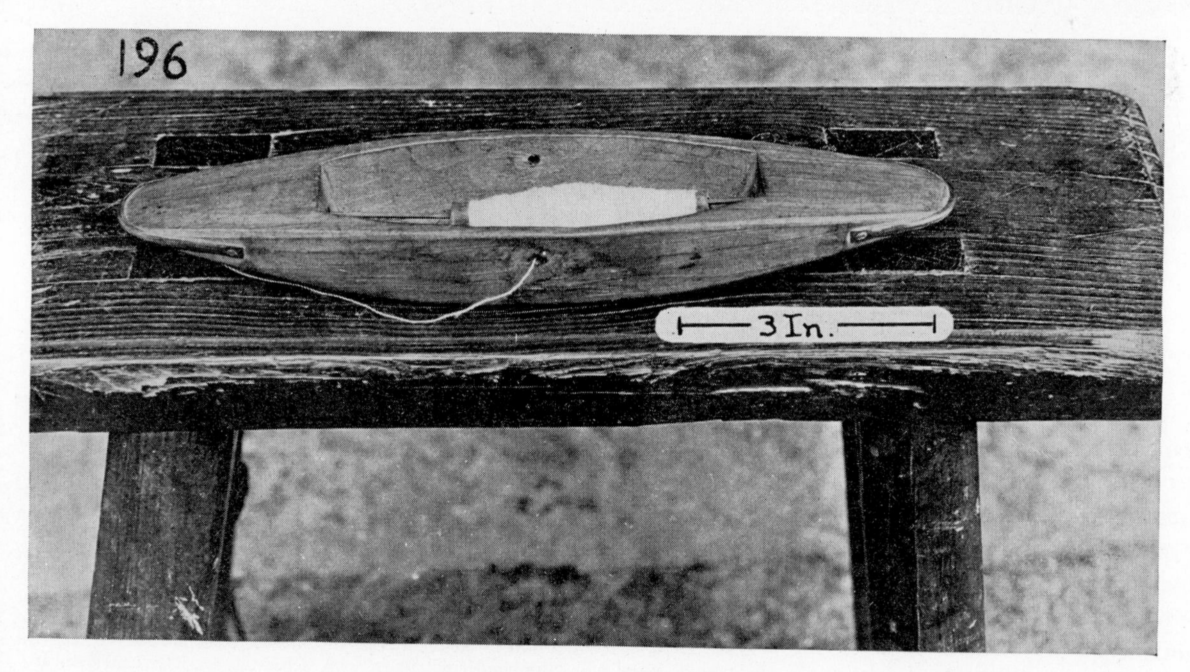

Fig. 265. Shuttle for Low-Warp Loom.

We see then, no matter from which side we look at the board that each groove has at its deepest part a round hole, and each space between the grooves a hole leading into a groove on the opposite side. The heald shown in Fig. 266 is an old one, the central row of holes from long usage had become too large, and the economic user instead of discarding it added a new row of holes and then again after the latter had served their usefulness, a third row. Not counting these mendings there were 120 openings in the new heald, and through these the hempen warp strings are passed. Each warp string starting from the upper horizontal beam passes downward through the heald to the lower beam, around or rather under it and then upward to the upward beam where it is tied to the starting point of the string. For a matting about 3 feet wide about a hundred warp strings are stretched over the horizontal beams in this manner. The heald is no longer suspended from ropes as shown in the picture, but is held by friction against the warp strings. The weaving is commenced close to the lower horizontal beam. The heald is manipulated by the wooden handles. By pushing the handles downward each string, entering on its downward path a groove, is pushed backward and each alternate string entering a space hole will be bent forward and thus a shed is formed immediately under the heald for the passage of the weft. To reverse the order it is only necessary to push the handles of the heald upward; then the readjusted warp strings again cross each other and form the alternate shed. Another important feature is that the heald serves the same purpose as and obviates the use of a reed. Each time a rush has been inserted across the shed to form the weft, the heald is taken by the handles, held horizontally and pushed down to drive home the weft. The inserting of the weft rushes is done with a long bamboo rod which has at its extremity a slot, into which the end of the rush is laid. This rod, about 4½ feet long is seen standing at the right of the loom and from this side the rushes are inserted. The whole process is slow. The rushes extending on each side of the warp, must be bent over and plaited into the warp strings, after each stroke, to form a selvage. The weaver, usually a woman or child, sits or stands in front of the loom and has an assistant who inserts the weft. As the fabric grows it

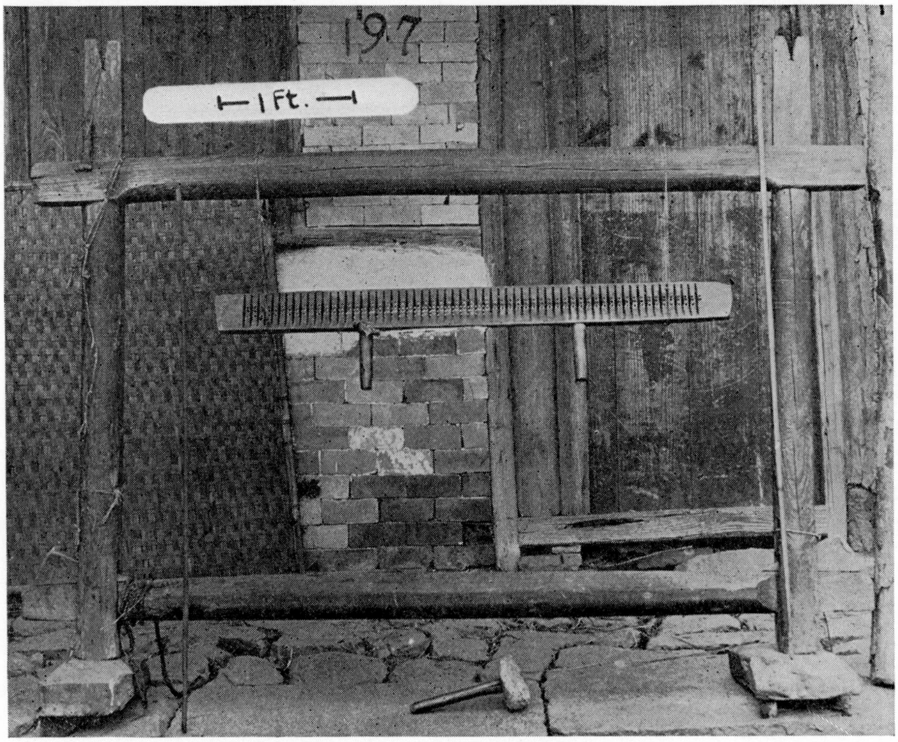

Fig. 266. Chinese High-Warp Loom.

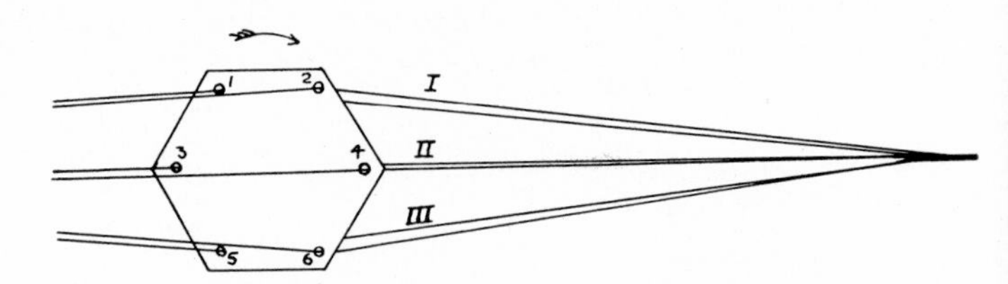

Fig. 267. Sketch for Figure Weaving on Belts. Sketch showing forming of sheds between warp yarns by means of a cardboard disk. For each six yarns there is one disk. The yarns pass through holes in the corners of the hexagonal disk and as the disk gets turned by hand, so that a fresh flat edge is on top, the arrangement of the yarns is changed. Now the layers of the warp correspond *I* to yarns 1, 2, *II* to yarns 3, 4, *III* to yarns 5, 6, but if a turn to the right is given different sheds are formed, and the layers will correspond *I* to 3, 1, *II* to 5, 2, *III* to 6, 4. This arrangement is used for figure weaving on belts combined with a purse which the Chinese use to keep their trousers in place and their pennies together.

has to be shifted periodically to the back of the frame. To do this the wedges at each end of the lower horizontal beam are loosened, the fabric is shifted, and, with the stone-hammer seen lying under the middle of the loom, the wedges are driven home again, which tightens the warp strings. A matting about 6 feet long can be made on this loom. When it is finished the fabric reaches from the top down in front to the lower beam, around it and up the back side. The warp strings are then untied and what is left of them used to secure the ends of the matting from unraveling.

From what we see now and then of the gorgeous garments which were worn by officials up to the revolution, we can testify to the perfection to which brocade and tapestry weaving had attained in China. Brocade weaving is done on a loom where all the warp yarns are connected to strings leading to a framework over the loom. Here on this framework sits enthroned the "heddle-boy" who is in charge of the array of strings and has the task of arranging the warp yarns after each shot of the shuttle so as to form the most intricate patterns. Three inches of warp length per day is a good average of such toilsome weaving.

Of the tapestry work done in China the so called *K'o Szu* is highly prized. Pieces which I inspected show that very fine silken warp yarns are stretched out in one way or another and that the weft is worked in with various colored silk yarns, depicting scenes and landscapes. The work is a combination of needle craft and painting. Some of the more intricate details, such as clouds and waves, folds of garments, contours of flowers and animals are painted with the brush.

The primitiveness of the high-warp loom is surpassed by another method of weaving where the warp is stretched out between two posts rammed into the ground. In Tatung, Anhwei province, I passed a place where wide cotton belts were made in this manner. The worker sits beside an array of parallel yarns, and pushes a spool of cotton instead of a shuttle, back and forth. There is a reed with three warp yarns passing through each interstice. The warp is divided into three layers, two of which can be shifted by a heddle. There are therefore two heddles and from the horizontal bars of these a rope passes to a pedal by means of which different sheds can be formed for passage of the woof yarn. The pedal is merely a slanting wooden stick, one end of which rests on the ground and the other holds the rope descending from the heddles.

Another loom, with the warp similarly stretched between two posts driven into the ground, has an ingenious shifting arrangement for forming different sheds in figure weaving. Six-cornered paste-board disks are used, measuring about 3 inches across with a hole in each corner. Through each of the six holes passes one yarn. The disks, one for six warp yarns, are held in a position parallel to the warp yarn so that one of the flat edges shows on top. Fig. 267 shows six warp yarns divided by means of a disk into three layers forming two sheds. If the disk is now turned (following the arrow) so that the next flat edge shows on top, the layers will have shifted so that layer *I* is composed of yarns 3 and 1, *II* of 5 and 2, and *III* of 6 and 4. By thus shifting the disks the following six combinations can be made:

Fig. 268. Ribbon Loom.

I 1,2 3,1 5,3 6,5 4,6 2,4
II 3,4 5,2 6,1 4,3 2,5 1,6
III 5,6 6,4 4,2 2,1 1,3 3,5

To form symmetrical patterns, for instance a meander, the worker gets his effects by arranging the disks in different positions and in this way is able to produce areas with figured surfaces. The shifting of the disks appears intricate, but the weavers I saw did it rapidly and wove belts with damask-like patterns. The observations were made in Tatung, Anhwei province, but unfortunately the hostile attitude of the people prevented the taking of photographs.

Fig. 269. Chinese Ribbon Loom at Close View.

RIBBON LOOM

In the country districts of China ribbons are still made in a very primitive way. Fig. 268 gives us a cheerful view of a peasant girl who, in between heavy work on the farm, weaves a few inches now and then on her primitive loom, and keeps well abreast of the demand without having to worry about overhead, competition, overproduction, or other industrial ills.

The construction of the loom is extremely simple, in fact it consists merely of a heald and a shuttle. The rest of the loom is improvised with a wooden bench and a rice measure, and you have the loom complete. Fig. 269 gives a closer view of the outfit, and we see from it that enough warp is unwound from the warp-string ball on the wooden stick to reach around the bench, over the rice measure, and leave free a stretch for conveniently carrying out the actual process of weaving. The sheds are formed by alternately raising and lowering the heald and the curiously formed shuttle is pushed back and forth to form the weft. A reed or spatha is not necessary, the shuttle is used for driving home each course of the weft. The heald is a wooden frame with bamboo slats each of which has a hole in the center. The 13 warp yarns pass through the frame in such manner that seven traverse the holes in the slats, one through each hole, and six go through spaces between the slats, also one through each space. The forming of sheds is thereby made easy by alternately lifting up and pressing down the heald.

From the closer view of the ribbon loom pictured in Fig. 269 we see that the warp is tied at the right of the bench to the end of the newly woven ribbon to establish the necessary tension. As in the process the ribbon grows in length, it is pushed downward over the edge of the bench. The closed circuit of warp and ribbon is from time to time untied to wind into a ball the stretch of woven ribbon and thus get it out of the way. An equal amount of warp must naturally be unwound from the warpstick and the warp is tied again to the ribbon a few inches from the point where the weaving stopped. The circuit around the bench is thus re-established and the weaving may be resumed once more.

Fig. 270. Tape Loom.

The essential parts of this loom were acquired for the Mercer Museum at a small place in the mountains, called Sung Yan, Chekiang province, and the pictures were taken to illustrate their use.

Comparing the Chinese ribbon or tape looms with the European types we find that the latter had also as an indispensable part a heald which however was much heavier and could therefore not dangle on the warp to be pushed up and down. The European process of weaving was therefore different, the loom was held between the knees of the weaver or when connected with a wooden box, was likewise necessarily stationary, and the sheds were in either case formed by lifting and lowering the warp by means of heddles.

The tape or ribbon loom just described was for household use, Fig. 270, shows a similar loom used by a rag dealer which is in constant use to produce tape for sale or rather barter.

This barter is an interesting feature of Chinese economic life, and I shall give a short account of it before proceeding to the description of the loom. In China nothing goes to waste, and many articles comprehended under the term junk, of such little account that no monetary value can be assigned to them, are obtained by the junk dealers in exchange for tape or candy. The women of the household carefully put aside all materials, which may interest the itinerant junk dealers, and the articles to be given in exchange are therefore designed to appeal to feminine taste. The ragman comes around with tape by the yard, and the dealer in old iron, brass, bones, etc., usually carries with him a batch of hard candy, of which he chisels off chips in varying proportions, according to the value of the articles traded in.

The loom referred to belonged to a ragman in Lingkiang, Kiangsi province, and I was able to persuade him to carry it to a convenient place for photographing. With the Chinese everything goes slowly, first I was given an old loom, Fig. 270, and finally the woman worker could be persuaded to come to the mission compound with her loom and pose to show the way it is worked, Figs. 271 and 273.

Fig. 271. Tape Loom at Work.

The loom proper, as shown in Fig. 270, is a jointed framework with two upright ends, one 14¾ inches high and the other 12 inches. The higher one carries the arrangement for shifting the sheds. The warp strings as shown in Fig. 271, are wound upon a wooden rod which is suspended under the bench. A working length is unwound, led to the end of the wooden pole which is fastened to the bench, there passes through an iron ring and thence is trained back to the smaller wooden frame. One half of the warp yarns pass through the lower perforated wooden cross strip in that frame and the other half through the upper perforated cross strip, thence the two trains pass to the rigging in the higher upright frame where by means of a pedal the two sheds can alternately be formed. It becomes clear by consulting the picture and the sketch, Fig. 272, that by that means a wide shed is formed and the shuttle, a short bamboo stick with the woof yarn wound upon it, can easily and rapidly be pushed through the sheds alternately formed by the pedal. The warp then becomes woven tape, and as such passes around a vertical peg seen at the right end of the bench. The warp as it comes from the stored roll under the bench is tied to the woven tape to give tension which is necessary to weaving. There is thus formed a circuit which is movable around the peg at the end of the bench and through the ring at the pole extending from the other end of the bench. As weaving progresses the woven part of the circuit is periodically pushed away from the harness, and before the knot, which ties warp to tape, gets beyond the reach of the sitting weaver, the tape is untied from the circuit, wound upon a ball and some more unwoven warp unwound, and in place of the woven tape incorporated with a new knot in the circuit. The operator sits beside the loom and handles the shuttle with the left hand. With the right hand she holds a wooden knife or spatha and drives home each layer of woof yarn. The product is a tape of 24 warp yarns arranged in such a manner that each half of the warp contains five double yarns with a single yarn at each selvage edge. The finished tape is dyed red and becomes then a desirable article which the women use to tie up their stockings or the bandages of their crippled feet. The photographs were taken in Lingkiang, Kiangsi province.

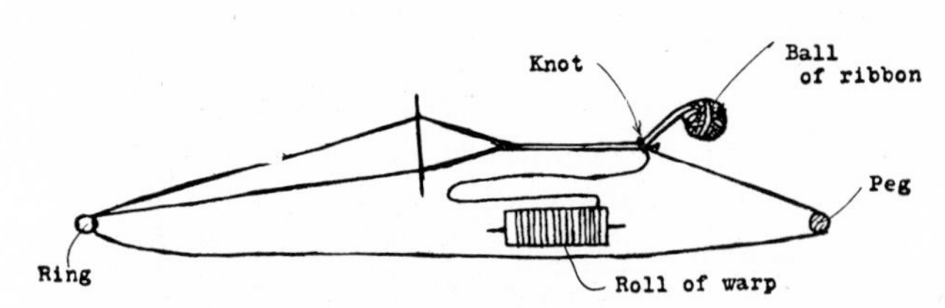

Fig. 272. Diagram to Show the Circuit of the Chinese Tape Loom.

FIG. 273. CHINESE TAPE LOOM. A close view of the same tape loom seen in Fig. 271 is here shown.

FIG. 274. DYER'S SCAFFOLD FOR DRYING ONE-COLOR DYED CLOTH.

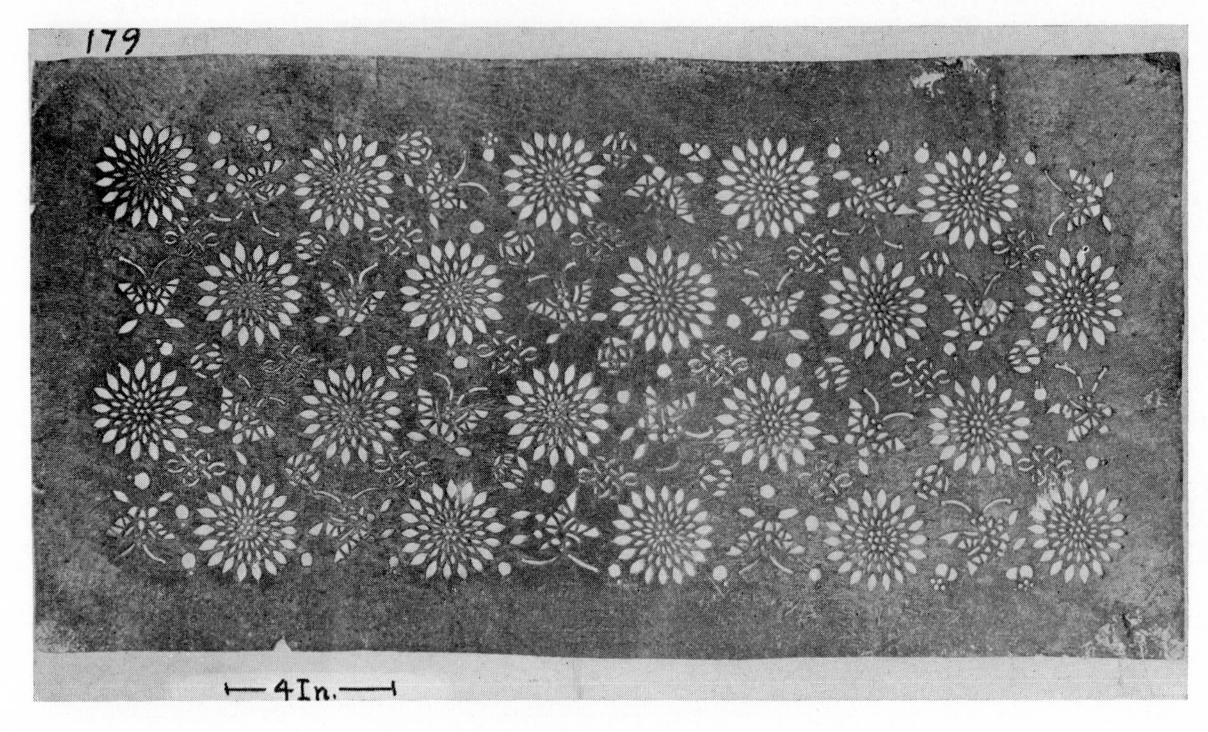

Fig. 275. Stencil for Dyeing Cloth.

DYEING

Fig. 274 gives a view of a dyeing establishment at Nanchang, the capital of Kiangsi province. These places are conspicuous on account of the high scaffolds upon which the goods of uniform color are hung up for drying after having been wrung out by hand. For putting the cloth upon the scaffolding a long stick with a crosspiece on top is used, an exaggerated T-square. In the front of the picture the ground is littered with garments which have been redyed and which after drying are ready for wear once more. A few vats can be seen made of glazed earthenware. The dyeing with more delicate colors is carried on inside the sheds. The majority of dyes used by the Chinese were of vegetable origin. Of minerals sulphite of iron is used for a black dye, and cinnabar for a beautiful vermillion. Alum is also used extensively in connection with dyeing, probably as a mordant, to make the dye adhere to the material.

The dyeing of cloth in China is an industry which is very hard to investigate. Of old the dyers kept strict secrecy about the various dyes they used and the methods of compounding, and while now these have been mostly supplanted by foreign dyes, the Chinese dyers still by force of habit keep the same secrecy. It is therefore of only one phase of the industry that I can report at this time in detail, but this is a highly interesting one. I refer to the making of cloth which shows a stencilled design in white on a background of dyed blue.

A stencil, Fig. 275, is the first requisite. It is made of oiled paper, and is 28 inches long and 14½ inches wide. The stencil is laid upon the cloth which is usually 17 to 18 inches wide. A thin lime mortar is then brushed over the stencil, and on removal of the stencil the pattern is left on the goods. With this white crust of raised pattern, the cloth is hung up to dry. It is a beautiful sight to see fold upon fold of a whole cloth hanging on bamboo sticks with the white design clearly standing out upon the cream-colored cotton cloth. After the lime upon the cloth is dry, the material is ready to be dipped into the vat for dyeing. I never saw any other color but blue used for dyeing such stencilled material. The purpose of applying the designs through a stencil is to cover these ornamental areas against the influence of the dye. The covered areas "resist" the action of the dye and this process is therefore called Resist Process of Dyeing.

The procedure with the stencilled cloth is necessarily somewhat different from the dyeing of one-color cloth. In every stage of handling, care must be taken not to break the crust of lime. After dipping this cloth in the vat it can not be wrung out. The dyer lets the dye drip off and then the whole cloth bolt is taken to a grass plot, spread out upon the ground and left exposed to the sun. After it is thoroughly dried, it is taken up by the workers (see Fig. 276), and scraped off with long knives which are shown in Fig. 277. These knives were photographed on the cloth to be scraped. They are made of iron with wooden handles. The lower knife is 22 inches long and the upper one 20 inches. Their edges are fairly sharp. After the scraping the cloth is still full of lime which has penetrated the fibres. The dyer does not bother about that but leaves the task of removing it by laundering, to the prospective purchaser of the goods. What he will still do for him, however, is to calender the material. The outfit for this process is shown in Fig. 278.

CALENDERING

There are three essential parts requisite for the process of calendering freshly stencilled or one-color dyed fabrics: a stone base plate, a wooden roller and a peculiarly fashioned heavy stone which is placed upon the roller to move it back and forth upon the base plate. They can all three be seen in Fig. 278. The heavy notched stone, shown tilted on its side, is 29 inches high, 2 feet wide at the flat bottom and 13 inches deep. Enough is seen of the base plate to perceive that its upper surface is concaved into a flat trough-like hollow, in which the roller of very hard wood can freely roll back and forth. The roller is 20 inches long and 3½ inches in diameter. A few feet of the cloth are laid under the roller on this curved base plate, brought over the roller and folded over on the side where the rest of the cloth bolt is lying. Then the heavy notched stone is tilted upon the roller so as to move the latter back and forth until the strip of cloth under pressure shows the desired gloss. The apparatus is operated by a bare-footed worker who jumps on top of the stone and with one foot on each of its horns dexterously does the tilting. To keep his balance he holds on to a horizontal bar fastened at a proper distance over the stone. It is really remarkable to see with what ease the worker pedipulates this heavy stone. Fold upon fold is thus fed under and over the roller until the whole bolt has been calendered. Each time a new part is ready to be shifted in, the worker tilts the stone on its side and rearranges the cloth. The pictures Fig. 275 to 278, illustrating dyeing and calendering were taken at a dyeing establishment in Chang-shu, Kiangsi province.

WASHING CLOTHES

Not only have I often seen Chinese women use a washboard, and that in regions where there was no sign of foreign influence in any of the activities of the people, but I have been generally assured that the

Fig. 276. Dyers Drying and Scraping Stencilled Cloth.

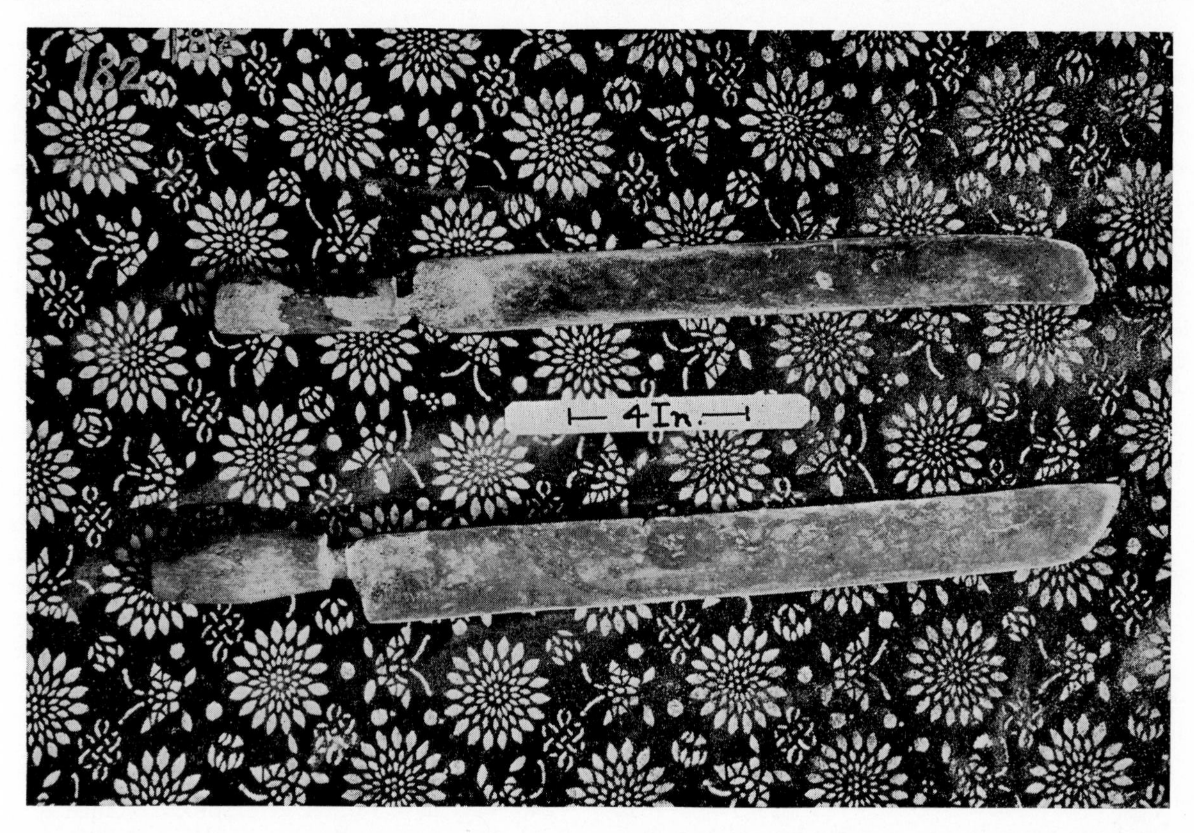

Fig. 277. Dyer's Knives for Scraping Stencilled Fabrics.

washboard is an age-old contrivance in the Chinese household. Its similarity to our type of washboard, in its horizontal, parallel grooves made me hesitate to accept it as a typical Chinese contrivance, until I saw in northern and central Kiangsi the type shown in Fig. 279. If the Chinese had adopted it from a foreign model, they surely would not have modified it to such an extent as the washboard here pictured, which with its crossed grooves, so noticeably deviates from the ordinary board with horizontal grooves. The fact seems to be that the washboard was introduced into America by Chinese laundrymen, and there improved, until it received its present form with corrugated metal insert. To Europe it came apparently from America. In Germany it is styled "amerikanisches Waschbrett."

The board is of hard wood 10½ inches wide, 3 feet 3 inches long, and ⅞ of an inch thick. The grooves are crudely cut crossing each other forming lozenge-shaped fields. The back side of the board is smooth. When not in use it is hung up against the wall upon a peg which passes through the square hole on the upper part of the board.

When using the board, it is placed slantingly in a wooden tub, the upper part resting against the rim of the tub, in very much the same way as we would use it. The clothing to be washed is soaked in cold water and vigorously rubbed against the board. While soap has now been introduced extensively, it is mainly used for personal use. It is too expensive to use for the family washing. In many parts of China a native soap is utilized, which is made from the pods of the soap-tree, *Gymnocladus Chinensis,* not unlike our Kentucky coffee tree. This is a large leguminous tree growing in central China. The reddish-brown pods, 3 to 4 inches long, are roasted and pounded into a pulp which is then kneaded into balls about 2 inches in diameter. These balls are then used like soap. Because of its unpleasant odor this soap is prohibited in public baths.

Washing with a washboard is a process used mainly about the house for clothing of better material. The ordinary washing is done without soap or board right at the river, brook, pond or whatever body of water is at hand. The water's edge, where the washing is to be done, is usually lined with large stones and on these the folded wet clothing is laid and vigorously beaten with a wooden bat. The washboard was photographed at Changshu, Kiangsi province.

Fig. 280 presents a typical example of one of the washing bats, fashioned out of one solid piece of hard wood. It was photographed at Se Aw, Chekiang province. Its length is 1½ feet and the diameter of its heavy end, above the handle, 3½ inches. After beating the clothing is rinsed in water, wrung out and beaten again. This process is repeated a few times until the woman judges the task completed. Much talking takes place when the women gather and thus work over the family washing, and many a time the garments get more beating than they deserve. After a final wringing the clothes are carried home to be hung up over bamboo poles or along the fence. Clothes pins and clothes lines are not known in inland China. In rare cases I saw a line made up of two separate ropes twisted together. In such cases no pins are used to fasten the garments, as one might assume. The line is stretched taut, the two twisted ropes pried apart wide enough to insert an end of the garment which is then held firmly between the rope twists. In taking off the garments the laundryman pulls, not too gingerly, and the foreigner wonders sometimes why a piece has been torn from his shirt or underwear, at places where he least suspected it.

Fig. 281 shows an ordinary wash tub. The women using it crouch down in front of it with bent knees. The handles are a part of the staves. The bottom rests in the usual croze-cut groove familiar in western tubs, but in this case caulked with a putty made of air-slaked lime and Chinese wood-oil. The height of the tub is 8 inches, the diameter is 22 inches, the thickness of the staves ¾ of an inch. The hoops are made of twisted bamboo strips.

IRONING

We might be led to think that the laundry business is a highly developed art in China but would be wrong if we did so. The Chinese who know anything about our methods of laundering live in the United States where, no doubt, they acquired their knowledge. In China where the methods of laundering are most primitive, ironing has no part, besides there are no establishments to take care of the family washing.

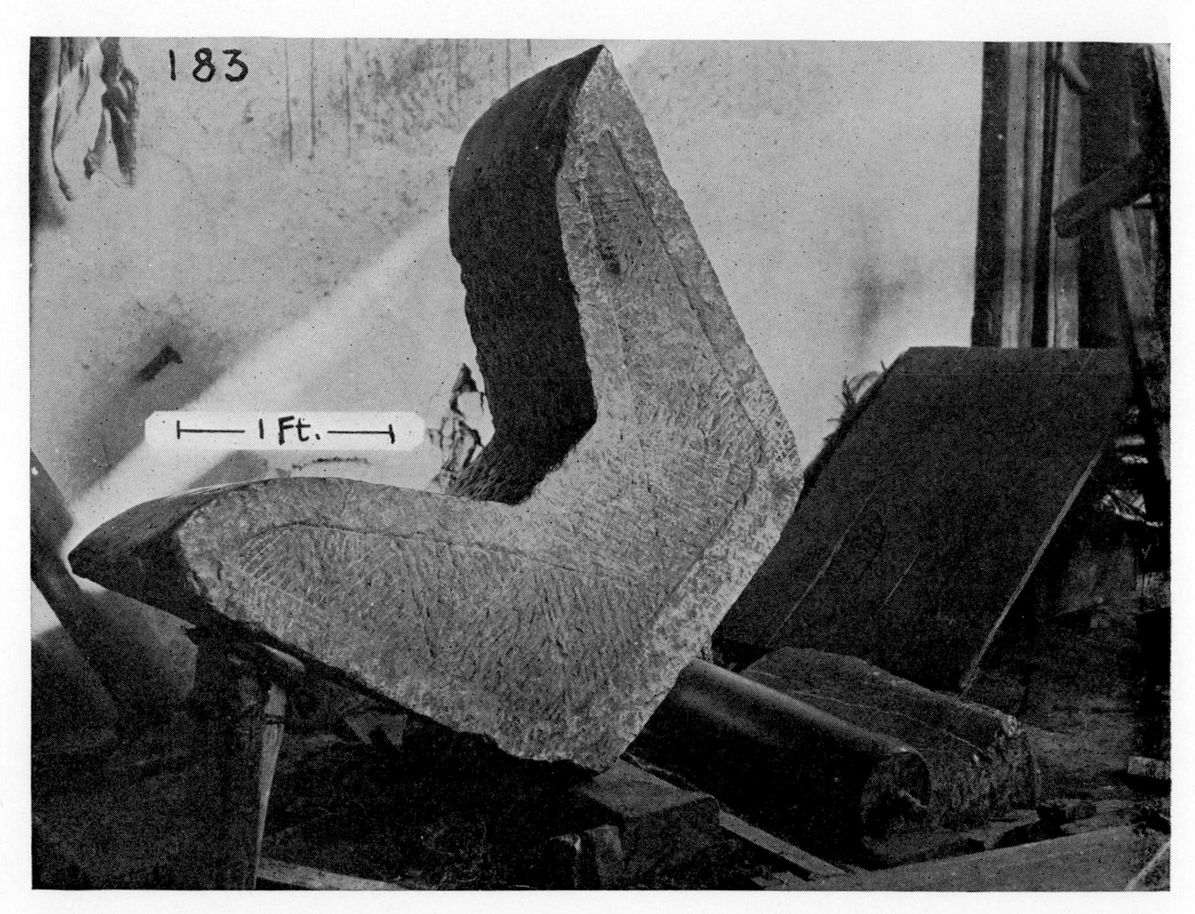

FIG. 278. DYER'S ROCKING-STONE AND ROLLER FOR CALENDERING FABRICS.

The women of the clan-household attend to that. The flat-iron which we associate with the laundry is well known to the Chinese tailor, but once a garment has left his hands, it will never again come in contact

Fig. 279. Washboard.

with the flat-iron, except it be once more entrusted to his care for repairs or alteration.

The flat-iron pictured in Fig. 282, is the kind used by the professional tailor, whether at his establishment, or at the homes into which he is called to work by the day. He uses it to flatten seams and smooth the material from creases due to handling. The bowl to receive the charcoal with a socket for a handle is cast of bronze in one piece. The outside of the bowl is usually decorated with scrolls of flowers cast in low relief. The bottom surface on which it stands that is the flat-iron proper is highly polished, and kept so by constant use. The shape of the bowl is elliptical at the bottom measuring 4 inches the long way and 3 inches the short way. The specimen was photographed at the Native City of Shanghai.

In the mountain regions of Chekiang, we saw another kind of flat-iron used for the same purpose. Two of these are shown in Fig. 283. The iron part is forged by the blacksmith. The triangular part is smooth on its under side, namely the surface which is applied to press down seams, etc. Both irons are of about the same dimensions. The thickness of the triangular, lancet-shaped part is $\frac{1}{4}$ of an inch, and the two longer sides are $2\frac{3}{4}$ inches long, the shorter side $1\frac{1}{2}$ inches long. To heat this iron the triangular part is put into hot embers of the kitchen stove or a hand-stove.

Another thing which we connect with ironing is the starching. The Chinese are well acquainted with the use of rice or wheat flour for starching clothing or yarn. The hanks of cotton yarn before they are wound upon spools for the shuttle, or used for preparing the warp, are put into boiled rice starch and then hung up to dry. Washable clothing is sprinkled with starch water, wrung out and hung out to dry. The starch water is prepared by pouring boiling water over wheat or rice flour and stirring it. When the clothing is almost dry it is folded up nicely, put on a table and a wooden bench or stool laid upside down upon it. Again, the flat-iron which would put nice finishing touches upon the clothing is not used.

In the Musée Le Brun, a collection of engravings published by the husband of Elizabeth Vigée Le Brun, a picture is shown by Isaac Ostade (1621-1649, a younger brother of the better known Adrian), where beside a fireplace an instrument can be seen hanging which resembles the solid flat-iron of the Chinese. The ironing surface there is square, however, as I remember it.

SEWING AND SEWING UTENSILS

LINE MARKER

The Chinese tailor for making lines upon cloth uses

Fig. 280. Beater for Washing Clothes.

a line marker in principle the same as the carpenter's line marker which will be described under Figs. 372 and 503, but more simple in construction. A piece of cloth is folded around some powdered ocher, and a string is laid through it. The little packet, with the string extending at both sides, is sewed together so that the contents do not spill. When a line is to be marked, the string is pulled through the ocher bag, held stretched over the cloth, taken in the middle, pulled up, and released, when the string thus twanged will deposit a line of the ocher dust upon the cloth. Fig. 284 shows such a line marker which was photographed in Se Kan, in the Wantsai district, Kiangsi province. The dimensions can be judged from the thickness of the string. The bag is about 6 inches long.

FIG. 281. WASH TUB.

THIMBLES AND NEEDLE-PULLER

Besides the thimble which is always part of the outfit of a Chinese needle-woman, the needle-puller is often to be found. Both implements seen in Fig. 285, I bought in Kiangsi province, and photographed at leisure in Kuling. The thimble shown near the point of the needle-puller is made of brass, and the other one of wrought iron. Both are about the same size, ¾ of an inch in diameter and ⅝ of an inch high. The indentations of the iron one seem machine-made, a sign of foreign manufacture, probably Japanese. The other appears to be of native make with the indentations individually cut with a punch. Whether the dents are foreign made or not, however, the type of thimble is Chinese. The thimble is worn upon the second joint of the right middle-finger. It is originally made small and can be easily adjusted to a larger finger by prying it open.

The needle-puller is made of brass. The two legs of it are brazed together at the curved end and reinforced with an iron rivet. In pulling the needle when stitching the cloth soles of Chinese shoes the needle-puller is quite handy, and yet there are districts in China where this device is not known. In use the needle-puller is held at the open perforated end between fore-finger and thumb. The extending point of the needle is taken between the legs of the puller, and held therein tightly by pressing finger and thumb together. The curved end which rests upon the material sewed furnishes considerable leverage and the needle is pulled through with ease. For a description of a wooden needle-puller see Fig. 293.

SPECTACLES

It is one of the familiar sights of Chinese street life to see an old Chinese granny sitting on a doorstep with her sewing outfit picking up chance business of mending a rent or tear in the habiliment of a passer-by. As often as not she has one of the bulky Chinese spectacles poised upon her flat nose, and I deem this association sufficient excuse to introduce here an account of Chinese spectacles. The pair shown in Fig. 286 is the type usually seen. The lenses are made of rock crystal or smoky quartz. The dark-colored ones of smoky quartz are plano-concave, and the others plain, of equal thickness throughout. The frame is of *peh tung* (white copper), an alloy of zinc, nickel and copper, used extensively in China. The bows have two hinges each, and can be folded flat over the lenses. The metal parts are fastened to the lenses with little pins which pass through corresponding holes penetrating the lenses. The thickness of the dark lenses is almost 3/16 of an inch at the edges, and of the light ones 3/32 of an inch throughout.

It seems that the Chinese originally used spectacles for shielding the eyes against the glare of the sun, rather than to aid the eyesight. Most lenses are made of smoky quartz, rarely of colorless rock crystal, but even the latter have sufficient opacity to soften the glare of the light passing through them. Among the literati and officials it was the custom (unavowedly, I dare say), to wear spectacles as an outward sign of superior intelligence. Dark color of the glasses was a further aid to the almighty officials for scrutinizing with searching eyes without being detected in doing so. That we find ground lenses indicates no more than an empirical knowledge that the eyesight in some cases will be benefited by varying the surface of the glasses, concave lenses for one disorder and convex glasses for another. It does not appear that the laws of refraction were understood in China before the Jesuit fathers brought enlightenment in this as in many other branches of science in the 17th century. A burning glass or a concave mirror has for a long

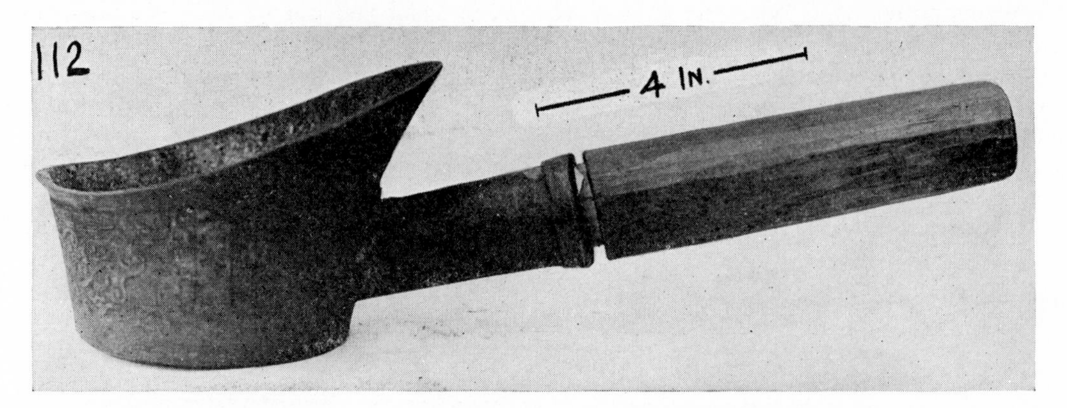

Fig. 282. Tailor's Flat-Iron.

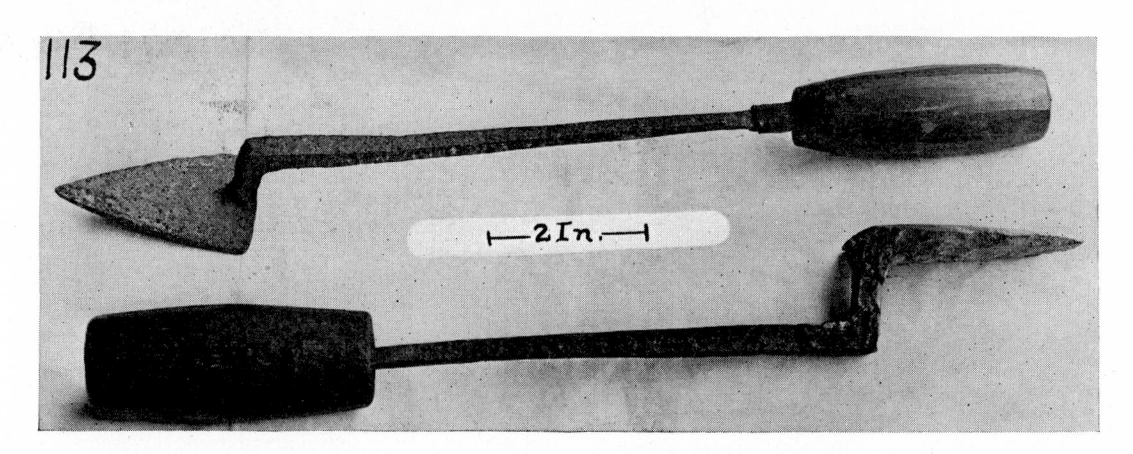

Fig. 283. Tailor's Flat-Irons.

:ime been used by Chinese doctors for igniting moxa, n the practice of cauterization. An empirical knowl- :dge of refraction of pre-Christian time, with a practi- :al application is indicated by an account of a Chinese writer, Hung Lieh Chuan [5] of Liu An (died 122 B.C.), who says: "Take a piece of ice and give it a round shape. Hold it against the sun and you can catch his rays upon tinder and ignite it."

The invention of spectacles is claimed by the Ital- ians. A tombstone in Florence bore the following in- scription (translated): "Here lies Salvino D'Armato degli Armati of Florence, the inventor of Spectacles. Died *anno domini* 1317." It has also been asserted that the Chinese were the first to use spectacles and others again have refuted this, as for instance Professor R. Greeff of Berlin, who wrote extensively about the history of eye-glasses. A missionary traveller A. Williamson, in 1868 observed that in the mountains between Tsi-me and Tsingtao (the famous Lao Shan group), Shantung province, rock crystals of various shades are found, from which the natives make spectacles. I was told in Tsingtao that the famous optical works of Zeiss in Jena has procured from the same locality rock crystal for optical instruments. Only in very recent times have Chinese opticians revolutionized their trade by the introduction of foreign

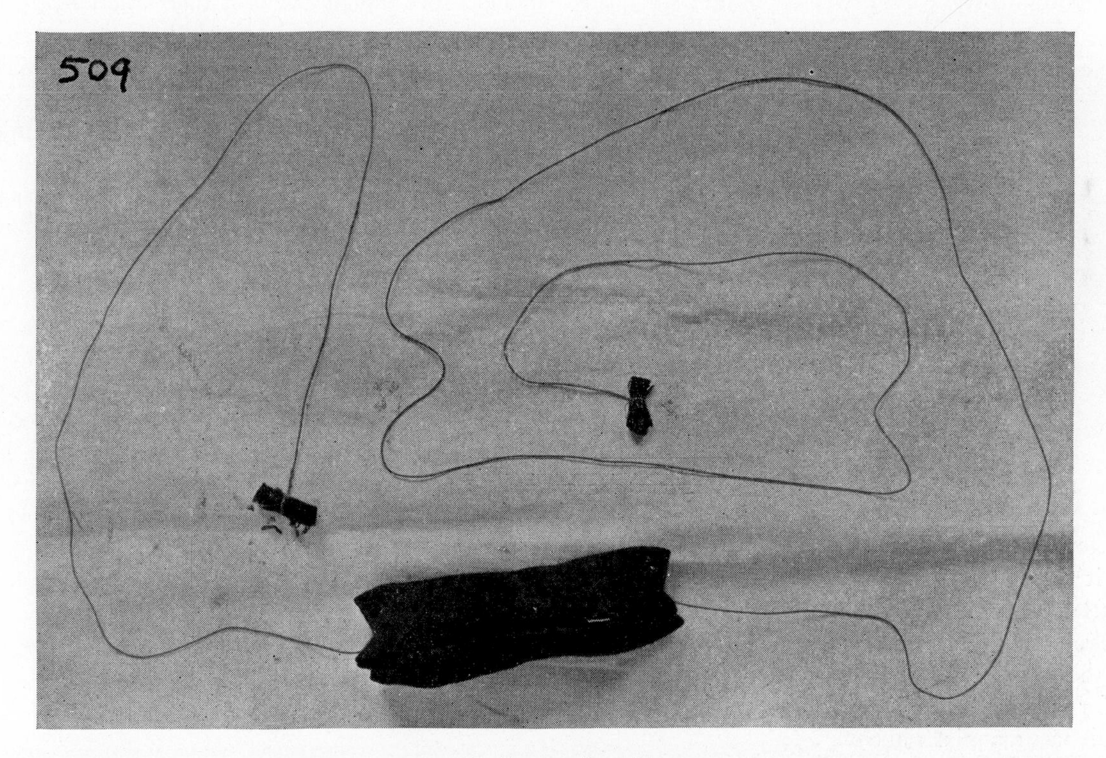

FIG. 284. TAILOR'S LINE MARKER.

FIG. 285. THIMBLES AND NEEDLLE-PULLER.

[5] Pfizmaier, "Kunstfertigkeit & Kuenste der alten Chinesen," Akademie Berichte, Wien, Volume 69.

methods for testing the eyesight and fitting glass lenses according to their tests. Chinese conservatism, however, still now and then rejects these innovations, and for friends of the old school, the optician must keep among his stock a number of Chinese spectacles

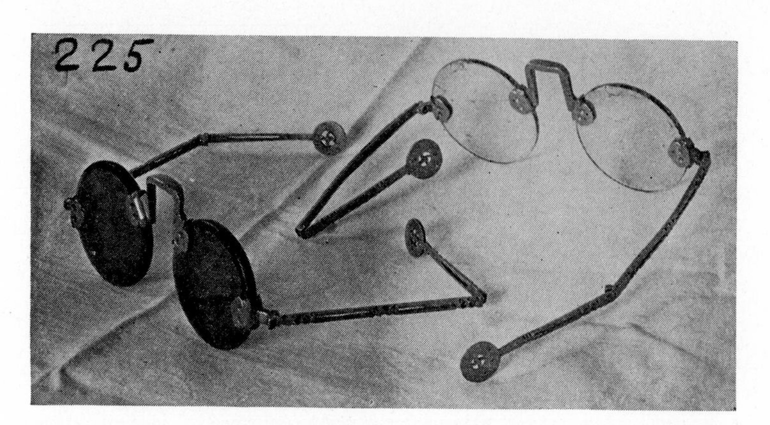

FIG. 286. SPECTACLES.

with stone lenses.

If it were true, as has also been asserted,[6] that spectacles were introduced from Europe in the 15th century, then the question arises, why the Chinese took the revolutionary step to abandon the use of glass for lenses, and employ instead a material but poorly fitted for the purpose. The use of glass had been known to them since the 5th century A.D., and in carving it like gems, they were masters.

It is not hard to cite facts which rather indicate that spectacles were invented by the Chinese, and found their way to the West. In the first place spectacles are mentioned by Chinese writers already before the 13th century,[7] at which time Venetian and Genoese merchants were in contact with China, and could easily have brought specimens home.

[6] Professor Hirschberg, quoted by Werner, "Sociology," London, 1910, p. 227.

[7] Werner, in his "Sociology," states on page 280, that spectacles have been mentioned in Chinese records pertaining to the period of the Tang dynasty (618-907 A.D.), viz. in *Pai Shih lei pien,* p. 22a, and in *Ming wu t'ung,* p. 22b, both reprinted in the Chinese encyclopedia of 1735.

It is recorded[8] that the Dominican monk, Allessandro de Spina, a native of Pisa (died 1313), was shown a pair of spectacles, succeeded in copying them, and made thereafter the construction public. The achievement of the Italians, who at that time already were famed for their skill in glass manufacture, may have been nothing more than to make lenses of glass. The German word for spectacles is "Brille," similarly as our adjective "brilliant," derived from beryl (Greek beryllos), a transparent gem stone. It has been suggested that the derivation of this word points to an original use of such stone for spectacles.

Summarizing we must keep in mind the two distinct uses of spectacles, one for improving the eyesight, and the other for shielding the eyes. The Chinese spectacles were primarily conceived for the latter purpose, to protect the eyes against the glare of a tropical sun, against sandstorms, and then to act as a screen for officials and literati from behind which, as it were, they could observe without being observed. The snow spectacles of the Eskimos belong likewise to the class for shielding the eyes. They were a covering for the eyes, carved of

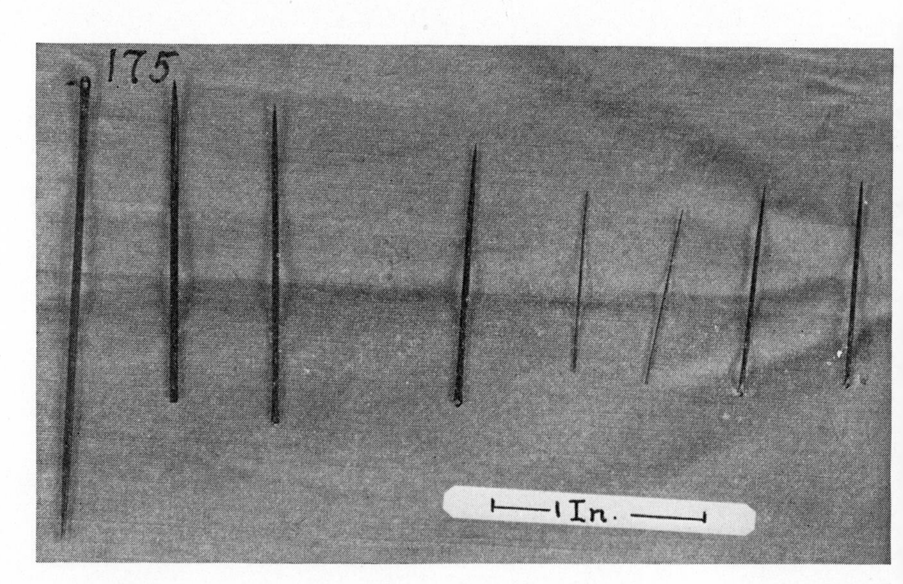

FIG. 287. CHINESE NEEDLES.

bone with two narrow slots placed horizontally over the eyes.

In Europe, by the 13th century, the ground had been sufficiently prepared for using convex glasses to

[8] Mitteilungen aus den Saechsischen Kunstsammlungen, Berlin, 1916, Vol. VII.

improve the eyesight. Burning lenses had been known already for centuries. The Arabian mathematician Alhazen had made known his views about refraction in the 10th century, and Roger Bacon, writing in 1267 about the magnifying power of glass, expressed the belief that old people with weak eyes could derive benefit from such glasses. The contribution made by the Italians, who were probably familiar with Chinese glasses through Genoese and Venetian traders, may have been merely the introduction of glass lenses as a substitute for rock crystal.

After this diversion let us return to our Chinese sewing woman and inquire into the manufacture of the needle with which she is skillfully putting a patch into the pants of a coolie who with rueful look stands beside her eagerly awaiting the return of this necessary garment.

NEEDLES

Fig. 287 shows an assortment of Chinese needles. One main characteristic is the round hole for an eye. The specimen next to the largest shown in the picture represents a piece of iron wire pointed, but not pierced. It is a pin as used by Chinese tailors. Nowadays foreign wire is used, while formerly the maker had to hammer out his own wire. I have previously mentioned that the Chinese are not able to draw iron wire in the same manner as they draw wire from more ductile metals such as gold, silver and copper.

Previous to drilling a hole for the thread at the blunt end of the needle, this part is flattened somewhat with a blow of a hammer on the little anvil shown at the left in Fig. 288. The pointed shank of the anvil is driven into a round wooden post, which is about 2 inches in diameter and 3 feet long. The needle maker holds the post between his knees.

For drilling the hole the needle is placed into a slight groove on the workbench and then the pump drill, shown in Fig. 288 is applied. The pump drill, a slender shaft of a very hard wood, about 23 inches long, has at its upper end a disk of slate as a whorl, which is 1½ inches in diameter and ⅛ of an inch thick. At the other end the very fine steel drill is inserted into a socket. The sliding crosspiece has at its center hole a cloth rag as a sort of packing which permits the crosspiece to slide smoothly up and down the highly polished shaft of the pump drill. It is a delicate operation to make the tiny eye holes in the needles. The drill is well adapted for it but one has to admire the consummate skill of the workman in

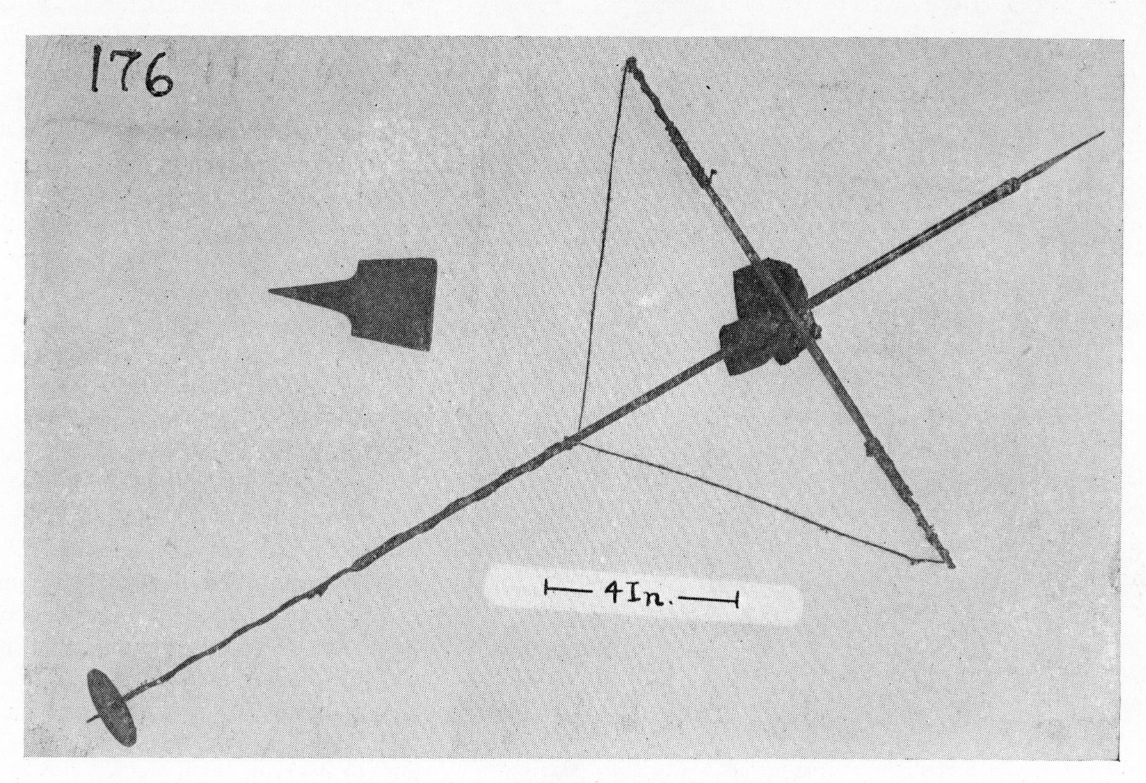

Fig. 288. Needle Maker's Pump Drill and Anvil.

using his tool. After the holes have been drilled the needles are hardened and then polished. For polishing they are placed upon a stone slab and rolled back and forth with a rag soaked in oil. Native needle making is one of the trades which can not hold their own against foreign competition and is fast dying out. The pictures were taken at the shop of a friendly old man in Teh An, Kiangsi province, who with little profit to himself held on to his old trade of making needles and fishhooks.

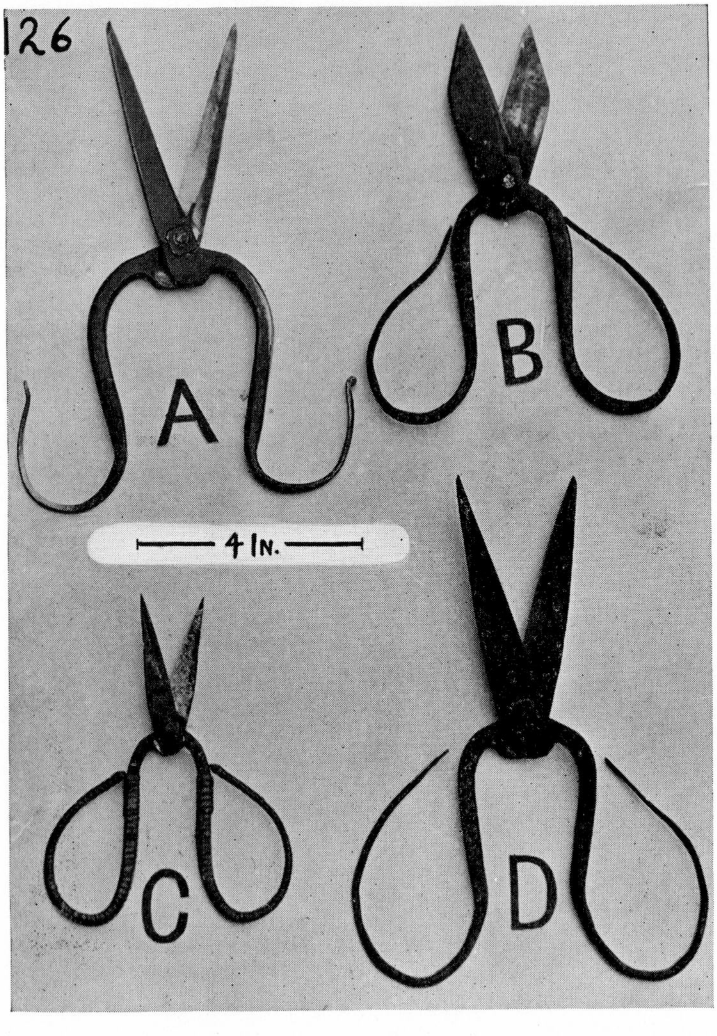

Fig. 289. Chinese Scissors.

SCISSORS

Fig. 289 shows typical forms of Chinese scissors. (*A*) is the one used by professional tailors. The handle loops are open which distinguishes this from all the others. It is a man's tool and a man's hand would not handle it comfortably if the loops were closed. Another characteristic but not so apparent in the specimen shown is its dull points. The story goes that a long time ago an aggrieved tailor forgot himself so far that he stabbed his adversary to death with his scissors, and thus brought disgrace upon his honorable calling. An imperial edict decreed that henceforth tailors must use scissors with dull points lest the example set by that culprit might lead to further tragedies. Thus runs the story, but on the other hand, it is quite evident that scissors with sharp points are not convenient for cutting out cloth, since the point of the lower blade is apt to catch in the folds of cloth underlying the piece to be cut. This pair of tailor's scissors is 8 inches long and the widest width of the blade measures $\frac{1}{2}$ inch, with a thickness of $\frac{1}{8}$ inch. The two blades are held together by an iron rivet. Between the hammered rivet head on each side, are usually two washers, first one of iron, and over this, one of brass. These washers are square, but the corners of the brass one are clipped off giving it an irregular octagonal form.

The scissors (*B*) are for rough domestic work. Their use even extends into the kitchen. In preparing beans in the pods, the pod ends are cut off with scissors, also in dressing fowls the intestines are sometimes cut out with scissors. In the rural districts where the people are more or less independent of the outside world there are of course innumerable uses for such a pair of scissors with strong, stubby blades. Rags pasted on top of each other forming sheets like cardboard are cut up with them for soles of shoes. The various weavings of straw hats, mats, baskets, etc., with straw, rush, sedge and fibres of all sorts require scissors. The length over all of this pair is $6\frac{3}{4}$ inches, the largest width of blade is $\frac{3}{4}$ of an inch and the thickness of blade $\frac{1}{8}$ of an inch.

Scissors (*C*) is a more delicate kind for general sewing and mending. It is adapted to the nimble fingers of the women of the household who usually do not partake in the rougher work around the house. The loops are wound with strips of cane and varnished red with a few spots of gold color, which however, together with the red varnish soon wears off. The whole length is 5 inches, the widest width of the blade 7/16 of an inch and the thickness 3/64 of an inch.

For home dress-making the scissors (*D*) are used, in size corresponding closely to the tailor's scissors, but with points sharp and handle loops closed. Apparently it is the tailor's privilege only to have scissors with open loops. The whole length of this pair is almost 8 inches and the largest width of the blade ⅝ of an inch with a thickness of 3/16 of an inch.

The making of scissors is a trade by itself, namely that of the Chinese cutler. He makes also razors, tweezers for removing superfluous hair, lancet-shaped knives for cutting toe-nails and callous flesh from feet and hands, burins, gravers, carver's tools, and many others. The material he uses is the best grade of steel or charcoal iron. The picture was taken in the Native City of Shanghai.

JAPANESE SHEARS

The usual assertion that the Japanese civilization has been derived from the Chinese, has many exceptions. Considering at random some of the Japanese tools we find that not a few are quite different. There is the Japanese board saw, an unwieldy blade, handled by one man in a horizontal direction, utterly unlike the Chinese tool used for the same purpose. There are other autochthonous types, of which more in their proper places. Scissors, early developed by the Chinese, are also found in olden times among the Arabs and in Persia, and it seems strange that in old Japan no scissors but only shears are known. They are used for all kinds of work, even tiny ones for embroidery.

The specimen of Japanese shears, Fig. 290 was procured from a Japanese lady in Kuling, Kiangsi province, who had brought it from her homeland. It measures 4¾ inches in length. On one of the blades the maker's name is incised in Japanese script. The blades are held in their relative position by the curved elastic piece which unites them, and in using the shears the two members are gripped by one hand and pressed together. After releasing the pressure the blades regain their former position by virtue of the elastic end-loop. The offset at the place where the lower blade tapers to the handle not repeated on the opposite upper blade, serves to prevent the pressing together of the blades more than is necessary for cutting. The whole pair of shears is made of steel of the finest quality.

Scissors, the implement with two separate blades held together by a rivet, and later by a screw, are said to have come to Europe from Venice in the 16th century. This statement is evidently wrong as far as the date is concerned and is interesting only in as much as it points to the Orient as the original source of the scissors. The Venetians were traders, especially with the Near East, and many Eastern customs and implements have passed through Venice on their way to Europe.

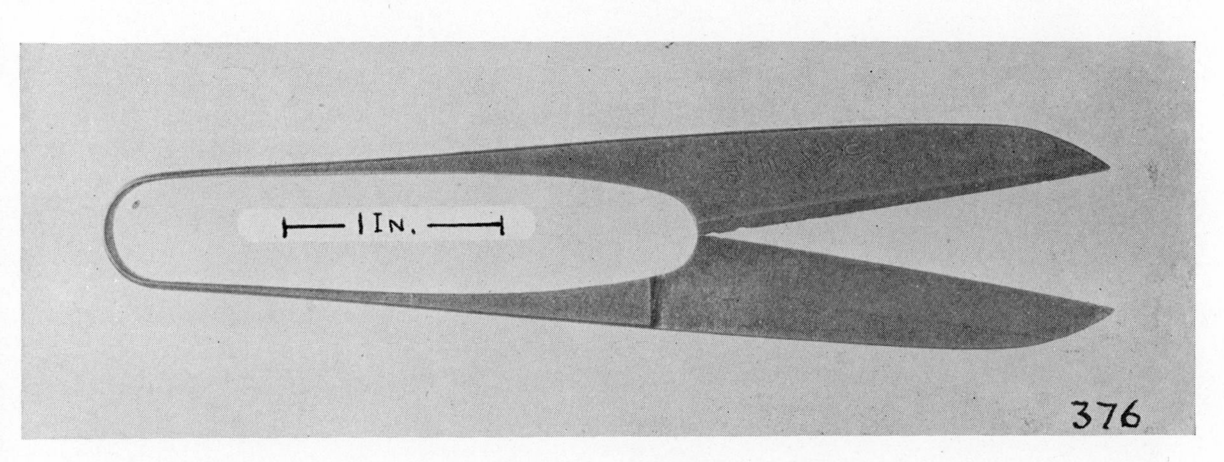

Fig. 290. Japanese Shears.

F. S. Meyer, in his "Ornamentik" (Leipzig, 1919), is authority for the statement that scissors, formed of two separate members, movable about a central point, occur sporadically after the 10th century in Europe.

STRAW FOOTGEAR

Fig. 291 pictures the bench used for making straw shoes. An ordinary low bench is pushed with one end against a wall, a column or anything to prevent it from moving in that direction. To the other end a wooden contrivance is hooked, which might be called a warp holder. The worker sits astride of the bench facing the warp holder, with the yoke, seen in the picture, held to his body by a string, which, attached to the ends of the yoke, passes around his waist. We could not persuade the owner to sit for us when taking the photograph, and as a makeshift, had to tie the yoke to the column, to show the relative position when tied around the waist of the worker. At the apex of the yoke a short wooden pin projects vertically and to this is hooked the loop of the hempen rope which serves as warp for the straw shoe to be made. The process is simple weaving. The work starts with the two warp strings. The two ends pass to the warp holder where they are tied to the large spike in the center leaving about the same length of warp hanging free from the spike. Next fibres of straw twisted together are woven to the warp-strings to form a strip about two inches long. Then the knot at the center spike is untied, the loose ends of the warp are passed around the end pegs on the warp holder, one string over each peg, and thence directed back to the newly woven part where they are tied to the original two warp strings. There are now four warp strings and the weaving of a wider surface is thereby made possible. Fig. 292, at the right, shows the four warp strings with a part of the woven shoe. According to the warp strings being hooked to the outer or inner pegs on the warp holder they are spread far apart or set close together. The weaving is now continued with the warp strings spread apart, then to narrow the fabric again after putting in a few wefts, the warps are moved successively from outer pegs to the inner ones, always putting in a few wefts between each shifting until they rest on the pegs nearest to the center spike of the warp holder, in the position shown in Fig. 291. This mode of weaving is in accordance with the outline of the shoe. The pointed part with two warp strings is the toe-part of the shoe to be bent upward when being worn. When the part which is immediately under the toes is reached the surface must be spread and hence four warp strings are used. A little contraction under the arch of the foot is produced by placing the four warp strings closer together by shifting them on the pegs of the warp holder and when nearing the heel part of the shoe they are spread again. The whole shoe

Fig. 291. Bench for Making Straw Shoes.

is brought to completion by attaching the warp strings to the center spike again and continuing the weaving as at the beginning except that in this case there are two warp strings together on each side instead of one.

The bench is 4 feet 6 inches long, and 16 inches high. The warp holder hooked to the bench is 16 inches long. The wooden block with the eight pegs is 15 inches long and 2½ inches wide. The wooden yoke measures on a straight line from tip to tip 19 inches and has an average diameter of about 1½ inches. The string on the ends of the yoke is tied to a groove at the one end and slipped over the hook wooden wedge, which can not be seen in the picture, driven across it through a hole in the part extending beyond the mortise. After the shoe is finished it is beaten thoroughly upon the ground, preferably a stone floor, with the mallet seen lying on the ground in Fig. 291. The straw then gets more pliable and soft, and the surface of the shoe more even. Then a long hempen latchet string is passed through the eye at the toe-tip of the shoe, and secured with a knot, and the shoe is ready for wear. To secure it to the foot this latchet string is passed through the separately attached loops on the side of the shoe and tied over the instep.

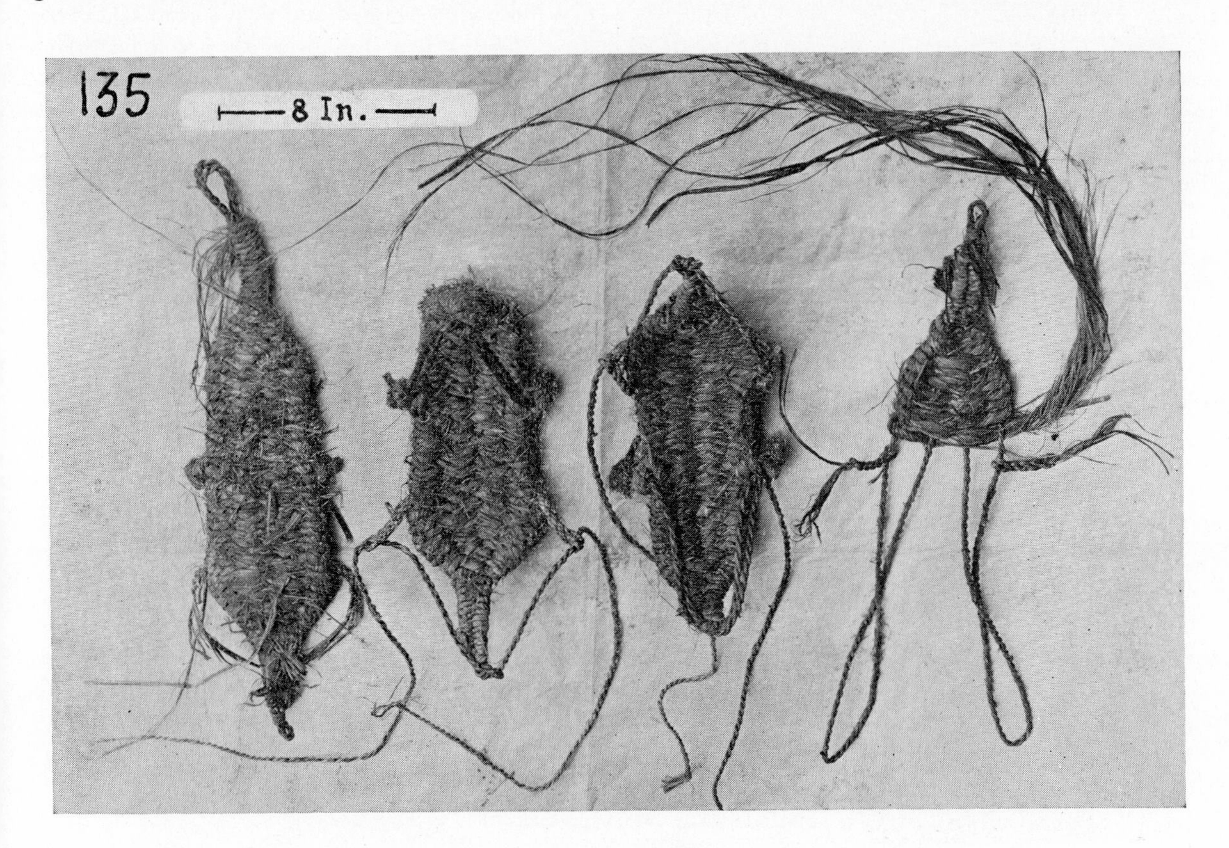

FIG. 292. STRAW SHOES.

carved at the other end. The man operating this contrivance keeps the warp stretched with his body. In ordinary weaving a reed is used for "beating up" the weft (pushing tight), but in this contrivance, the straw weft is pushed back once in a while by putting the fingers between the warp strings and pushing up the twisted straw. Whenever this is done, the operator first hooks all the warp loops upon the center spike, and then with his fingers against the weft pulls with all his might in a direction towards his body. The large horizontal wooden hook passes through a mortise in the warp holder and is kept in place by a

In Fig. 292 we see straw shoes in various positions and one partly finished. The one on the left, stretched out all the way, presents the bottom view. The two in the middle are a finished pair with latchet strings, for fastening to the foot, attached. As the unfinished specimen shows there are loops braided from hemp fibres, attached to the outer warp strings which ultimately serve for holding the latchet strings. The weaving is started at the tip of the shoe and ends in two loops at the heel end. These loops are fastened at the side of the shoe, so that the end is bent up forming a secure resting place for the heel. This heel upbend can better be seen in Fig. 291, where a finished straw shoe is seen lying on the bench, presenting a side view.

In the country the peasants wear this type of straw shoe in rainy weather or on stony ground. Otherwise they go barefooted. Cross-country carriers, chair bearers, wheelbarrow men and ricksha coolies always wear them. Straw shoes of other districts may vary slightly from the ones described, but nevertheless the same kind of apparatus is used for making them. The pictures were taken at Se Aw in Chekiang province.

CLOTH SHOES

Chinese shoes for every-day use are not made of leather. The chemical process of converting hides into leather, by means of tannic acid, does not seem known in the parts I have visited. Lime is used for dressing hides and the resulting product looks more like raw-hide than leather. It is not surprising therefore that the Chinese make very little use of their hides. Only foreign contact has taught the Chinese various uses of leather, as for belts, straps, trunks and shoes. Inquiries in the country revealed that it was customary until recent times to bury the carcasses of cattle, hide and all, when any of the animals died. The Buddhist belief forbids the consumption of beef, and the lack of a proper tanning process makes the use of the hide a matter of small importance. It is the same as with the utilization of feathers. The Chinese don't know how to free feathers from their natural oil which is apt to give rise to putrefaction, and therefore they cannot use them for pillows or bedding.

Cotton cloth is used for making Chinese shoes, and silk sometimes for the uppers. The making of uppers is simple needlework. For winter use the shoes are frequently padded with cotton. The making of the soles is more complicated. In the Chinese household every bit of cotton rag is kept to be finally utilized for making the soles of the cloth shoes. The rags are first thoroughly washed and then spread upon boards for drying. When thus dried they will lie perfectly flat as if ironed. In Ningpo I passed once an establishment which makes a business of collecting rags all over the city. When washing them they hit them with flails, in construction the same as the one described previously, Fig. 111. By pasting the rags together, rectangular sheets are formed from which pieces conforming to the outline of the sole with a liberal margin are cut. In pasting up these sheets a large piece of cloth is used as a base upon which smaller rags are pasted with a paste made of wheat flour. The product looks like a Chinese puzzle in which the irregular shaped bits of rags have been fitted together without any overlapping. Each sheet consists of three or four

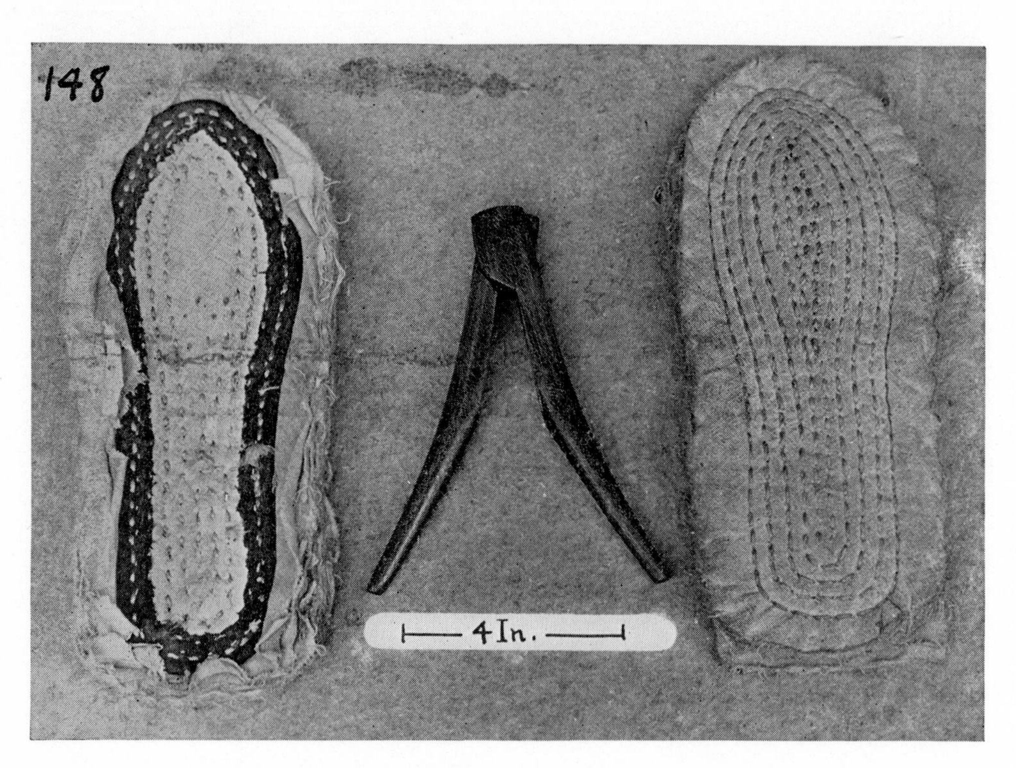

Fig. 293. Chinese Cloth Shoes.

layers of rags upon the cotton cloth as a base. About 20 to 30 pieces, cut from the large sheets, are laid one upon the other, and then, applying a cloth welt at one side, are sewed together. The cloth welt usually conforms in color and material to the upper which is next sewed to it. For sewing hemp is used, which the women making the shoes twist upon their thighs. The sewing is commenced with the row of stitches which fasten the cloth welt to the sole. It is hard work to push the needle through so many layers of pasted cloth even with the aid of a thimble. The women usually push the needle through the sole and then getting hold of the point with the wooden tweezers, made expressly for the purpose, shown in Fig. 293, pull the needle through. On the left of the picture can be seen a sole with the stitching not quite finished and the dark cloth welt showing plainly. The sole at right presents the opposite or bottom view. After the soles are sewn together, the edges are trimmed off close to the welt, and then they are ready to receive the uppers. The work of sewing on the uppers is usually entrusted to the cobbler, who likewise trims the edges with his half-circular knife. The country people, however, frequently make the complete shoes themselves and then trim the edges with their scissors or chisel them off, if a chisel is part of their inventory. Poor people who even suffer from want of rags, use strips of paper for part of the inside layers of the sole, and claim that it serves the purpose just as well as the rag layers.

The needle puller in the picture is made of a hard wood. One of the legs is forked at the end and the end of the other leg fits into the fork. A wooden pin passes through both and forms the pivot joint below which the needle is seized. The soles shown are about 10½ inches long and their thickness is ¼ of an inch.

In rainy weather leather shoes with large hob-nails are worn a good deal. They are heavily oiled, to preserve the poor leather from putrefaction. The picture was taken at Se Aw in Chekiang province.

Fig. 294. Rain Hat.

RAIN PROTECTION

The Chinese are very sensitive to rain. We are inclined to ridicule this propensity, especially when we see soldiers walking about with umbrellas. We should remember, however, that it is not pleasant to be caught in torrential rains, such as are prevalent in China, which drench you to the skin in a few seconds. The wadded clothing of the Chinese would be completely spoiled if it became saturated with rain, and to protect this is probably the main cause of the Celestials' sensitiveness to rain.

The peasants who have to toil for their daily bread, must brave all kinds of weather. Tilling the fields they cannot very well carry an umbrella and have to protect themselves in some other way. This they do with the large hat shown in Fig. 294. The diameter of these hats is about 3 feet. They are formed of large dry sheath-like leaves, woven over on both sides loosely with thin bamboo splints. Some of these hats have two handles on the rim opposite each other so that they can be hung up or tied over baskets when coolies carry loads overland.

The photograph, taken in Tatung, Anhwei, gives two views of the hat, one to show how it is worn and the other from above, revealing the structural detail. Mr. T. Y. Pong, my faithful interpreter for several years, posed for this picture, which the peasants would not do. The sheath like leaves used are taken from bamboo shoots, which in their early growth are covered by such sheaths. The splints being also derived from bamboo it appears that the complete hat is a product of the bamboo.

KNITTING

In Kansu province, where over one half of the population is Mohammedan, the art of knitting is well known and practiced extensively by men and women. In fact it seems to be a characteristic of the Moslem in China to be acquainted with this art. Stockings and gloves are knitted and the knitting started contrary to Western usage at the toes or finger ends. In Bulgaria knitting is started in the same unchristianlike manner, an inheritance of Turkish rule very likely, and curved knitting needles are used.

Heretofore it has been held, according to various accounts in present-day encyclopedias that the art of knitting was a European invention of which no certain allusion occurred before the 15th century. There is, however, a much earlier reference to the art in the "Travels of Marco Polo," Book I, chapter xii. Marco Polo here speaks of the Saint Barsamo Monastery, near the border of the territory of Tauris (Tabriz, the capital of Azwebaijan, Persia), which he visited in about 1272. He relates that the numerous monks "to avoid idleness are continually knitting woolen girdles. These they place upon the altar of St. Barsamo during

FIG. 295. CHINESE STOCKINGS. This picture shows Chinese stockings hung up for drying. They are sewed of stout cotton cloth and conform as closely as the inelastic material will allow to the shape of the foot. The sole is usually of coarser material for better resistance to wear. This type of stocking seems to be the original foot covering of the Chinese. Knitted stockings of foreign manufacture in recent times have found ready favor and are gradually crowding out the hand-sewn stockings shown.

the service, and when they go begging about the province, they present them to their friends and to the gentlefolks, for they are excellent things to remove bodily pain; wherefore every one is devoutly eager to possess them." Sir Henry Yule's edition, from which I quote, states in a note that the monastery doubtless meant here was near Malatia. Thus we see that knitting was practiced in Persia in the last quarter of the 13th century. Marco Polo speaks of knitting without any further explanation, and the art seems therefore to have been common knowledge in Italy in his time.

FIG. 296. LEATHER MAKER'S "BEAM BOARD" FOR SCRAPING OFF THE FLESH AND HAIR OF HIDES.

Exploration of graves in Achmim, Upper Egypt, of the Byzantine period (ca. 400-650 A.D.), yielded knitted caps and short knitted stockings, knitted of differently colored wool, with the foot divided into two parts, one for the big toe and the other for the remaining toes. This arrangement was necessary for the fastening of the sandals, the latchet of which passed between the large and the second toe. The Japanese wear similar sandals and their stockings sewn of cloth like the Chinese ones have also a space provided between the toes for the latchet.

Some claim (as recorded in Meyer's Konversations Lexikon) that the art of knitting was already known to the old Greeks. No evidence supporting this claim is adduced. It may be, however, that what gave rise to it are human figures pictured sometimes on old Greek vases, draped with a short sleeveless robe which shows only those parts of a tricot-like undergarment that cover arms and legs. Zigzag ornamentation upon it is singularly suggestive of knitted ware. So, for instance, on the Darius Vase in the Naples Museum and on a pail-shaped Apulian vase found in Ruvo di Puglia.

More convincing evidence we can offer that knitting was known at the time of the Roman Empire. At Carnuntum[9] many interesting pieces of armor have been found dating from the time of the Roman Empire, and among them fragments of mail knitted of iron wire. Although these fragments present a texture of iron wire, it proves that the principle of knitting is employed, and therefore must have been known to the Romans. It is of interest to note here that in the Italian language there is a term for knitting, *far la maglia,* in addition to the more usual *far la calza. Maglia,* of course, refers to mail or the loops of it.

In bog graves of Denmark woolen knitted caps have been found, and a knitted bonnet has been recovered from an oaken tree-coffin in Trindhoë, Jutland. Forrer, in his dictionary of prehistoric antiquities (Berlin & Stuttgart, 1907), deals with these finds, as well as those from Achmim, mentioned above, and comes to the conclusion that they were knitted. Of caps from Achmim he says that some are knitted of white linen yarn, and some of colored woolen yarn, in a manner resembling netting and at times with various openwork patterns. This characterization rather suggests that we have to do here with knitting done with a crochet-hook. Crocheting in its simplest form is really a primitive mode of knitting, and quite likely

[9] Old Celtic settlement in Pannonia on the Danube. Winter quarters of the Roman legions and station of the Danube flotilla. Marcus Aurelius spent 3 years in C., and Sept. Severus was here proclaimed Roman Emperor. Extensive ruins are still to be found at Deutsch-Altenburg, near Hainburg, east of Vienna. The reports of the association "Carnuntum," published since 1888, give accounts of the excavations carried on.

preceded knitting with two needles. The fact that in lake dwellings of Switzerland a wooden (at Moerigen) and a bronze (at Wollishofen) crochet-hook have been found only tends to corroborate this view.

Up to the end of the 18th century only two needles were used in Germany for the knitting of stockings and one was fastened to the bodice of the worker. It is not quite clear how this was done, the result, however, of such knitting was that the stocking had a seam along its whole length. In English the term knitting-sheath is known, a small cylindrical socket attached to the dress of a knitter for holding one end of the knitting needle while in use. From this we deduce that English knitting was similar to the German method. I recently read[10] that in "southern Italy knitting-needles are curved, and in knitting the end of one of the needles is placed in a socket which is either tied to the waist or slipped inside the apron-strings. These sockets are usually attached to a heart-shaped plate. Old silver ones are to be found, beautiful specimens of the silversmith's art."

Europe certainly cannot claim the invention of the art of knitting. To China it probably came through the Arabians in the 7th or 8th century when Arabian mercenaries were brought in large numbers to China to help repress rebellions, and settled there afterwards. The finds of Achmim belong to the Byzantine period and cannot be connected with the Arabians who took possession of Egypt much later. We can however suppose that the Arabians became acquainted with the art of knitting in Egypt and were the carriers who brought it to other nations. We know for instance that the cultural influences of the Arabians (Moors) were very extensive in Spain (711-1492), and in fact a tradition persists that the art of knitting was brought to the rest of Europe from Spain.

Among the earliest mention of knitted goods in

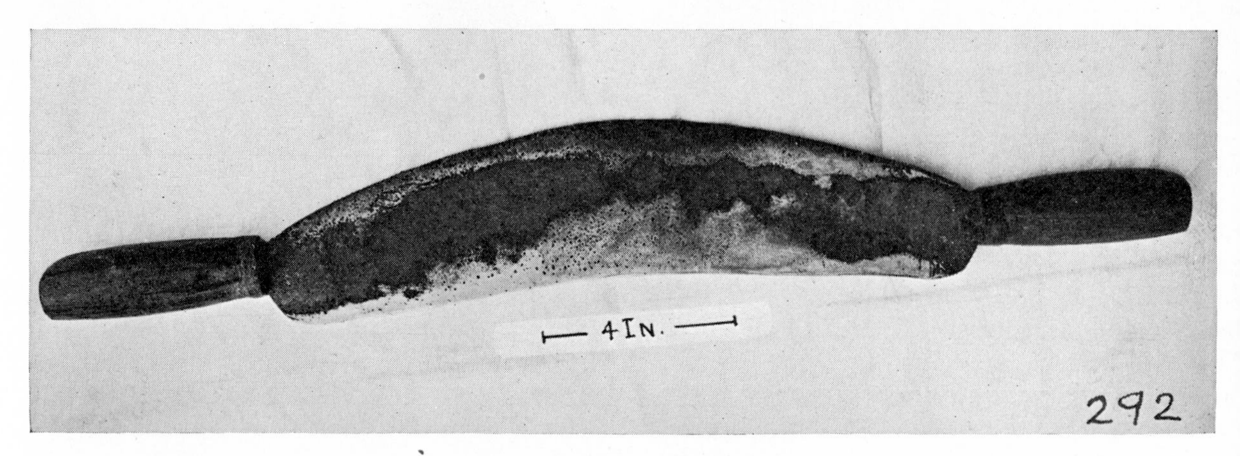

FIG. 297. LEATHER MAKER'S FLESHING KNIFE.

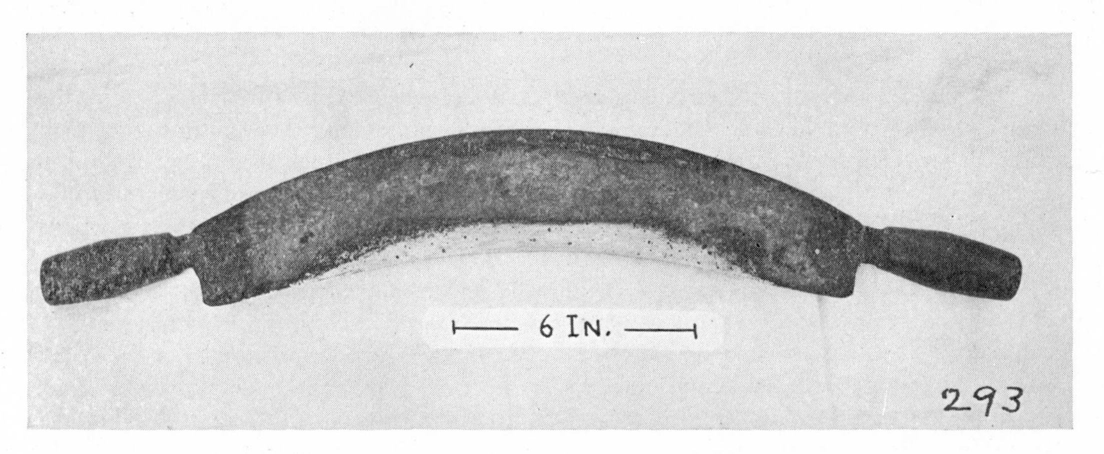

FIG. 298. LEATHER MAKER'S FLESHING KNIFE. This other fleshing knife is 23½ inches long, and the blade, rather more curved than the other, is 3 inches wide.

[10] "Notes & Queries," 1930, Vol. 158, p. 87.

European accounts we find Spanish silk stockings as worn by English royalty in the 16th century. How advanced methods of knitting were introduced into Scotland is explained by a local tradition of Fair Island according to which the art of knitting colored stockings, the dyes having been derived from various plants and lichens found locally, was introduced by surviving mariners of one of the ships of the ill-fated Spanish Armada, which was wrecked in 1588 on the shores of the island [11].

LEATHER MAKING

The Chinese have never attained to the art of true leather making, namely the converting of skins and tannin. The cocoons of the wild silkworms which feed on oak leaves and which furnish the silk for pongee, have to be softened in water with soda in order to loosen the gummy cover, rich in tannin. Further, the spent tea leaves which are thrown out from millions of teapots daily contain also tannin. As primitive as the East Indian method of preparing leather is, they, the East Indians, are at least acquainted with the fundamental principle, the use of a tanning agent. The mode of procedure in India is to fill the hide with moist tanniferous bark, sew it up, and hang it up on a tree. The only care expended is to keep the bark always moist for the duration of suspension. The hide thus gets gradually converted into

Fig. 299. Drying Leather.

hides into leather through a tanning agent. This is the more surprising as there is an abundance of tannin-producing plants and trees. Of oaks in China the botanists count over 40 varieties. The gall-nuts of commerce come from China and they contain largely leather. Leather of a sort is produced however in China, and this by the process not of tanning but of tawing.

The raw material used is zebu or water buffalo hide. The hide stripped from a carcass is spread upon the ground covered with powdered quick lime and then sprinkled with water. The hide is thereafter folded together and left lying for about an hour. After

[11] The account of knitting, here slightly expanded, first appeared in Vol. 158 (1930) of "Notes & Queries," London, submitted by the Author in answer to a query about the history of knitting.

that it is extended over a wooden beam with convex surface, the so-called beam-board, to be scraped in a downward motion with a fleshing knife. Fig. 296 shows an example of a beam-board. The beam-board consists of two parts, the beam proper, and a supporting frame which rests loosely in mortises of the beam. The length of the beam is 32 inches. In some places the beam alone is used. The worker props it against his knees, and bending over it, scrapes off the slimy covering of the inside of the hide.

For the scraping of the hide upon the beam-board the fleshing knife, Fig. 297, is employed. For his protection the worker wears a large leather apron. The hide is then laid in water, in a brick-lined tank, set into the ground, for from 10 to 15 days. The hair on the outside of the hide, after that time, is easily taken off with the fleshing knife, the edge of the blade of which is concave, to correspond with the convex shape of the beam-board. The stench accompanying this process is beyond description and imagination. After a few whiffs of the atmosphere I had to retreat, and yet a little child sat there beside the tank playing, wholly unconcerned, and the tradesman with the rest of his family work, eat, and sleep there apparently in no way affected by this aroma.

Fig. 300. Drying Leather. The face of the freshly scraped hide stretched on a framework of bamboo poles is here shown.

The fleshing knife, Fig. 297, is 2 feet long, the handles take 9 inches of that length, leaving 15 inches for the metal between handles. The greatest width of the blade is 3¼ inches.

Figs. 299 and 300 show how the hides, now tawed to leather of a sort, are stretched out with bamboo rods for final drying in the sun. Along one edge of the hides the notched ends of bamboo poles catch the skin in marginal slits, and along the other edge of the hide the skin is tied with twisted straw through other slits to the other ends of the poles.

Leather prepared in this manner is of poor quality. Shoes made from it are used for rainy weather, but the soles must be well studded with hobnails, as the leather gets soft and slimy from the water. To keep the shoes from spoiling they must at all times be well oiled.

A somewhat better quality of leather I saw made in Kienchang, Kiangsi province. The process is practically the same as described. After the final drying, however, the leather is exposed to the smoke of burning rice chaff, alternately on both sides. The top of a brickstove, constructed similar to the square kitchen stove, has a round hole in its top, about 5 inches in diameter, and the hide is held over this hole and moved about until the whole surface has been exposed to the dense smoke issuing from the opening. As the stove has no chimney, the smoke pours readily out of the orifice.

In either of these cases of leather making, the finished hides are folded up and laid by, weighted down with heavy beams of wood, until used. The maker of rain shoes thus prepares his own leather and when he takes a hide from the pile, he has to put on a few finishing touches. One is to even the inside surface of the hide with a knife, which is shown in Fig. 301.

The dried hide is next laid over the curious trestle shown in Fig. 302. In a direction parallel to the beam of the trestle the leather maker shaves irregularities off the surface of the hide by pressing down the knife, Fig. 301, in a direction away from the body. The yoke-shaped handle he presses against his stomach, at the same time grasping the handle near the socket of the blade to guide it. The trestle, a long pole, with only one rigid support at the one end, the two legs mortised into its left end, is placed in the position shown in the picture. If only a small stretch of its length is required, it is placed so that part of the round beam extends out through the door into the street where it is in everybody's way, but that does not matter, the passers-by walk around it. The patient Chinese has not that western irascibility which sees a personal affront in any inconvenience caused by another person. Human acts are fate to him the same as rain, storm, and the like.

To make the leather soft and pliant, another similar instrument with a dull blade is employed, see Fig. 303, in which case the same trestle is used for a support, and the instrument handled the same way, i.e., being pressed against the leather over the beam in a downward direction.

An inexpensive and efficient method of making leather pliable I saw at a country market in Shantung. Before the crowds had arrived to do their buying, selling and bargaining the enterprising leather maker had spread his whole supply of hides upon the ground where most people would congregate and trample them smooth.

The photographs were taken in different places. Fig. 297 and 303 in Chienkang, Kiangsi, and Fig. 296, 298 to 302 in Kienchang, Kiangsi. In the former place the smoking of the leather is not practiced, nor known. The shoemaker there making his own leather was rather discouraged with his product, having seen so much of tanned leather which came from the treaty ports, and found ready favor with the Chinese. In Kienchang, the other place, more inland, near the

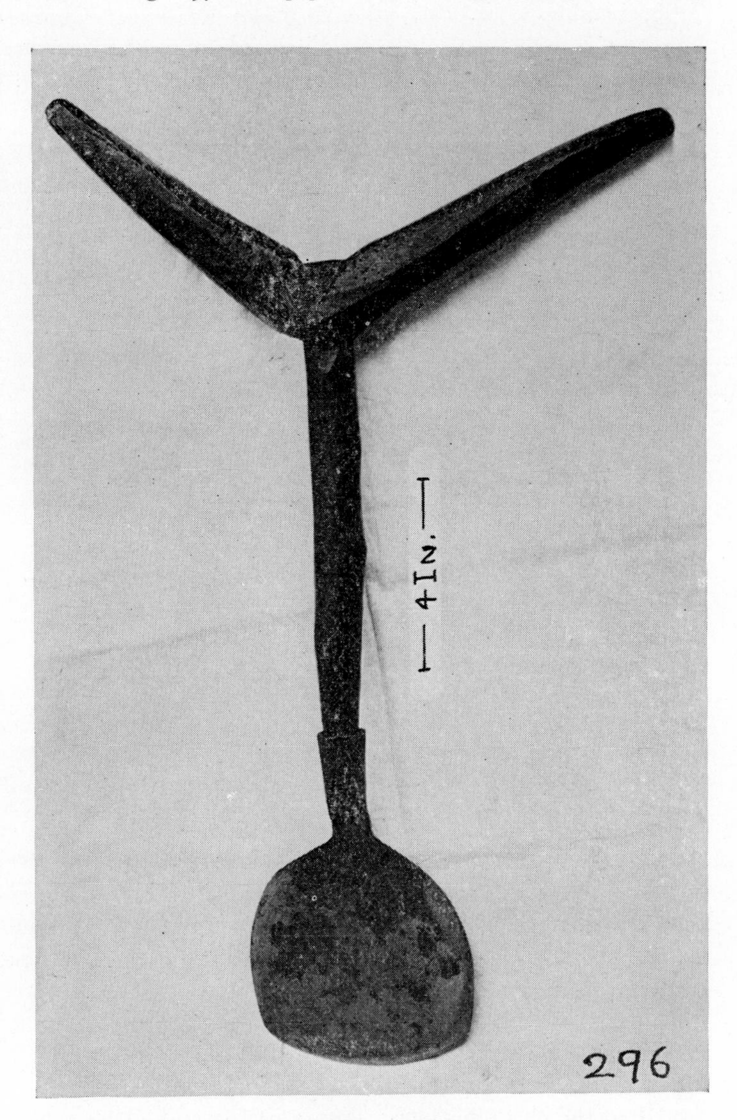

FIG. 301. LEATHER MAKER'S TRIMMING KNIFE. This instrument measures 17 inches from the crotch to the edge of the blade. The sharp edge, slightly concave is 5 inches wide. The metal part is 7 inches long from its edge to the end of the socket.

Fukien border, smoking of leather is practiced as described above. I also saw the curing of leather with smoke in Hupeh province.

SHOEMAKING

Shoemaking is one of the itinerant trades in China. The shoes mostly worn are of cloth, used for both sole and uppers, the making of which has already been described. The soles are usually sewn by the women at home, likewise the uppers. Both are then given to the shoemaker, hailed from the street, who trims the soles with his knife, shown in Fig. 305 (another knife is shown in Fig. 306), and sews the uppers to the welt upon the soles. A section of a tree, similar to the chopping block, shown in Fig. 198, is used as a lap-board. The sewing is done over a wooden last, like the one photographed in Fig. 304, to give the proper shape to the shoe. It consists of two parts, one for the vamp or forepart of the shoe, and the other for the heel. Between these two pieces a few wooden blocks are inserted and finally a wedge to ensure the proper length of the shoe. The Chinese do not distinguish between right and left shoes. The shoemaker has usually only three sizes of lasts, one for a shoe to fit a foot 10 Chinese inches long, another for 9.9 Chinese inches, and the third for a foot 9.8 Chinese inches long.[12] The heel part is the same for all three. Anybody who has an abnormally large or small foot keeps his own last and furnishes it to the shoemaker to make shoes accordingly.

The last, Fig. 304, is made of hard wood. The length of this composite last is $9\frac{3}{4}$ inches. In inland China the crippling of female feet still persists. Shoeing these deformities is outside the realm of the shoemaker. The women make their own shoes or their servants make them for them. A last is not used, in fact the "lily feet" are such formless stumps, different in every individual, that each woman would have to have her own last.

Fig. 302. Leather Maker's Trestle for Trimming Hides.

SHOEMAKER'S TOOLS

A clever clamp is used for holding the shoe while sewing. It is shown in Fig. 307, and consists of two wooden boards which are mortised at one end into a wooden block. The other ends meet and are kept in this position by a rope tied around the two upright boards. Thus a vise is formed and the material to be sewn is held between the ends of the boards which represent the jaws of the vise. The contrivance rests upon the ground and the shoemaker who sits upon a

[12] The Chinese foot measure is decimally divided into 10 inches. It is very indefinite in regard to length, varying with trades and localities.

low stool or his tool box holds the clamp between his knees. Working in this position he is just as liable to become knock-kneed as his occidental brother. The clamp or vise, Fig. 307, is 23 inches high, 8½ inches wide across the bottom opening. The boards forming the jaws are 3½ inches wide, ½ inch thick, and the base plate is 1¾ inches thick.

Fig. 308 shows a more elaborate clamp for sewing the soles of Chinese cloth shoes. The principle is the same, only in this specimen the tightening of the two jaws of the clamp for holding the working piece, is done with a wooden key which passes through long vertical slots in the uprights of the clamp. The tightening is done by pressing the horizontal wooden key downward when the knobs on both ends of the key draw the jaws together and hold them in place by mere friction. I saw and photographed this contrivance at a lone farmhouse in the Wantsai Mountains, North-western Kiangsi.

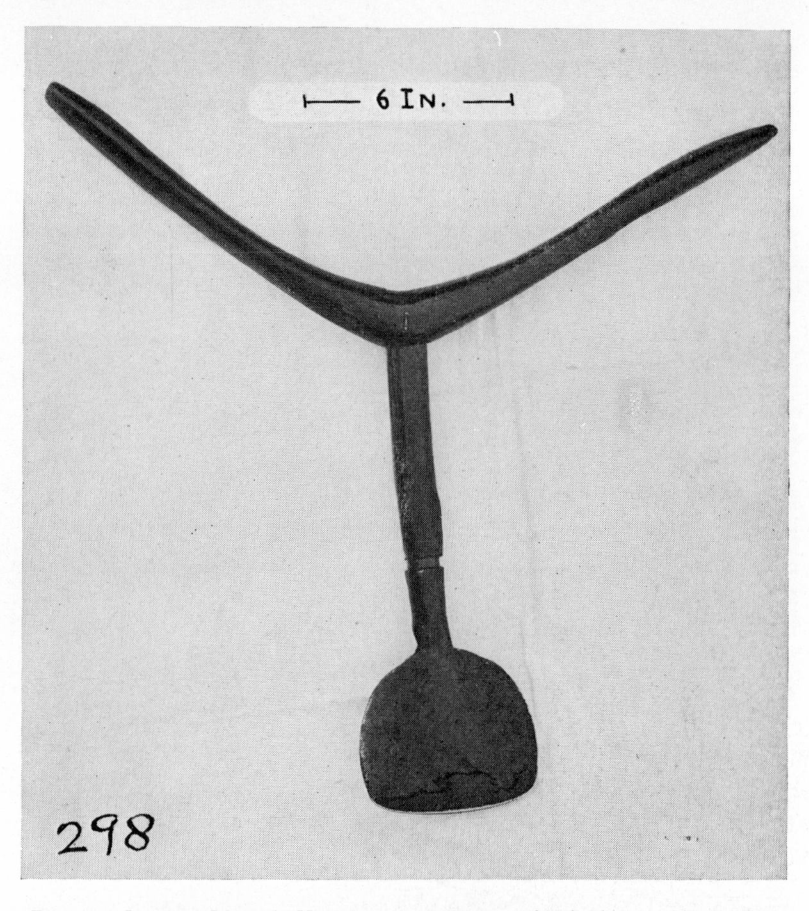

Fig. 303. Leather Maker's Hide-Softening Knife. This knife resembles in shape Fig. 301 and is handled over the same trestle in the same way. Its blade is dull and it is not used to cut clean the under surface of the hide, but to soften the leather and make it pliant.

Shoemakers as a rule use such clamps, but they are also occasionally found in isolated farmhouses where the women supply the whole household with shoes. In Germany the harness makers, in my childhood days, had a similar clamp, which, holding the leather worked upon, left the hands free to sew with two needles. The western shoemaker, who sews in the same way with two needles, used to hold the shoe on his knees and had a leather strap

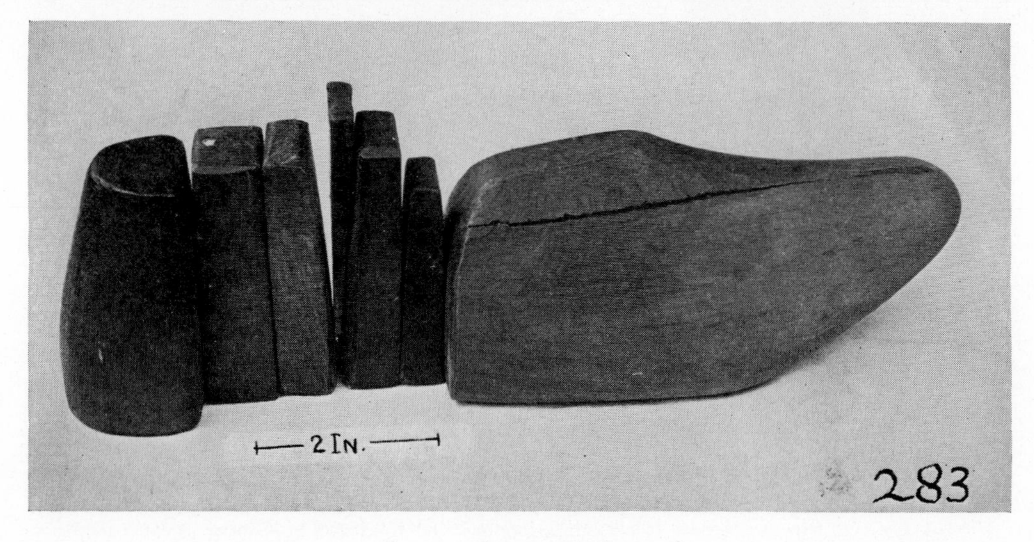

Fig. 304. Shoemaker's Last.

FIG. 305. SHOEMAKER'S KNIFE FOR TRIMMING THE SOLES OF SHOES. This knife was photographed at Teh An, Kiangsi. The blade is 4½ inches square, with one corner rounded off. The tang rests in a wooden handle 3¼ inches long. The thickest part of the blade is ⅛ inch thick. The edge is kept razor-sharp

passing over it which he kept taut with his feet.

The Chinese awl sticking in the soles, has a large ball end, admirably fitted to exert pressure with the palm of the hand. Householders rarely use an awl for such sewing. They produce better soles by sewing with one needle so that only one thread passes through one hole. The work is then more cumbersome and a needle puller has to be used to pull the needle through the heavy cloth soles. Another important point is that in that case one continuous thread has to be used for the sewing of the whole sole. This the expert woman worker gauges properly when twisting the thread.

With the awl in the right hand and a round piece of wood in the other the shoemaker works at his sewing. First he makes a hole with

FIG. 306. SHOEMAKER'S KNIFE. This represents another type of shoemaker's knife. The blade is 4½ inches long, the edge 2 inches. The tang rests in a wooden handle 3½ inches long and 1¼ inches in diameter. An iron ferrule secures the handle from splitting. Photographed in Kienchang, Kiangsi.

the awl, and then pushes through it the two hempen threads, tipped with hog's bristles, each in an opposite direction. Laying the thread over the handle of the awl in the one hand, with the round piece of wood in the other, he pulls the threads tight, and so proceeds sewing from hole to hole in the same manner. In some districts, instead of the wooden stick or puller, the shoemaker holds in his hand a bamboo tube, about 4 inches long and ½ of an inch in diameter, with one end closed and the open end stuffed with oil-soaked cotton. Before every stitch he lubricates the point of the awl by pushing it into the oiled cotton. This sewing with two threads which cross each other in the hole through which they pass, is the same method practiced by our shoemakers and workers in leather. For sewing of short stretches the shoemaker does not trouble to attach hog-bristles to the thread,

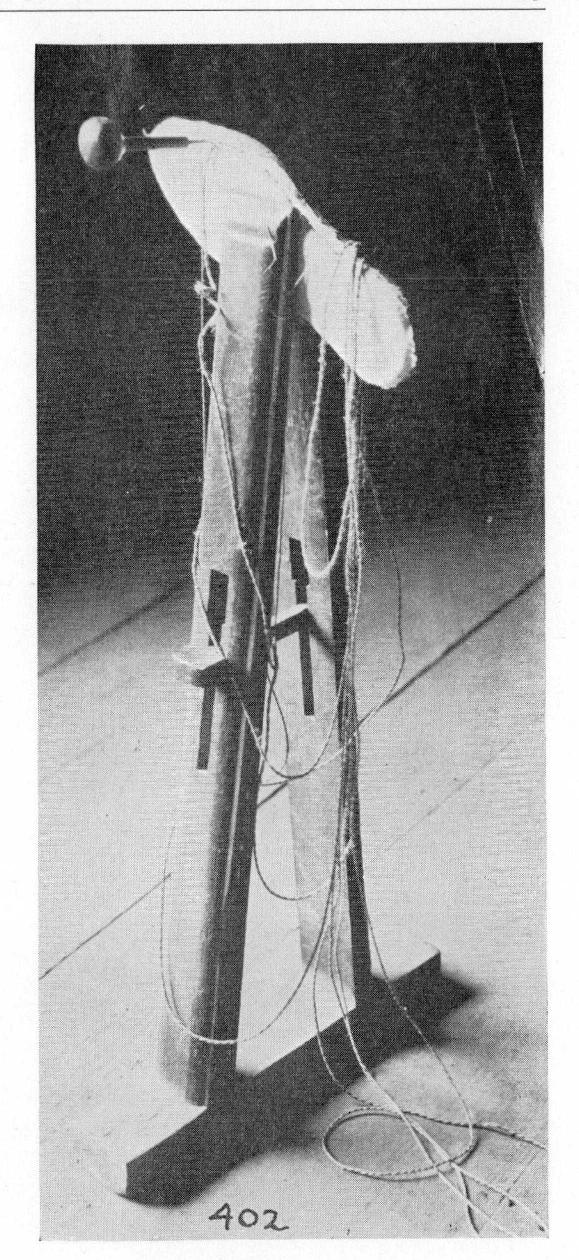

Fig. 308. Shoemaker's Clamp.

he sews them the same way with two threads, but with steel needles at their ends.

The mode of sewing with awl and bristle-tipped thread is peculiarly reminiscent of the most primitive sewing before the advent of needles. We know that then thorns, splinters of bone or fish bones were used for perforating the material to be sewed. Whether at the same time bristles were attached to the thread, has not been proved, although it seems likely. Another question we would like to answer is whether the Chinese shoemaker tipped the

Fig. 307. Shoemaker's Clamp.

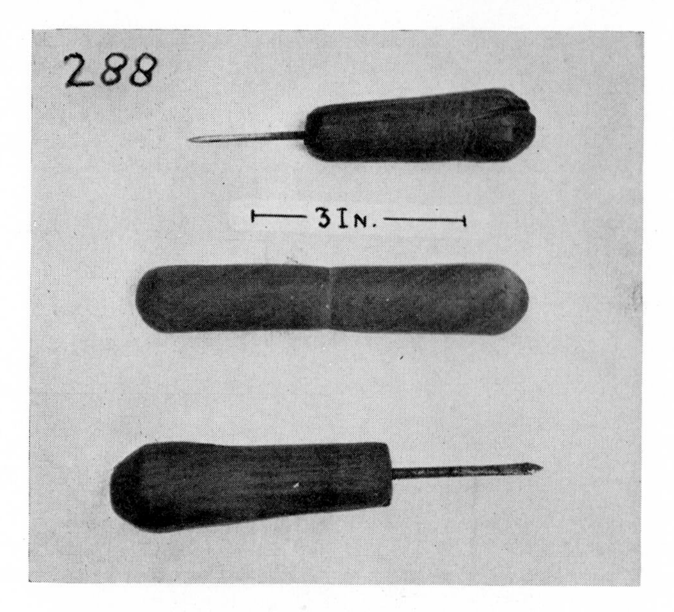

Fig. 309. Shoemaker's Awls and Thread Puller.

thread with bristles, before this was done in Europe.

Fig. 309 shows two awls and the piece of wood used for pulling the thread. The larger awl has a flattened point 3/32 of an inch wide, the smaller one a similar point 1/16 of an inch wide. The former is used for perforating soles and the latter for the uppers. The thread puller, a round piece of hard wood, 5½ inches long, shows in the middle a groove worn by much usage from the thread. To attach the hog bristles the thread is first twisted to a fine point. The end of the bristle is then frayed, the frayed end split and the thread end laid into the split fissure, and wound a few times around the one half of the split bristle. Next the two frayed halves of the bristle are twisted around the thread and finally the pointed bristle pushed through a loop made by pulling apart the strands of the thread, and this repeated when the procedure is finished.

Cloth shoes soon show wear, the part covering the toes usually gives way first, the soles get thin, and the heel part becomes trodden down. Here again the shoemaker has to help. He carries leather with him and sews on patches where needed. The leather he cuts with his big scissors shown in Fig. 312. They are 9¾ inches long and have the characteristic, comfortable handle loops which we have noticed already on other scissors. The worn soles the cobbler often reinforces with big hob-nails. To drive them he puts the shoe over his pegging jack. This instrument, made of forged iron, is shown in Fig. 313. The top is shaped to fit the shoe.

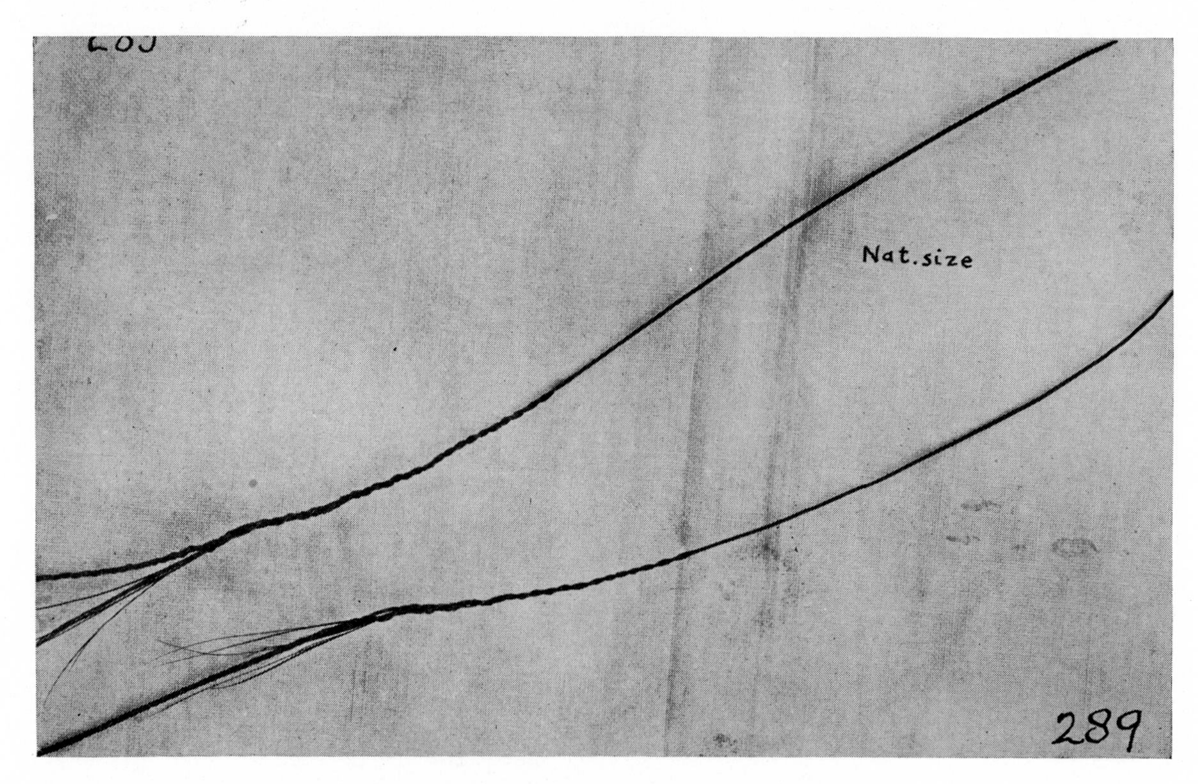

Fig. 310. Shoemaker's Thread Tipped with Hog Bristles.

On the stem is a knob, up to which the shoemaker pushes it into the ground or between flagstones of paving, wherever he happens to be working to give the necessary stability. The pegging jack is 10 inches long, the head 5¾ inches long, 2 inches wide at one end and 1½ inches at the other.

The claw hammer, Fig. 314, is used, for driving hob-nails, and for hammering new cloth-soles to make them pliable. The head of the hammer is 3¾ inches long, the butt end 1 inch square. The other end is cleft for pulling nails as I was told, although it is hard to see how that is done with the battered specimen shown. The whole length of the hammer with handle is 5½ inches.

The itinerant shoemaker carries his whole shop with him. Over his shoulder he bears a carrying pole at one end of which dangles a box with drawers for tools while at the other hangs a basket containing the rest of his equipment. The box also serves as a seat. A bundle of hemp he always carries with him for

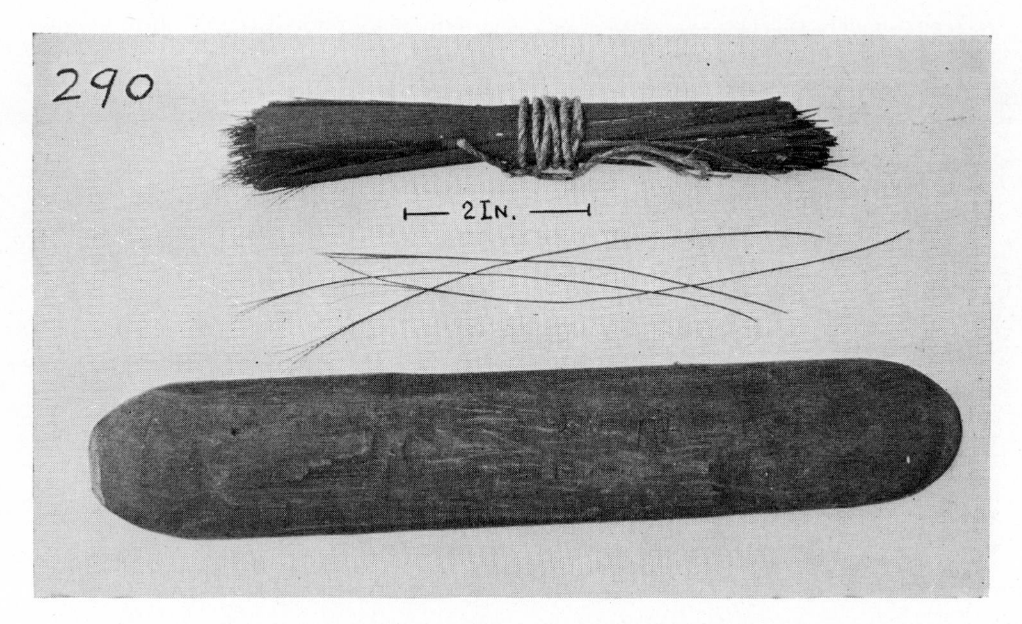

FIG. 311. SHOEMAKER'S BRISTLES AND BAMBOO BURNISHER.

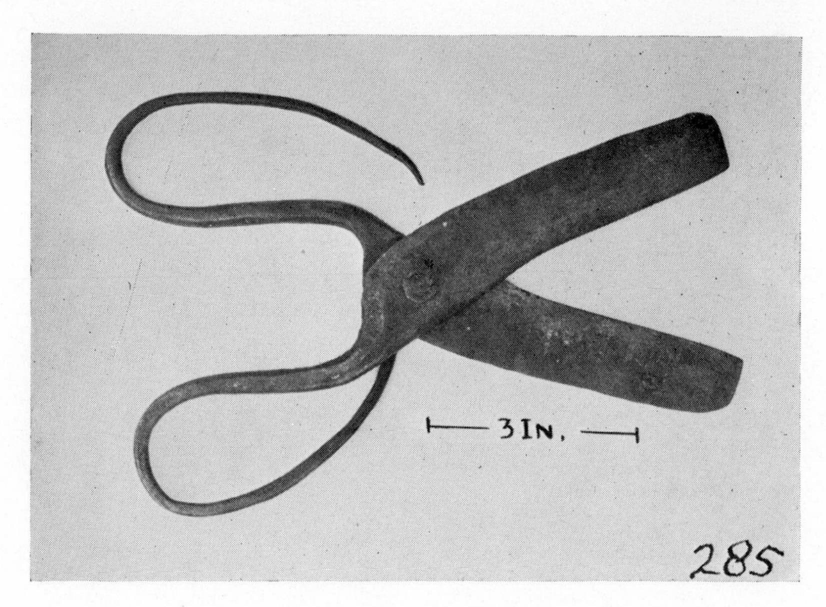

FIG. 312. SHOEMAKER'S SCISSORS.

making thread. I never saw a shoemaker wax his thread. In Kiangsu he twists his thread with the bone-spindle (cf. Fig. 245), in other places he twists the hemp upon his bare leg or upon a roofing tile which he places upon his thigh.

There are also permanent shoemaker shops, in fact the itinerant shoemakers are usually apprentices of the former. These stationary shoemakers work usually in leather which they prepare on their premises. As has been explained, their product is of a poor kind, made without a tanning agent, not worthy name of leather.

In many details the procedure of Chinese shoemaking is similar to the European. What I have described is based upon observation in country districts where foreign influence is not to be suspected. If some points seem to be introduced from Europe the question arises why not other important ones as the waxing of thread and the shoemaker's globe or reflector. The latter was an adjunct in every German shoemaker shop to comparatively recent times.

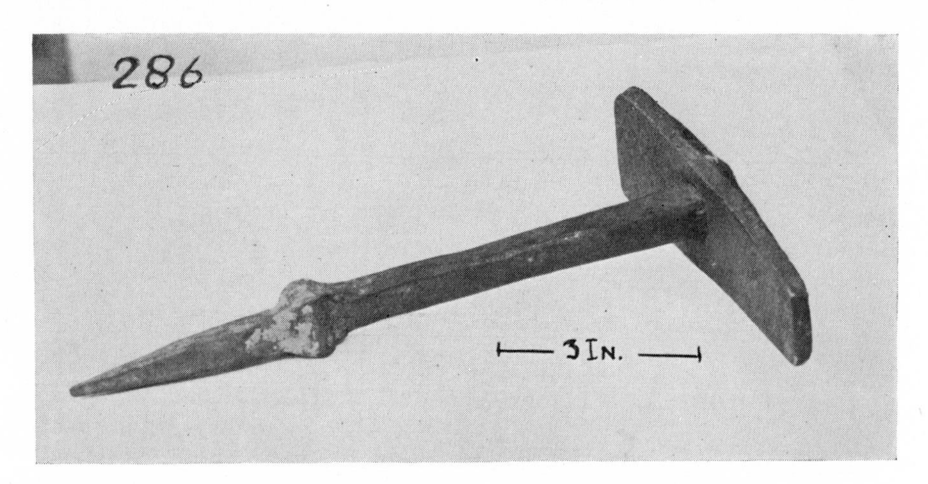

Fig. 313. Shoemaker's Pegging Jack.

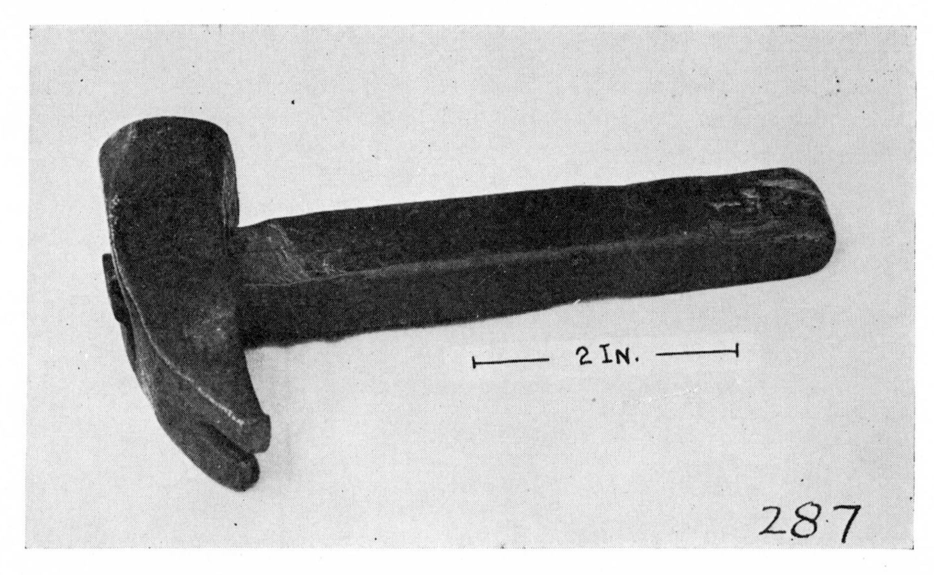

Fig. 314. Shoemaker's Claw Hammer for Driving and Extracting Hob-Nails.

Chapter IV

TOOLS FOR PROVIDING SHELTER

TREE FELLING

IN CHINA as in America the forests are gradually disappearing. The phenomenon of wholesale deforestation is a feature of modern civilization and has produced certain methods and implements to attain its end, especially in America where the virgin forests of a whole continent have fallen victim to the greedy lumber merchants. In China deforestation was a slow process, extending over centuries, and the ordinary felling tools and methods were always sufficient, when plenty of time was on hand and the cost of labor was of little consequence. In the mountain regions in Central and Southern China there are still large forests and when a tree is needed by a peasant he cuts it down with his axe or a bill-hook, lopps off the branches, saws it in convenient lengths on the spot, and then carries the sections away on his shoulders. If it is the full length trunk he wants, and it has to be carried some distance, he sometimes drives a wooden wedge into the log near the center of gravity, which serves him as a handle to steady the beam resting on his shoulders. Thus a single man can be seen carrying a tree 25 feet long and a foot in diameter at the butt end, upon his shoulder from the Poyang Lake up to Kuling, a trip of two hours through rising ground to the foothills and then after that a two hour climb continuously upgrade. In Kuling such trees are sawed up for building construction. Larger trees if they have to be transported are moved by mass labor with rope and carrying poles, each end of which rests upon the shoulder of one man. There are no other mechanical means, nor is animal power used.

In other districts where larger supplies of lumber are cut to be united into rafts and thus conveyed along the rivers, an ordinary pike or boat hook is used by the river-drivers to handle the logs. In southwestern Chekiang, high up in the mountains, I saw piles of cut timber along the mountain streams. As soon as the spring freshets come, the logs are rolled into the stream and it is the task of the lumber-men to follow the mountain stream, for many miles at times, until it flows ino a less rapid river. Armed with the boat hook they look for logs stopped in their downward path, and set them off anew on their voyage. In quieter waters the logs are then collected and united into rafts.

Here I wish to register a protest against the wanton deforestation carried on in the hinter-land of the port of Wenchow, Chekiang, instigated by Japanese interests, I was told. China has a bureau of forestry, and forest stations in many provinces, among them one in Chekiang. The officials, who should protest, get their bribes, and that settles the matter. In Chuchow, a two or three days' trip up the river from Wenchow, there has been more high water in the last five years, than at any time before within the memory of the people. Farther up the same river, in the Lungchuan district where the hills have not yet been entirely despoiled of their forests the local gentry have refused to have any more charcoal exported. The tax collector went raving mad over this refusal and swore he would have this lucrative business resumed, if necessary by force, "for the good of the country."

AXE

As a result of the almost total disappearance of the forests in China, a real tree-felling axe is a rarity. I finally ran across one in Kien Chang, Kiangsi, near the Fukien border, a natural border formed by a thickly wooded mountain range. The photograph, Fig. 315, shows the complete axe. The head, from poll to bit, measures 9 inches, the poll is square, with sides 1⅛ inches long, and the edge of the bit is 1½ inches long. The entire length of the axe with handle is 2 feet.

It is interesting to establish (as it is also the case in the Chinese hatchet, Fig. 350) that the Chinese are quite aware of the advantage gained by making the poll of such weight, that it outweighs, or at least

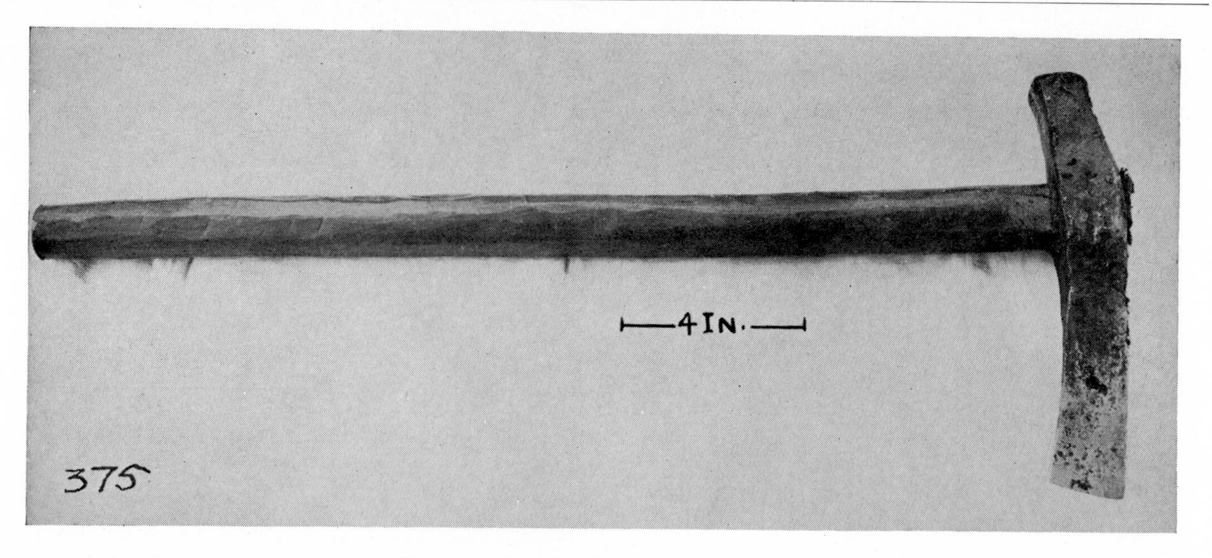

FIG. 315. CHINESE FELLING AXE.

balances the weight of the bit. If this were not the case, as for instance in the German axe, the handle would have to be gripped much more firmly, in order to prevent the heavier bit from deviating from the intended direction. The Chinese are not unique in making use of this principle. A Roman heavy iron axe, excavated at the Saalburg, a former Roman stronghold on the Limes in Germany shows this construction, as do Swedish axes from the oldest times to this day. A Swedish missionary, Mr. G. Nystroem, formerly engaged in the carpenter trade, told me that the present-day axe in Sweden is of that type. He estimates the proportion of length of poll to length of bit as 1 to 2, that means that the distance from the face of the poll to the eye is about one half the distance from the cutting edge to the eye. Most of these Swedish axes are now factory-made, but in the country districts many are still made by the village blacksmith. In the meantime I have acquired a Danish axe which shows the same characteristics and proves the statement of the Swedish missionary.

LOG HOOK

The Chinese do not know our type of cant hook, but in its place use the tool shown in Fig. 316. It consists of a slightly curved steel point projecting sideways from an iron ring, forming therewith one piece, about 6 inches long, mounted and rammed upon the end of a bamboo pole about 4 feet 8 inches long. Powerful leverage can be obtained by setting the hook under a beam and forcing the handle backward. The Chinese carpenter starts with logs as his raw material and usually has a pile of them in his yard, and for handling them employs the hook shown herewith. Another way of working this tool is to jab the log by swinging the tool point down upon it with some force, and then pull the handle so as to shift the log. This tool was photographed in Linkiang, Kiangsi.

LOG MARKING HAMMERS

The marking hammers, Fig. 317, were procured from a junk dealer in Nanchang, Kiangsi province.

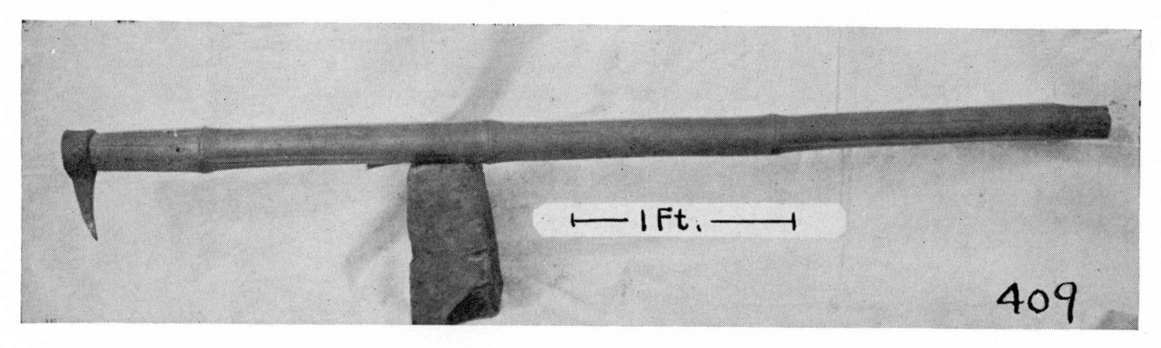

FIG. 316. CHINESE LOG HOOK.

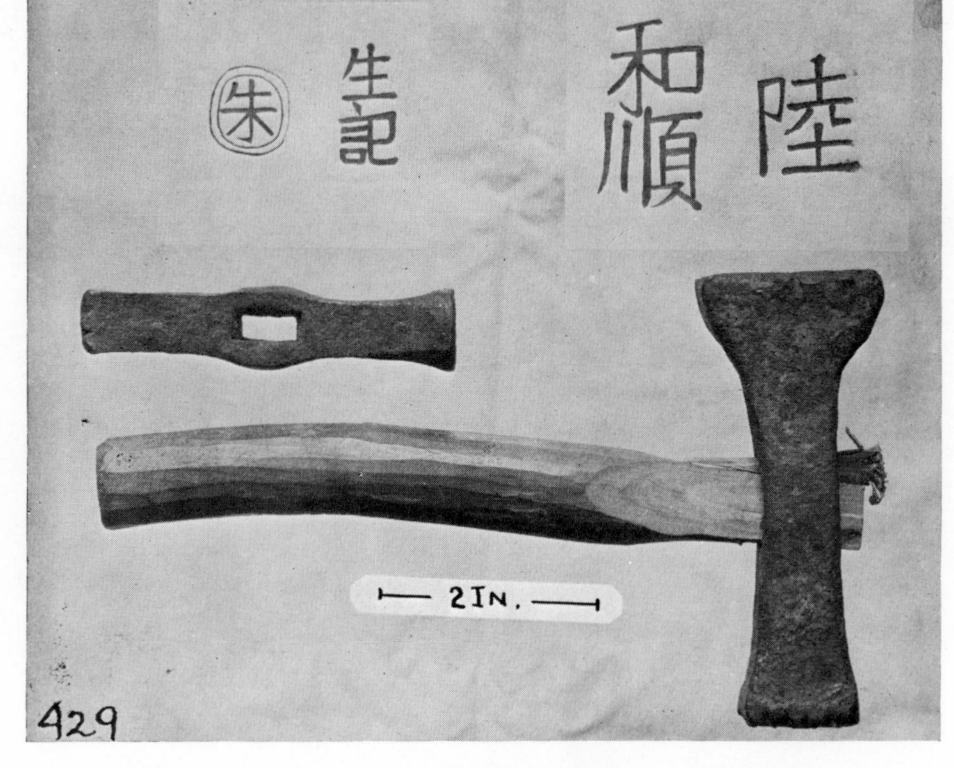

Fig. 317. Log Marking Hammer.

They are both of forged iron, and the dies on the faces are hand-cut. In each instance there is the shop-name on one pounding face and the personal name, on the other and we were told that the hammers were used for marking lumber. The procedure was to press the die into red marking ink, and then mark the lumber by hitting the wood a sharp blow with it thus leaving the impression sunk in the wood outlined in red. The smooth cross-cut log ends are marked in this manner to identify the logs easily when they stray on their downward path in the mountain streams. I never saw evidence of burning the marks into the wood. The handle shown on the one hammer is not original.

The large hammer with handle is 4 inches long, meaning only the metal part. The other one is 3¾ inches in length. The Chinese characters on the picture from left to right are: Chu (personal name), Sheng Chi (shop name), Ho Shun (also a shop name), and Lu (again a personal name). These characters, shown on the picture, are the actual impressions of the marking hammers.

The marking of articles with a die with more or less force is a common idea with the Chinese. Pewter is thus marked, jewelry of gold and silver, iron tools, cutlery, sometimes also earthenware, porcelain and bricks. The material of the dies, of course, varies according to the hardness of the material to be

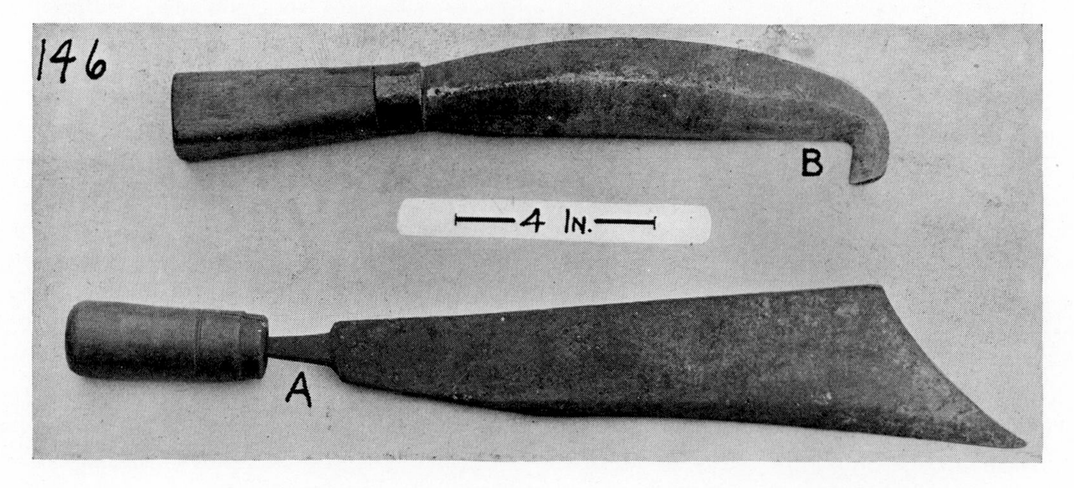

Fig. 318. Knife for Felling Bamboo (*A*), and for Splitting (*B*).

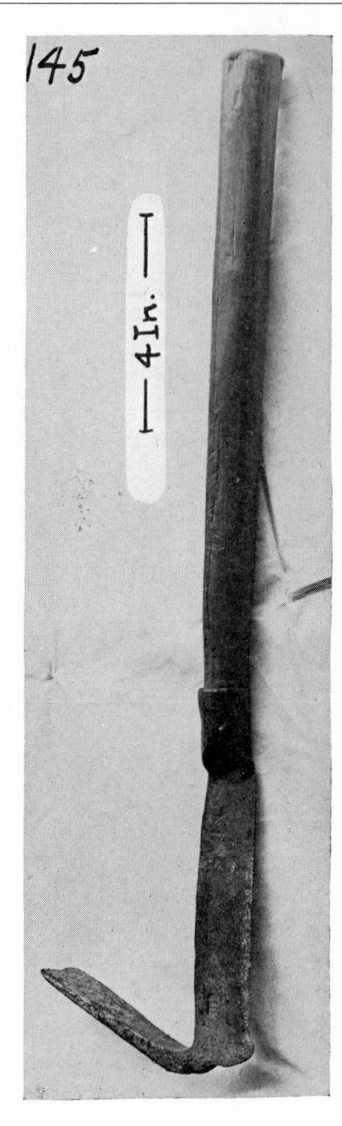

FIG. 319. KNIFE-HOE FOR CUTTING BAMBOO.

marked. It ranges from hardest steel to soft wood. It is interesting to note that the Chinese, in spite of this technical knowledge, have never struck coins, but clung until very recently to the old method of casting coins.

UTILIZATION OF BAMBOO

The bamboo tree is of the greatest economic importance in China, and its uses seem endless. I give at random a few of the thousand and one applications which confronted us at every turn in going through the country. The whole unsplit stems, or parts of them, are used for ships' masts, for scaffolds in building construction, for fences, water pipes, walking sticks, carrying poles, furniture, fishing rods, well-sweeps, tool handles, containers. The wood of the stems split up is utilized for mats, baskets, hats, musical instruments, bows and arrows, chairs and stools, tables and shelves, screens, staves, tallies and token money, chopsticks, fans, combs, umbrella frames, torches, candle wicks, ropes and many other things.

The botanists distinguish a great variety of bamboo trees. But as the species produces flowers and fruit only once in from 30 to 60 years, very little has been done to classify its various kinds systematically. Some grow to a height of over a hundred feet, another black-stemmed type, does not exceed the height of a man. The regular distance between the joints, varying in different species, affords one means of classification. There are also some trees with joints close together near the root, the distance between the joints however increasing from joint to joint on their way upward. Most of the trees are hollow between the joints, a few are solid throughout. Most of them are round, but some form a square stem.

There is no cultivation of these trees worth speaking of. They grow most prolifically anywhere in Southern China, as far up as the Yangtse River. A mature tree sends out a number of suckers in the ground in all directions, and from these grow, towards the end of winter, and in early spring, the bamboo shoots from which new trees develop. The growth is rapid, in one season a height of from 20 to 100 feet may be reached, depending on the species. I once took measurements of the growth of a young bamboo stem in Spring and found that in 24 hours it had grown 25 inches. The shoots have the form of a cone, and have a diameter up to 4 inches at the base, reaching a height of a foot or more. They are tender and have the most delicate flavor and are shipped by the thousands to the markets to be used as vegetables. It is an unwritten law that after the Ching Ming festival, on the fifth day of the fourth moon, no more shoots are to be cut. Any shoots missed by the diligent searchers have now a chance to grow up into trees.

To fell a bamboo tree the knife marked *A* in Fig. 318 is used. The tree is severed immediately under a joint as near as possible to the ground by hacking the hollow stem all around with the knife. The whole length of the instrument is 19 inches. The handle is not original, it had a handle like *B* on the same photograph. The edge from tang to point measures 13 inches. The greatest width of the blade is 3 inches. The thickness of the back increases from ¼ inch at

FIG. 320. KNIFE FOR SHAVING BAMBOO.

the tang to ½ inch at the point where the back ends. This makes the instrument rather heavy at the end, which however, is an aid in dealing a forceful blow.

A worker in bamboo buys a whole stem, saws it in convenient lengths and splits these sections with the knife *B* to suit his purposes. Holding the section vertically he starts splitting at the top. Once a start is made, the splitting proceeds easily, thanks to the triangular cross-section of the knife. The blade, here shown on the downward side of the tool does the cutting and the triangular shape acts like a wedge forcing the split parts asunder. The cutting edge is as sharp as a razor and to press the knife downward until a slit has been started, is all that is required. The bamboo to be split stands on the floor and the knife on its downward path will finally reach the ground, the nose at the end of the blade, however, protects the edge from getting dulled. The whole length is 14 inches the greatest width 2 inches and the thickness of the ridge in the center ⅜ of an inch. The tang passing through the handle is clenched. An iron ferrule strengthens the handle. The picture Fig. 318, was taken in the Native City, Shanghai.

Fig. 319 represents an iron hoe and knife combined. The metal part of the tool ends in a socket which holds the wooden handle. The other end is bent at right angles to form the hoe. The straight shank of the tool has been fashioned into a knife and thus the tool serves two purposes. The ground around the tip of the bamboo shoot is removed with the hoe, the whole shoot laid bare and then cut off at its base with the knife of the implement. The photograph of the tool discussed was taken at Se Aw, Chekiang.

The implement is 18½ inches long, handle included. The width of the knife, i.e., the flat blade, extending downwards from the handle to the hoe-end, is 1⅜ inches wide and the thickness at the back ¼ of an inch. The length of the part forming the hoe is 5⅝ inches. The edge of the hoe is concave and measures 1⅛ inches from point to point. Note the projecting nose at the lower end of the knife-blade for the protection of its edge. A socket forged on the blade-top received the wooden handle.

For cutting bamboo shavings which are used to

FIG. 321. BAMBOO SHAVE.

stuff mattresses and pillows, the tool shown in Fig. 320 is used. The large oval flat part is made of bamboo, and has round holes for attaching the iron knife seen in place upon the wooden part. The two round holes below can be used for attachment of a larger knife to the same holder. The knife forms a square iron block-bevelled blade. Under the square part of the knife is a hole, 1 inch by two inches, through which the shavings pass. The edge of the knife is set to leave a space of about 1/16 of an inch between it and the wood. The tool is held with the hand grasping the oval wooden holder at the back of the knife where, as seen at the bottom of the picture, the wooden oval has been hollowed away. For cutting shavings the instrument is pushed along the bamboo like a plane. The metal part is $1\frac{1}{8}$ inches wide and $2\frac{1}{2}$ inches long, not including the projections which bent at right angles form the tangs passing through the wood. The tangs are held in the holes by friction only. They are 2 inches in length although the average thickness of the wooden holder is about $\frac{5}{8}$ of an inch. Immediately in front of the knife edge, the bamboo holder is cut slanting to allow purchase for the blade. Similar tools with narrower blades are used for cutting strips and splints of bamboo. The distance between blade and bamboo determines the thickness of the strip or splint or shaving to be cut. This and the tool described in the next paragraph represent an early attempt to produce a tool similar to our wood plane. The photograph was taken in the Native City, Shanghai.

Bamboo stems have a thin cover, rich in silica, which the Chinese remove before the stem is cut up for making utensils. This skin is originally dark green, becomes lighter in color from year to year and finally turns a light yellow. This color is the only means for judging the age of a bamboo, as the stem reaches its full thickness and height within a few months. The instrument shown in Fig. 321 is used for scraping off this skin from the bamboo stem. A curved knife-blade with two tangs is stuck through a short bamboo tube. The distance of the blade edge from the bamboo tube is just sufficient to allow scraping without cutting into the bamboo stem along which the instrument is pushed. The diameter of the bamboo tube is $1\frac{1}{2}$ inches and its length is 6 inches. The instrument is held with the right hand, the ball of the thumb over the blade, and pushed over the stem of a bamboo in a direction away from the body. The photograph was taken in Foochow, Kiangsi province.

Fig. 322. Board Saw or Pit Saw.

WOODWORKING TOOLS

SAWING

Boards are sawn from a log with saws like the one shown in Fig. 322. The height of the saw is 5 feet and the length of the crosspieces holding the saw-blade 30 inches. The round wooden pole, about 2 inches in diameter, run-

Fig. 323. Board Sawing and Sawyer's Scaffold.

ning parallel to the saw-blade, is held between the crosspieces by mere compression without mortise and tenon. The saw-blade, made by a native blacksmith, is 4 feet 7 inches long, 2½ inches wide, and about 1/16 of an inch thick. The teeth are set starting from the middle of the blade in such a way that they point in opposite directions towards the ends of the blade, in other words the teeth from one end to the middle of the blade cut one way, and thence to the other end of the blade they cut in the opposite direction. This arrangement of the teeth compels each of the two sawyers using this saw to do an equal amount of work. With our old pitsaws, the pitman in drawing the saw downward did the actual cutting while the topman merely pulled the saw up again. At each end of the blade a loop is attached formed by a strip of iron, the ends of which are folded over the end of the saw-blade. The blade with these iron loops is drawn taut by the side arms of the saw frame, and can be shifted to accommodate the saw to various sized logs. If the blade is adjusted farther away from the center brace, naturally boards can be sawn from a thicker log. The saw-blade is kept taut by the rope with the toggle stick. Hard wood is used for the two side arms of the saw frame but the center brace is usually of pine. The saw is always handled by two men, one at each side arm. They grasp the side arm with the blade between their hands. The saw is held with the frame against either side of the log, as convenience dictates.

The ways of placing the log to be sawed are various but the professional sawyers usually adopt the method shown in Fig. 323. To construct a saw scaffold two round beams are tied together at one end and the other ends spread apart. Next the log to be sawed is raised up into the air at one end and the scaffold beams with the tied ends, placed over the log. Another short beam is then placed under the log so as to rest upon the two scaffold beams and is tied securely to them with ropes. The topman lays a board against the log for him to stand on. The position of the log on the scaffold can be changed to suit conditions. When the sawing begins the log is so placed on the scaffold that the one end can readily be reached by the sawyer. As sawing proceeds the position of the log is changed to form a larger angle with the ground. The kerfs are sawed as far as possible and then the log is reversed and sawing resumed until kerf meets kerf. A wedge is used to keep the kerf at which the men are sawing, from pinching the saw blade. Heavier logs are made to rest against boards or beams placed over other large logs and the end is weighted to the ground with large stones. The end sticking up into the air is in addition sometimes supported by a short perpendicular pole. Logs of heavy hardwood are stood on end and the men do the sawing with the saw in a horizontal position. They saw them as far down as possible and then break the boards apart.

The equipment of the sawyers consists of saw, saw-set and file, linemarker and oiler. Fig. 324 shows a saw-set and file combined, the whole length of

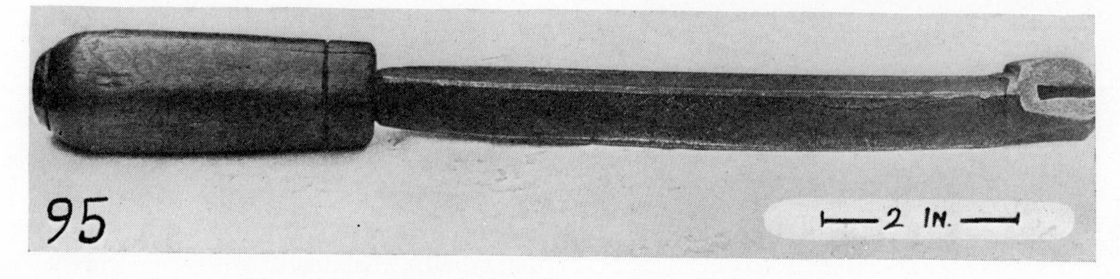

Fig. 324. Carpenter's Saw-Set or Saw Wrest and Saw File.

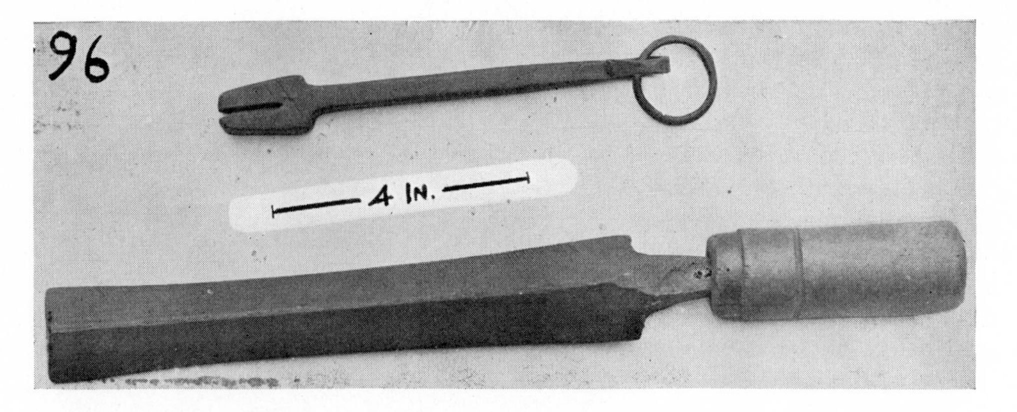

Fig. 325. Carpenter's Saw-Set or Saw Wrest (Single Tool Above) and Carpenter's Saw File.

which including handle is 11 inches. The file is triangular with its two upper faces smooth and only the

Fig. 326. Carpenter's Saw Oiler.

lower face is ridged with indentations. Saw-set an file as separate tools are seen in Fig. 325. With th notched saw wrest or set the saw teeth are twisted t the right and left alternately so as to widen the ker or cut of the saw.

As an oiler to oil the blade occasionally, a bambo tube stuck onto a base is used, the other end bein open and filled with a wad of cotton, saturated wit oil. This open end with the cotton extending a littl therefrom, is rubbed against the saw-blade. Fig. 32 shows a representative sample, blackened with dir and oil. Its whole height is 6½ inches, the diamete of the bamboo tube is 1½ inches.

Fig. 327 shows sawyers at work. It will be notice that they have been sawing kerfs only as far as th wooden props. The log was afterwards turned aroun to saw from the other end. This and the othe pictures, showing board sawing and tools, were take at different places, Figs. 322, 324 and 327 at Ch Tsuen, Chekiang, Fig. 326 at Se Aw, Chekiang, Fig 323 and 325 at Shanghai, in the Native City.

Fig. 328 gives a view of the type of board saw use in Kiangsi. The log from which boards are to b sawed is supported horizontally upon two trestles t which it is fastened with iron "dogs," or staples. Th sawyers, one at each side of the log hold the sa frame vertically, blade downward, and with the blad set at right angles to the frame, so that when the pull the frame back and forth the blade works in horizontal position. They walk slowly along th whole length of the log as the sawing progresses, an lift off the boards sawn, one after another. The spac between the saw blade, and the central pole of th saw need therefore not be very wide, and we fin indeed that saws used in this manner, are alway rather narrow compared with their length. The entir length of the saw is 4 feet 2 inches, the length of th end cross-pieces 11 inches. The width of the saw blade is almost 2 inches. As pointed out before the teeth are arranged in the peculiar Chinese way, one half of them up to the center of the blade pointing toward one end, and the other half toward the other end of the blade. The center pole of the saw is held by compression between the cross-arms, not mortised into them which would weaken them.

Fig. 329 gives a close-up view of the type of saw used in Central China. It was procured in Kuling for the Mercer Museum. The blade hammered out by the blacksmith, is about 2 inches wide and 4 feet long with riveted loops at each end. The center brace is loose, not even notched. Nevertheless, it is held firmly in place between the two end arms solely by leverage of the latter, caused by the strain of several strands of rope twisted with a toggle stick. The rope is made of the fibres of the chamærops palm. The overall dimensions of the saw are 4 feet 5 inches for the length and 1 foot 1 inch for the width. This saw is an entirely unbalanced contrivance, but the secret of working it is rice three times a day. The Chinese working-man consists of bones, muscles and skin; handling such a saw for twelve hours a day does not bother him. The muscles keep the saw balanced and what a strain is the sawyer does not know.

Fig. 330 shows a log squared with the hatchet, and resting horizontally upon two supports, ready for sawing. This way of propping the log, practiced throughout Kiangsi province, seems far more convenient than the fixing of the log in a slanting position, as we saw it done in the eastern part of China. The supports are formed in a simple manner of two sticks nailed together crosswise with one end of a slanting beam resting in the crotch. The lower end of the slanting beam is rammed into the ground or, if the sawing is carried on on a wooden floor as is shown in the picture, nailed to the floor. At the upper end of the beam a heavy stone is suspended with rope or wire to give rigidity to the structure. The log is fastened to the upper ends of the slanting beams by means of iron "dogs," stapling the log to the beam. This can be better seen in Fig. 331, which gives a closer view of the support. These iron dogs or staples secure the log firmly to the slanting beam. Two dogs are shown separately in Fig. 332. One is

Fig. 327. Chinese Board Sawyers, Sawing a Log into Boards.

5 inches long, and the other $6\frac{3}{4}$ inches. They were wrought by native blacksmiths. The sawyers, one on each side, walk alongside of the log, holding the saw-frame vertically at a convenient height, the blade, set at right angles to the frame, sliding back and forth horizontally, about 3 feet from the ground. Lines are carefully drawn on each side of the log with the line-marker (see Fig. 372 and 503). As the kerf widens the sawyer inserts for a wedge the head of the little hatchet seen hung on the wire in Fig. 331. The hatchet serves also for a hammer to drive in the iron dogs.

Fig. 328. Board Saw.

The frame of the carpenter's bow saw, Fig. 333, is made of hard wood. The entire length along the center rod is $27\frac{1}{2}$ inches. The center rod is held in mortises in the sidepieces. The length of the sidepieces is $14\frac{1}{2}$ inches. The saw blade, 23 inches long and $1\frac{1}{8}$ inches wide, was made by a native blacksmith and is held in the slotted ends of wooden pins, by iron nails passing through pin slot and saw-blade. The wooden pins are $\frac{1}{2}$ inch in diameter and have a wooden knob on one end which prevents them from slipping through the hole in the sidepieces where they revolve. The stretching of the saw-blade is accomplished by tightening the rope joining the other ends of the sidepieces with a toggle stick. The saw-blade is always set at an angle to the plane of the frame. This enables the carpenter when sawing to watch the saw-blade cutting along the desired line. Another advantage of setting the blade at an angle is that pieces of any length can be cut. If the saw-blade were in the same plane with the frame, then only kerfs corresponding in depth to the distance between the cutting edge of the blade and the center-rod of the frame could be cut. The teeth of this saw are set in such a way that sawing is done on the push. Various saws of this type are kept in a carpenter shop,

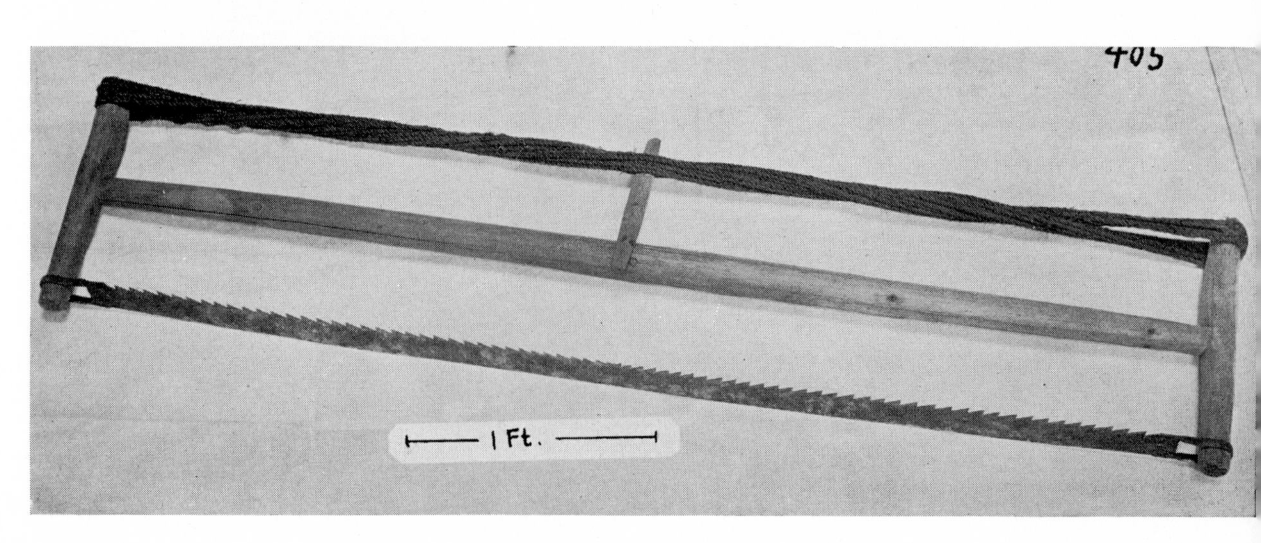

Fig. 329. Board Saw.

FIG. 330. LOG READY TO BE SAWN INTO BOARDS.

distinguished only by the size of frame or saw-blade, but never by the shape of teeth as far as my observations went. The use of a specially toothed rip-saw for cutting parallel to the line of grain is not known. The photograph was taken in the Native City of Shanghai.

The saw in Fig. 334 is merely a frame-saw of larger dimensions. The distance between saw-blade and center-rod, almost two feet, reveals that it is used for cross-cutting large logs. The tightening is the usual one with twisted rope and toggle-stick. The additional rope is a make-shift to hold the rickety frame together. The arrangement of the teeth in this saw, see Fig. 335, is rather unusual, and introduces a type I had never seen before in China. The teeth of the ordinary board saws and carpenters' frame saws are usually V shaped. In this saw between two teeth there is always a lower ridge, which is an aid in expelling accumulated saw-dust. Besides the teeth are not raked but with equally sharpened sides cut both ways. The saw is used for cutting thin slices about 10 by 4 inches and 3/16 of an inch thick, across the grain, from a log of camphor wood. These boards serve for the slabs on the endless chain of the irrigation wheel described under Figs. 79-83. The width of the saw-blade is 1½ inches and the distance between the points of the saw-teeth is one inch. The teeth are set. The length of the whole saw is 5½ feet, and the width a little over 3 feet. The enormous size of the saw is explained by the fact that it is employed not only for sawing the small slabs, but also for cross-cutting the whole camphor-wood log to convenient smaller lengths from which the small slabs are sawed. Two men work the saw with the frame held vertically and the rigid blade, teeth downward, cutting in a perpendicular downward direction. The camphor-wood log from which the slabs are cut is wedged against a post in the workshop in the same manner as is shown in Fig. 532.

BOAT BUILDER'S COMPASS SAW

Fig. 336 gives a view of a compass saw used by boat builders, photographed at Foochow, Kiangsi province, a center for the making of excellent river craft. To cut openings into timbers or boards, a hole is first drilled large enough to insert the point of the saw and then this hole is enlarged with the saw as desired. Among carpenters I never found such a saw in use. They employ for the same purpose a wire notched for teeth at close intervals with a file or chisel, and stretched between the ends of a bent bamboo rod. A hole is first drilled, the wire passed through the hole, and fastened to the ends of the bamboo rod. The length of the compass saw with handle is 1½ feet.

CROSSCUT SAW

A crosscut felling saw is also used in China. The blade appears curved from much sharpening and the teeth are on the concave part. The saw is handled by

FIG. 331. LOG DOGGED ON ITS TRESTLE TO BE SAWN INTO BOARDS. The squared log already line-marked, to be sawn horizontally into four boards, indicated by parallel lines dimly seen is stapled (dogged) fast upon the top log of one of its trestles.

two men. As the direction of the teeth indicates the saw cuts by being pulled by the hinged handle which is held at right angles to the blade. The length of the saw stretched out as shown on Fig. 337 is 2 feet 10 inches. The photograph was taken in Foochow, Kiangsi province.

BAMBOO WORKER'S SAW

A modification of the frame saw is shown in Fig. 338. Here the rope and toggle for stretching the saw-blade are ingeniously replaced by a flexible bamboo rod, hooked at its extremities through mortises upon the end pieces of the saw-frame. The tightening is accomplished by bending the bamboo rod toward the central member of the frame and fastening it thereto with rope or bamboo-splints. This kind of saw is used in various parts of China by workers in bamboo. The specimen shown was photographed in Nanchang, the capital of Kiangsi province.

FIREWOOD SAW

In the mountainous hinterland of King Teh Chen, which supplies all the wood for the voracious kilns (nearly a thousand coolie loads are used in a single heat per kiln), the type of saw shown in Fig. 339 is regularly used for cross-cutting the trees into convenient size, sticks about a foot and a half long. The saw is a one-man tool and held to cut on the push. The length of the blade is 3 feet 9½ inches, the width 1¾ inches. The bow is of willow wood and about 1¾ inches in diameter. The ends of the blade rest in slots of the bow and iron pins passing through holes in the blade-ends furnish a hold for the ends of the curved willow stick.

This saw is perhaps the earliest type of a saw-blade stretched by a frame. The problem of the primitive saw-maker was peculiar. To make the saw-blade efficient, strength was necessary, and hence sufficient thickness to keep the blade from bending or breaking. Thickness of blade, however, was a disadvantage, it meant the cutting of a wide kerf, correspondingly the expenditure of so much more energy. The problem was finally solved by making a thin blade, and stretching it taut upon a frame so as to overcome the tendency to bend or break, and at the same time enable it to cut a narrow kerf. The first attempt to do this was probably to stretch the blade between the ends of a wooden stick bent like a bow. One of the earliest reproductions of such a saw is pictured on an Attic vase of the 6th century B.C., found at Orvieto and now in the Fine Arts Museum at Boston.[1] A Greek smithy is shown on this vase and in the background, among other tools, the saw clearly depicted.

TREE FELLING SAW

A tree felling saw is represented in Fig. 340. The length along a straight line from handle to handle is

[1] The picture on this vase is shown in Neuburger, Albert, "Die Technik des Altertums," Leipzig, 1920.

3 feet 8½ inches, the widest width of the blade is 2¾ inches. The teeth are arranged in the usual Chinese way for a two-man saw, i.e., up to the center they point in one direction, and thence in the opposite direction. The handles are pieces of wood, 8 inches long, wedged into iron loops which are riveted to the ends of the saw blade.

This and the saw in Fig. 339, I found and photographed in a place called Ta Yao (Big Kiln) in the Lung Chuan district, Chekiang province. The name "Big Kiln" refers to the porcelain works which flourished there in the Southern Sung Dynasty (1127 to 1279 A.D.) and supplied the famed Seladon porcelain exclusively for the Imperial Court, then at Hangchow, the Kinsai of Marco Polo.

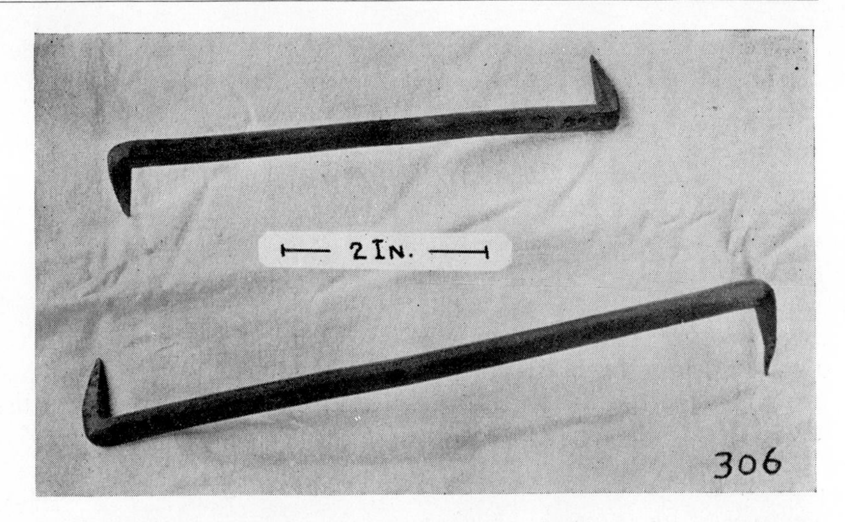

FIG. 332. LOG DOGS.

JAPANESE FELLING SAW

There is a tendency among Japanese workers to do things single-handed. Boards are sawn from the log by one man, and trees small or large are felled by one man. The saw represented in Fig. 341 is used for the latter purpose and the procedure is rather unique. When I first saw this implement which was in the possession of a Japanese in Kuling, Kiangsi province, and used by him occasionally, the end was stained with soil, a fact which is intimately connected with the use of the saw.

The Japanese peasant, previous to felling a tree, lays bare the top roots, and then takes his saw with both hands and pushes its end into the soil immediately over a root, and proceeds to saw through it. This he does with root after root, until the tree is ready to fall. In this manner a single man, patiently laboring, can bring down a mighty tree with a small saw which looks entirely inadequate for such an undertaking.

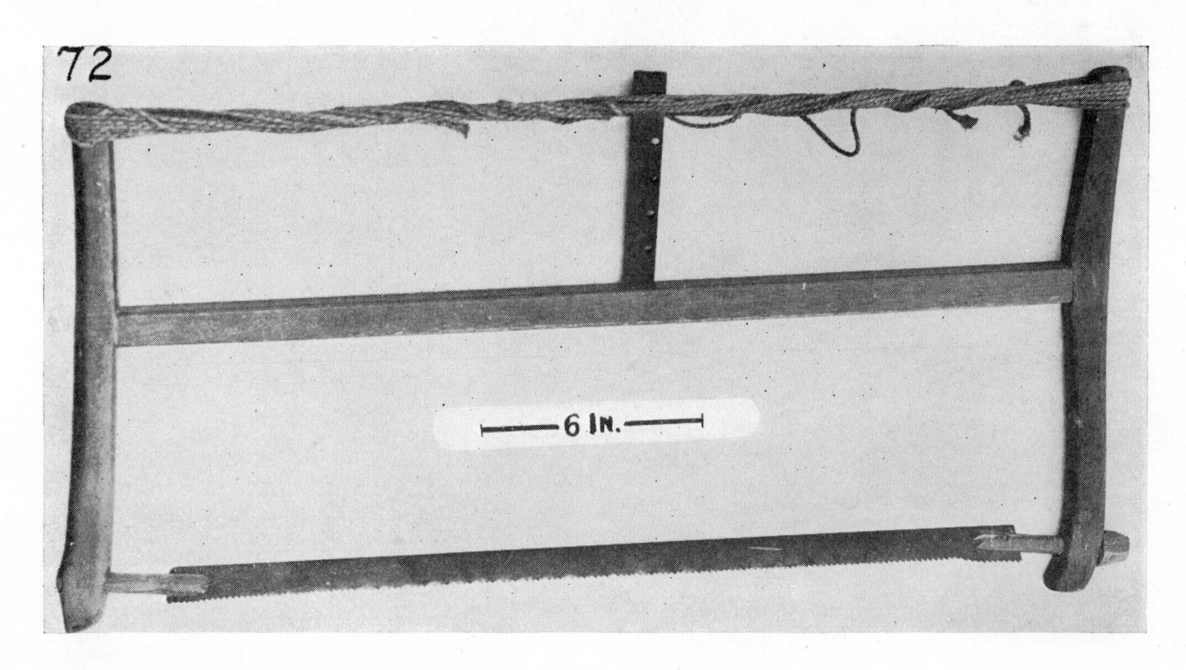

FIG. 333. CARPENTER'S BOW SAW.

The length of the saw is 35¾ inches. The part of the blade fitted with teeth is 16¾ inches long, and the greatest width of the blade is 3⅛ inches. While the whole saw is quite primitive in type, the blade is machine-rolled and not hammered out by hand. The thickness is 1/32 of an inch, which at the handle and tang is increased to 3/32 of an inch. The tang, flat as the blade and almost as wide as the diameter of the handle, rests in a slot of the wooden handle, which is wound for quite a distance with a strip of rattan, to hold the blade firmly in place, and at the same time afford a good grip for handling the saw. As the picture shows, the teeth point toward the handle and the saw, therefore, works on the pull.

The limited compass of the space in which those people work, who usually dwell on the floor and possess no furniture on which to sit, is demonstrated by the manner in which they use their tools. Thus, the Japanese carpenter with the floor for his work-bench uses saw and planes on the pull. A man like the Chinese, working at a bench, standing up can reach out and does better work by handling saw and plane on the push. Henry Disston & Sons, Philadelphia, assert in their interesting little book "The Saw in History" that Turkish saws cut on the pull, and we know that the Turks sit on the floor and use no chairs.

Fig. 342 shows an array of different Japanese saws. The uppermost is the felling saw already described. The blade is shown here on a larger scale and near the handle may be observed the impression of Chinese characters serving as trademark. Next comes a compass saw with the teeth peculiarly arranged. In the first place they are not set and the blade is thickest at the points of the teeth, getting thinner thence towards the back of the blade. This arrangement is necessary when the teeth are not set, to prevent the blade from jamming in the kerf. Another feature is that there are two parallel rows of teeth. Looking at the blade from the side, as it is presented in Fig. 345 (top), one can see that one tooth of the one row is between two teeth of the other. A wide kerf can be cut rapidly with this saw, a feature by no means primitive, and I am inclined to think that it is a foreign introduction. I have a small saw in a pocket-set of the same type which is of German manufacture. This compass saw is employed to make larger holes in wood. First a small hole is drilled with the whirling drill (see Fig. 368) and this is enlarged with the saw to whatever size is required. The length of the saw with handle is 14¼ inches, the toothed edge is 9⅛ inches long, and the largest width of the blade is ⅜ of an inch.

The third saw in the picture is toothed on both sides of the blade. It is

Fig. 334. Cross-Cut Saw.

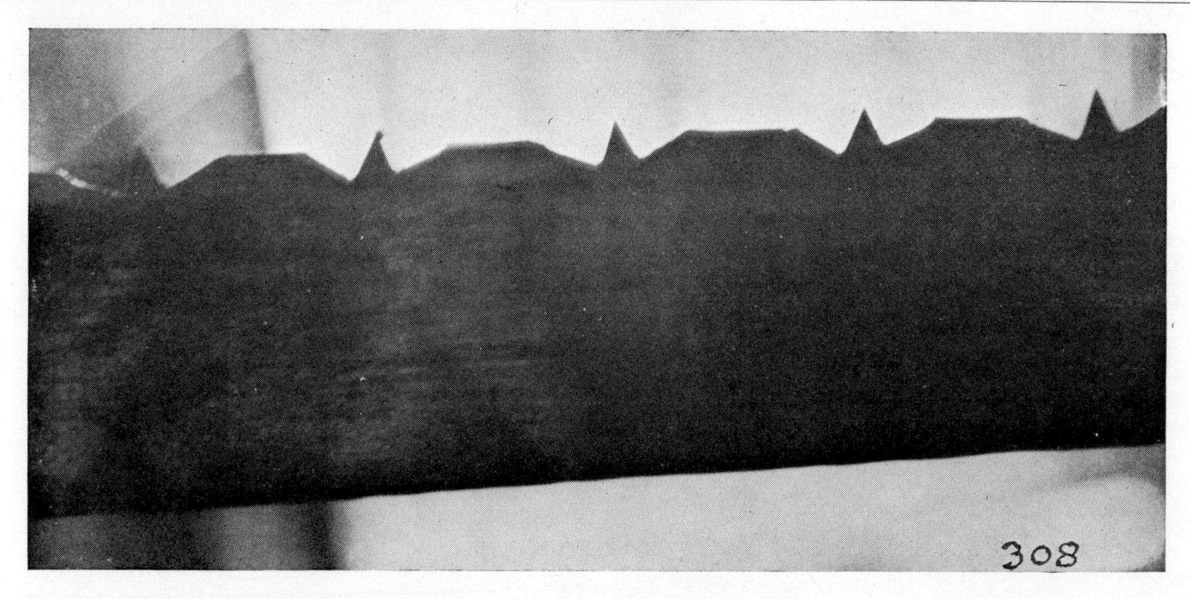

Fig. 335. Blade and Teeth of a Cross-Cut Saw. The picture shows the saw-blade and construction of saw-teeth, in the Chinese cross-cut saw, Fig. 334.

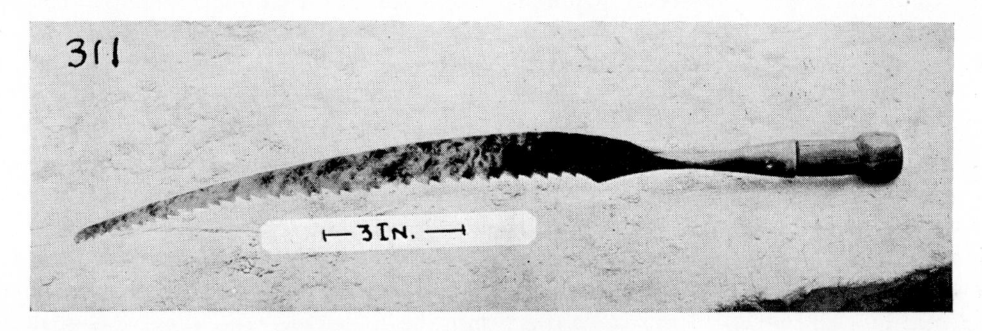

Fig. 336. Boat Builder's Compass Saw.

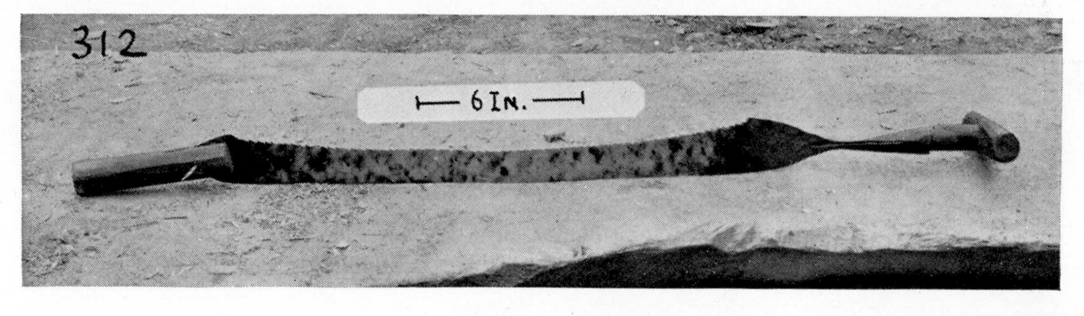

Fig. 337. Cross-Cut Saw.

shown separately in Fig. 343 with the handle removed. The tang is flat, 1/16 of an inch thick, and the blade itself less than 1/32 of an inch. The blade by itself measures 15 inches in length and the largest width is 3⅛ inches. The toothed edges are 8 inches long. The teeth on the one side showing considerable rake are for ripping, Fig. 345 (bottom) shows these and the peculiar teeth on the other side on an enlarged scale.

JAPANESE TENON SAW

Fig. 344 presents on a larger scale the blade of the tenon saw (Fig. 342, bottom) with its extremely fine teeth. To cut with this saw is a recreation, one has the feeling in handling it that every tooth is active and doing 100 percent work. The straight handle on Japanese saws seems extremely awkward, because we are used to a handle which we can firmly grip with a

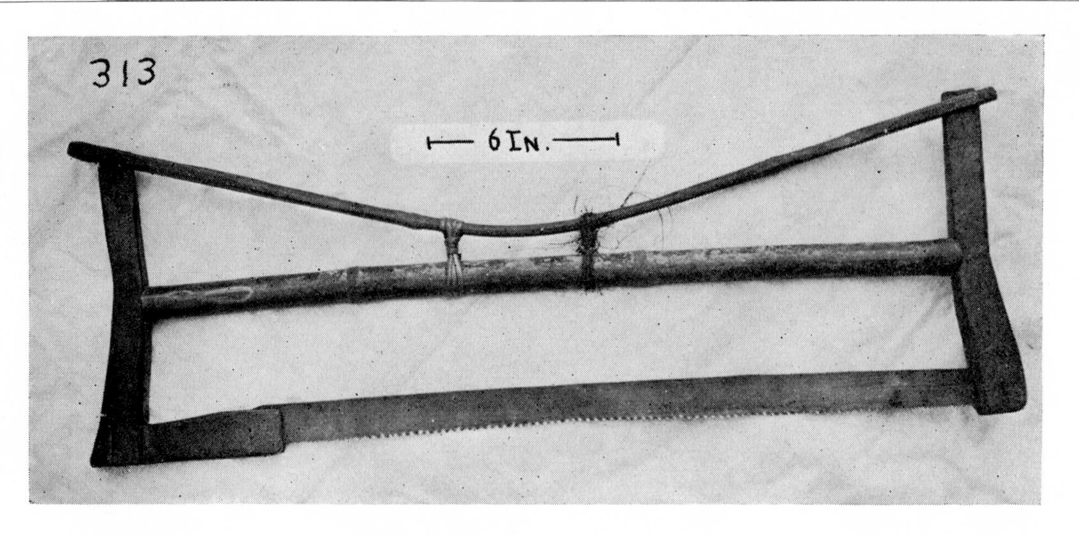

Fig. 338. Bamboo Worker's Saw.

strong downward pressure. With such sharp and well-arranged teeth much less pressure is required and on experiment we find that the straight handle on such a saw is not so awkward after all. The thin blade has a stiff back formed of a folded strip of metal held in place by friction and not soldered in place. The whole length of this saw with its handle is $20\frac{1}{2}$ inches. The width of the blade at the end is $2\frac{1}{2}$ inches, near the tang 2 inches. The toothed edge is about $9\frac{1}{2}$ inches long. The very fine teeth are filed alternately and slightly set. Our saws are usually filed with the file held at right angles to the blade, the Japanese assume more of a slant and produce thereby a sharper edge.

Fig. 339. Firewood Saw.

Fig. 345 (bottom) shows the teeth of the double edged saw described under Fig. 342. The upper teeth are constructed for cutting wood with the grain (ripping). These teeth for ripping are set, and show an aggressive rake. Each tooth is filed slantingly to produce a sharper cutting edge. The lower side of the blade is used for cross-cut sawing. The teeth of the latter are unusually long and pointed, and are also set. I have tried to saw with it and it works like a charm, none of our hand-saws can compete with it. The sharpening, however, of these fine pointed teeth must be a laborious task. Only with small knife edge files as shown in Fig. 346 is it possible to sharpen such close-set teeth. The handle of this combination, double-edged saw is wound with wire to hold the blade firmly in place. This feature, the use of a wire, and the fact that the blade is made of machine-rolled steel shows the modern influence in Japan, and yet we cannot help perceiving a certain grade of conservatism among the trades-people who keep on demanding the ancient non-European shape of the tool.

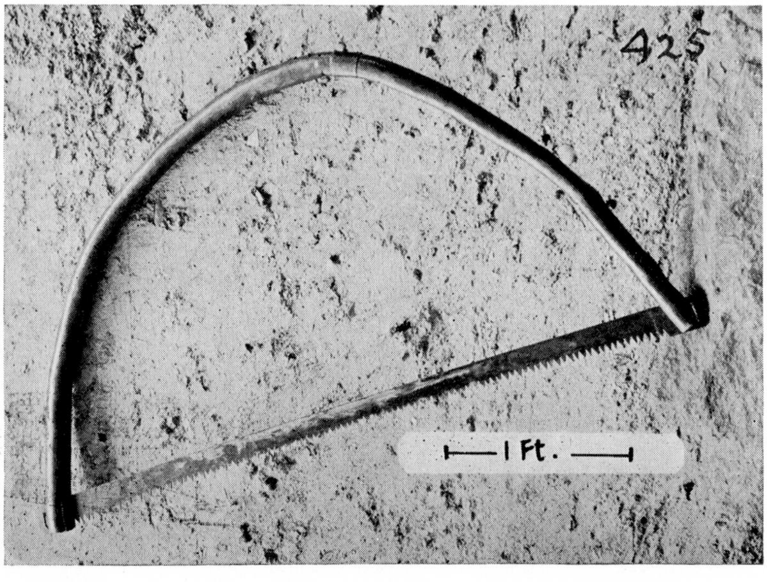

HAND SAWS

The Chinese one man hand saws work on the pull, as the rake of the teeth indicates. They are special saws for cutting grooves, corresponding to our dovetail saws, and are never used for ordinary sawing.

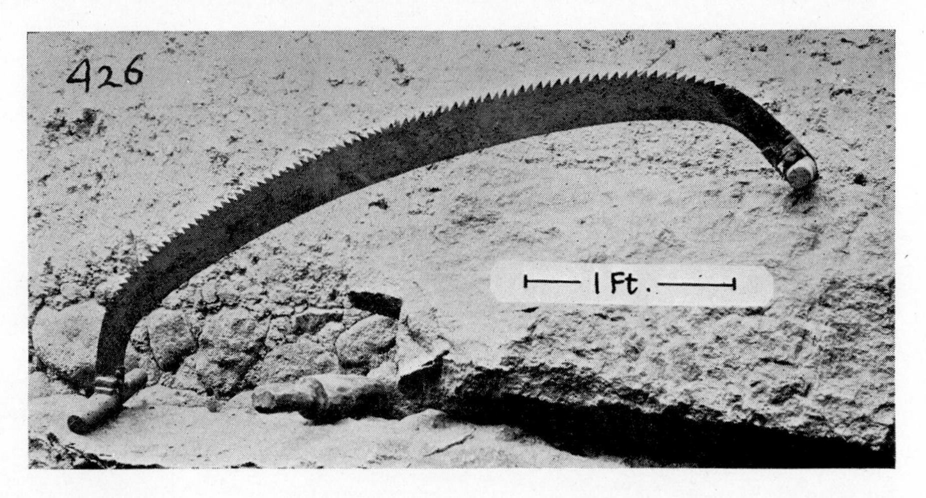

Fig. 340. Tree-Felling Saw.

In the making of coffins, a special trade in China, a saw, like the specimen in Fig. 347 is always employed. To understand its use we must consider the shape of the Chinese coffin (see Fig. 358) which is composed of four half-logs, with square panels at each end. The panels consist of thin rectangular boards, resting in grooves, and these grooves are cut with the aid of this saw. The entire length of the saw is about 14½ inches. The cutting edge of the saw-blade is 7 inches long and the width of the blade is 2 inches. The photograph was taken at Fuchow, Kiangsi.

Another interesting saw, a dovetail saw from the tool kit of a carpenter in Fuchow, Kiangsi, is shown in Fig. 348. It is employed for sawing grooves in making furniture. It is a native product although similar to the foreign handsaw, and has a handle shaped to fit the hand. The length of the blade is 5½ inches. I found a local carpenter in Kuling who had a similar saw, and he informed me that it is indispensable for making highgrade hardwood furniture.

The dovetail saw in Fig. 349 has a different handle and is shown to call attention to a peculiarity in the arrangement of the teeth. The small, one-man hand saw, with the free blade, such as the coffin-maker's saw, Fig. 347, and the compass saw, Fig. 336, or the stiff-backed saws, Figs. 348 and 349, all cut on the pull. The dovetail saw here shown, however, and the coffin-maker's saw, Fig. 347, have the last few teeth nearest the handle raked in an opposite direction to the remaining teeth. The Chinese carpenter found by experience that he could not cut a clean-cut corner in a dovetail or groove which ends squarely within the wood like a mortise with a saw in which all the teeth point in one direction. To overcome this the carpenter hit upon the expedient of reversing the direction of the last few teeth.

To strengthen a surface made up of parallel boards Chinese joiners frequently make use of cross battens set into straight-edged mortises, and for cutting these the saw with the few reversed teeth is used. It will be understood that these mortises do not extend clear across the boards to be held together. They terminate an inch or two from the edge of the outer boards forming the surface.

The length of the saw, Fig. 349, with the handle is 13 inches, the saw blade inserted into the wood measures 6 inches. The wooden part is painted red, and for this reason did not photograph well. The picture was taken in Changshu, Kiangsi.

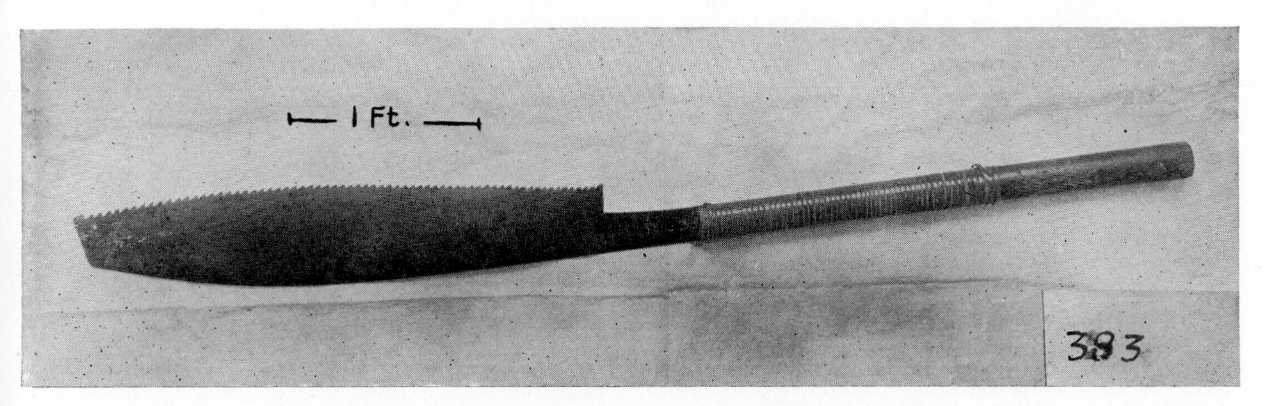

Fig. 341. Japanese Felling Saw.

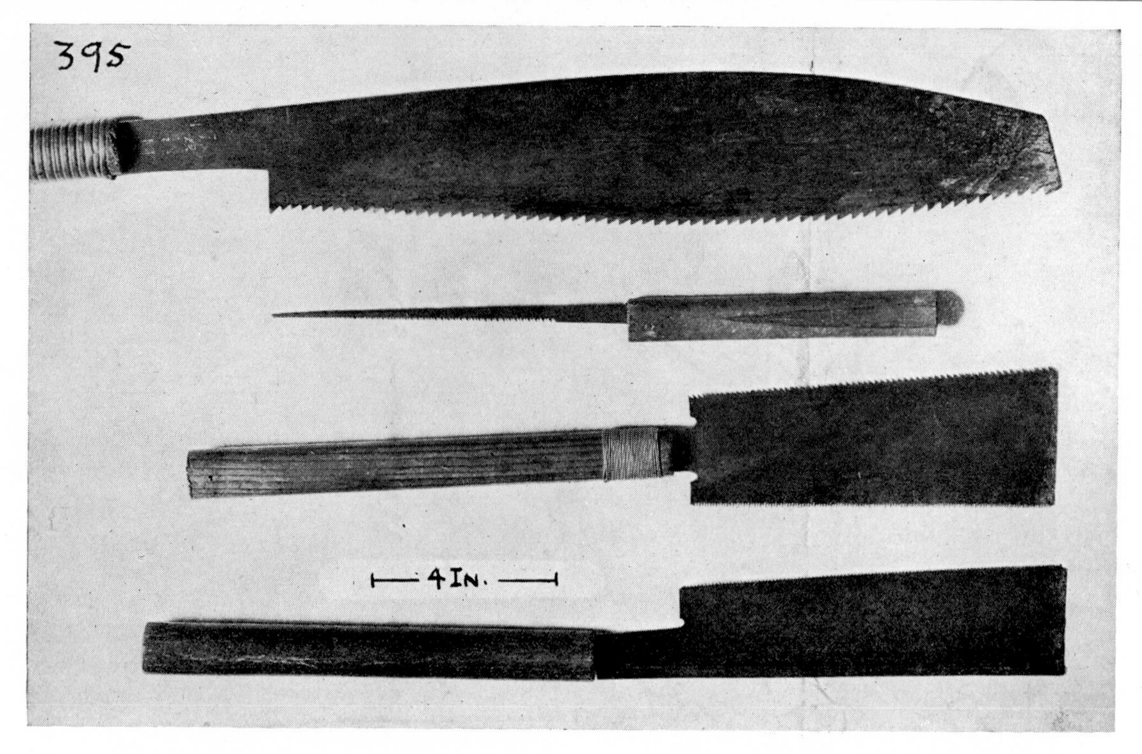

Fig. 342. Japanese Saws. From above downwards: a felling saw, a compass saw, a double-edged saw, and a tenon saw.

HATCHET AND ADZES

One handy tool of the Chinese carpenter is the hatchet which serves him as a hammer, for pointing stakes, rounding square pieces, and roughly dressing surfaces before using the plane, and for many other similar operations. The hatchet, Fig. 350, is wedge-shaped, at the poll it is 2 inches wide, and 1⅛ inches thick, decreasing gradually in thickness towards the edge or bit, where it is 4 inches wide. The length from poll to edge is 5 inches. The rectangular hole for the handle passes right through the metal and measures 1 by 7/16 of an inch. The handle is made of a hard wood.

An important feature of the Chinese hatchet is that one broad side forms a right angle with the face of the poll and the hatchet is sharpened only from the other side, the side shown in Fig. 350.

This peculiar shape of the hatchet enables the workman to cut wood along a straight line, so that the plane is often not needed afterwards. This plain surface of the hatchet is always kept very smooth, and as the user does not hit metal with the poll, the edge formed by the plain surface with the poll will

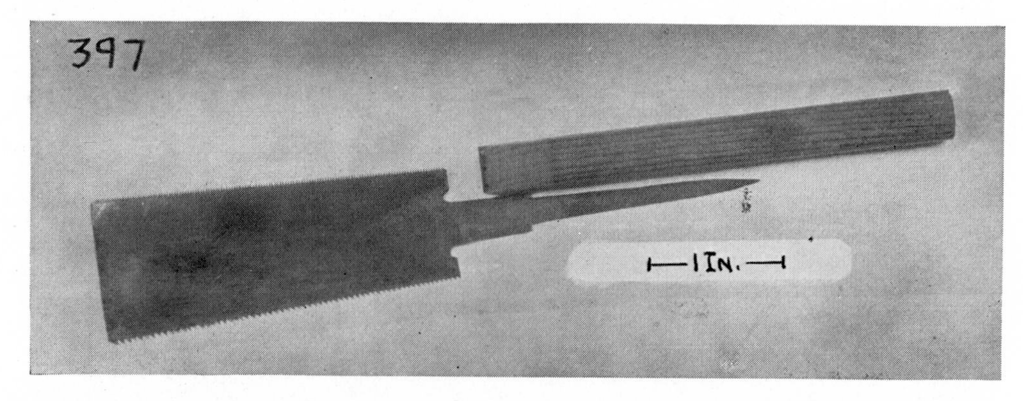

Fig. 343. Japanese Double Edged Saw with Handle Removed Showing Method of Mounting. This double edged saw used for two purposes, "ripping," or cutting wood with the grain, and "cross-cutting," or cutting wood at right angles to the grain.

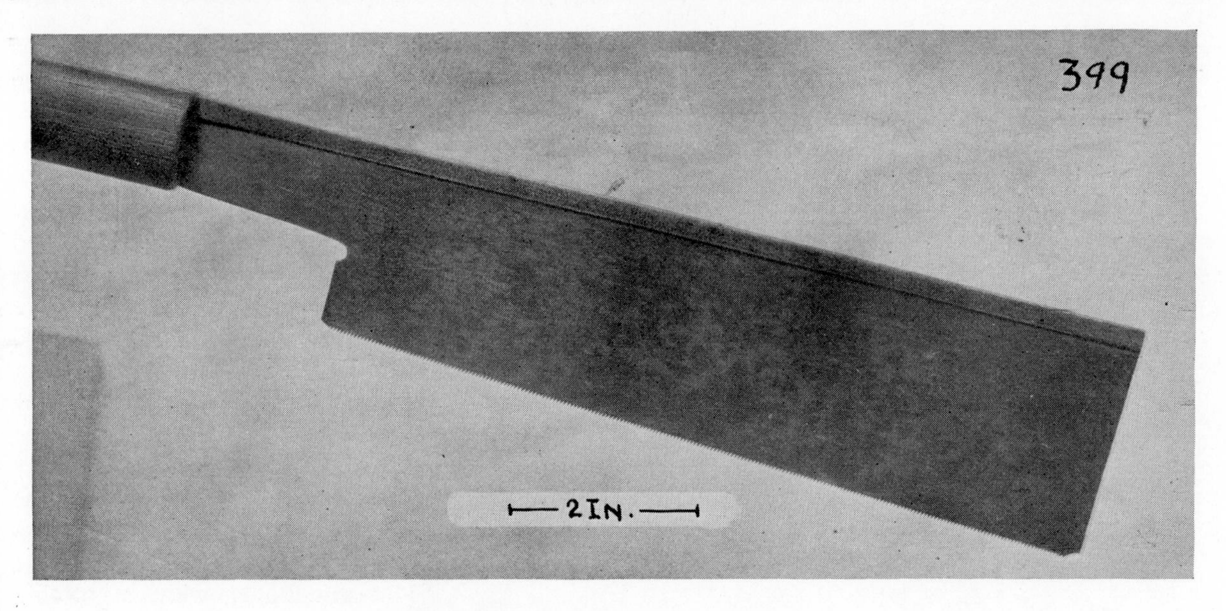

FIG. 344. JAPANESE TENON SAW.

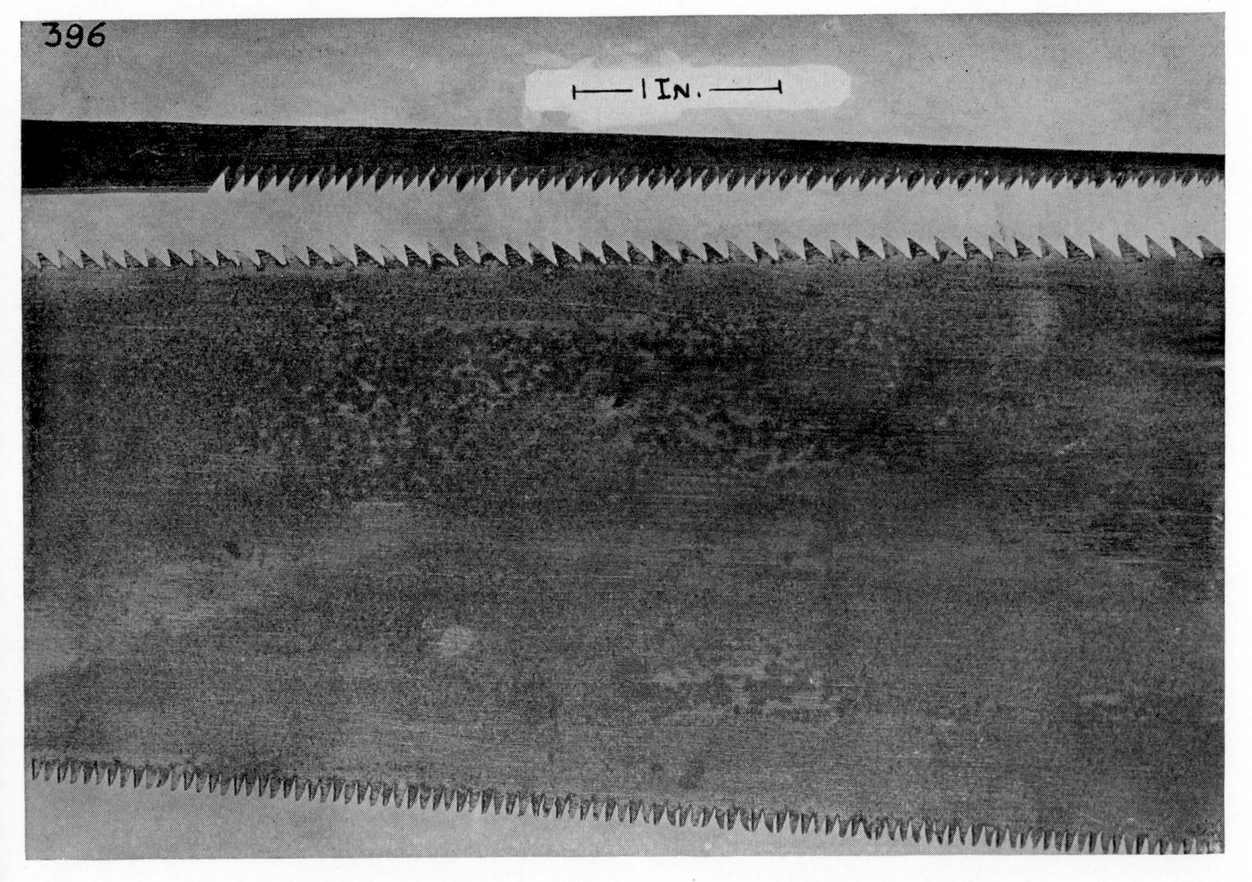

FIG. 345. JAPANESE COMPASS SAW, AND DOUBLE-EDGED SAW. SIDE VIEW OF THE BLADES.

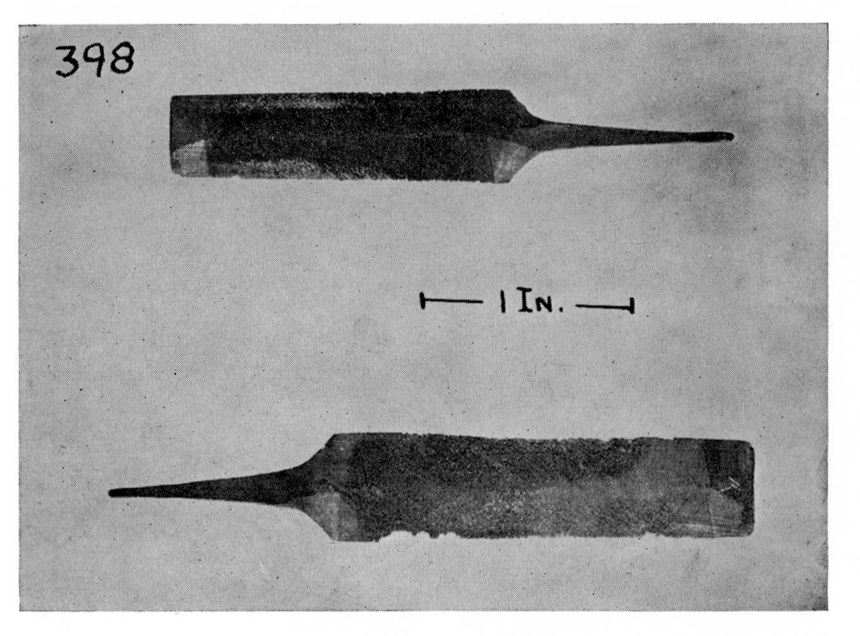

Fig. 346. Japanese Saw Files.

not get ragged. The native carpenter in the coastal regions readily adopted the claw hammer. There he frequently has to use foreign nails for the driving of which he never uses the poll of his hatchet.

The principle of balance, illustrated by having the handle hole in the hatchet pass through the center of gravity, is instinctively understood by the Chinese. When swinging this Chinese hatchet it is not necessary to grasp the handle tightly to prevent the hatchet from turning, as would be the case if the handle hole were much closer to the poll. The photograph of this hatchet was taken in Shanghai, in the Native City.

One can find scarcely any implement made of metal without the Chinese "chop" or trademark. On the hatchet can be seen on the iron near the poll end, two stamps, the marks of the maker. These chops are for the Chinese a guarantee of excellence, and if a man once buys goods, with a certain chop and finds them to his liking, it is hard to persuade him that another brand might be as good or better.

One characteristic of the Chinese workman is that he keeps his edged tools very sharp. For sharpening the hatchet and other tools he uses a flat whetstone. The circular grindstone, with a turning crank is not known.

The adze is not often found among the carpenter's tools, and it was a surprise to see the one shown in Fig. 351 in a carpenter shop in Lingkiang, Kiangsi.

The head of the adze is all of metal in the shape of an asymmetric wedge. This feature reminds us of the hatchet described under Fig. 350. The edge is sharpened only from the side facing the handle and the other side forms a perfectly plain surface from edge to butt. The hole through the head is slanting and the inserted handle forms less than a right angle with it. The length of the whole adze is 14½ inches and the length of the metal part 4¾ inches, the butt, or pounding end, is one inch square.

In coffin-making, a distinct and separate trade, the workman always makes use of an adze, but then usually in the form of a socketed celt, where

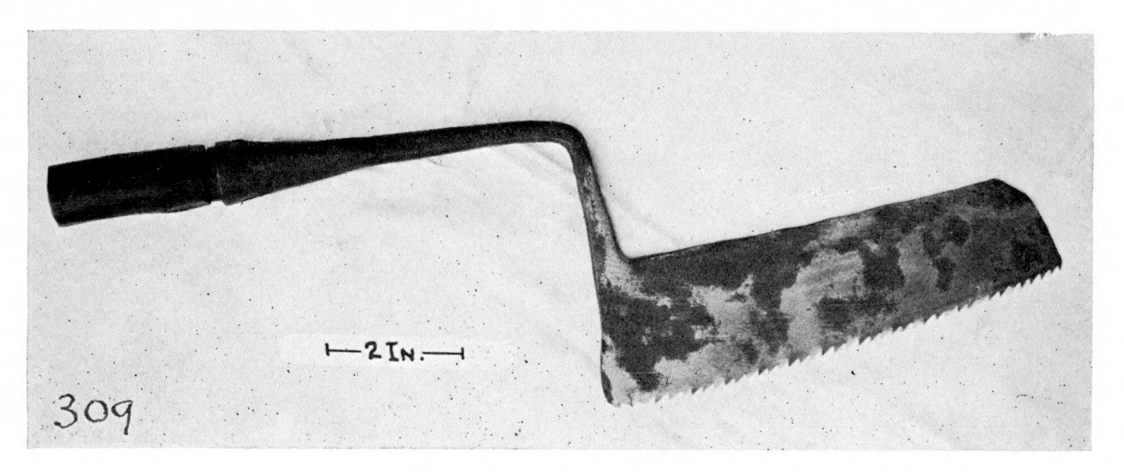

Fig. 347. Coffin-Maker's Saw.

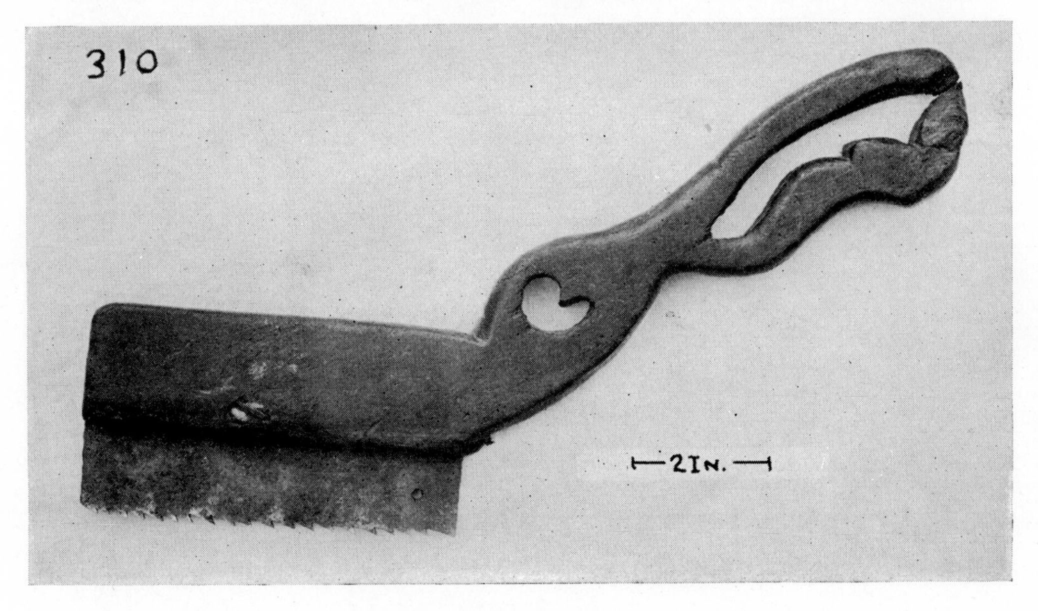

FIG. 348. DOVETAIL SAW.

only the celt is of metal and the rest of the head wood.

In Fig. 352 we are confronted with such an adze, apparently a survival of prehistoric times. An asymmetric socketed celt is mounted upon a wooden head. The prehistoric prototype was made of bronze, while the modern example is a product of the blacksmith shop. Thus we find the economy of socketing a metallic blade upon a wooden head, both in ancient and modern examples.

The length of the adze head is 13 inches, the length of the handle 10 inches. To properly balance the head, the wooden part had to be made of enormous size as compared with the metal blade stuck to it. The tool is handled with both hands, and it is of further significance, that it also takes the place of the plane in smoothing logs.

Chinese conservatism is proverbial, and innovations reach slowly a trade, such as the coffin-maker's

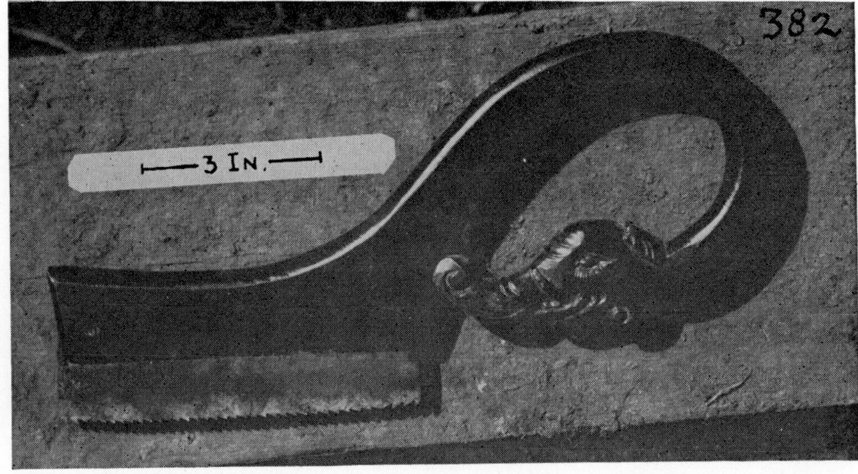

FIG. 349. DOVETAIL SAW.

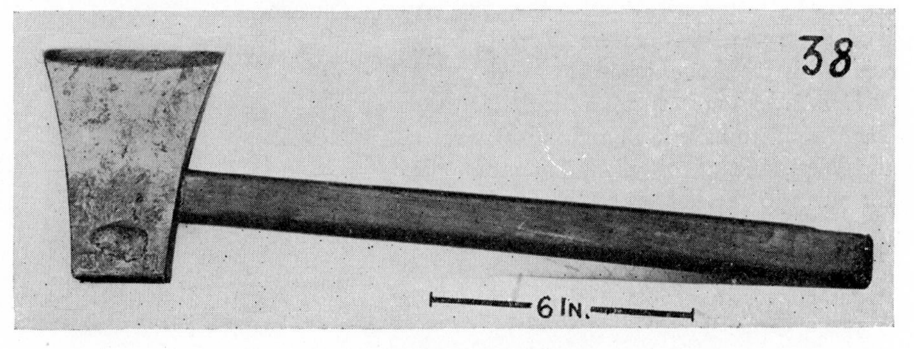

FIG. 350. CARPENTER'S HATCHET.

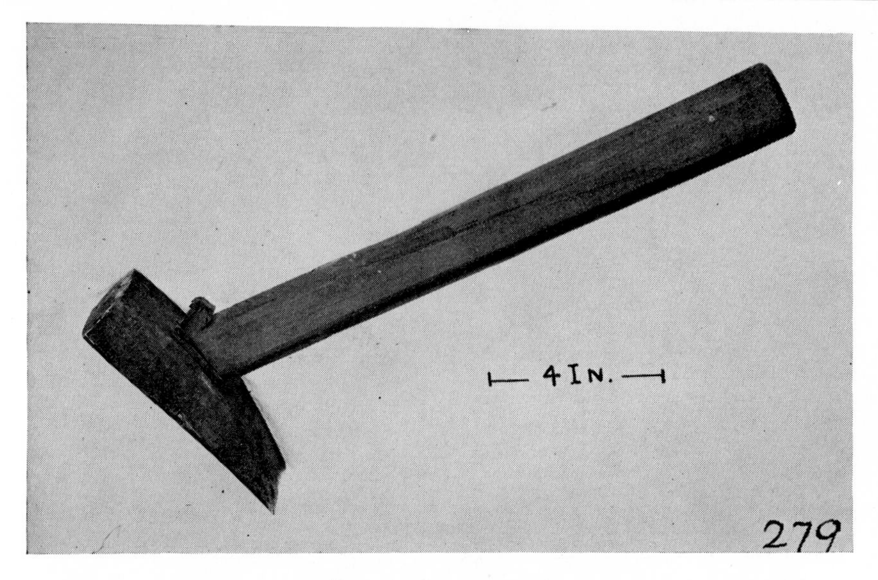

Fig. 351. Carpenter's Adze.

forms a right angle with the direction of the handle. The Chinese carpenter employs the adze for squaring large wooden beams lying on the ground. For trimming smaller pieces he holds them in an upright position and uses an axe. If it is correct that a majority of the Chinese bronze celts found are adzes we may conclude that the early Chinese confined their work in wood chiefly to trimming large beams which had to be handled lying on the ground. This is quite in accordance with the mode of building practiced in rural China today, a mode which cannot be much different from ancient methods, owing to the extreme conservatism of the people. The houses are of one story, the roof rests on heavy wooden posts, and the walls

which is closely linked with religious traditions and ceremony. Thus we see him use as his main tool the ancient form of adze to build up the coffin formed of four half-logs as has been done for centuries. Fig. 353 gives a view of a peasant's coffin of Kiangsi which clearly shows the construction. The ends of the logs are cross-grooved at each end and joined together by a square board, set in the grooves. For trimming these logs an adze is admirably fitted. The Chinese stick tenaciously to that shape of coffin which no doubt traces its origin to a time when large logs were still easily procured. At present with the forests mostly gone very often smaller stems are skillfully joined together and when finally varnished give the appearance of solid half logs. The adze, Fig. 352 and the coffin, Fig. 353, were photographed in Kien Chang, Kiangsi. The coffin was the proud possession of a prosperous peasant who had it constructed in his lifetime and in wistful moods would stroll out to the shed and tenderly regard his future habitation for which his forethought had provided.

Dr. Andersson [2] expresses the opinion that there seems to have been a liking for axes in the West, and an equally pronounced taste for adzes in the Far East. The fundamental difference between axe and adze is in the direction of the cutting edge. In the axe it is parallel to the handle, and in the adze it

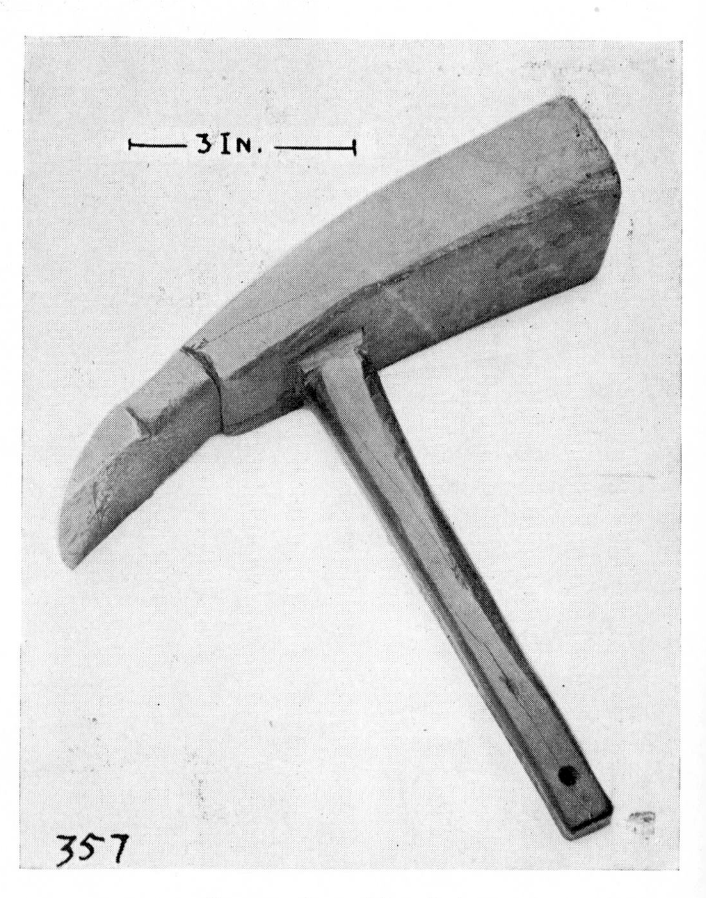

Fig. 352. Coffin-Maker's Adze.

[2] Bulletin, Geological Survey of China, No. 5, Peking, 1923.

fill the intermediate spaces, not supporting the structure, but merely enclosing it; the door and window frames, especially in older times, were usually of stone, and the floors without boards, simple mud surfaces smoothed and hardened only by the passing of feet.

FIG. 353. CHINESE COFFIN.

PLANING

Fig. 354 shows a typical plane for all-around work. The lower surface or "sole" measures 7½ inches by 2¼ inches. The blade which is of foreign make (witness the hole in it which serves no purpose on the Chinese plane) is 7 inches long, 1¾ inches wide and ⅛ of an inch thick. The opening in the plane stock shown in the picture, terminates in a bottom slot 1¾ inches by ¼ of an inch. Blade and apron (the wedge in front of the blade) are held by two shoulders which narrow the opening in the plane.

FIG. 354. CARPENTER'S PLANE.

The cross handle, 10½ inches long, is inserted into a groove immediately back of the blade. The front edge of the slot where the blade protrudes is bounded by a rim of iron. When planing the shavings pass through the space between the blade and the iron rim.

All Chinese carpenter planes are pushed away from the body, being held with both hands by the handles if they have any, or else held with one hand near the one end and with the other near the other end. This latter mode of holding applies especially to longer planes which do not have the characteristic handles shown in Fig. 354.

Another plane, which we would call a rabbet-plane, is shown in Figs. 355 and 356. It is about 16 inches long and 1½ inches wide.

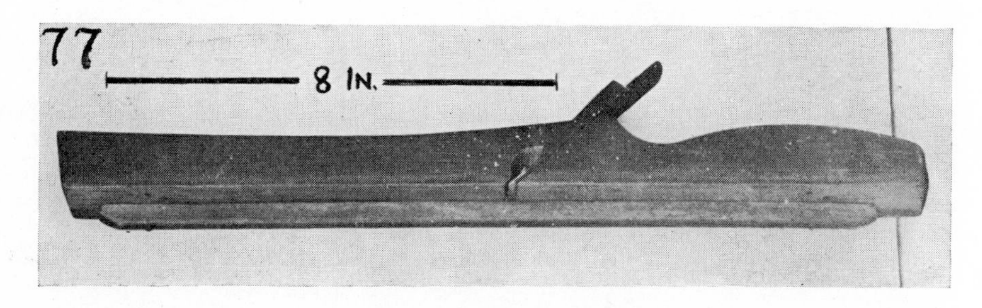

FIG. 355. CARPENTER'S RABBET-PLANE.

FIG. 356. CARPENTER'S RABBET-PLANE. The picture gives another view of the Rabbet-Plane shown in Fig. 355.

A tapering opening holds the bit in place, fixed there with a wedge. A half round hole on the side of this opening allows the shavings to escape. On the bottom an adjustable guide strip is held in place with dowels, which are fixed in the guide strip and fit into holes in the bottom surface of the plane. The space between edge and guide strip can be varied by shifting the guide strip with its dowels into other holes in the bottom of the plane. The bit measures 4 by 1 by 1/8 inches. Confronting the face of the cutting edge of the blade, a piece of iron is inserted across the blade opening so that the shavings pass between it and the blade edge. Rectangular rabbets are cut with this plane. The photographs were taken in the Native City of Shanghai.

Figs. 357-A shows a grooving plane or plow, bottom up, with its attached gauge or adjustable fence. The accompanying sketch, Fig. 358, shows at

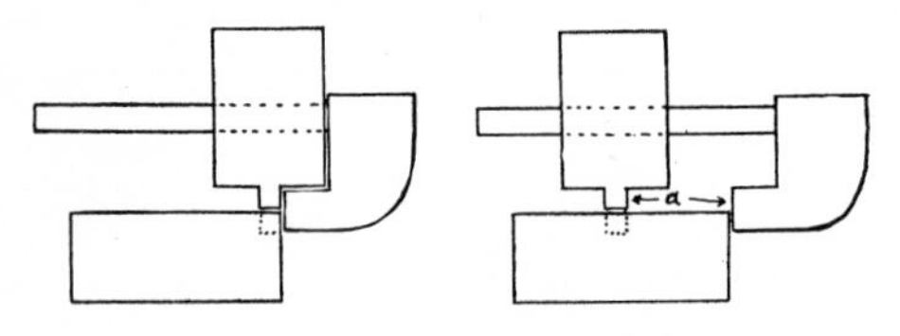

FIG. 358. SKETCH SHOWING MOVEABLE FENCE ON CARPENTER'S GROOVING PLANE.

the left, the plane with the "fence" pushed all the way home, in which position it is fitted to cut a rabbet, and at the right, with the gauge pulled out, ready to cut a groove the distance "*a*" away from the edge of the material. The gauge once adjusted is held in place by a wedge. The ledge running along the longitudinal center of the sole corresponds to the contour of the blade which cuts the rabbet or groove, as the case may be. In using the plane it is held so that the projecting piece of the gauge slides along the edge of the wood upon which the groove is to be cut. The blade is wedged into a groove passing diagonally through the plane-stock and downward through the bottom ledge at the sole, from which the cutting edge slightly protrudes. On the top of the plane the discharge hole is enlarged to permit the shavings to pass through. The length of the plane is 7 inches, the width 1½ inches, the thickness including

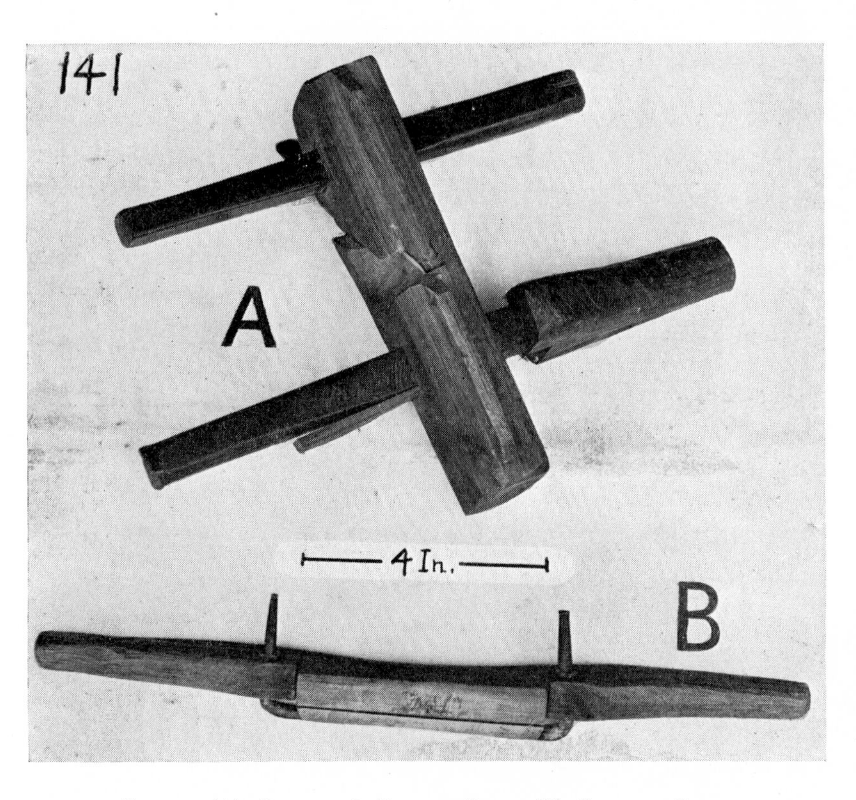

FIG. 357. (A). CARPENTER'S GROOVING PLANE. (B). ROUNDING SHAVE.

FIG. 359. JAPANESE PLANE.

the rectangular ledge at the sole is 2¼ inches. The steel blade is 5 inches long, ⅜ inch wide and 3/16 of an inch thick.

Fig. 357-B shows a shave used for smoothing or planing rounded surfaces, as stakes or handles, or for planing irregular pieces necessary for the making of plows, harrows, etc. A steel blade, 5 inches long has tangs at right angles to the blade at each end. They pass through holes in the wooden holder which is 12 inches long. The blade is ¾ of an inch wide, and the distance its edge is set away from the wood of the holder, determines the thickness of shavings which can be cut with this tool. The carpenter using it holds it with both hands, one on each handle in such a manner that looking down at it, it would present about the same view as the picture. The cutting is done with a motion towards the body. The photograph was taken at Se Aw, Chekiang province.

Fig. 359 presents a Japanese carpenter's plane. It is very similar to the Chinese plane but has not its characteristic handles. The stock is of oak and the slot has an offset on each side, or shoulders, to hold the wedge-shaped bit in place. There is no wooden apron as in Chinese or foreign planes and it is a skillful piece of work to make the mortise of such shape that it holds the steel bit firmly in place so as not to shift when using the plane. It is due entirely to the wedge-shape of the bit, that the latter keeps itself in place by mere friction without the aid of a wooden apron. The bit is hit with a hammer to put it in position, and to loosen it the end of the stock nearest to the bit is tapped with a hammer.

The most curious feature of the instrument is its manner of use, namely that it is not pushed away from but pulled toward the body of the workman. While different from the Chinese mode of handling a plane it is in keeping with the Japanese manner of sawing wood which is always done on the pull. The length of the plane shown is 9½ inches, the stock is 1 inch high and 2½ inches wide. The plane is simplicity itself, it consists only of two parts, the stock and the metal bit. A Japanese resident of Kuling, Kiangsi, lent me the plane for photographing.

It appears that planes were introduced into Japan in the 16th or early 17th century by the Portuguese

FIG. 360. JAPANESE CARPENTER'S PULL-PLANES.

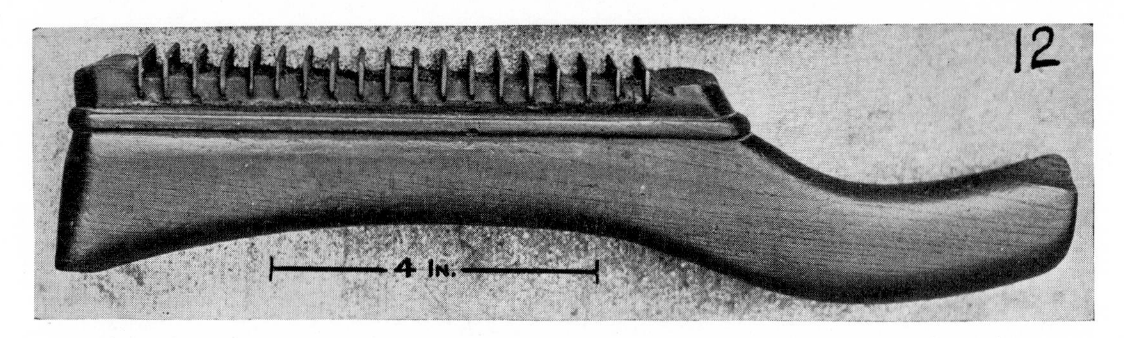

FIG. 361. WOOD SCRAPER.

or Dutch, or possibly by the English navigator Will Adams.[3] Necessarily these planes must have been push-planes and the singular fact confronts us, that the Japanese adopted them but transformed them into pull-planes, as they use them to this day. In the absence of any definite information it appears that wood was made smooth in Japan before the introduction of the plane with an adze which is worked towards the body. The Chinese coffin-maker still uses the adze for this purpose. Century-old custom then may have linked this motion toward the body with the action of smoothing wood, and when suddenly a new tool was introduced for this purpose, it does not seem unreasonable that the new tool was made to conform to an innate urge.

The Japanese have an adze, called "chona," with a wide sharp blade. It takes considerable skill to wield this tool, and the people proficient in its use, cut accurate surfaces. They wear shoes with a high projection over the toes to protect them against accidental contact with the sharp blade. The "chona" wielders were the workmen who gave a preliminary smoothness to wood before the advent of planes in Japan. According to native historians a long-handled curved knife, called "yari ganna," meaning spear plane, was then used for the final touch and finish. It has disappeared from the tools of the carpenter since the introduction of the plane, but its generic name "ganna" was retained and given to the plane.

Fig. 360 shows two more of the Japanese planes which cut on the pull. The lower one has already been described under Fig. 359, the other presenting its sole or lower side is $8\frac{3}{4}$ inches long, 1 inch high and $2\frac{3}{8}$ inches deep. The steel blade is $3\frac{1}{2}$ inches long, 2 inches wide and, being wedge-shaped, $\frac{3}{8}$ inch thick at one end and $\frac{1}{4}$ inch thick at the other where the bevel starts which forms the cutting edge.

[3] William Adams, a native of Kent, England, was sailing-master of a fleet of Dutch merchantmen, which set out for the East Indies on a trading expedition in 1598. Most of the ships were wrecked, but Adams arrived at Bungo, on April 19th, 1600. Because of his superior knowledge in shipbuilding, mathematics and foreign usages in general he was retained in "friendly captivity" as the Japanese historians put it. He was well treated and became a favorite of the Shogun Ieyasu. A Japanese wife and the fief of Hemmimura were bestowed on him. Much liked for his honesty, which contrasted sharply with that of the fawning Dutch and the shifty Jesuitical Portuguese, he acted as intermediary with the foreign traders and exerted considerable influence upon the Tokugawa dynasty which was to dominate Japan for several hundred years. Will Adams died at Hirado May 16th, 1620.

WOOD SCRAPER

The climatic conditions in China, snow in winter, a rainy season in spring and tropical heat in sum-

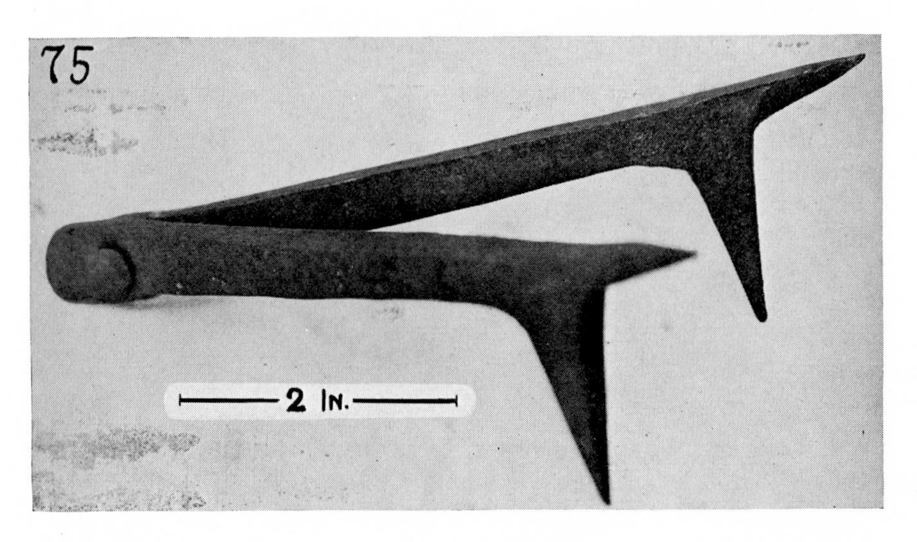

FIG. 362. CARPENTER'S BENCH-STOP.

mer, make it desirable for the people who can afford it, to have their furniture constructed from wood which can withstand these severe changes. We find therefore that a great variety of hard woods, partly of native growth, but more frequently imported from the tropical regions of South-Eastern Asia, are employed in constructing the furniture of the Chinese house.

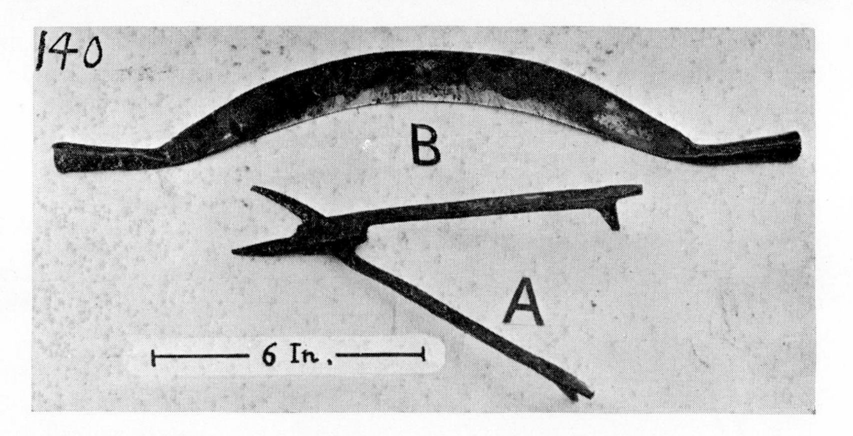

Fig. 363. Carpenter's Bench-Stop and Drawing Knife.

Teakwood, blackwood, redwood, ironwood and many others, sometimes not easily identified, are used. Some of them are so hard that their surfaces can not be smoothed with an ordinary plane. Chinese ingenuity has overcome this by producing an instrument, shown in Fig. 361, with which the surface of the wood, after sawing, can be made smooth, just as softer woods are with the aid of the plane.

The instrument is 12½ inches long. It consists of a wooden holder and 19 steel knives fastened permanently in the wooden part. These knives are ¼ of an inch wide, 1⅜ inches long, and 1/16 of an inch thick. The cutting edge of each is bevelled. The steel blades are forced into kerfs sawn across the grain of the wooden holder. The wooden part of the tool is fashioned out of a single piece of wood taken from a kind of elm, called *chü* which is found in Kiangsu Province. This wood is not affected by any changes of temperature, or moisture in the air, and the knives are never dislodged through shrinkage.

The scraping is done by pushing the instrument the handle of which is held in the right hand away from the body and pressing it firmly down with the left hand. This specimen was procured from a second-hand shop in Shanghai, Native City.

CARPENTER'S BENCH-STOP

To hold a board in place when planing it, the carpenter uses an instrument like the one shown in Fig. 362. The two spikes pointing downward are driven into the bench or the top of a wooden horse. The board whose surface is to be planed is laid flat upon the work bench and its edge pressed against the two end spikes of the stop. To plane the narrow edge of a board, the board is set upon edge, pushed between the two legs of this bench stop and thus held firmly in place. The length of the two parts, held together by an iron rivet, is 6¼ inches. The bench-stop was photographed in the Native City of Shanghai.

Fig. 364. Carpenter's Working Trestle.

Another bench-stop is shown in Fig. 363-A. It resembles a pair of plyers and in fact can be used as such for pulling out nails if they are ever encountered. This resemblance is incidental, however, as the purpose of the instrument is to hold boards in planing. The method of use is precisely the same as that of the other stop described. Its structure, however, is different. The two levers of the stop are joined together by the one passing through a slot in the other. The levers hinge upon an iron rivet also passing through the two members. The length of the instrument is 9 inches.

The drawing-knife in Fig. 363-B is used for

stripping bark from logs before proceeding to saw them into boards, or to trim them for beams. This tool is forged in one piece, measures $16\frac{1}{2}$ inches in

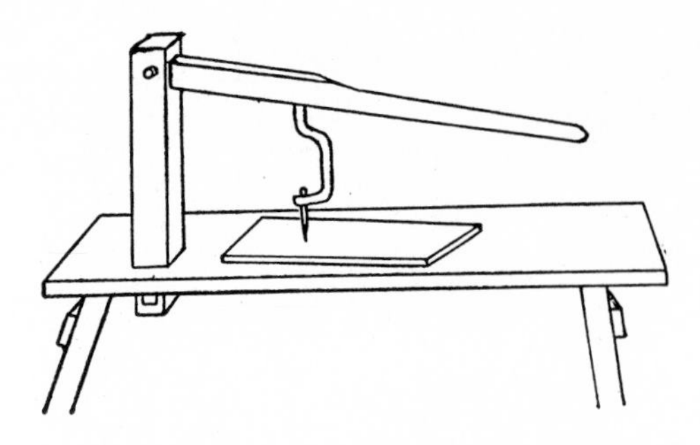

Fig. 365. Drill Press Used in Solnhofen, Bavaria. Sketched after a photograph in Bayerischer Heimatschutz, 1919, XVII, 160.

length and is $1\frac{1}{4}$ inches wide in the middle. The thickness of the blade is $\frac{1}{8}$ of an inch at the back and tapers to a sharp edge. The iron handles are socket-shaped only to give them a round form for convenient holding, and no wooden sticks or grips

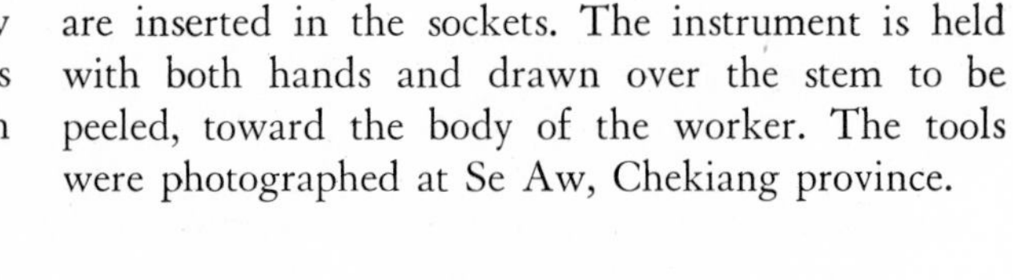

are inserted in the sockets. The instrument is held with both hands and drawn over the stem to be peeled, toward the body of the worker. The tools were photographed at Se Aw, Chekiang province.

CARPENTER'S WORKING TRESTLE

The Chinese carpenter's trestle illustrated in Fig. 364, is not a saw-buck, but a so-called "horse," or substitute for a carpenter's bench. The Chinese name for it is "horse," despite the fact that its three legs bear little resemblance to the four legged contrivance which we call a saw horse. Work to be planed or trimmed with the hatchet is laid over two of these trestles between the two arms. The device is never used for sawing boards from logs, but when long pieces are to be sawed off cross-wise, they are laid upon this trestle which serves as a support. The upper ends of the cross-arms serve also for chopping blocks. The height is 32 inches, about the height of a table, and the diameter of the beams forming the cross is 6 inches. This unusual trestle was seen and photographed in Lingkiang, Kiangsi province.

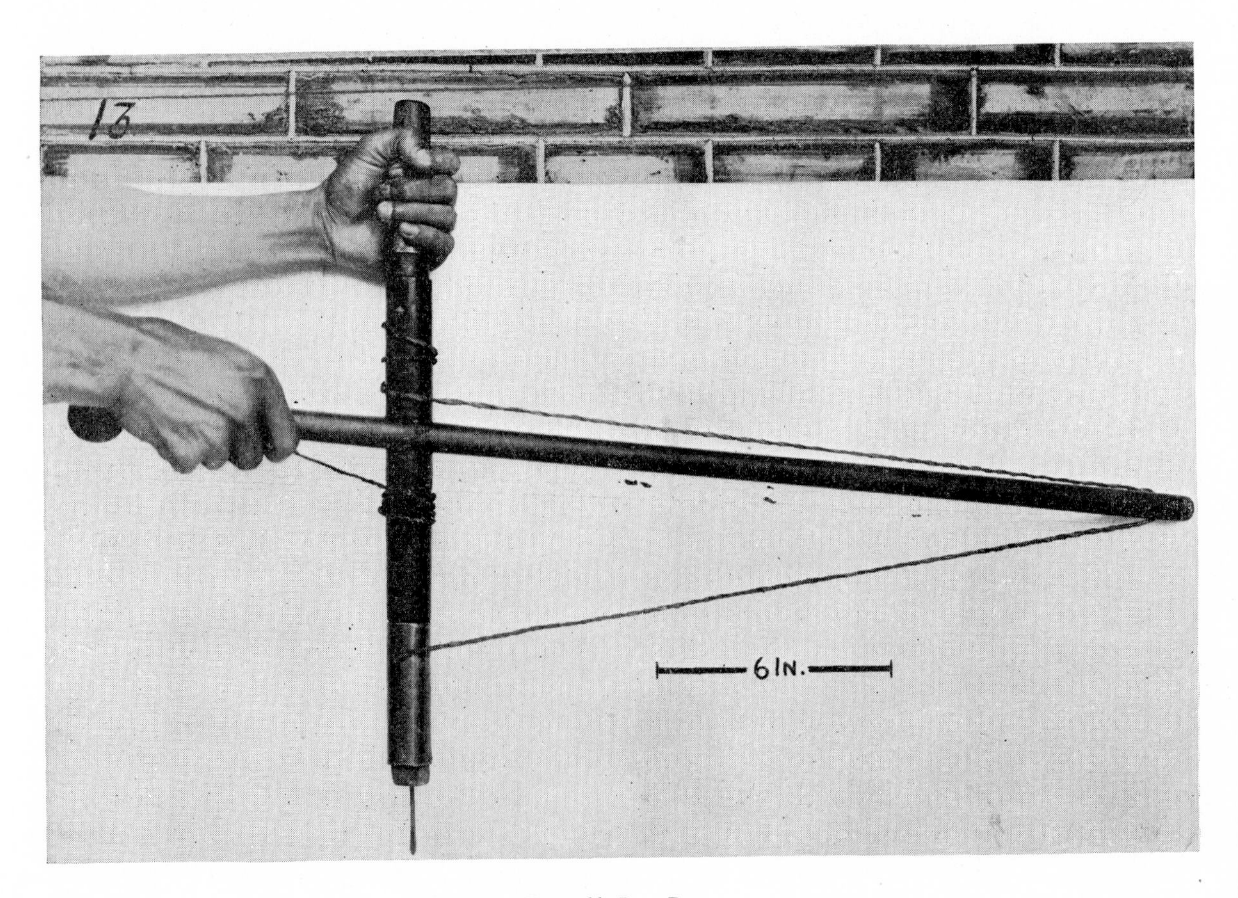

Fig. 366. Bow Drill.

DRILLING

The Chinese have not reached that stage where the continuous rotary motion is substituted for a reciprocating motion, in technical contrivances, such as the drill, lathe, saw, etc. To take this step familiarity with the crank is necessary. The crank in its simple rudimentary form we find in Chinese windlasses (conf. Fig. 172), which use of the device, however, has apparently not given the impulse to change reciprocating into circular motion for other contrivances. R. Forrer has reconstructed a neolithic drill-press actuated by a bow of which every detail is authenticated by actual finds of the period. For thousands of years then it appears, that the world had not made any decided progress in the mode of drilling. Drills, with reciprocating motion, have survived in Europe until quite recently with clock-makers and jewelers, who for fine drilling, use a bow drill or a pump drill.

The sketch, Fig. 365, represents a contrivance for drilling holes into lime-stone roofing tiles, as it is used to-day in Solnhofen, Bavaria, where the world's supply of lithographic stones is quarried. The work carried on there is very primitive, and the roofing tiles produced fill only a local demand. The contrivance is similar to the neolithic drill-press, and was probably, in former times, used also with a bow, until the introduction of the crank changed conditions. The operator presses the lever with the left and turns the crank with the right hand.

The bow drill shown in Fig. 366, is from a set of carpenter's tools, seen in the native city of Shanghai. All the wooden parts are of Chinese black wood, namely, the bitstock which is 1¼ inches in diameter, the grip which revolves on the bitstock and is to be seen in the left hand of the operator in the picture, and the bow, or horizontal rod, which is ¾ of an inch in diameter and has a wooden handle knob at one end.

The picture demonstrates the mode of handling the drill. When pushing the bow away from the body, the two ends of one string wound onto the bitstock will unwind while the other string which terminates in a hole in the bow under the right hand of the workman will be wound onto the bitstock. It is clear then, that the bitstock will revolve back and forth as the bow is pulled back and forth.

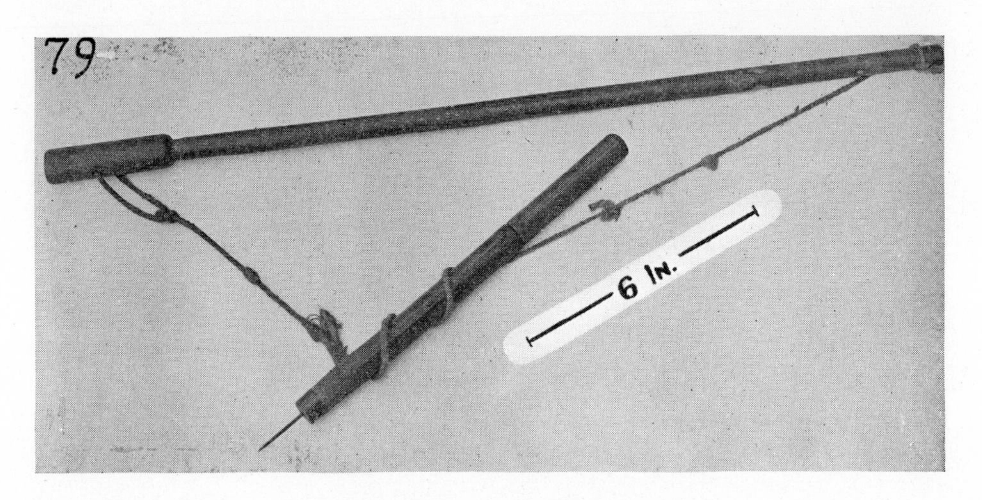

Fig. 367. Carpenter's Bow Drill.

The steel bit is driven into a square wooden block and the block is inserted into a square opening at the bottom of the bitstock. The bits used are always reciprocating drills shaped at the end like an arrowhead. To strengthen the end of the bitstock a brass sleeve is forced over it. The grip of the bitstock is a piece of wood 2½ inches long and 1 inch in diameter. Over one inch of its length a brass sleeve 2½ inches long is forced, which leaves 1½ inches of the brass sleeve hollow. In this hollow space, the upper end of the bitstock whose circumference has been reduced to fit the hole, revolves. Hempen strings, made of two strands, are fastened to the bitstock and bow by passing them through holes and tying a knot at the ends projecting through the holes.

Drills like this are used in all kinds of trades. At one time I saw a large one used in drilling a hole one quarter inch in diameter. This was worked by three people; one held the bitstock, while the other two operated the bow, each pulling as his turn came. Instead of strings it had leather thongs. This type of drill is used on wood only. For drilling holes in metal the pump drill is used.

A simpler kind of bow drill is shown in Fig. 367. The string-holder or bow, a wooden rod 21 inches long has a diameter of one half of an inch, the thicker handle part is 3 inches long and ¾ of an inch in diameter. The drill holder is 10½ inches long excluding the drill, and ⅝ of an inch thick. The steel drill driven into the end projects 1¼ inches and has a diameter of 1/16 of an inch. A ferrule keeps the wood of the drill holder from splitting where the drill is inserted. The other end or top of the drill holder is reduced to a smaller diameter, to receive a bamboo tube which turns freely upon the top. When using the bow-drill, the bamboo sleeve is grasped with the right hand, the string laid around the drill holder, as shown on the picture, and the string-holder or bow, is held at the thicker end, with the left hand and moved back and forth, thus turning the drill back and forth. The photograph was taken in the Native City of Shanghai.

Fig. 368 shows two drills for making holes in wood, as they are to this day in use in rural districts in Japan. This instrument was the only drilling apparatus until recent years, when the western brace and bit, and similar tools were introduced. I was assured by Japanese that the bow and pump drill were never known in Japan. This is a curious fact and we are forced to the conclusion that the Japanese mode of drilling has never advanced beyond the stage which was in vogue in palæolithic times in Europe, for the neolithic people, going a step farther, had devised a drill held in a frame, and worked with a bow.

The bits of the drills shown are of steel, the one is quadrangular with sharp edges merging into a point, and the other has a flattened tang inserted into the wood, and near its end a thickened triangular head with sharp edges tapering to a point. The wooden shafts into which the bits are driven are round, about ¾ of an inch in diameter and taper to about ½ of an inch at the other end. The drill is twirled between the palms of the hands, back and forth, which process is fascilitated by the tapering of the wooden shaft. The longer one of the two unique tools is 9¼ inches long, and the other one 8¼ inches. They were lent me by a Japanese in Kuling for photographing.

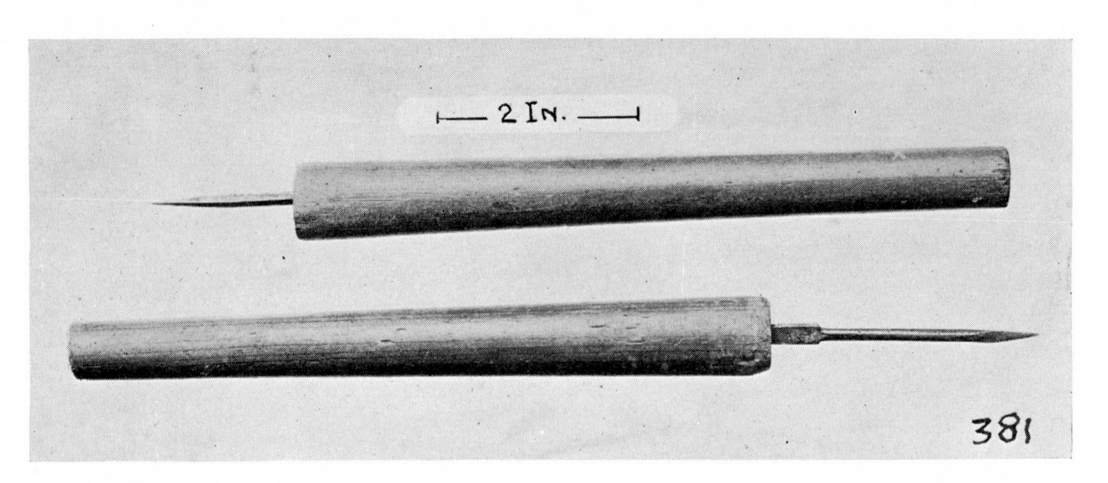

Fig. 368. Two Japanese Twirling Drills.

The Japanese carpenter tools discussed and some other implements described in these pages are sufficient indication that the primitive trades of the Japanese have been developed in insular seclusion. Chinese trades as a whole remind us very much of ours in the western world, as they have been plied until the era of modern industrialism.

A singular and ingenious mode of Chinese wood drilling was observed in King Teh Chen, the famous porcelain center. It was in the shop of a pipe maker, who was engaged in drilling a hole through a wooden pipe stem about 3½ feet long. A pith core about 1/16 of an inch in diameter which ran through the whole length of the stem facilitated the drilling and prevented the drill from deviating from the center. The drill consisted of a long stiff iron wire, with one end flattened into a lanceolate point. The other end of the wire was inserted loosely into a short bamboo tube fastened to a bench. In drilling the point was applied to the pipe stem, and the wire as it lay on the bench was turned around its own axis, by sliding a wooden board over it, in a direction at right angles to the length of the wire. Every once in a while the drill was pulled out to shake the drillings from the pipe stem.

The Chinese apply the lever in various forms, one important application of it, however, namely the screw, is not known to them. Ever since the Jesuit Matteo Ricci brought western clocks to China (in 1583), the native artisans have successfully copied these clocks, and in this way became acquainted with the principle of the screw, yet, to this day, it has not been applied in any other way. It is therefore not surprising that the gimlet or auger is not known to the Chinese.

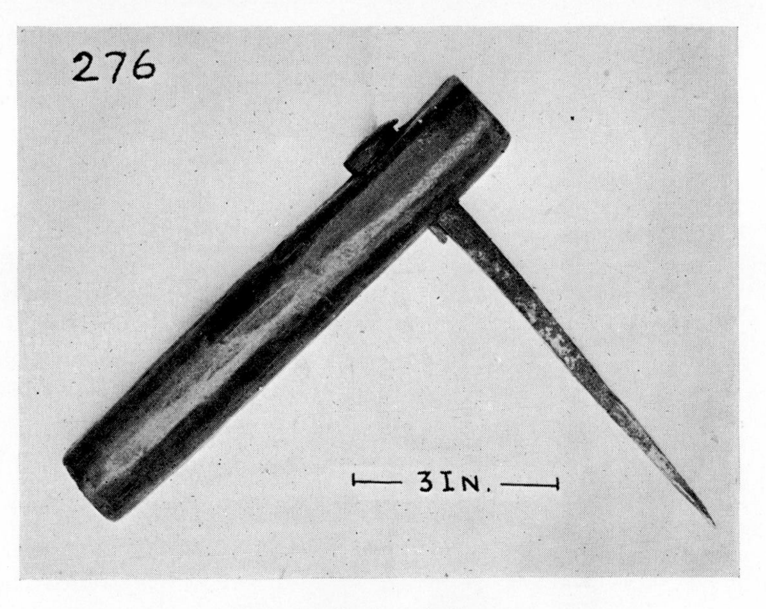

Fig. 369. Carpenter's Reamer.

CARPENTER'S REAMER

In joinery, dowels are used a great deal, and to make holes in the wood for their insertion, use is made sometimes of a reamer as shown in Fig. 369. With it a tapering hole can be made to suit the form of dowels. The metal part is a tapering spike with square cross-section, 7¾ inches long, set into a wooden handle, 1½ inches in diameter and 8 inches long. To make a hole the reamer is driven into the wood and then turned back and forth, about its own axis, with the wooden handle.

It must be added, that the usual method of making holes in finer work is with the bow drill, in fact, I never saw this square tapering spike, except at Lingkiang, Kiangsi province, where it was photographed.

The rudiments or first feeble attempts to make a drill with continuous rotary motion we find in Egypt. Rexford Newcomb, Professor of History of Architecture, University of Illinois, writes [4] that the old Egyptians in drilling out vases from stone early invented a crank drill. "These, plainly shown in the hieroglyphs and dated at from 3,500 to 3,000 B.C., appear to have been the earliest known machines. This type of drill was composed of a vertical shaft with a crank at the top and a forked termination at the base to accommodate the bit in the form of a very hard cutting-stone. Near the top were attached two stones of equal weight, which, acting like the weights of a governor, really supplied the place of a fly wheel and kept the drill revolving."

In the same publication pictures are shown of this type of drill, Fig. 3, Egyptian Craftsmen Drilling out Stone Vases with Crank Drill, after de Morgan; "Recherches sur les Origines de L'Egypte," Vol. I.; and Fig. 4, Egyptian Crank Drill, invented in early Dynastic Period (3,400 to 3,000 B.C.), after Borchardt.

[4] In the "Architectural Monographs on Tiles and Tilework, No. 2," "Ceramic Architecture in Ancient Egypt, Babylonia and Assyria." Published by the Associated Tile Manufacturers, Beaver Falls, Pa.

CHISELS

CARPENTER'S FORMING CHISELS

Fig. 370 shows three chisels which are indispensable to the carpenter. Whenever called out for repair work, he carries these along. They are made of steel with wooden stocks inserted into conical sockets. Their dimensions are, exclusive of wooden stock, (*A*) 6 inches long, with an edge ⅜ of an inch wide, (*B*) 7 inches long with a curved edge ¾ inch across, and (*C*) 5 inches long, with an edge one inch wide. The photograph was taken in the Native City of Shanghai.

JAPANESE CARPENTER'S CHISELS

The chisels shown in Fig. 371 are Japanese. They are well finished and profiled, and remind us of a European type, namely the bevel-edged "firmer" chisel. The wooden handle seemingly rests in a socket of the chisel proper, but this is not the case. The chisel blade ends in a pointed tang, which penetrates the wood, and between an offset on the blade shaft

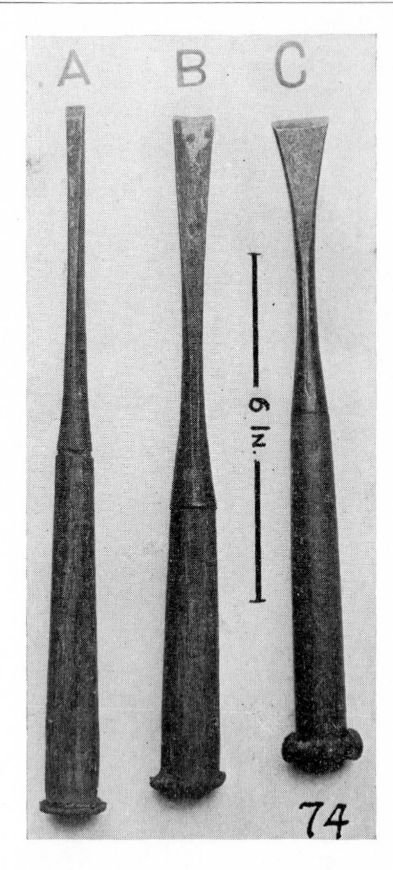

FIG. 370. CARPENTER'S FORMING CHISELS.

of the chisel and the wood, rests a tapering wrought iron sleeve, which gives the appearance of a socket. The butt end of the wooden handle is protected with an iron ring against fraying. I was told that this type of chisel is generally used in Japan. The length of these chisels is 7⅜ inches and 4¾ inches respectively. The cutting edge of the longer one is 9/16 of an inch wide and of the other 5/16 of an inch. The wooden handle is made of oak and the steel of the tool is of excellent quality.

LINE MARKING

The carpenter's line marker, Fig. 372, is a compact little instrument consisting of an inkwell made of bamboo, a handle, roulette and string fastener. The square little wooden block, at the right in the picture, holds a pointed iron pin and to this pin the hempen string is fastened. The string passes through the inkwell, which is filled with silk-waste saturated with black ink, and thence to the drum or roulette around which it is wound.

To mark lines the block with its iron point is pressed into the lumber worked upon, and the line is run out from the roulette through the inkwell and stretched taut over the place to be marked. Then the string is picked up with thumb and forefinger and let go, when it flies back into its former position, leaving a black line along its path. The length from the inkwell to the end of the handle is 13 inches, the height of the bamboo inkwell is 2½ inches and its diameter 2½ inches. The drum revolves on a wooden axle stuck into the handle. The disks of the drum are of teakwood, as is the handle, and the spokes are of bamboo. A nail inserted in the disk in the line of its spokes, serves to turn the drum. The brush shown sticking in the inkwell takes the place of a pencil for marking short lines. It is not much of a brush at that, being merely a bamboo stick with its ends finely sliced with parallel cuts about one half inch deep. The result is a fairly good semblance of a brush.

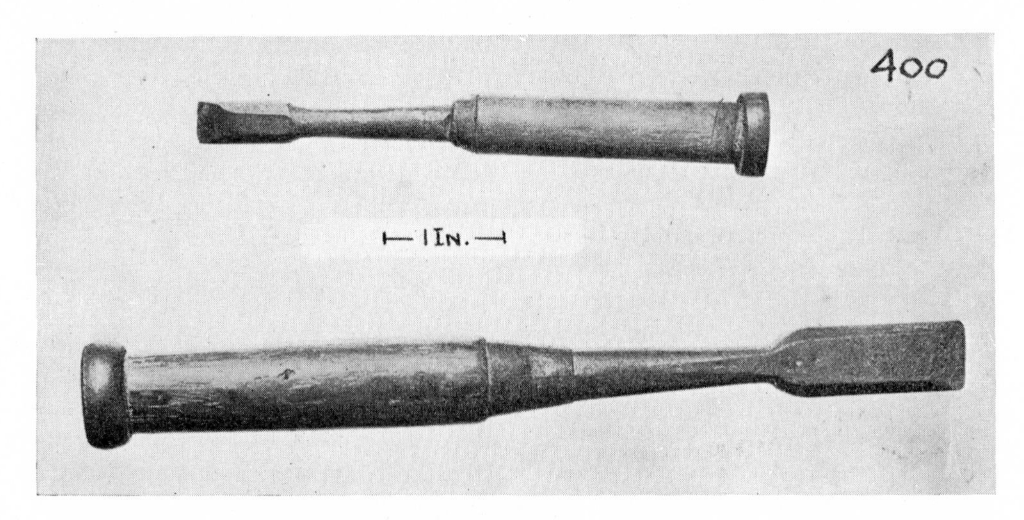

FIG. 371. MODERN JAPANESE CARPENTER'S CHISELS.

This line marker was photographed in the Native City of Shanghai.

Fig. 373 shows three line-marking brushes. The bottom specimen is the ordinary carpenter's brush. It is 9¾ inches long and made of bamboo. It is similar to the one seen sticking in the ink pot of the line-marker in Fig. 372. The ink pot contains a small amount of moxa or some silk waste, saturated with black ink, and the brush is dipped into it to take up ink, which is retained between the thin slivers of bamboo.

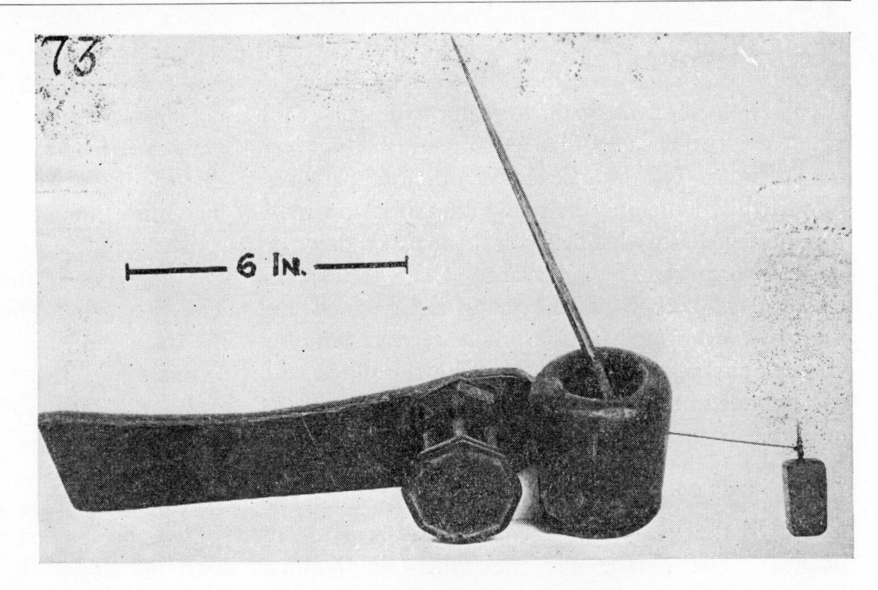

Fig. 372. Carpenter's Line Marker.

The brush in the middle of Fig. 373 was picked up in a Chinese stone quarry, where it had been used to mark on granite the lines along which the stone was to be split. Part of the slitted end is broken off, probably the reason why the brush had been discarded. It is stained with reddle or red ocher, which the quarry men use in liquid form for marking. Only the end of the brush is shown, its whole length is 15½ inches. It is made of bamboo, as are the other two brushes shown.

The most interesting of these implements is the top specimen which the Chinese carpenters use for scribing. To understand its use we must recall the process of scribing as practiced by our carpenters. To fit a board against an uneven wall, the board has to be cut in such a manner that its edge will show the same unevenness as the wall. The problem is to draw a line on the board which coincides with the uneven wall surface, and then saw along this line. When properly sawed the board will fit exactly against the uneven wall. Our carpenters accomplish this with the use of compasses. The straight-edged board is held against the uneven wall and the compasses are opened to fit the greatest distance between board and wall. While one leg of the compasses is passed over

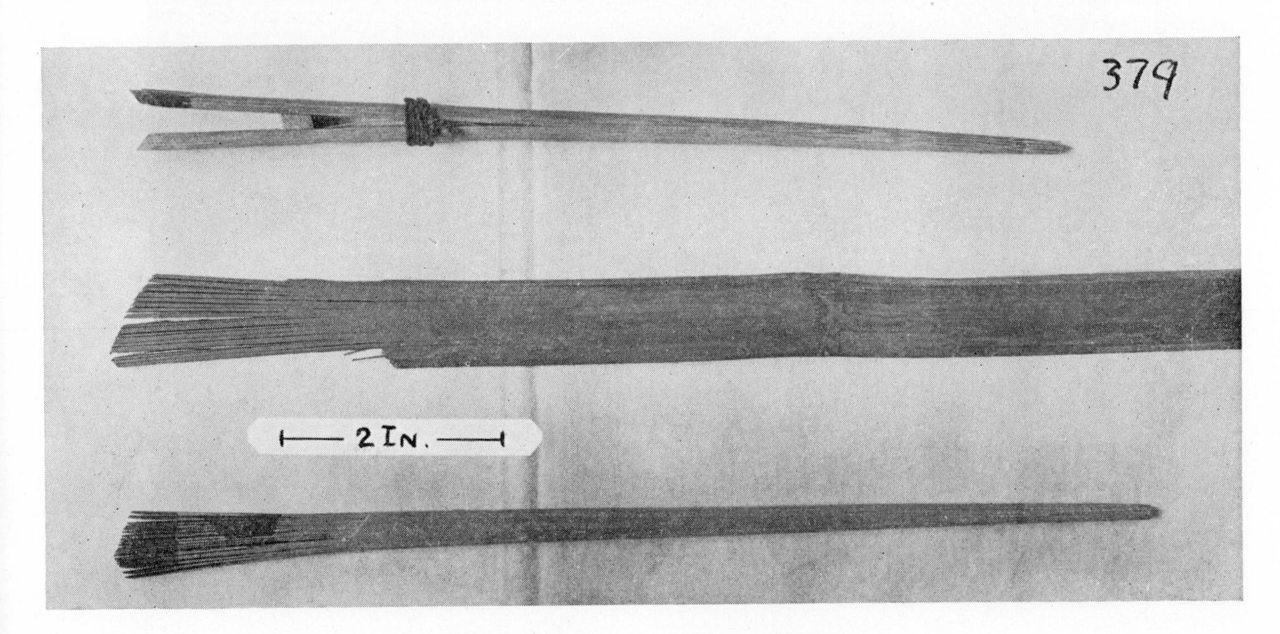

Fig. 373. Chinese Line Marking Brushes.

the surface of the wall the other leg makes a scratch on the board, marking a line closely corresponding to the unevenness of the wall. Instead of compasses the Chinese carpenter uses this scribing brush, Fig. 373, top specimen. The distance between the two parts can be varied by loosening the string around it and moving the wooden wedge between them up or down to decrease or increase the distance. Once the proper distance has been fixed, the string is tightened and the two parts remain in the proper relative position. One leg of the scribing tool, that with the slitted end, corresponds to the Chinese carpenter's brush, and the other leg is merely pointed and used as a guide to slide along the uneven surface, to fit which the straight-edged board is to be scribed and cut. The length of the tool is 8¾ inches and it is made of bamboo. The photograph was taken in Kuling, Kiangsi.

The prototype of the painting brush, a bundle of fibres or hair at the end of a rod, might well be a wooden stick with frayed ends. The Chinese have apparently gone through several stages of brush development and finally arrived at the writing brush, which is a perfect piece of workmanship. It is one of the paradoxes found in China that to this day the carpenters use a brush which is exceedingly primitive, though very efficient for drawing lines along the edge of a ruler or the like. The most perfect brush would not answer for this purpose, and as the Chinese do not have any pencil, we may take this for the reason that the primitive brush, a wooden stick with parallel incisions at the end, has been retained.

The Chinese are also pioneers in using oil paint. For applying it they use however no paint brush. They get a handful of cotton waste and dip it into the paint and apply it in this manner. It is a dirty business and the hand of the painter gets full of paint, yet they paint efficiently and cleanly. After all there is much more "feel" in applying paint with the hand than with a brush.

Among Chinese artists there exists also a curious conceit, the painting a picture or writing characters with the finger or fingernail dipped into the ink. There are illustrious examples named in the annals of art and specimens are treasured by the art collectors.

RECIPROCATING LATHE

Fig. 374 shows a reciprocating lathe which is used to turn small pieces. This particular one was photographed in a pewterer's shop in Nanchang, Kiangsi province. The same type is used by wood-turners,

FIG. 374. RECIPROCATING TURNING LATHE.

FIG. 375. A POLE LATHE OF THE 17TH CENTURY. Pictured after the Dutch painter-engraver, Jan Joris Van Vliet, born at Delft in 1610.

bone-workers, gem-cutters and the like. The lathe has a sort of chuck which holds the material to be worked but has no tail-stock. For abrasion processes the working piece is held in the hand free against a reciprocating cast iron disk fixed on the lathe-head, which disk with the aid of water and sand accomplishes the grinding or abrading.

The lathe proper is similar to the Japanese lathe in Fig. 376 and consists of a wooden base with two short uprights, slotted on top for receiving the wooden spindle or lathe-pin. Around the spindle between the supports, a rope is coiled with the two ends hanging down. A wooden framework, four uprights, with various cross-pieces to give it sturdiness, serves as a support for the lathe proper. In the center it furnishes a seat for the workman on a board (not shown) which is laid over the horizontal cross-pieces.

At the lower right part of the framework two pedals are attached which connect with the two rope ends dangling from the lathe-pin. The turner sits within the framework facing the end of the lathe-pin and works the pedals with his feet to give it reciprocating motion. Wood to be turned is driven into a cup-shaped socket upon the end of the lathe-pin. The tool is applied to the working piece when it moves in one of the reciprocating directions, namely when the right pedal is being pressed downward.

The underlying principle of this lathe is the same as in our pole-lathe, which was used in former times. The accompanying reproduction of an old Dutch print, Fig. 375, gives a good view of a pole-lathe. When the turner presses down on the pedal the pole is bent downward and the piece to be turned revolves in the wrong direction for cutting. The actual turning takes place when the pole is released and moves upwards. It is interesting to note that the western worker is thus free to center more of his attention upon applying the tool, without at the same time expanding too much bodily energy in moving the pedal, as the Chinese turner has to do.

For polishing the wood after turning the Chinese use scouring rush [5] (*Equisetum hyemale* W.). It contains a large amount of silica, 97 percent of the whole ash, and is therefore well fitted for an abradant. Sandstone with water is used for polishing hard wood, this is especially the case for smoothing the large wooden poles of Chinese steelyards.

Although there is a similarity between the western pole-lathe and the Chinese lathe, inasmuch as there is reciprocating motion in both of them, the pole-lathe is not used nor known in China.

The attached sketch, Fig. 376, copied after the detail of an old Japanese woodcut, shows the simple principle of the Chinese lathe once more. The rope is passed once or twice around the lathe-pin and the ends are pulled alternately by an attendant while the worker applies the tools to the working piece fastened

[5] Also called Dutch Rush or Horse Tail. It is "the best species for polishing wood and metal, and is imported from Holland for that purpose under the name Dutch Rushes. It is much used by whitesmiths, cabinet makers, and comb-makers, and formerly it was in demand for scouring pewter and wooden articles in the kitchen." (Loudon, Enc. of Plants, London 1836).

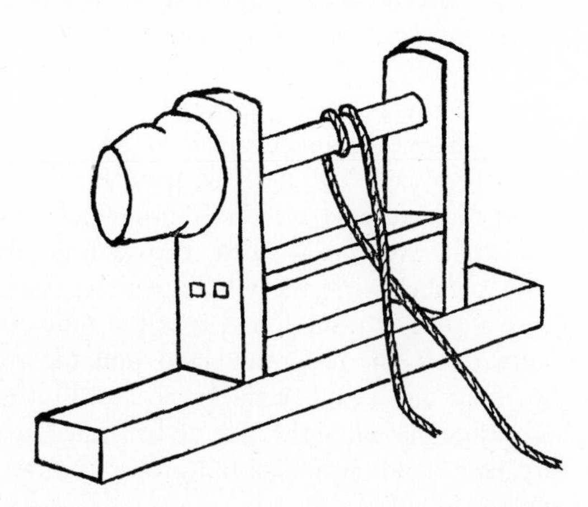

FIG. 376. JAPANESE LATHE (AFTER A JAPANESE WOODCUT).

to the lathe-head. See for comparison also Fig. 525 which gives another view of the lathe shown in Fig. 374.

For turning long pieces the Chinese carpenter rigs up on his workbench, as occasion may require, a simple turning lathe arrangement which can easily be dismantled when no longer needed. The workbench itself is merely a trestle, about 20 inches from the ground. The working piece is held between two hard wood strips, which are nailed across the top of this trestle at right angles to its length, and protrude over the trestle-edge. Fig. 377 shows this arrangement, and how two iron spikes, passing through the hard wood strips, hold the piece worked upon, so it can revolve around its own axis. To guide the hand holding the chisel and to serve as a primitive sort of tool-rest a a board is laid over the wooden strips a little away from, but parallel with, the working piece. Around this latter a rope is wound, and it is the task of an apprentice to sit on the ground and pull the rope-ends, now the one and then the other, and thus give a reciprocating motion to the piece to be turned, while the carpenter stands behind leaning over the trestle, and applies the chisel.

I saw this turning arrangement in Changshu, Kiangsi, and the carpenter serving it said apologetically that somebody had ordered a piece of furniture to be made in foreign style. He was therefore adorning it with turnings instead of carving and shaking his head over the depraved taste of the foreigner. It is a pity that foreign taste is thus misunderstood. This country carpenter did not know that economic considerations compel us to substitute turnings for carving. A Chinese wood-carver will work a whole week, twelve hours a day, for about a dollar, and if we could get wood carving done as cheaply we would soon discard turnings for carving.

Fig. 377. Wood Carver's Turning Lathe.

Wood turning is a much later art than wood carving, in fact we may call it a mechanization of wood carving made possible by the introduction of the lathe. In the fictile arts we have a striking analogy, the shaping of wares by free hand, which preceded the use of the potter's wheel.

There seems to be a close connection between the cutting of moldings and wood turning. Here also the primitive molding was undoubtedly made by the carver. The invention of the hand plane made the first machine-made moldings possible. In the subsequent development the blade of the plane was given all sorts of profiles in order to shape the wood into the type of molding desired. Now the surface of a turned piece when flattened out produces the profile of a molding and the whole process is closely related to wood turning although arrived at by different means.

ACCESSORY CARPENTER'S TOOLS

The Chinese carpenters use the three squares shown in Fig. 378. There is the L-shaped square, with the shorter leg graduated and measuring one Chinese foot, equivalent to nearly 13 of our inches. Chinese measures are rather flexible, not only do they vary in different parts of the country, but even in one city, the various guilds fixing a standard to suit their own trade. The foot is divided into ten inches and each inch into ten subdivisions. The scale is painted white and the division marks applied with Chinese ink. The length of the long leg of the L-shaped square is 21 inches.

The longer part of the T-square is 8⅛ inches in length, and the shorter leg, mortised into the other, is 4¾ inches long.

The mitre-square consists of a straight piece, 11¾ inches long, with another strip, 9⅞ inches long, attached at an angle of 45 degrees.

Lines are marked against the sides of these squares with the bamboo brush of the line marker described under Fig. 372.

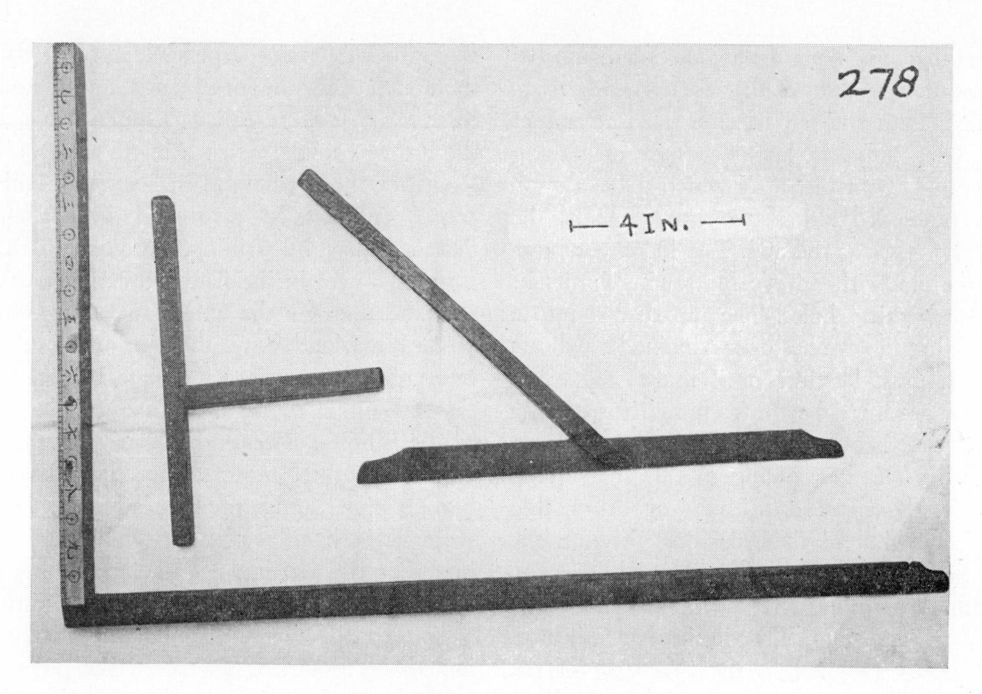

Fig. 378. Carpenter's Squares.

USE OF DOWELS IN CHINA

HISTORY OF DOWELS

For economic reasons the Chinese carpenter uses wrought iron nails but sparingly. Treenails or bamboo dowels serve his purpose as well. Producing them and drilling holes for their insertion means more work but it keeps him independent of the blacksmith who laboriously makes the wrought iron nails. Nevertheless there are occasions when a metal dowel, a nail without a head, is necessary for added strength. This is the case in Chinese shipbuilding where boards, the sheathing of the hull, are united butt against butt with wrought iron dowels.

The *raison d'etre* of pin, dowel, needle, bodkin and awl is the desire to join separate parts together. This desire first manifested itself apparently in connection with the need for clothing. The finds from the early epochs of human culture from the age of stone through that of copper, and bronze to the iron age, show the development of the pin of which the earliest forms are the thorn (according to Forrer some Abyssinian women held their garments together with thorns until quite recently), fish-bone, and bone-splinters. The development does not proceed along one line, but branches out into different channels.

One result of this branching out is the art of sewing. First the pin made the holes and, left in place,

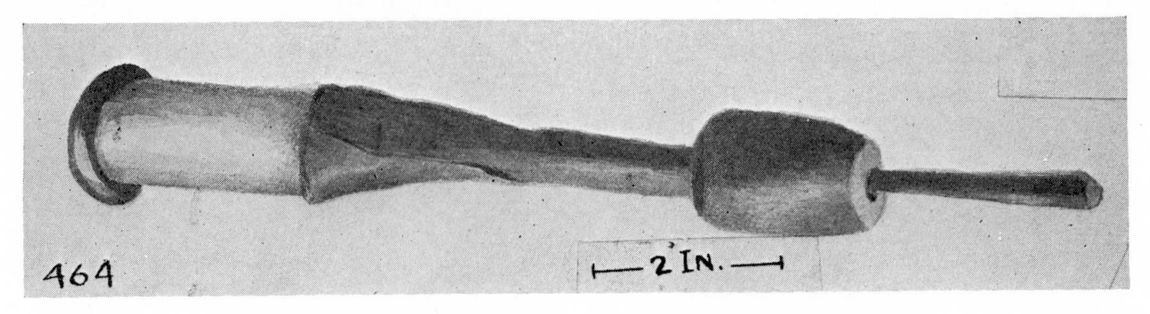

Fig. 379. Chinese Dowel Driver.

joined pieces together. Next a fibre threaded into the holes reduced the function of the pin to merely making the holes. Thus the pin became the fore-runner of the awl. Then came the happy thought of making a hole in the end of the pin, after which the evolution of the pin proceeded along two lines, one as the needle and the other as the awl. The increase of usefulness of the pin with an eye for sewing limits its usefulness for making holes. The pin turned into a needle by adding the eye has ever remained a delicate instrument. It must be thin, or it makes too big a hole, and yet, it should be thick enough for a large eye to receive a heavy thread. For sewing heavy material, such as leather, owing to this inadequacy of the needle, the more primitive way of making holes with an awl, and then pushing through the holes the thread, tipped with hog bristles, has survived to this day among the shoemakers in China (conf. Figs. 310 and 311). The diminished utility of the needle as an awl, led to the invention of the thimble, and in China of the needle-puller (see Figs. 293 and 285). The further development of the needle shows few variations. Traceable to the stone age, when they were made of bone, we find needles in the copper age made of copper, with the eye formed by bending the end into a tiny loop, in the bronze age of bronze, with sometimes a round and sometimes an oval eye. In the iron age we finally find them made of iron. In Germany, in the middle ages, one end of a wrought wire was sharpened, the other flattened and then cleft and the open ends hammered together. Such needles were called "Glufen." An advance in the art was made, when a blank wire of double the length of the needle was sharpened at both ends, the center flattened, cut apart and the eye made in the flattened part by drilling. Another method was to form two eyes in the flattened center part by punching, and then cut the wire between the two eyes.

As remarked above, the pin, no longer left in the holes of textiles to join the material together, became the forerunner of the awl, an instrument for merely making holes. The end, then, was made heavier, bulbous, to offer more surface for pressure with the hand. Copper and bronze awls for economy of metal were set in handles of wood or bone. To pierce soft materials the awl has not undergone any changes to this day. When, however, the primitive worker attempted the piercing of harder materials the awl had to be modified. To flatten the point allowed of leverage on the principle of the wedge, the form of the cobbler's awl for piercing leather. To make the point three or four cornered (as the Japanese wood drill used to this day, conf. Fig. 368), the principle of abrasion came into play with rotary, reciprocating motion. Thus we are led into another interesting channel which comprises the drill with its various modifications.

Returning to the pin we remember that its primary function was to make a hole and remain therein to unite the material. The pin used by the Chinese tailor (see Fig. 287, the second of the specimens from the left) illustrates the primary function of the pin, still without a head. The Japanese with their pins are a step ahead of the Chinese, having added as a

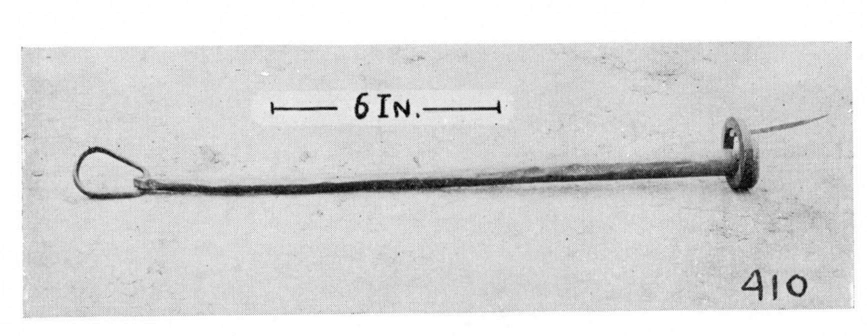

Fig. 380. Nail Puller.

head a cylindrical piece of wood, or wound the dull pin end around a flat piece of wood. In Europe a head was soon added to the pin, to keep it from sliding through the material and at the same time to aid the pushing, by thickening the end, by flattening it or by furnishing it with a cross-piece, the latter product being called a "crutch-pin."

To apply the pin to harder material for example for the purpose of joining two pieces of wood, the mere pressure of the hand was no longer sufficient. To surmount the difficulty two methods presented themselves. One was to make the pin strong enough to be driven into the material without bending or breaking (result: the nail), and the other, to aid the pin to penetrate by preparing the hole beforehand with the awl or its modification the drill. In the latter case the pin becomes the dowel and need not be of unusual strength to be driven.

Fig. 381. Chinese Whetstone.

DOWEL DRIVER

Metal dowels are used a great deal in Chinese shipbuilding. For the unusual mode of driving these dowels, without making a hole beforehand, an unusual tool is used. The instrument consists of two parts, the one shaped like a socketed chisel with wooden handle inserted and protected against fraying with a ferrule, and the other, a heavy wrought iron sleeve. Instead of a chisel edge the blade of the tool has a square or dull end, not seen in the picture, Fig. 379, because it is covered by the bulbous sleeve. The blade of the tool proper is wedged within the sleeve against the side of the tapering dowel, and the tool can be hit to drive the dowel, large end foremost, into the wood. This is done until the dowel has penetrated the wood to half its (the dowel's) length. A short, smart blow against the sleeve of the instrument, loosens the wedged combination, and the task is accomplished. Fig. 379 has been sketched from an unsatisfactory photograph taken in Fuchow, Kiangsi province, in a shipbuilding yard.

NAIL PULLER

The planks of boats are nailed to the ribs with iron nails and, as has been said, are joined butt to butt by wrought iron dowels. But whether nails or dowels are used it becomes necessary at times to draw them, especially in repairing boats, and for this purpose the Chinese use a nail-puller like the one shown in Fig. 380. A wrought iron rod, about 1 foot 4 inches long, has a flat knob at its end, and a loose iron ring sliding on the rod. The head of the nail to be pulled has to be cleared of surrounding wood, and then it is gripped between the knob-edge and the ring, exactly as the nail is held in the picture. Pushing the rod downward exerts leverage and tightens the grip, and the nail is easily extracted from the wood. When not in use the instrument is hung up by the ring on the other end of the rod. The photograph was taken at Fuchow, Kiangsi, where it was in use by shipbuilders.

WHETSTONE

The picture, Fig. 381, shows a whetstone held between two little bamboo posts rammed into the ground, aside of a wall on a Chinese farm. The stone is a fine-grained sandstone and is wedged into slots cut into the tops of the posts. It is placed conveniently near the entrance gate and used by the peasants to sharpen their various implements. The process of whetting is carried on much as we would do it, with water poured occasionally upon the stone to keep it moist. The revolving grindstone is not known nor an arrangement for periodically dripping water upon the stone.

Usually the whetstone is set into a mortise of a block of wood not much larger than the stone. Carpenters usually have a stone of their own among their tools, and when engaged at a job of some duration, make a wooden block to hold it, which they abandon when moving on to another job, where they spend again much time in fixing the whetstone into another base. They keep their tools keen-edged and it is ever the complaint among foreigners that a carpenter called in for some work spends half the time sharpening his tools.

A fixed whetstone on a farm, as the one shown, is not the rule. In this respect the Chinese are usually opportunists, and sharpen their knives and tools in the street on any stone convenient, be it a stepping stone, railing of a bridge, or a tumbled down monument. Similar conditions prevailed in Europe as is indicated by an entry in the register of a London parish under date of April 23, 1646, which runs as follows: "A child found at Mr. Sawyers in the street on a place to whet knives and was named Edward Sharp."

The photograph, Fig. 381 was taken at a lonely farm in the Wantsai Mountains, northwestern Kiangsi, where dwell a people distinct from the Chinese in the surrounding country. They are termed K'o-Chia, guest tribe, a name indicating their status as a people who have settled in these mountains in comparatively recent times, after having been driven from their original abode in Kwangtung through war and untoward economic conditions.

Fig. 382. Adobe Bricks.

BAMBOO ROOFING TILES

The low wall in Fig. 381 is made of Pisé de terre, and is part of an enclosure of the vegetable garden and is protected with bamboo tiles against disintegration by rain. Chinese records of the Sung Dynasty (960 to 1280 A.D.) speak of the splitting of bamboo and levelling of the joints and the subsequent use of these gutters for roofing tiles. Among the K'o-Chia this mode of covering must be a remnant from the South, I have not seen it anywhere else in China. It is used among these mountain people only sparingly, for covering pisé walls, small out-houses and lean-tos. The main houses are covered with earthenware roofing tiles. In the Malay Peninsula bamboo roofing tiles were still used in recent times.[6] The semi-circular form of the Chinese roofing tiles may have been derived from these bamboo tiles. The clay tiles are much superior and need not be weighted down with heavy stones as is the case with the bamboo tiles in Fig. 381.

[6] "The mode of tiling is derived from the use of split bamboos as it is practised to this day by the Malays." Davis, "The Chinese," Vol. I, p. 366. London 1836.

BAMBOO LIGHTING SPLINTS

The bundles of bamboo splints lying on top of the wall, Fig. 381, deserve also a word in passing. The splints are used individually for lighting. At night one or two can be seen sticking each in a separate hole in the mud-wall of the room, slanting a little bit downward. They give a dismal light and burn up to the wall where they leave a black streak extending upwards from the hole. The ashes and charred embers drop on the mud floor. In preparing these bamboo splints old bamboo trees serve the best. After being cut to size, about 3 feet long, and bundled as seen on the picture, they are submerged in the rice fields for about a week and then exposed to the sun to become thoroughly dried out, when they are fit for use.

BRICK MAKING

The development of Chinese habitations started with "caves on declivities." As culture advanced huts were formed of branches and covered with clay. Historians compared them with the shape of a potter's kiln. These huts were succeeded by houses formed of stamped clay walls and covered with thatch. In the Shih chi by Sze-ma Ch'ien, the Herodotus of China, it is related that T'ang (1766 B.C.) and Yü (2205 B.C.) built habitations with thatched roofs and clay steps. The clay steps very likely were the blocks of tamped clay which are a characteristic feature of building walls in the manner of pisé de terre. In the 23rd century B.C. the mausoleum of Shun of Yü was surrounded by a brick wall, we read, and thereafter the mention of bricks becomes more frequent. First they were most likely only sun-dried or adobe bricks, but by the time of the Han dynasty the art of burning bricks had become fully developed.

In the country districts of Kiangsi one can frequently see peasant houses built of adobe bricks. The country is watered by streams and creeks, which carry considerable silt and the fields which are periodically inundated for raising rice and other crops gradually get so deeply silted that it is impossible to get the proper water depth and it becomes necessary about once in ten years to lower the surface. In autumn, after the harvest, the field is plowed over and the surface smoothed with a stone roller. Some days after a heavy rain, when the moisture has evaporated to such a degree as to leave the ground similar in consistency to putty, with a perfectly smooth surface, the top layer of a field to be brought to a lower level, is cut with a spade into sections corresponding to the outline of an adobe brick and these pieces are lifted off after a final cut with the spade from the side. The bricks measure about 14 by 9 by 4 inches, and thus the fields are uniformly lowered by about four

FIG. 383. BRICKMAKER'S SPADE.

inches. It is necessary to do this cutting in autumn, when the heat of the sun is not so strong. In summer the drying of the field would be too rapid and the field would develop irregular cracks, a condition quite unsuitable for the cutting of adobe bricks. The bricks after cutting are piled up in rows (as shown in Fig. 382), covered with straw, as a protection against subsequent rains, and left to dry for several weeks, when

FIG. 384. BRICKMAKER'S BOW FOR CUTTING PLASTIC CLAY.

they will be ready to be used for building walls. The wall foundations are built of stones, and upon them rests the adobe brick wall. As a binding material or mortar, wet mud mixed with straw is used. Information about this process was gathered at Sha Ho, Kiangsi province, where also the picture, Fig. 382, was taken of the removed surface layer, cut into rectangular pieces which form the adobe bricks.

KILN BRICKS

At Sa Sau Dung Gao, Chekiang province, we visited an establishment where bricks are made of river mud. The mud is dug from the river's edge

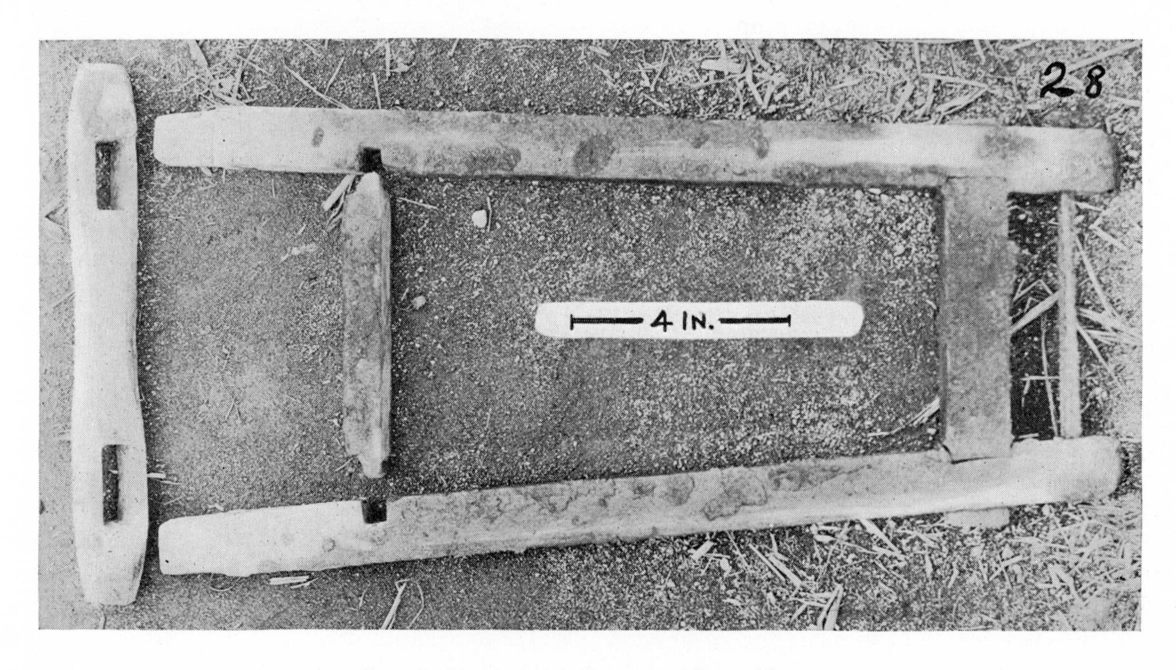

FIG. 385. BRICKMAKER'S RELEASABLE BRICK MOLD.

with a type of spade shown in Fig. 383, and carried in shallow baskets on bamboo poles higher up the bank to the huts of the brick-makers. Here the transported clay is moistened with water and tramped and kneaded by a workingman's feet to get an even mixture. The heavy crosspiece on the handle of the spade suggests that all the strength is applied with the hands and arms when digging. The poorly shod Chinese cannot exert any pressure with his foot.

As soon as the mud is well tempered by the treading, batches are cut from the mass with the bow shown in Fig. 384. The straight wooden arm of the bow with the wire is forced down into the mass from the top. The curved part of the bow is then swung sideways so that the wire cuts horizontally. The wire is then drawn upward. The batch cut out has thus a triangular shape. This batch is then carried to the brickmakers, each of whom has his own straw covered hut. Here the brickmaker kneads the batch of mud thoroughly with his hands and puts it upon a deal table where he has his implements. These consist of the mold, as shown in Fig. 385, several wooden slabs about ⅛ of an inch thick and of a surface measuring 12 by 6 inches, and the small bow shown in Fig. 387. A little heap of wood-ashes completes the outfit. In order to make a brick, the closed mold—shown open in Fig. 385—is placed upon one of the wooden slabs, so that the form of the brick to be made is bounded on the bottom by the wooden slab and on the sides by the inner sides of the mold. Next ashes are sprinkled over the inside of the mold, and then the brickmaker lifts up a batch of mud and throws it with considerable force into the mold. The top of the mud is then levelled off with the wire of the small bow, Fig. 387, and then the finished brick, 10 by 5 by 1½ inches, lies in the mold. The mold is opened by withdrawing the mortised end-piece, and spreading the side-pieces apart as can be readily understood by looking at Fig. 385. The slab with the soft moist brick resting upon it, is then put aside. Other bricks thus formed and thus supported on slabs are set one upon the other

FIG. 386. BRICKMAKER'S TWO BRICK MOLD.

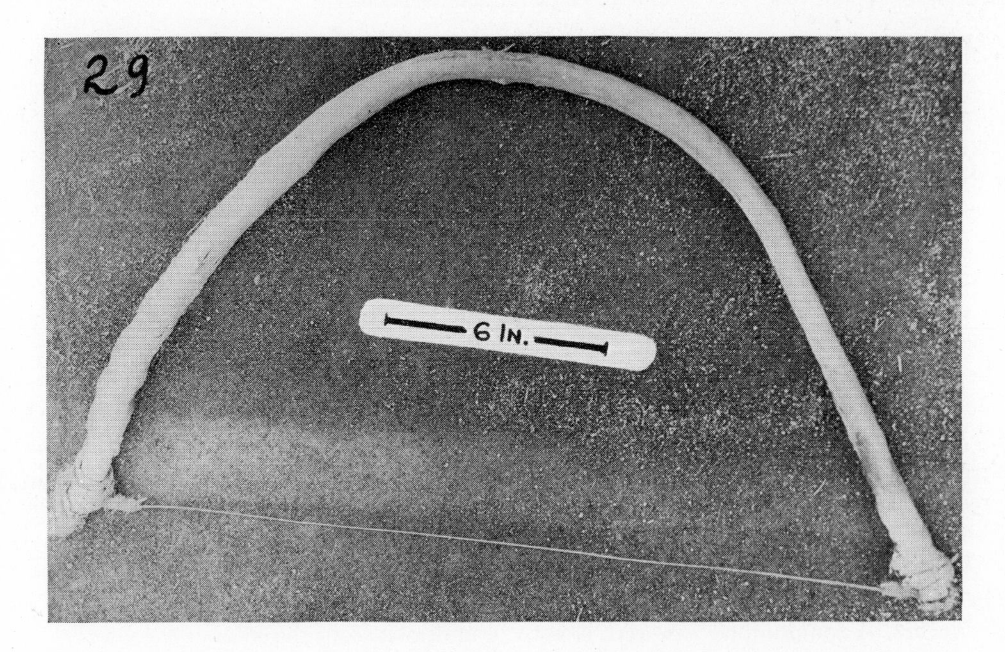

FIG. 387. BRICKMAKER'S SMALL CUTTING BOW FOR CUTTING SUPERFLUOUS CLAY OFF THE BRICK MOLD.

FIG. 388. BRICK KILN SHOWING FIRING HOLE.

and when a pile of about a half a dozen is finished, the brickmaker takes this pile, carries it into the yard, and taking the bricks from the slabs stands them on edge, one close to the other. These rows are left exposed to the sun for about a day and when they have become somewhat dried and firm, are piled up on top of each other five bricks high, in rows, as can be seen in the backgrounds of Figs. 383 and 384, and the top of the rows is covered with straw. After about a week's time the bricks are dry enough to be burned in the kiln.

At another brickyard in Anhwei province bricks measuring 10 by 5 by 1 inches were made in a mold constructed so as to make two bricks at a time instead of one but otherwise similar to the mold shown in Fig. 385. The thickness of the mold frame shown in Fig. 386 is 2 inches. A longitudinal saw-kerf is cut through its side-pieces starting at the right-hand end of the mold in the picture and extending as far as the grooves which hold the loose piece terminating the opening of the mold on the left. Instead of one mold frame there are now practically two mold frames still fast together, because not entirely bisected by the saw-kerf. The cross-piece and end fastenings on the right are duplicated so that the saw-kerf is free for the passage of a wire for the entire length of the brick. After the mud has been thrown into this closed double mold, the wire of the bow is passed through the kerf, and then across the top of the mud mass to level it off. Now there are two bricks in the mold, one on top of the other, each one inch thick. These are dried sticking together, but are easily separated by tapping their edges before placing them in the kiln. The advantage of the double mold as a time saver is evident.

Fig. 388 shows the front of a brick kiln with the firing hole. The diameter of its vaulted roof is about 12 feet, with an opening on top about 3 feet in diameter. The bricks are piled into the kiln through this circular roof opening by a man who enters it with a ladder. In setting the bricks in the kiln a space is left in the middle with a passage to the firing hole. When the kiln is filled, the top is closed up with slabs of stone and mud is plastered over these. On the other side of the kiln, opposite the firing hole, just where the cupola or vaulted roof projects from the surrounding earth work, is a draft hole. The fire is regulated by a graduated opening or closing of this orifice as circumstances demand. Boughs of pine trees are used for fuel, piles of them are shown in Fig. 389, and the fire is kept up for twenty-four hours. Then the firing hole and the draft hole are closed up until the kiln has cooled which takes from four to seven days, when the operation is finished and the burned bricks are ready to be withdrawn from the kiln.

A different method of making bricks is practiced

FIG. 389. FUEL OF PINE BOUGHS, USED FOR BURNING BRICKS, AT BRICK KILNS SEEN IN BACKGROUND.

in various places in Kiangsi province. The mold shown in Fig. 390 is used there. It is in the form of a wooden box with two compartments and a bottom. The length is 27½ inches, the width 6¾ inches, and the height 3¼ inches. The size of the bricks formed is 11 by 5½ by 2½ inches. The three crosspieces of the mold are mortised into place and the bottom board is nailed to the frame with foreign nails. The clay is worked with much water and is therefore rather soft and sticky. The man who prepares a batch

FIG. 390. BRICKMAKER'S MOLD, NON-RELEASABLE VARIETY.

FIG. 391. BRICKMAKER'S CLAY FORK, CLAY SPADE, FLOOR LEVELER AND CLAY BAT.

FIG. 392. KILN FOR BURNING BRICKS AND ROOFING TILES.

for throwing, rubs his hands previously with wood-ashes, or with powdered stone derived from a disintegrating rock. Another takes these batches, and throws them into the mold, one batch for each compartment. Previous to throwing, he pours wood ashes into the mold, shakes them around and pours out what does not adhere to the bottom and sides. After throwing the clay into the mold, the top of the protruding mass is cut off level by means of the wire on the small bow seen hanging on the brickmaker's trestle. The mold is then taken from the trestle to the yard, turned upside down upon the ground, when the bricks drop easily from the mold and come to rest flat on the ground, not on edge, as we saw it done in Chekiang. After drying in the air until sufficiently firm, they are piled in rows for further drying. The kilns are in construction the same as those previously described. The bricks are piled up in the kiln rather loosely to allow of air passage between them, and the burning lasts from 7 to 12 days. After that the firing and draft holes are closed up and left for a day. Then water is poured into the draft hole on top, altogether 560 buckets. The kiln holds 12,000 bricks. The fuel consists of green boughs indiscriminately gathered from various kinds of trees. The burned bricks have a gray color which is due to the quenching with water.

For the mixing of clay a circular pit is dug about 1½ feet in diameter. The mixing is done by men who trample it with bare feet, and the wrought iron flat-pronged fork or stirring tool, two specimens of which are shown in Fig. 391, is also used. The iron part of this tool is 6¾ inches wide at the bottom, and 2 feet 10 inches long, ending in a socket which receives the wooden handle. The same picture shows a wooden spade with a long handle for slicing off batches from the heap of clay in the background, against which the tools lean. A wooden leveller, shown in the middle, is used for smoothing the ground upon which the bricks are deposited for drying. Finally, on the extreme right, is shown a large rectangular wooden bat for hitting the bricks when standing in a row and partially dry for burning, to get their surface even and flat. Figs. 390 and 391 were taken near Kuling.

High up in the Ten Tai Mountains, in the hinterland of Ningpo, Chekiang province, we got some more pictures and information on brick making. In the circular kiln shown in Fig. 392, there are four draft holes in the wall of the structure near the

FIG. 393. BRICKMAKER'S TOOLS AND TABLE, BRICK MOLD, LIFTING TABLET, BRICKS AND CLAY CUTTER.

FIG. 394. CHINESE BRICKMAKER AT WORK.

of the kiln. The large firing hole seen in the picture is walled up and only a small opening left in it to keep the fire going with pine tree boughs. The kiln is vaulted with bricks, and on its outside the brickwork is strengthened with earth heaped against it. The projecting upper part of the kiln is encircled with bamboo hoops, lest the heat burst the vault.

The same place where the foregoing picture was taken furnished Figs. 393 and 394. The former shows the whole outfit of the brickmaker. There is the releasable brick mold, three bricks on the supporting slabs, which are placed under the mold when forming a brick, and one slab in the background, ready for another brick. The bow is seen hung up, to be handy when needed, and wood ashes are in a box hidden from view beside

bottom. They are about the same distance from each other and lead to vertical smoke passages in the wall

FIG. 395 ANCIENT CHINESE DECORATED BRICK.

the empty slab. The clay on the ground to the right is cut up into convenient batches for throwing into the mold. After four bricks have been made the worker takes the pile and carries them to the rows shown in Fig. 394.

Back of and close to the bench in Fig. 393 there are some bricks piled up to form a stand. They show grooves along their whole length, to make which the brick mold is modified by putting cross pieces into it which hold a wooden rod just the size of the groove. The flimsy Chinese house walls are sometimes reinforced with wooden rods fitting into these grooved bricks. Now and then, as the fancy takes the wall builder, a wooden rod is placed horizontally along the whole length of a wall, on top of a finished layer of bricks, and the rod then covered up by laying these grooved bricks over it.

The brickmaker in Fig. 394 is just reaching for wood ashes to strew over a finished brick in the mold. His uncanny look is prompted by fear for his soul, or at least that part of it which according to peasant superstition is easily detached and captured by a cameraman to become part of the picture he takes. I was ever careful to respect the beliefs of the Chinese even if I could not share them and avoided taking pictures of individuals who were afraid to be photographed. In this case however the worker had tempted fate by deliberately stepping between camera and object and spoiling pictures. The momentary resentment made me point the camera at the picture despoiler and let it do its soul-damaging work.

The dimensions of Chinese bricks vary with the various provinces. A Japanese scholar has evolved a system by which he claims to be able to tell to which historical period a brick belongs by its dimensions. Thus the bricks of the Han Dynasty he claims were of a different size from those of the Sung Dynasty. I fear, however, that in such a system the exceptions would by far outnumber the rules. I adjoin a list giving the dimensions of a number of Chinese bricks with some foreign ones for comparison.

Brick						
Shantung adobe brick for kang *	12	by 12	by	4	inches	
Kiangsi adobe brick	14	by 9	by	4	inches	
Chekiang brick	10	by 5	by	1½	inches	
Chekiang brick	10	by 5	by	1	inches	
Kiangsi brick	11	by 5½	by	2½	inches	
Kiangsi brick of Han Dynasty	13	by 6	by	2	inches	
Anhwei brick	9½	by 5	by	1½	inches	
Anhwei brick of Sung Dynasty	15	by 7	by	3¼	inches	
English standard brick (1839)	10	by 5	by	3	inches	
American standard brick	8½	by 4¼	by	2	inches	
German standard brick	10	by 4¾	by	2½	inches	approx.
	(25	by 12	by	6½	cm.)	
German medieval brick	11¼	by 5⅓	by	3¾	inches	approx.
	(28.5	by 13.5	by	9.5	cm.)	

* Chinese heated bed.

If there were any fixed dimensions for bricks in the various dynasties it appears that in one or the other province the historical conscience went to sleep, and that some brick makers are one or two dynasties behind.

Regarding the releasable mold (Fig. 385) the question may be asked, why use a collapsible mold, when wet bricks can be made and released just as readily from a firmly fixed frame, by turning the mold upside down.

In my wanderings through various parts of China I saw now and then fragments of bricks, in the walls of poorer houses or in enclosing walls around yards and vegetable gardens which had one or more of the

Fig. 396. Ancient Decorated Brick.

side faces decorated with raised lines, formed undoubtedly in a mold. These walls were usually constructed from old bricks which are dug up in and around the older cities wherever one chooses to dig. Inquiries concerning these decorated fragments revealed nothing more than an entire ignorance of the natives as to their origin. They are not now made or used, and I never saw them used in old temples or pagodas, but only in humble dwellings and garden walls. It seems that these fragments bear witness to a

FIGS. 397-400. EFFECT OF ANCIENT DECORATED BRICKS IN PANEL FORMATION. The decorations lend themselves exceedingly well for repeat-designs with which we are familiar in floor tiles. The shape of the bricks with their narrow sides decorated, point however rather to their use in walls.

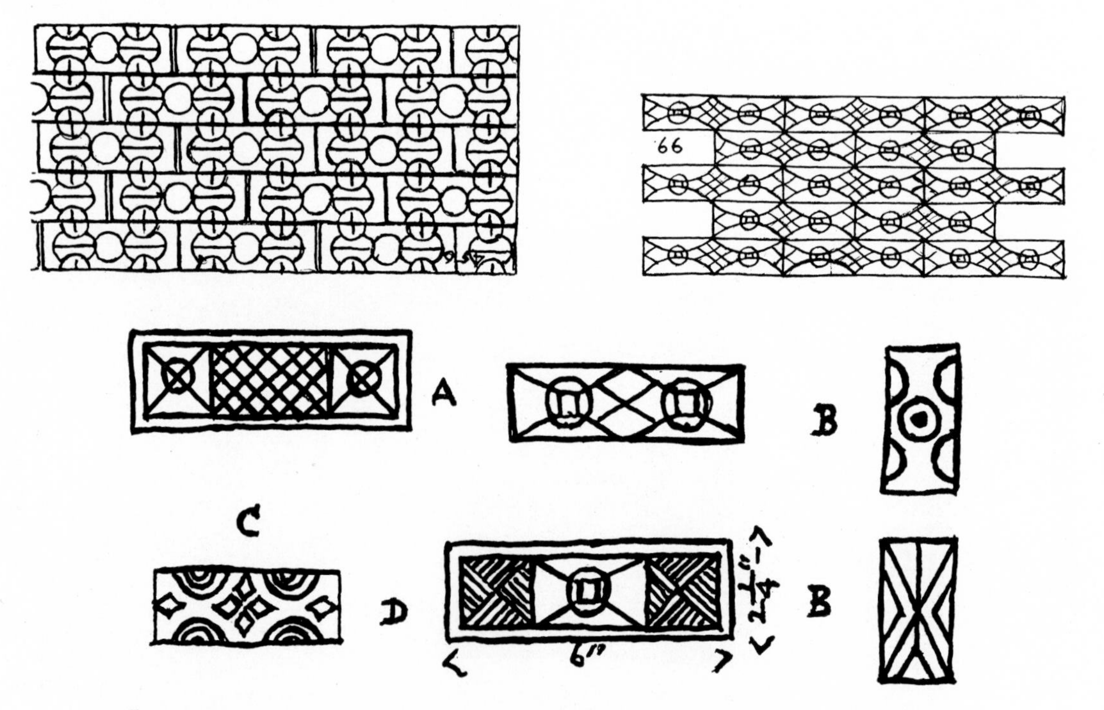

FIGS. 401-403. DESIGNS ON ANCIENT DECORATED BRICKS, AND THEIR APPLICATION IN PANELS. Figs. 401 and 402 show again the formation of panels and Fig. 403 gives the designs of single bricks found in the debris of ancient places in Anhwei, Chekiang and Kiangsi.

long forgotten art of the Chinese. Fig. 395 shows a typical example of such a fragment, found near Changshu, Kiangsi. If we try to picture to ourselves how these bricks were made, we at once find an explanation for the fact that some of the present-day brickmakers in China, use releasable molds for forming ordinary plain bricks. When making these decorated bricks a releasable or "draw" mold must needs have been used with one or more of its side-pieces carved in intaglio with the design to be imprinted upon the brick. To release the raised design the mold had to be opened and "drawn" away from the brick. It is highly characteristic of the Chinese, that long after the discontinuance of making such decorated bricks, they should still use the same releasable mold—now with undecorated sides—, although a rigid mold would answer the purpose just as well and simplify the work.

FIG. 404. ANCIENT DECORATED BRICK. This picture shows a type of burnt brick no longer made in China, often found in city debris and used in building common brick walls.

In Anhwei province I saw also a releasable mold in use, which proved that the releasing process for making modern bricks is not a necessary feature. The brickmaker using it had transformed it into a rigid mold by nailing the various parts together. Questioned about it, he said that he found that it was not necessary to open and close the mold continually, accordingly he had nailed his mold shut. Was he perhaps the first Chinese brickmaker in centuries who had the courage to break all tradition and modify this time-honored contrivance?

In China the art of brickmaking and the utilization of bricks seems to go back as far as the Hsia Dynasty. A Chinese account treating of that period (22nd to 18th century B.C.) says that brick enclosures were built over the coffins. By the time of the Han Dynasty (206 B.C. to 220 A.D.) we find the art fully developed, as peculiarly decorated bricks still to be found in debris around old cities testify (conf. Fig. 395). No longer satisfied with the pleasing effects which variations in bond afforded, the Chinese, at that time, apparently enlivened whole flat wall surfaces with decorated bricks, of which art we find now only fragments of bricks which may have been used in such manner. Figs. 395, 396, 404 and 405 give a few examples of decorated bricks gathered in various parts of Central China, and the sketches, Figs. 397 to 403 show the effect which walls with decorated bricks might have produced. All the designs have been copied from old bricks, found in various places in Chekiang, Anhwei, Kiangsi and Hunan provinces.

FIG. 405. ANCIENT DECORATED BRICK. A now obsolete type of ornamental brick, sometimes found in the debris of cities, and dug up and used in cheap wall building, as noted under Fig. 395.

Wherever I found such decorated bricks they seemed an indication that the founding of that particular place

Fig. 406. Clay Slicing Tool of the Roofing Tile Maker.

went back to the Han dynasty. Often I have tested it by confronting the local literati with the statement "I see your city goes back to the Han dynasty" which was invariably correct whenever I had found decorated bricks in the debris. Likewise in the absence of these the founding of the place was invariably of a later date.

ROOFING TILE MAKING

The most extensively used roof covering in China is the semi-circular or hollow terra-cotta tile. Two of these slightly tapering gutters lying adjacent have their abutting side edges covered with the concave part of another tile. Architecturally they are called the normal or Asiatic tile, and the German in blunt picturesqueness call them "monk and nun."

We had the opportunity to observe the making of the Chinese roofing tiles at five different potteries in different parts of Chekiang province. Of outstanding interest was that the roofing tile-maker used a sort of potter's wheel, while the potter in these regions from the smallest pot to the largest jar built up his ware with strips of clay. This stone-age method seems strange in China, where in other parts of the country the fictile art has been brought quite early to the highest perfection.

The procedure of roofing tile making was essentially the same in all the five places investigated. The raw material, river mud, cut from the banks of a river, or clay, cut from the hillside, or dug from the fields, is taken to the pottery and deposited upon the ground in the open. It is sprinkled with water, and thoroughly worked over by the workmen who tramp it with their bare feet, but is not worked so wet that it would spread unduly or run. The worked clay or river mud is then left in a big heap on the ground. The potter for his daily needs cuts big chunks from the heaps outdoors and carries them into his hut, where he thoroughly kneads them until he gets them into the proper consistency for working.

For cutting chunks from the big heap of raw clay the potter uses a bow, similar to the brickmaker's bow described in Fig. 384. It is strung with a wire extending from the lower end of one of its long arms to the other, as shown in Fig. 407, where the bow can be seen leaning against the pile of bricks. The bow is held by its top bar and one arm of the frame is pushed vertically down into the clay. The bow is then swung around with the arm in the clay as an axis, at an angle usually not exceeding 90 degrees, and then the arm sticking in the clay is pulled out. Following the motion of the wire of the bow we can readily understand how a triangular piece has been cut from the heap. To cut clay with a wire or string seems to be one of those universal inventions which sooner or later is bound to occur to some worker in clay, no matter where, or perhaps even in different parts of the world, as the best means for the purpose. The wire makes a clean cut, impossible to attain with a spade or other instrument to which the clay would adhere.

The tile maker forms from the chunks he has brought into his hut a big rectangular batch of clay, about 4 feet long. In doing this he is guided only by his eyes. Before the batch receives its rectangular shape it is worked into the consistency desired by having pieces repeatedly cut from it and then thrown forcibly upon it. Such a batch on the floor of the tile maker's hut is shown in Figs. 406.

On top of the batch can be seen a unique instrument, a slice-cutter with which a slice of clay, about ⅜ of an inch thick, is cut from the top surface of the batch. This slice is laid around a cylindrical mold to form a clay cylinder, which cylinder is finally broken up into four even parts and furnishes four of the Chinese roofing tiles. The slice-cutter is a crudely made affair. There are three different ones shown, one in Fig. 406, one in Fig. 410, and another one, without handle, in Fig. 412. At other places we saw more carefully constructed ones which cut slices with great precision, but in all cases the principle was the same. The instrument may be compared to a wooden rake with only two outer teeth. The cross bar is about 15 inches long, with a handle attached to it. Near each end of the cross bar are the square teeth mortised into square holes and a wire is stretched between them. Sliding this cutter along the top surface of the batch of clay, keeping the cross bar in close contact with the clay, the wire will cut a clay slice from the batch of a thickness corresponding to the distance of the wire from the cross bar, which is about ⅜ of an inch.

The tub-like roofing tile maker's mold, shown in Figs. 407, 408 and 409, is made up of wooden staves like a flexible window shutter or roll top of a desk which are hinged upon three separate strips of stout fabric which pass through slender cross mortises penetrating the staves. The end staves are longer than the others and serve as handles for the mold. The mold, consisting thus of strips hinged together, forms a many-jointed, flexible cylinder, and when stood up on end a hoopless tub is formed. The mold is stiffened by slipping a tightly fitting moist cloth cover over it, to hold the whole thing together. Four vertical bamboo strips equidistant from each other, and parallel to the joints of the staves, are fastened with wooden pegs, or with wire, on the outside of the staves. In Fig. 409, where the mold without cloth cover is shown, one of these bamboo strips is clearly in evidence. The object of these strips is to indent the inside of the clay cylinder to be formed upon the mold, so as to form guide-lines along which the clay cylinder when dry will easily break up into four roofing tiles.

When the tile-maker proceeds to make clay cylinders, he places the mold upon the top of his wheel. Fig. 408, taken near Cha Tsuen, Chekiang province, shows a typical tile-maker's turning wheel. The height from the ground to the disk is 25½ inches, the diameter of the disk is 13 inches. The top of the disk is flat without any projection. The center post, rammed into the ground has an iron pin inserted in its top upon which revolves the wooden disk or wheel. To steady the wheel it is supported by two braces which connect it with a perforated crosspiece lower down the post, about 3 inches from the ground. Wheel and crosspiece united by this rigid bracing revolve together when the wheel is set in motion. The bracing of the wheel in Fig. 407 is ingeniously split into four arms, out of a single bamboo tube.

When using the wheel the worker strews some wood ashes upon the top and places the mold with the cloth around it in the center. He turns the wheel to assure himself that the mold rests in the center and adjusts it if necessary. Then he cuts a slice from the batch of clay, takes it up with both hands and lays it around the mold. Next he gets his shaping tool (Fig. 412 on the left), and turning the wheel slowly, smooths the surface so as to obliterate the joint

Fig. 407. Mold for Making Roofing Tiles, and a Tile-Maker's Potter's Wheel.

formed when the clay is laid around the mold. The wheel does not make more than three or four revolutions to accomplish this. One more revolution of the wheel and the cutting gauge, Fig. 412 in the center, is applied to cut off the uneven top rim and then the mold with the wet clay cylinder sticking to it is lifted off the wheel and carried to the yard. A picture of such a drying yard is given in Fig. 410 and 411.

Next the mold is ingeniously collapsed by turning the two projecting end staves towards the center of the mold, whereupon the mold is rolled up inside the cylinder and easily withdrawn. When finally the cloth is pulled out, the cylinder is finished and is left to dry in the sun. In withdrawing the cloth cover the worker reaches down into the cylinder, takes hold of the cloth at the bottom rim and pulls it out gently. To prevent the cylinder from caving in during this releasing process, a bamboo hoop is put over it just previous to withdrawing the mold, and left there until it is needed for the next cylinder. A cylinder with this bamboo ring can be seen on the left of Fig. 410.

After a day the cylinders are hard enough to be piled on top of each other (as seen on the left of Fig. 410), where they await the time when enough material has been made to fill a kiln. Before being put in the kiln the cylinders are broken up into four tiles. The workman takes the cylinder between his hands, each palm over one of the impressed lines and pushes the cylinder inward with the result that it collapses, breaking into four concave segments, exactly along the guide lines. Four broken segments, finished roofing tiles, produced by breaking up one cylinder, are shown in the foreground of Fig. 411.

At some places the enterprising tile makers have their chop or trademark embroidered four times on the cloth sleeve used in making the tiles. The result is that the raised lines of the embroidery leave their imprint on the tiles.

Three of the tools of the tile maker are shown separately in Fig. 412. The shaping tool on the left, usually made of wood, is here of cast iron with a socket cast at the back to receive the wooden handle. The gauge in the center, for cutting the top rim of the clay cylinder consists of a piece of wood with a slot into which is wedged an iron pin. The third object is a simple slice cutter without a handle. The pictures, Figs. 411 and 412 were taken at Teh An, Kiangsi province.

104

8 In.

Fig. 408. Mold for Making Roofing Tiles.

LIME BURNING

The use of lime in modern Chinese building construction except in areas where European influence had made itself felt is rather restricted. It is used in small quantities in brick walls and these are built only by richer folk. Closer inspection of pagodas and old city walls reveals that in olden times pure lime was generally employed for mortar. It is evident then that only economy restricts the wider use of lime at the present time.

The Chinese method of burning lime is cumbersome and yet the resultant product is all that is to be expected from the best of lime. A kiln is used, but it is not a permanent structure. It is built up for the occasion, and after burning, demolished to recover the lime. Fig. 413 shows the general aspect of such a kiln. Preliminary to building the kiln, little cones are formed by mixing clay and sifted coal ashes together with water. The ashes are taken from previous operations of lime burning and are apparently incompletely consumed coal dust. The cones which have a diameter of about 9 inches and a height of 4½ inches are roughly formed by hand from the mixture after it has thoroughly been trodden out with the feet. In some parts they are slightly baked upon a platform under which a straw fire is kept burning. This platform has the nature of the hearth of a bakeoven, as a thatched hut is raised over it which confines the heat. In Changshu, Kiangsi, where the pictures were taken, this preliminary baking is dispensed with, and the cones are merely allowed to dry in the sun. From these cones a large circular wall is formed upon the ground and the included space filled with a layer of coal dust which is succeeded by a layer of lime-stone. Over the first circle of the cones another is formed, and the enclosing space similarly filled with a layer of coal dust and another of limestone. The circles of cones are held together by imported iron wire. This was formerly done with hoops of bamboo. In this manner the kiln is built up until it reaches a height of about 8 feet. The shape of the kiln is an inverted truncated cone. The fire hole, which can not be seen in the picture, is a small trench in the level ground leading from the outer base of the kiln inward to the center. A wood fire is built in this trench so as to start the burning before the kiln has been built to its full height. As the burning proceeds the building up of the fuel layer and limestone is continued, until on the fifth day of burning, the kiln is finished. After this it is kept burning for two more days, when the process is considered completed. The fire is then quenched with many buckets of water poured on top of the kiln. If a heavy wind is blowing upon the kiln while in action, the more or less porous structure is protected from its blast by a bamboo mat tied to the kiln side as shown in the picture.

After the kiln has cooled sufficiently, the workmen begin to demolish it from the top down to recover the calcined lime stone. For each heat this kind of kiln has to be dismantled. The wires are removed and circle after circle is broken up with hoes, and the rubbish thrown down upon the ground. The pieces of burned lime are gathered and put aside on one pile, the cones which are now burned fairly hard are dumped nearby, and the ashes are used for forming new cones. Fig. 414 shows the dismantling of this type of temporary lime kiln. The picture was taken at the same place as Fig. 413, in Changshu, Kiangsi province. There are enormous refuse heaps outside the city, partly the result of lime burning, and partly debris from the manufacture of sulphate of iron, which has also been carried on in Changshu for a long time. The dumped cones of the lime kilns largely crumble in the course of time. But some of them which were more exposed to the heat of the kiln than others, become as hard as clinkers, and are collected by the thrifty Chinese to be utilized in building enclosure walls, and walls for houses. Fig. 415 shows a house in process of erection and the mode of using these cones. This house stood about a stone's throw from the kiln depicted.

Fig. 409. Roofing Tile Maker's Collapsible Mold.

The process of burning lime in the circular kiln is undoubtedly old. That coal, apparently some easily

Fig. 410. Roofing Tile Clay Cylinders on the Drying Floor Not Yet Broken Up Into Four Roofing Tiles Each.

Fig. 411. Clay Cylinders on the Drying Floor. One is Broken Up Into Roofing Tiles.

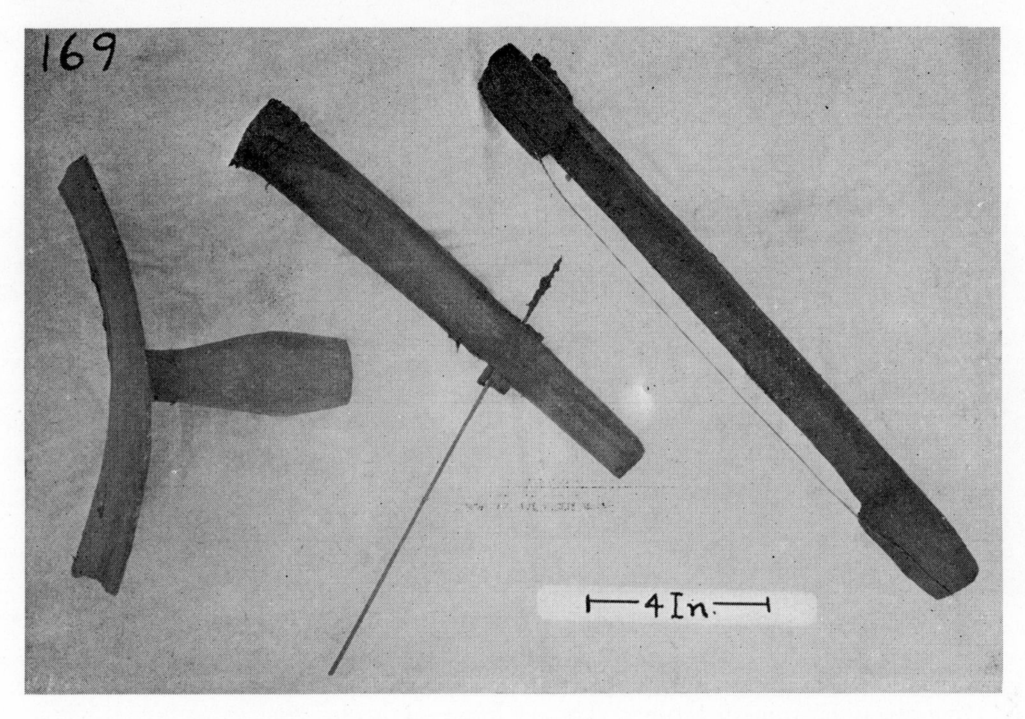

FIG. 412. ROOFING TILE MAKER'S SHAPING TOOL, GAUGE, AND CLAY SLICER.

powdered sort of stone coal, is used must not deter us from believing so. According to citations by M. G. Pauthier, the learned editor of a French edition of Marco Polo (Paris 1865), stone coal was in use in China before the Christian era, and Marco Polo himself speaks of the extensive use all over Cathay of a kind of black stones dug from the mountains and burned like firewood. The Chinese solved in their own peculiar way the problem of how best to use this fuel, as I had many opportunities to notice in Chekiang and Kiangsi. The powdered coal is mixed with clay and with the addition of water the whole mass is formed into a paste. In this moist condition it is put upon a wood-fire where it readily ignites. It burns very slowly with a red glow and gives off a powerful heat. In some places, notably in Kweichow, Szechuan and Peking, a similar mixture is placed into molds whence it issues as

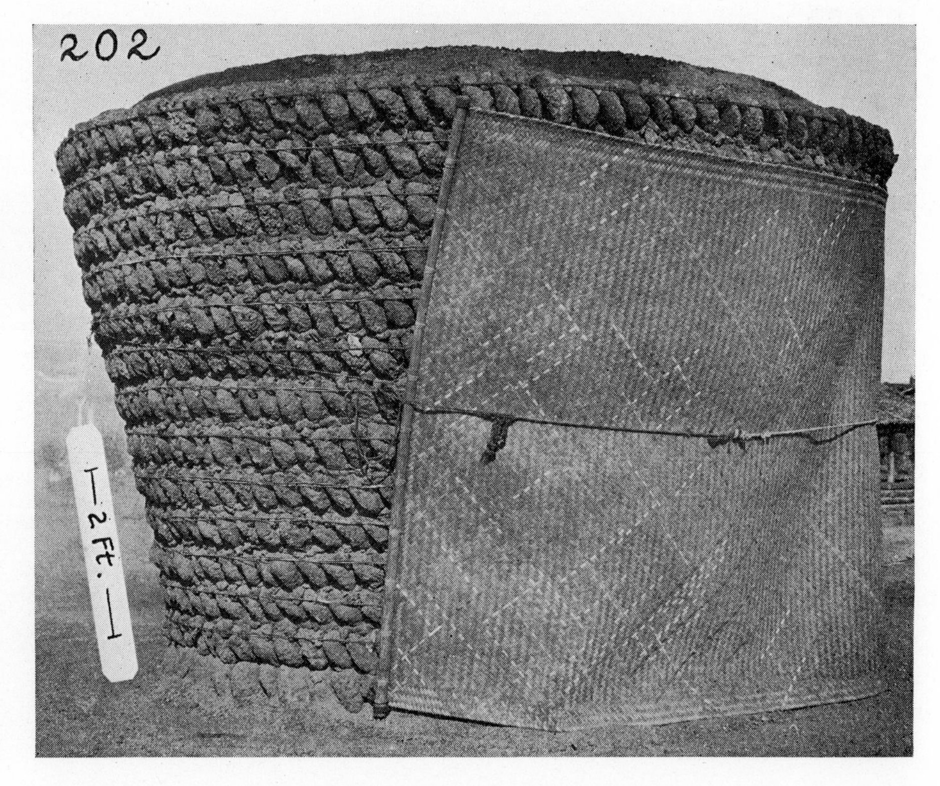

FIG. 413. TEMPORARY LIME KILN.

FIG. 414. DISMANTLING A TEMPORARY LIME KILN.

briquettes in the shape of truncated cones. These after being dried in the sun are ready to be used for fuel.

The type of temporary lime kiln is however not the rule in China. On our way from Yuanchow to Wantsai, Kiangsi, we saw lime kilns very similar in construction to those at home. Against the slope of a hill, beside a road, the kiln is built of stone, open on top and with a firing-hole below. The fuel used is stone coal which is abundantly found in the neighborhood. There is consequently no dismantling of the kiln as observed elsewhere in Kiangsi. Lime is used in great quantities in the paper making industry, which is carried on extensively farther up on the wooded mountains which form the border between Kiangsi and Hunan.

Chinese literature furnishes data which indicate that lime was first burned from shells. In describing a temple of the Hsia dynasty (2205 to 1766 B.C.), the K'ao Jung Chi, a historical treatise, relates that lime made of shells was used in ornamenting the building. The details of this process of producing lime are not given, but after 4000 years a primitive way of burning lime from shells is still carried on, on the sea coast of China, a

FIG. 415. HOUSE WALL PARTLY BUILT OF DISCARDED BRIQUETTES FROM LIMESTONE BURNING.

process which S. W. Williams describes: "Shells are burned into lime in a space enclosed by a low wall, ten or twelve feet across, in the middle of which a hole communicates underneath the wall through a passage to the pit, where the fire is urged by a fan turned by the feet. The wood is laid loosely over the bottom of the area, and the fire kindled at the orifice in the center and fanned into a blaze as the shells are rapidly thrown in until the wall is filled up; in twelve hours the shells are calcined. Toward evening scores of villagers collect around the burning pile, bringing their kettles of rice, or vegetables to cook in the fire thus furnished them. The lime is taken out the next morning and sifted for the mason." The use of a fan turned by the feet instead of the highly efficient box-bellows makes it seem probable that the complete process has been practiced thus without modification since the dawn of Chinese history, until the present time.

In Pergamos, Asia Minor, lime was burned from the shells of snails about 200 B.C. Such at least are the indications from finds of old mortars which have been analyzed and show an unusually high amount of phosphoric acid. The mortar contained besides sand and pebbles, snail-shells which had been incompletely calcined.

FIG. 416. WOODEN FRAMEWORK OF A TEMPLE IN COURSE OF CONSTRUCTION.

VARIOUS USES OF LIME

Cement House Walls.—S. W. Williams describes Chinese cement (*ni chuen* or sifted earth) as a compound of decomposed granite or gravel and lime mixed with water, and sometimes a little oil, of which durable walls are made by pounding it into a solid mass between planks secured at the sides and elevated as the wall rises, or by beating it into large blocks. When stuccoed and protected from the rain, he says, this material gradually hardens into stone. I have never seen this, personally.

For Preserving Eggs.—Eggs are preserved by lime if it may be called a preserving process. Fresh ducks' eggs are enveloped with a paste of straw ashes, salt and slacked lime and then covered with rice husks. After remaining for thirty days in a sealed earthenware jar they are ready for consumption. The white has hardened, become dark green in color and the yolk has turned into a dark brown jelly-like mass. It is these preserved but discolored though not putrefied eggs which have started the popular misconception abroad that the Chinese eat rotten eggs.

For Making Sulphate of Iron.—In the manufacture of sulphate of iron the concentrating pans of cast iron are smeared with lime to protect them from the corrosive action of the concentrated liquor.

For Dyeing.—The dyers use lime to stop out stenciled patterns on the cloth, which should not be colored by the dye.

For Paper Making.—In paper making the bamboo fibres are converted into pulp with lime.

For Tanning Hides.—Skins are tawed with lime to form the poor Chinese leather. The action of the lime is not sufficient to convert them into real durable leather.

For Putty.—Putty for caulking is usually made of a mixture of wood-oil and lime.

For Water-Proofing Ropes and Fish Nets.—Very often fishing nets and ropes used for the sails on boats are made waterproof with a mixture of pig's blood and lime.

For Embalming.—A layer of lime is usually placed in the coffin before depositing the body. At best this is only a temporary preventative of too rapid decay. I could not find out how old this custom is. I suspect that the so-called Han-jades discolored from long interment have undergone a chemical surface change from the lime in coffins. Otherwise it would seem strange that such a hard and densely fibred stone as Jadeite and Nephrite should be considerably affected by merely being buried in soil, be it moist or dry.

BUILDING CONSTRUCTION

Ordinarily Chinese building construction is very primitive. The most substantial buildings, which have endured for many centuries are the pagodas. Here we have solid masonry construction for the greater part. According to locality, where the material could be easily procured, many of them are built of hewn stone. The reason for the endurance of the pagodas

FIG. 417. WOODEN FRAMEWORK OF A CHINESE TEMPLE IN COURSE OF CONSTRUCTION.

lies in the massiveness of their construction, and the freedom of their walls from perishable material. Wood has usually been used only for balconies, staircases, and floors, and many a pagoda is standing where all these accessories have become a prey to time, until only a structure remains like a huge thick-walled cylinder perforated by windows or doors which formerly led to wooden staircases, from story to story all the way up. In some pagodas the staircases are contained within the wall, the steps are of

FIG. 418. CHINESE BOX BOND. MADE WITH BRICKS OF TWO DIFFERENT SIZES.

stone or brick with a slanting arch overhead. Very often the various floors are supported by circular vaults formed by stepping inward each course of brick or stone, until the circular opening has become so small that it can be closed by a round slab about two to three feet in diameter.

With all this knowledge of substantial construction, too substantial in many cases, it is surprising that more care has not been expended upon other

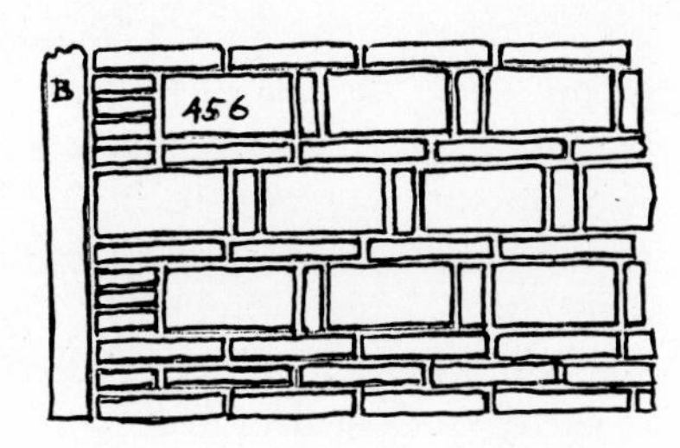

FIG. 419. CHINESE BOX BOND. BRICKS ALL OF ONE SIZE ARE USED. The sketch shows a section of a wall with an abutting lintel.

buildings such as temples and dwellings, to make them more enduring. Wooden construction is universal. A finished house with brick walls is usually very substantial looking, it will, however, not endure any longer than the wooden beams will hold out, upon which the whole structure is supported. The brick walls usually only enclose and fill out but they do not support any structural parts.

In reviewing the process of building we have to start with the site. For safety's sake people cluster

FIG. 420. CHINESE CROSS BOND.

together in cities, towns or villages, and new houses are usually built upon ground where at one time or other stood some habitation, destroyed by fire, flood or decay. Chinese houses never have any cellar, and removing debris, levelling the ground, and placing the pedestals in their proper location, is all that is necessary. The arrangement of the houses is very uniform, and the pedestals serve as a guide for the columns which define the dimensions of the different rooms. The owner is usually in charge of the

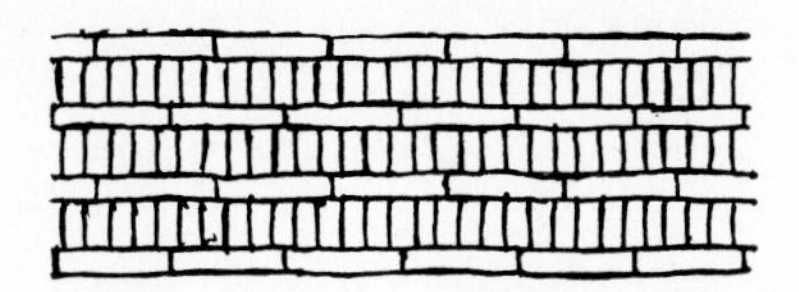

FIG. 421. CHINESE BOND FOR FOUNDATION WALLS AT TIMES EXPOSED TO THE ONRUSH OF WATER IN INUNDATIONS.

enterprise. He buys all the material, such as wooden beams, bricks, roofing tiles, lime, and hires the working people.

Plaster and lath do not seem to be a Chinese idea. Partitions are built of brick, of wooden or of plastered bamboo wattle. In the half-timbered construction of Continental Europe, the spaces between the beams were spanned with interwoven willow matting, and then plastered over from both sides. Lath plaster developed later from this medieval process. The Chi-

FIG. 422. BONDS FOR FOUNDATION WALL, VARIATION OF Fig. 420, USED FOR THE SAME PURPOSE.

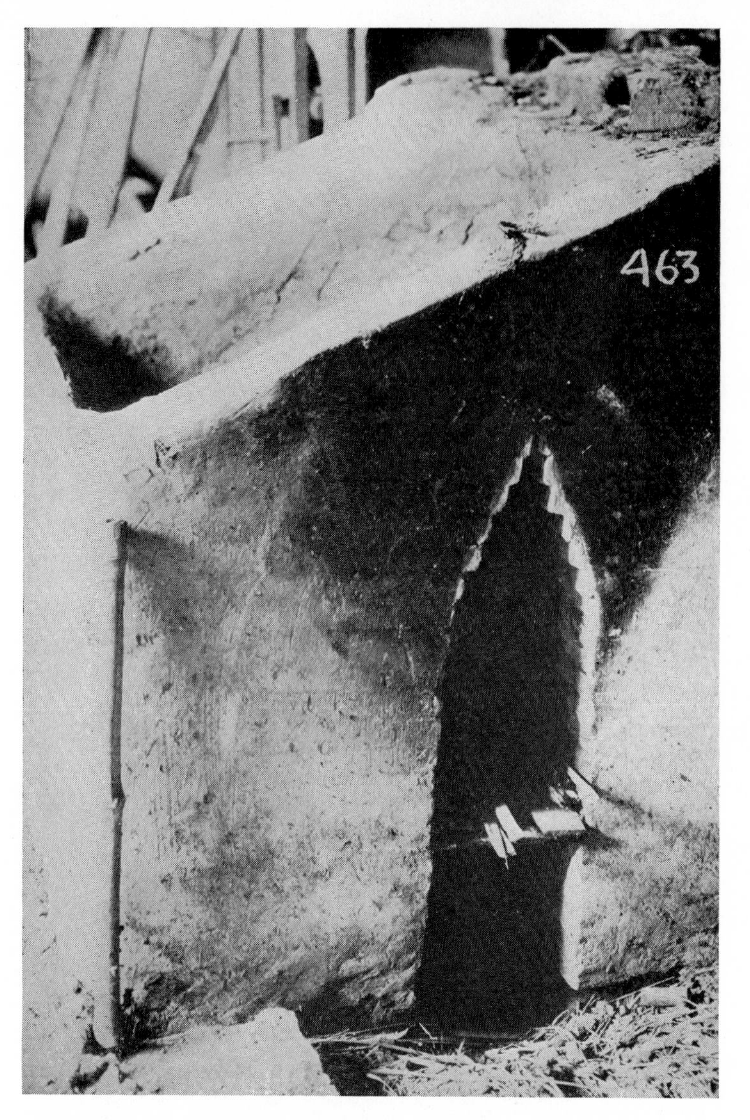

FIG. 423. STEPPED-IN BRICK ARCH.

nese plaster is paper and lime, or clay and lime, usually covered with a coat of whitewash. Wooden partitions are often covered with wall-paper, ordinary white Chinese paper, pasted with paste of wheat or rice flour. Of late the Chinese have developed a taste for papering their rooms with foreign newspapers. Ceilings are of boards, if the tent shaped garret space above the flat ceiling is utilized, otherwise woven rush matting is laid across the rafters, and pasted over with paper or the space is left open, affording a view of the inside of the roof.

The floors in the poorer Chinese houses are mostly of soil pounded until a hard smooth surface results. Such floors after a number of years become an asset in the Chinese household which can be turned to good account. The producers of saltpetre buy up the surface layers of mudfloors, which have become heavily charged with nitrates, until they show a whitish efflorescence, an indication that they are ripe and will yield the coveted calcium nitrate. A more elaborate flooring is made of Chinese cement, a mixture of lime, clay and sand, beaten hard and made waterproof as far as I could learn with the slippery substance leached from a certain plant or bark. The finishing touches of such a floor are to mark the surface with lines crossing each other at right angles, which gives the appearance of a floor covered with square tiles. The background of Fig. 432 shows such a cement floor. Square brick tiles, or flagstones, which the cement floor imitates, are actually used for paving at times. This is a more costly process and can be seen in older buildings or temples where throughout much more care has been expended. In the same way ordinary bricks serve also for paving occasionally, otherwise, where the locality yields the material, slabs of limestone are used.

Board floors are usually found in the bedrooms, and in the shops behind the counter. Boards are always sawn, never riven. The boards are laid butt to butt, and rest loosely upon the joists. At opposite ends of the floor a wooden beam passes over the board-ends to keep the boards from shifting. This is a slovenly way of fastening boards, but a fair substitute, in view of the disinclination to nail boards down to the joists.

As described under Fig. 413, rough hand-rolled briquettes of partly consumed coal dust mixed with

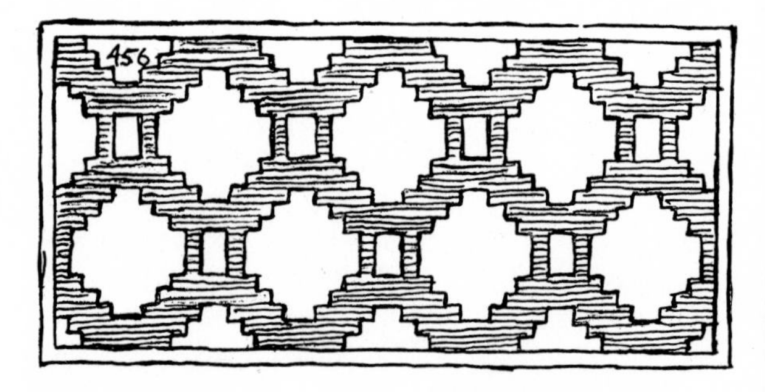

FIG. 424. A CHINESE WALL SCREEN OF OPEN BRICK WORK. The Chinese are to this day masters in forming pleasing panels in brick walls of open work. The panel shown is built entirely of bricks the pattern being formed by leaving spaces between some of the bricks in regular array.

FIG. 425. A CHINESE WALL SCREEN OF OPEN TILE WORK. A square or rectangular opening in the wall is filled by roofing tiles arranged symmetrically to form a design with regular open spaces.

plastic clay in the shape of rounded wedges or cones, a by-product of the lime burning process, are utilized for building walls of houses. It should be noticed, that while the cones set in horizontal layers in the

FIG. 426. A CHINESE WALL SCREEN OF OPEN TILE WORK. More elaborately designed this screen fills also a rectangular opening in a wall with roofing tiles symmetrically arranged.

kiln, Fig. 413, are all tilted to the left, here, in this house wall, Fig. 415, they tilt alternately to right and left, with much wider intervening mortar joints.

Fig. 415, primarily serving as an illustration for the use of burned cones, the by-product of lime-burning, shows also to good advantage various principles peculiar to Chinese building construction. The building is usually started by placing on the ground in their proper place the foundation bases for the upright beams which are to hold the roof. By consulting Fig. 279 and especially 249, it will be seen that a square stone is embedded in the ground and on this is placed a globular stone from which rises immediately the wooden beam. The beams are connected by crosspieces which are always horizontal and in this way are formed the trusses so peculiarly Chinese. The roof is laid and completed before the builder proceeds to any other details. These structures with the heavy tile roofs look exceedingly precarious. The walls are then built all around the structure, meant to enclose but not to support. This is the usual custom, but roofs resting on walls can also be seen in this land of contradiction, especially where timber is not to be had, and there are many such places. Another method of wall construction is to fill out the spaces between the beams with interlaced bamboo strips and plaster the latter both inside and out, leaving the beams, however, exposed. This gives the pleasing effect of half-timbered construction which we pointed out on the left of Fig. 1.

In many parts of China the towns and cities are still surrounded by walls and the gates are closed at nightfall as in medieval times. The walls are usually built of bricks. The plan of construction is to build two face walls or enclosing shells, leaving an open interior space filled with earth excavated in digging the adjacent moat. There are no connection-ribs between the face walls, but they are usually built slanting so that the base of the complete structure is wider than the top. The top is flat, usually not less than six feet wide. The outer enclosing wall is carried higher to form a parapet, plain on top or embattled, and pierced with embrasures. To embattle in the shape of a flower, two steps up, two steps down seems an imperial prerogative. I saw it on the city wall of Yenchow, in Chekiang province, where Marco Polo passed on his way home, and was told that only in Nanking and Peking, both imperial cities, this design is used on the walls. An old scholar, after many years' service at the court, educating the young princes, went to spend his declining years at his home town Yenchow, and in memory of the imperial wall which

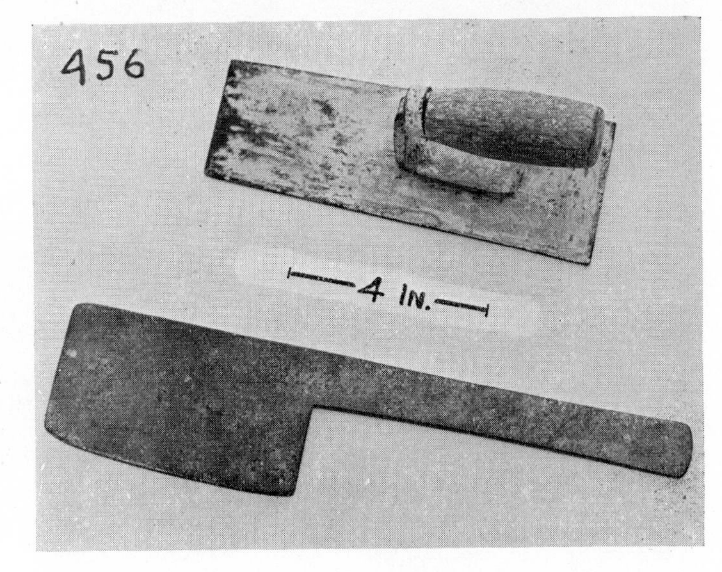

FIG. 427. BRICKLAYER'S JOINT-STRAIGHTENING TOOL AND TROWEL.

FIG. 428. BRICK MASON'S SPACING TOOL.

he had seen daily for such a long time, he adorned the crest of the walls in his native city with the flower-like design. Through some malignant knave news of this presumptuous action reached the court, and the result was a mandate from the emperor, asking the unfortunate scholar to either remove the city wall or else himself. He chose the latter course and saved the town from humiliation. Henceforth Yenchow was allowed to retain the distinguished embattlement to tell of the old scholar's noble self-sacrifice.

It was the duty of the country people to keep the city walls of their district-town in repair, and the various districts in turn had to keep in good order the walls of the provincial capital. This arrangement is reflected in the walls themselves. One section may be built of red sandstone, if it happens that such stone abounds in the district of the people who are in charge of that section. To the right and left then may follow sections of bricks, one perhaps with enormously large bricks, an indication that the people who furnished them made ordinarily use of adobe bricks only, and when called upon to burn bricks made them of the size they were familiar with. A difficulty would arise in such a case from the fact that the unusually large brick thus furnished would not get baked through to the core. This difficulty I have seen overcome by the simple expedient of having the brick perforated through its longitudinal center, perhaps by pushing a chopstick through it before it was baked. Another fact of archeological interest is that the bricks very often bear the impression of a seal, giving the date and name of the district which furnished them. For the Chinese this was a safeguard to prevent the theft of accumulated bricks previous to laying them.

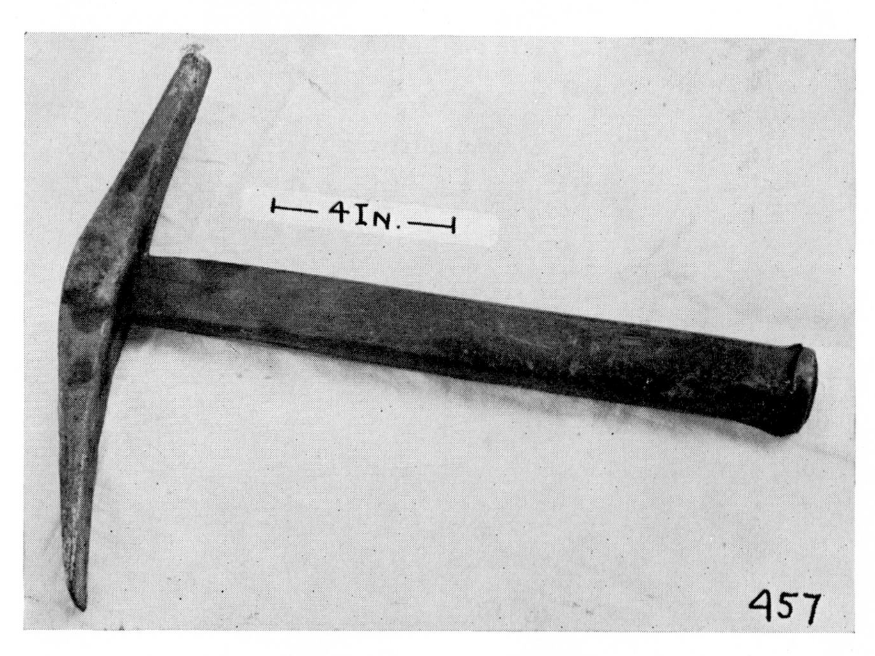

FIG. 429. BRICKLAYER'S HAMMER.

Any Chinese building is erected in about the way shown in Figs. 416 and 417 picturing the framework of a new temple which was being built in Changshu, Kiangsi. Wooden beams rise up to carry the whole superstructure, and in that service are weakened by numerous mortises to receive horizontal members for the support of floors and the roof. The uprights are not even anchored in the ground, they rest merely upon stone or brick pedestals. The most notable fault is the absence of any wind-bracing, and the utter disregard of the principle that a beam is never stronger than

FIG. 430. BRICKLAYER'S TROWEL.

its smallest cross-section. For instance a favorite decorative feature of the main hall of a building, is the stringing across the lofty ceiling an enormous beam, which is, at each end, reduced to a ridiculously small tenon, and mortised into an upright column.

Another interesting feature is that Chinese houses can be built without a bit of iron, such as nails, hinges, clamps, etc., entering into the construction. The modern influence is, however, making itself felt in this respect, and the carpenter uses now more and more foreign nails. Nevertheless nails do not advance him over former methods, and must be rather looked upon as a time saving shortcut, since the original Chinese method of wood bracing by means of wooden and bamboo dowels and wedges, was, although a more tedious, nevertheless a more enduring way of uniting the various members in building construction.

The several layers of horizontal beams, one above the other are to give strength for floor supports, or the support of the roofs. The roof trusses are also quite unique. The weight is distributed, and directly carried down in a vertical pressure upon the supporting horizontal beams, and only in these trusses have we an indication of triangular windbracing, not adopted consciously as a sound mechanical principle, but incidentally, formed by the oblique slant of the roof.

FIG. 431. BRICKLAYER'S TROWEL VARIETY USED IN KIANGSI PROVINCE. BOUGHT IN KULING AND NOW IN THE MERCER MUSEUM.

Fig. 432. Wooden Rammer Used in Making Chinese Composition Pavements.

Ordinarily dwelling houses have only one story, with, occasionally, sleeping quarters under the slanting roof, reached by a ladder. Stairs whenever used, are simply made, two slanting beams hold between them in slots the planed boards for the steps, sometimes the step boards are mortised into the beams.

The building material is mostly soft wood. In older temples one sometimes sees immense columns of hard wood, and even now temples, for new construction or rebuilding use hard wood, if it so happens that the temple property comprises stretches of woodland whose growth has not been disturbed for centuries. Whenever I saw on my travels clusters of gigantic trees, I could be sure that they belonged either to temples, or were shading some old graves. In either case they are not counted upon for utilitarian purposes.

The timbers for Chinese buildings are dressed by hand on the ground. The mortises and tenons are made with chisel and hammer. Whole sides of the framework are assembled at one time and, with the help of many people raised into perpendicular position are propped to stay in place. Other sections, similarly raised, are roped to adjoining ones and then united by horizontal cross beams to remain permanently in place. It is always a great concern of the Chinese to have the roof finished as soon as possible, whereupon the rest of the work can leisurely proceed. The roofs in the two illustrations, show the modern influence. They are being covered with boards to make firmer foundation for the roofing tiles. At right angles to the ridge of the roof following the slant downward from the ridge to the eaves, are placed parallel rows of wooden bars, at a few inches distance from each other, to form an adequate resting place for the curved tiles. Row after row of tiles is placed with the convex side downward, and the contiguous upturned edges are covered by a row of tiles with the concave side downwards, their edges resting in the gutter formed by the tiles first placed. Needless to say, each tile in one row always overlaps the next below it. To keep these rows from getting into motion, and sliding down the incline of the roof, the pitch must be rather flat, and as an additional safeguard the roof is made to curve upward slightly towards the eaves,

Fig. 433. Wooden Bats Used in Beating Down (Solidifying) Chinese Composition Pavements. The smaller one is 19 inches long and the surface resting on the ground 12½ inches long and 4½ inches wide. The larger one is 2 feet 8 inches. Photographed in Kien Chang, Kiangsi.

FIG. 434. BAMBOO KNIFE OR JOINT MARKER USED TO INCISE DECORATIVE JOINT LINES IN CHINESE COMPOSITION PAVEMENTS. The length of this Bamboo Knife, for marking the cement floor with intersecting lines, is 21 inches, width 2⅞ inches, length of edge 14¾ inches. It was photographed in Kien Chang, Kiangsi.

resulting in that graceful curving sweep so characteristic of Chinese roofs.

A unique feature is that the whole structure rests as it were on stilts, a construction thought to have been derived from lake dwellings or the similarly constructed huts found in the Malayan Archipelago. A very practical reason for such construction however, is that it enables the dweller to protect the house much easier from the inroads of white ants. This destructive pest must come through the ground to get to the wood, and the columns in Chinese houses, as they rest upon stone or brick foundations are therefore not within their reach. Sometimes through careless placing of wooden partitions reaching to the ground contiguous to columns, a bridge is formed for the white ants and the whole house endangered.

As we see from the pictures the next step after the framework is up is to build the enclosing wall or filling between the posts. This outer wall may contain windows, but usually the Chinese prefer not to have

FIG. 435. STONE CUTTER'S HAMMER, CHISELS, AND PARTLY FINISHED TOMBSTONE.

any windows on their outside walls. There is always a judicious arrangement of courts on the inside of the building and the rooms get sufficient light from them. A main door, and sometimes a smaller one, if the area is extensive, such as we would call a backdoor, connects the house with the outer world. If a small yard is attached to the house, a high wall encloses it. This latter wall is indistinguishable from that of the rest of the buildings, and, from the outside, it is impossible to tell whether a part of the house is behind it or only a yard.

BRICK BONDS USED IN BRICK WALLS

As far as bonds in the laying of bricks are concerned, the Chinese have an interesting variety. Besides the bonds we are familiar with, the Chinese make use of a few others. The one most in evidence is what one might style Chinese box bond. It is an economical placing of bricks in walls which do not support any superstructure. Fig. 418 and 419, give typical examples.

In England the introduction of bricks came from the Continent as the names of Dutch bond, Flemish bond, Dutch tiles, Dutch clinkers, etc., sufficiently indicate. Whether we can make the same deduction by inspection of the German names of some of the bonds, as Polish (the one called Flemish in England) or Wendic, to indicate that they point to the country of origin, or source, whence the Germans received knowledge of them, as yet remains an open question. I think it is not without significance that in the old Lusatia, the lowland of Northern Germany, after it had been wrenched in bloody struggles from the Wends in the 10th century, arose a period, in which the building with brick was brought to great perfection. This apparent spontaneous arising of the art of building with brick in those parts, and its speedy development into excellence, as exemplified in the cathedral of Lubeck (ca. 1160 A.D.) is puzzling, and still awaits satisfactory explanation.

In Fig. 418 use is made of bricks of two different thicknesses, the other dimensions being the same. Usually the wall is started with a few courses of stretchers of the thicker kind, and then follows a course with the box-construction made of the thinner bricks. Headers laid on edge pass through the wall,

Fig. 436. A Chinese House Built of Pisé de Terre.

and between each two of them are laid, also on edge and flush with the outer faces of the wall, two of these thinner bricks, exposing their largest or side surface to view, that is, one on each side of the wall. Thus boxes or spaces are formed, which are closed up on top by the next course of thicker stretchers.

A bond of very pleasing and harmonious appearance is shown in Fig. 420. It might be called Chinese cross bond. In each course there are always three stretchers followed by a header, and in the next upper course a header is always centered above the middle one of the three stretchers in the course below. The shading has been added to emphasize the pattern. There is some similarity between this bond and a German medieval one (from the Brandenburg District) called "Märkisch" or "Wendic." In this always a header follows in each course after two stretchers, and above and below the header, is placed the joint of the two stretchers.

Fig. 421 shows a bond which is used sometimes in walls which in inundations have to withstand the onrush of water. Here a course of stretchers is followed by a course of headers stood on edge and the courses of stretchers break joints with one another, in other words, the joints of the second stretcher course come in the middle between the joints of the first. This construction is unusually rigid and as far as I know has no parallel in the Western world.

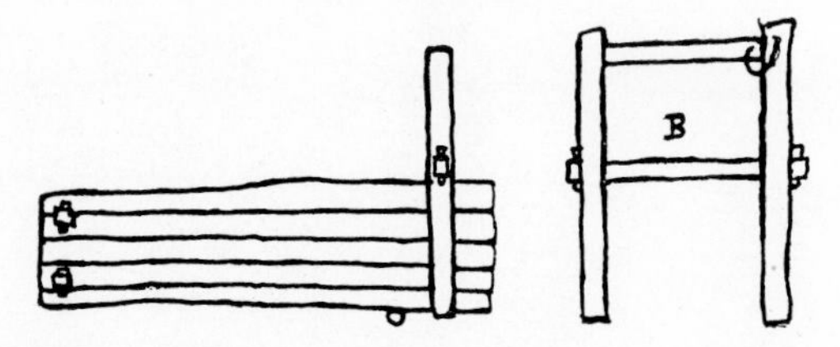

Fig. 437. Frame for Making Pisé de Terre Walls.

Fig. 422 shows also two types of very rigid bonds for foundation walls. The upper sketch shows three stretchers, one above the other, followed on either side with a header stood on end. The lower sketch has on either side of the three stretchers, three headers stood on end. In building up courses the headers stood on end are always placed in the center of the stretchers below.

Fig. 438. Wooden Form and Ramming Stick Used to Build a Pisé de Terre Wall, Here Seen Partly Built, Resting on Its Stone Foundation.

FIG. 439. TWO MEN RAMMING EARTH INTO A SHIFTABLE WOODEN FORM, IN BUILDING A WALL OF PISÉ DE TERRE.

Fig. 423 illustrates one method of building a brick arch. This type of arch, usually called a step arch, is formed by drawing the courses of bricks gradually closer together stepwise until they meet at the top of the arch. The arched opening illustrated is the fuel door of a stove used for heating oilseed before pressing. The photograph was taken in Lee Go Gao, a small village near Ningpo, Chekiang province. The plate is of interest because it furnishes a simple example of the style of masonry frequently found in Chinese pagodas especially in window arches.

Great skill has been shown in building pagodas ever since the Han dynasty. Various books give 250 A.D. as the date when the first pagoda was built in China, at Nanking. Chinese records[7] however enumerate among the various occupations during the Han dynasty a "builder of pagodas" and we may assume that pagodas were built years before the date given above.

In Chi Chow Fu, Anhwei province, a little way out of the East Gate, I saw a pagoda, dating according to local tradition from the Sun dynasty (960-1279 A.D.). It is built of bricks measuring 15 by 7 by 3¼ inches, and laid in pure lime. Each of the seven stories is dome-vaulted and each vault has a hole in the center of the dome. Standing in the lowest story one can look up through these successive holes to the very top of the pagoda. The stairs run up in the wall of the structure. The circular vault is formed by letting each row of bricks extend a little beyond the one immediately below it, and step by step the circular inside wall is drawn in to form the vault, until the opening at the top is about two feet in diameter. In a ruinous pagoda, where the interior layers of a heavy wall were exposed, I noticed that the courses crossed each other diagonally, a very sound principle which is made use of in Germany for dykes and fortification walls (called *Strom* or *Festungs-Verband*).

The arches of the windows and doors of pagodas are sometimes built semicircularly without centering in the same way as the Egyptians built them of old, and still build them today (Flinders Petrie). Two men, one on each side, have to build on such an unsupported arch until their work meets in the middle. The horseshoe arch of Moorish architecture is also found in China and may have been necessitated by building arches without centering. The rather steep sides of such arches seem to confirm this. At least for

[7] Quoted in "Yuan chien lei han," Cyclopedia of K'ang Hsi, 1710 A.D.

China this is very probable, for we find now and then perfect horseshoe arches in old Chinese pagodas of the Sung or Ming dynasties in the interior of China and there is no evidence that centering was used. One notable example is the pagoda in Ningpo which it is said, was built in 696 A.D.

As the houses in China consist mainly of a framework of wood, and since the brick walls, if used at all, only fill out spaces, and do not support any of the constructive framework, very little care is expended in manufacturing bricks, and in laying and cementing them.

The tools of the bricklayer are the trowel, the hammer, and an instrument for properly forming the interstices between the bricks and ramming down the cement, namely, the joint-straightening tool, here shown in Fig. 427, which looks like a cleaver with an unsheathed handle. The whole length is 13 inches, and the width of the blade 3 inches, while the tang is only 1 inch wide. The thickness is 1/16 inch, and the material iron. To shift bricks in laying them, so as to form even interstices between them on the walltop, the tool is held in a vertical position, edge downward, and forced in between two bricks, when a slight motion sideways will easily push one brick aside from its neighbor.

FIG. 440. BUILDING A WALL OF PISÉ DE TERRE AT KULING, SHOWING THE POSITION AND END LOCKING OF THE FORM AND ONE OF THE WALLED-IN WINDOW FRAMES.

The other tool shown in Fig. 427 (top) is the bricklayer's trowel. It is used in the same way as our bricklayers use the same tool for taking the mortar from a wooden bucket and applying it to the bricks, spreading it evenly and catching what oozes out from the joints. The blade of the trowel is of steel, 8½ inches long, 3 inches wide at one end and 2½ inches at the other, with a uniform thickness of 1/16 of an inch. The handle is riveted to the blade. Fig. 427 was photographed in Shanghai.

Fig. 428 represents another example of the spacing tool described under Fig. 427. It was photographed in Fuchow, Kiangsi province, and proves that this type of tool is not confined to Shanghai.

The length of the instrument is 13 inches, the length of the dull edge 6¼ inches, and its widest width 2½ inches. Its use has been described, but I might add, that I was told, without being able to confirm it, that this tool serves also to break bricks as it becomes necessary in laying, further to separate pairs of bricks which come sometimes stuck together from the kiln. Such pairs of bricks are not an accidental feature, the mode of making them in one mold and cutting them in the mold with a wire has been

FIG. 441. BUILDING A WALL OF PISÉ DE TERRE AT KULING, KIANGSI PROVINCE, SHOWING THE STONE FOUNDATION, AN INSERTED WINDOW FRAME, AND ONE OF THE METHODS OF END-LOCKING THE SHIFTABLE WOODEN FORM.

described under Fig. 386. Usually they are separated before being put in the kiln, but sometimes they are left sticking together and burned as a pair in the kiln.

Fig. 429 shows the bricklayer's hammer. The length of the forged head is 11¾ inches. The chisel-shaped blade on the lower arm is 1⅛ inch wide and placed at right angles with edges flattened giving it almost an octagonal appearance. The length of the handle including the head is 1 foot 2½ inches. At the end of the wooden handle is an iron ring to keep the wood from fraying when hitting the bricks with it, which is done to put them in proper horizontal position. The hammer was photographed in Kien Chang, Kiangsi.

In Kiangsi province the trowel is somewhat different, as Figs. 430 and 431 reveal. Here the end of the blade has been bent up to form the back support for the wooden handle, and the other support of the handle is riveted to the blade. Fig. 430 was photographed in Kien Chang, and Fig. 431 shows the trowel purchased in Kuling, now in the Mercer Museum.

For a plumb line and plumb bob the Chinese bricklayer uses a string with a stone tied to its end. For a level, if the Chinese bricklayer is called upon to set a window or door frame into the brickwork, he gets an ordinary rice bowl, fills it to the brim with water and places it upon the inserted wooden sill. By inspecting the surface of the water he can tell if the sill frame is level.

The mortar for brickwork is a mixture of lime and sand. The mixing is done on the ground in an enclosure made by banking up freshly dug soil. The Chinese are not very careful in such processes, and it does not matter if some humus gets into the mortar. Interior plastering is done with a mixture of lime and paper and this gives an excellent surface. The paper is not much more than pulp made of straw, roughly made up into sheets of a loose texture and about 1/16 of an inch thick. This beneficial action of straw paper upon lime mortar, suggests experiments with straw upon clay made by Dr. E. G. Acheson.[8]

[8] ". . . experiments led me into a study of clays, that had rather an unlooked for result. I discovered that when a clay moderately weak in strength and plasticity was treated with

Such paper mortar is especially efficient for stoves and chimneys, as it withstands heat and does not crack. The Chinese it seems, however, are not unique in having found out the beneficial effect of the admixture of straw or plant fibre with clay for brickmaking or for mortars. The Tibetans on the northern slope of the Himalaya Mountains, a region which is frequently rocked by slight earthquakes, use for building their houses a lime-mortar mixed with the needles of a native pine tree which has edible cones. This admixture gives almost elastic strength to the mortar, for the walls of the houses are said not to show cracks even after earthquakes.

Fig. 442. Inner House Door.

Another noteworthy accomplishment of the Chinese is the making of a cement for paving courts, passage-ways and sometimes the rooms of their buildings. I was told that it is a mixture of lime, clay and sand, sometimes with the admixture of some slippery substance for water-proofing, leached from a plant or the bark of a tree. A porous foundation is first formed of bricks broken into small pieces and this is rammed down tight with the rammer, Fig. 432. Upon this comes the floor mixture proper which is applied in a pasty condition from two to three inches thick and also rammed down. The moisture gradually evaporates in an upward direction and is absorbed from the porous foundation below. After one or two days, the floor is beaten with a short bat of wood, two specimens of which are shown in Fig. 433. The flooring still remains somewhat elastic, and receives a further beating, with the bat, after about a week, and then the lines are incised which give the floor the appearance here shown, as if laid with square flagstones. The edge of the bamboo knife, Fig. 434, is put down upon the floor and pressed into the cement by hitting the back of the knife with the bat or the fist. In a hot climate like that of China, the setting of this cement progresses at a fairly rapid rate. When erecting some of the buildings of the Rockefeller Foundation in Peking, old Chinese cement floors were encountered, and it was a hard task to break them up for removal.

The rammer shown in Fig. 432, is entirely of wood. It lies upon a Chinese floor in whose construction it is used. Its whole length is 3 feet, 8 inches, the square head is 6¼ inches high, 5¼ inches square at the bottom and 4 1/6 inches square on top. It was photographed in Kien Chang, Kiangsi.

Mr. N. Kullgren of Hwangchow, Hupeh, a Swed-

tannin, extract of straw, and other plant extracts, it was increased in those properties. The particles of the clay were reduced so fine that they would pass through a fine filter paper, and would remain permanently suspended in water. I believe this to be an explanation of why the Egyptians used straw in making brick, and I call clay so treated and dried "Egyptianized Clay." From "Pathfinder," an autobiographical sketch by E. G. Acheson, published by the Press Scrap Book, New York 1910. A fuller account of "Egyptianized Clay" may be found in the transactions of the Am. Ceramic Society, February 1904.

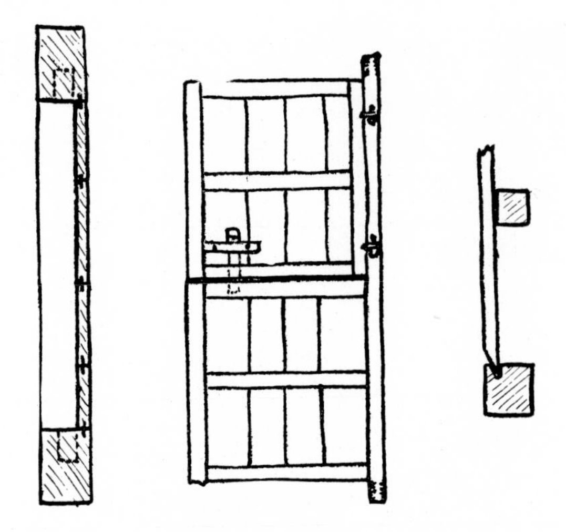

Fig. 443. Chinese Double Door, and Details of Door Shown in Fig. 442.

ish missionary, told me, (in August 1927), that he supervised many times the laying of Chinese cement floors at various mission stations. The practice of natives in Hupeh province, is to use a mixture of two parts lime, two parts sand and five parts old bricks broken to the size of a chestnut mixed with water to a doughy rather than a liquid consistency. Three parts of lime is considered preferable but seldom used for economic reasons. Mr. Kullgren has heard that boiled rice is mixed with the surface layer if a cement floor is intended, which has no protective overhead covering, in other words, the addition of rice, besides giving a smoother surface finish, was believed to make the floor waterproof. The tool, Fig. 428 is, according to Mr. Kullgren, also used in connection with laying cement floors. The mixture placed upon the ground is first of all beaten down with the dull edge of this tool to still further reduce the brick particles, but especially to pack the mass solidly. On the second day the wooden beater is used. Although the process requires the exertion of much muscle power, it is well spent effort and the floors become well nigh indestructible.

When in Fuchow, Kiangsi, we stumbled upon a stone mason engaged in preparing a tombstone. He had the stone, a large sandstone slab, lying in the middle of the road, and was working away unconcerned with the traffic passing him right and left. He was engaged in chiselling an intricate panel in relief. I exclaimed here is an artist at work, let us stop and watch him. We stopped, but my interpreter informed me that the object of my interest was not an artist, only a stone-mason. And so he was ranked in China. Art has not been dissociated from the trade. The man will execute for you with equal fidelity a mill-stone or a door-sill.

His tools seen lying on the tombstone in Fig. 435, are a handful of chisels, a hammer, compasses, a wooden square and a foot rule. With the hammer we are already familiar. It is the same type as used by the miner, (Fig. 15). The chisels are made by the blacksmith according to instruction of the stone-mason. The compasses are made up of two flat iron rods riveted together, not at their ends, but near their

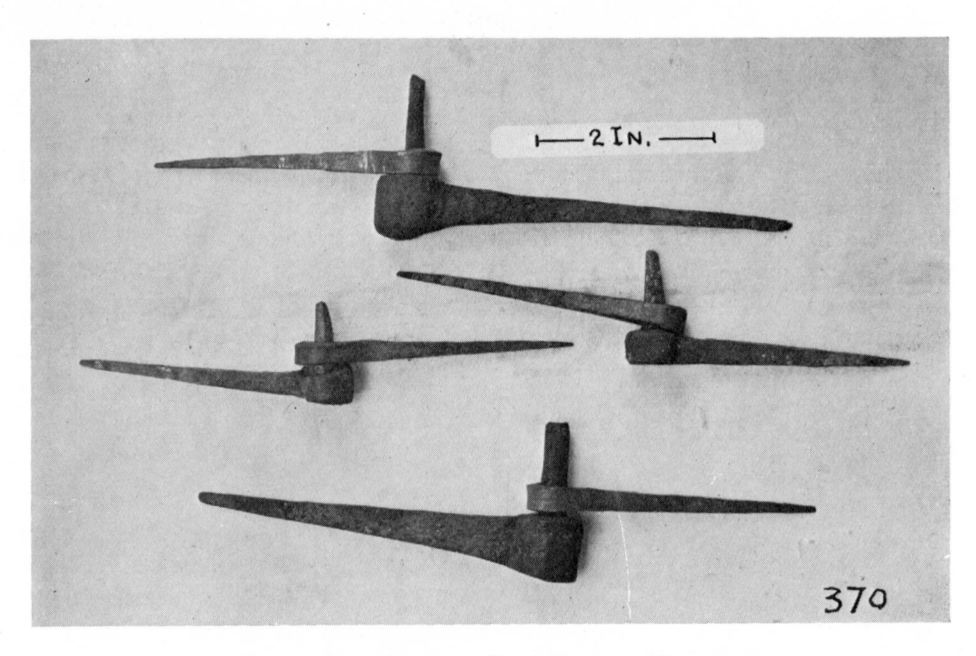

Fig. 444. Iron Hinges for House Doors and Windows

middle, so that the instrument is, as it were, double jawed, that is, there is available a shorter and a longer pair of legs, the ends of which are pointed. If inscriptions are to be placed upon stones, they are carefully written in the size desired upon a thin sheet of paper, usually by a skilled pen-man, and this sheet is pasted with rice paste upon the flattened surface of the stone. If the characters are to be raised the white background of the design is chiselled away, paper and all, or if they are to be cut into the stone the black areas on the paper indicate to the stone-mason how to proceed.

Alexander Hosie [9] gives an interesting account of the polishing of stone-slabs in Szechuan. There he saw the huge irrigation wheels adapted for the purpose. "A part of the horizontal axle of the wheel was removed, and an iron elbow inserted; to the elbow a long iron rod was attached by an eye; to the lower end of the rod was fixed a polisher, which, as the wheel revolved, was drawn backward and forward over the surface of a stone pillar being prepared for building purposes. On exactly the same principles, except that the axle of the wheel was vertical instead of horizontal, the rod was made to blow a blacksmith's bellows."

PISÉ DE TERRE WALLS

The making of walls by the method known in French as Pisé de Terre, for which we have no word in the English language, is an art which has been practiced in China for many centuries. In fact Chinese tradition calls Fu Yueh, the Minister of King Wu Ting, who ascended the throne in 1324 B.C., the first pisé mason.

A typical Chinese pisé de terre house is pictured in Fig. 436. The round holes left by the supporting brace rod of the casting form show plainly. Several courses of bricks are laid on the pisé wall top, immediately under the roof. The earth walls absorb moisture, and the roof timbers are therefore laid, not directly on the pisé, but on bricks to preserve them from untimely rotting. Specimens of the two most common modes of roofing are likewise here in evidence. Tiles are usually laid in this straggly fashion, while thatch has ordinarily not so unkempt an appearance. Fig. 436 was photographed

FIG. 445. CHINESE HINGE FOR AN INNER HOUSE DOOR.

[9] Alexander Hosie, "Three Years in Western China," London 1890.

beyond the South Gate of Chi Chow Fu, Anhwei province.

Figs. 438 to 441, showing the various stages of making pisé walls were taken in Kuling, Kiangsi. The chief of police of the Kuling Estate, a summer resort for foreigners in Central China, erected a police hut in this style. Infected by my enthusiasm for this time-honored mode of building, he decided to give it a trial and engaged the services of expert pisé masons from the country. The result was an inexpensive and perfectly adequate police hut for the Estate and the opportunity for me to photograph the process in perfect peace without arousing the hostility of a Chinese mob, which was ever the danger when taking pictures in the interior of China.

Fig. 446. Wooden Door Bolt, and Iron Door Bolt and Iron Hasp and Staple for a Padlock on a House Door.

The best practice, followed in this case, is to build a stone foundation. Rough stones were piled up without binding material. On this rises the wall of rammed earth. In building up the wall a three sided form is used, a sketch of which is shown in Fig. 437. The sides are built up of narrow pieces, held together by dowels. At one end the two side pieces are connected with an end piece mortised into position. The other end is held together by a removable framework or brace looking like the letter *H* (see Fig. 437 at the right) the crossbar of which is mortised in the center of the two legs. The lower legs of the *H* are placed over the side boards of the form so that the cross bar *B* rests on top of the boards. A wedge about the same length as the crossbar *B* is then driven between the ends of the upper arms of the *H* which causes the lower legs to grip firmly the side boards thus preventing the latter from spreading after the earth is thrown in.

The wooden form rests at one end upon the cross endboard which holds its long sidepieces together. At the other end these sidepieces rest upon a round wooden stick which has been pushed through the upper section of the finished wall.

The tamping of the earth, which is taken freshly dug from the ground is done with a rammer which has a smaller wooden block at one end and a larger one at the other end. Ramming is done first with the smaller end to get the earth into all the corners and then with the larger end. After the form is filled and well pounded down the *H*-shaped frame is removed and the wooden form set up anew for further filling and ramming.

The same method of making pisé walls is pursued in Chekiang. What ever soil is at hand is used. If the soil has not sufficient binding power it is mixed with wood-oil, pressed from the seeds of *Dryandra cordata,* in parts where this plant abounds, at other places with strawpaper soaked in water. The strawpaper is specially made for this purpose. It is of very loose texture and about 1/16 of an inch thick. It has more binding power than straw alone, probably because of its admixture with lime, which is used to rot and disintegrate the straw when making this paper.

Fig. 438 shows, resting on its side, the wooden form in which the earth is rammed. Lying upon it is the wooden rammer. The

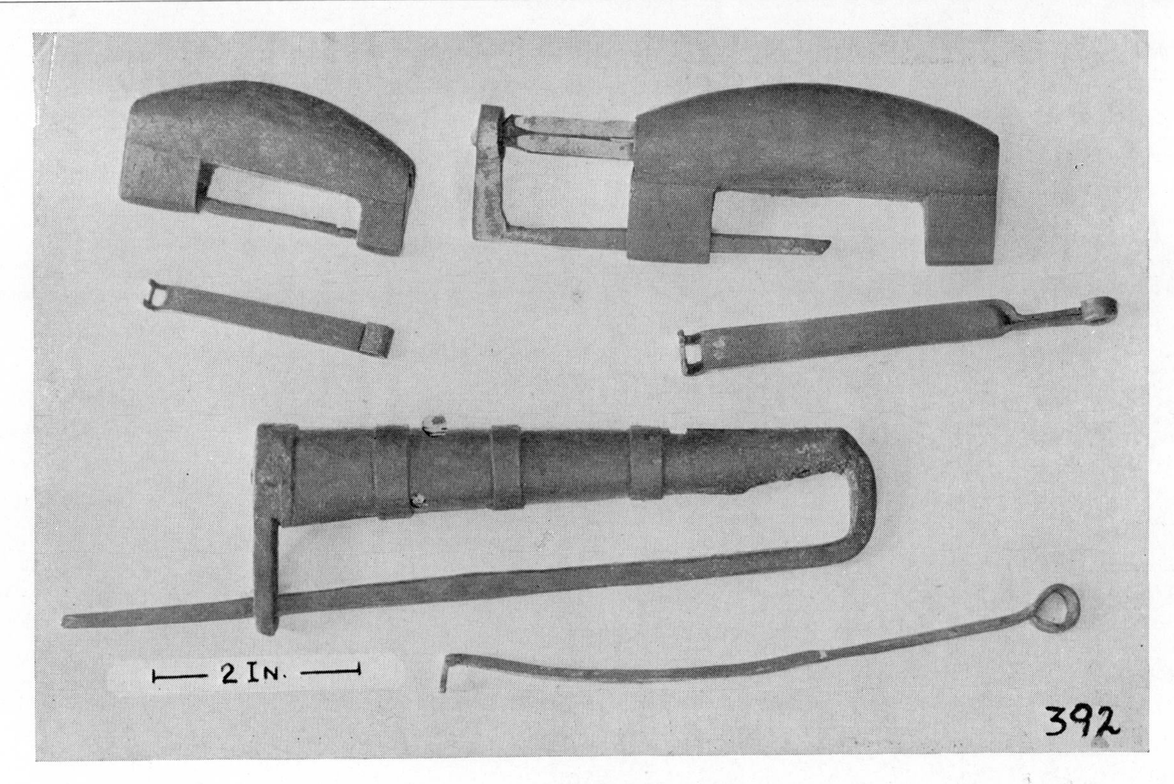

FIG. 447. PADLOCKS.

two side boards of the form are 5 feet 7 inches long, 13 inches wide and 1½ inches thick. The connecting end-board is of the same width and thickness, and has a length of 18 inches. The width of the wall to be formed with this form, therefore, is 18 inches. Projecting tenons from this endboard, pass through mortises in the long side boards of the frame, and are secured by a locking pin, as can be seen in some of the other pictures. The rammer is 5 feet 8 inches long. One enlarged end is round, and 3¾ inches in diameter. Its other end is squared with sides 1¾ inches wide.

The form in Fig. 439 is set level and braced for work on a partly built wall top. The right end with the 18-inch crosspiece rests across the wall top. The other end is supported by a wooden rod laid under the side boards also across the wall, with both its ends extending beyond the side boards. To keep the loose end of the form together in this case wooden brace sticks are inserted into round holes in the extending ends of the supporting rod under the form. The upper ends of these brace sticks fit again into end-holes, near each end of another stiffening cross-rod of the same dimensions as the one supporting the form. This is a modification of the *H*-frame previously described and usually seen where pisé walls are made. The form thus fixed is ready to receive loose earth, which is then rammed into it, as shown in the various pictures. To ascertain if the form rests horizontally across the

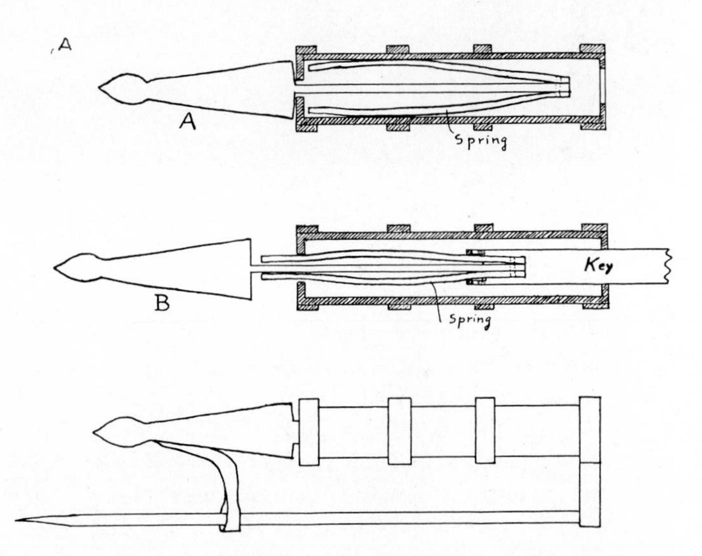

FIG. 448. DETAILS OF CHINESE PADLOCK, SHOWING THEIR CONSTRUCTION. (*A*) shows the inner springs expanded and the mechanism locked. (*B*) shows the key inserted from the right, the springs compressed and the detachable part which opens the lock partly withdrawn. The lower part shows the complete lock from the side.

FIG. 449 DOOR LOCK.

wasting undertaking in ordinary practice as we might imagine, since the Chinese have usually only a few and very small windows, and a lot more time and patience than we.

Fig. 441, like Fig. 440, clearly shows the method of adjusting the end-clamp on the movable form, slightly differently applied from that in Fig. 439. The top of the window frame, inserted in the wall under the form, prevents the placing of the brace in the usual manner. A bundle of bamboo rods, none thicker than one quarter of an inch, is ordinarily spread out between the rammed layers. In the walls here shown under construction, small flat stones have been laid between the layers. This was our suggestion and is foreign to Chinese practice. Ostensibly the layers of bamboo rods allow of a thorough drying-out of the walls in the hot summer months, and we figured that the layers of stone instead of a perishable material would serve the purpose as well if not better. The earth used was freshly dug from the ground nearby and thrown into the form without admixture of any sort. The nature of it was a clayey loam, and the form had to be scraped clean after each application.

wall a plumb-line is fastened in the center of the upper edge of the small connecting piece of the form, with a Chinese cash piece—a coin with a square hole in the center—tied to the end. In Fig. 439 this primitive level can be faintly seen.

In Fig. 440 the foundation built of rubble stone without any binding material is clearly in evidence. Over this follow the layers of rammed earth. The framework for windows is laid as the work progresses. After the whole wall is completed the rammed earth is cut out from the spaces enclosed within the window frames. This method assures smooth edges around the windows, and is not such a time and labor

DOORS

In China there are still walled cities whose gates are closed at night, when passing in or out is denied, excepting to a few privileged persons holding a pass issued by the chief magistrate. The enormous size of these gates is not as apparent in the daytime, when the passage-ways are thronged with people going in and out. At nightime, however, when all the streets are deserted, it is an impressive event to pass through such a gate. I was once detained in a city, and at about 10 o'clock hastened towards the south gate, armed with a pass, to be sure, to regain my lodgings, situated outside the walls in a suburb. The street seemed to terminate with the vast structure of the gate tower, beside which stood the guard-house to which I directed my steps. I handed my pass to a soldier who went within to verify its authenticity. The pass is a thin tablet of wood, a few inches long, and covered with Chinese characters. When issued, a duplicate is made and kept in the guard-house. Patiently waiting I heard the shuffling of wooden passes as if they were kept in a bushel basket and had to be picked out one by one until by chance the right one is found. After finally finding the duplicate which verified my pass, the soldier detailed two coolies to open the gates and let me proceed. A heavy wooden beam, which only two men could handle, was then lifted from its position across the two enormous wings of the gate, and one wing pulled open wide enough to let me pass through. Thus we entered a spacious barbican with houses right and left, and after walking a few hundred yards arrived at the outer gate, also surmounted by an imposing superstructure. Here the second gate was opened by similarly removing a large cross-beam, and as soon as

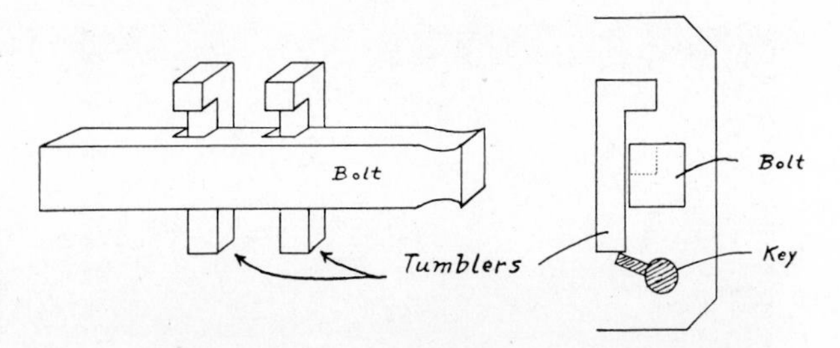

FIG. 450. DETAIL OF CHINESE DOOR LOCK SHOWING ITS CONSTRUCTION. The tumblers on the perspective view on the left are shown raised, in which position the bolt can be moved freely forth and back. The cross-section on the right shows how the key raises the tumblers. When the bit of the key is turned downward, the tumblers drop down by their own weight and engage in the notches of the bolt, thereby locking it.

I had passed out, the barring of the gate resounded in the large vaulted passage of the tower. With the feeling of all security being locked away behind me upon the closing of the gate, I took a firmer grip of my cane and rapidly walked away to reach my lodgings.

The wings of the gate are formed of roughly squared beams placed vertically aside each other and held together by several horizontal planks which pass

FIG. 451. DOOR LOCK, INNER SIDE.

FIG. 452. DOOR LOCK, OUTER SIDE. The vertical, upper slot is for insertion of the key and releasing the bolt from its tumblers, and the lower horizontal slot for the push pin to prick and slide the wooden bolt sideways to open the door. Key and push pin are shown in Fig. 453.

through mortises in these upright beams. Through the center of the places of intersection of the vertical beams with the horizontal planks, a treenail is driven and thus the whole wing presents a remarkably solid structure. The hinging is the usual Chinese one, on two pivots, one projecting upward, the other downward at the upper and lower gate corner, the upper one passing through a pierced projection of the stone lintel, and the lower one revolving in a round hole in the stone sill. The whole outer surface of the gate wings is imbricated with iron plates, hammered out on the anvil. The plates are nailed down and placed as we arrange slate roofing, the nail-hole always covered by an overlapping plate.

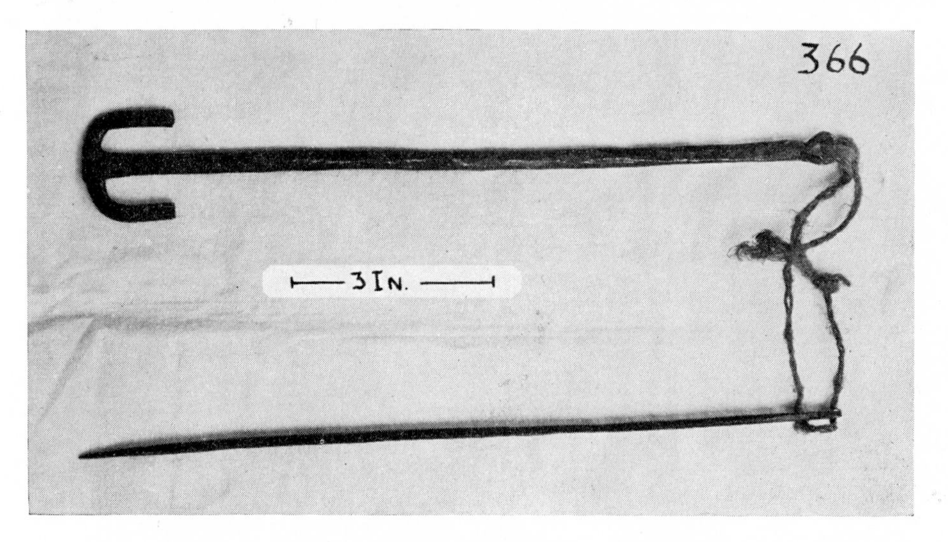

FIG. 453. KEY AND PUSH PIN OF THE DOOR LOCK, FIGS. 451 AND 452.

To gain admittance to the city at night is more time-consuming. Approaching the gate you see the vast extent of the imbricated wings, and if you look sharp, you are sure to find somewhere, a few feet from the ground, a horizontal slot just large enough to insert your wooden pass. First, of course, you have to make a big noise by shouting, or by pounding the gate with a stone, to attract the attention of the guard within the inner gate. This is usually aided by the inhabitants within the barbican, who, as it were, hand on the shouting, till it reaches the ears of the guardsmen beyond the inner gate. Finally when the watchman is thoroughly aroused he gets his coolies to open the inner gate, walks through the barbican and takes your pass through the slot. Next, if you are inclined, you have sufficient time to light a pipe and smoke it, while the watchman returns to the guard-house to verify your pass. After he is quite certain that it is no treason to let you in, he walks leisurely back with his two helpers and opens the gate, and your troubles are ended.

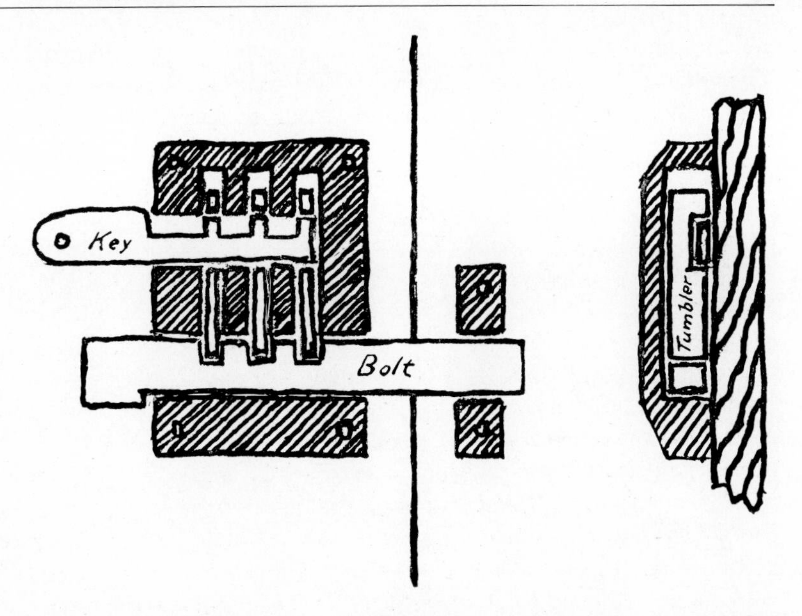

Fig. 454. Sketch of Another Chinese Lock, a Type Also Used by the Old Romans. Attached for comparison this sketch gives details of a lock which has been common in Europe since Roman times and scarcely passed out of the memory of peasants in Alsace and Hesse, and can to this day be found sporadically in remote parts of Germany, countries around the lower Danube, Egypt etc.

A Chinese family house is an entity which usually can be closed to the outside world by one big door. If a yard or garden is attached, the latter is surrounded by very high brick walls, never lower than 8 to 10 feet. A large compound or lot reaches often from one street or alley to another and a gate opens then upon either street. The construction of these outside doors is usually sturdier than that of the doors within the compound. Usually they are built up of roughly squared wooden beams, keyed together as in the wings of the city gate described. Nailed-on battens involving the use of precious nails are not popular. Doors made of boards are, in the absence of battens, strengthened by a mortised frame similar to the one shown in Fig. 442. Mortises are an infatuation of the Chinese carpenter. He loves them and makes them to fit their corresponding tenons with great precision. The boards are fitted edgewise together with dowels of bamboo, and the whole board surface or panel rests above and below in a groove of the frame. The boards contiguous to the horizontal ribs of the frame are not nailed on as one might expect. The vertical edges of the panel are joined at intervals with dowels to the frame along their whole extent. The accompanying sketch, Fig. 443, shows the details of construction. On the left is shown a transverse section through the door pictured in Fig. 442, and on the right a section showing how boards rest in grooves on top and bottom of the door frame. The sketch in the middle shows a Chinese double door, cut hori-

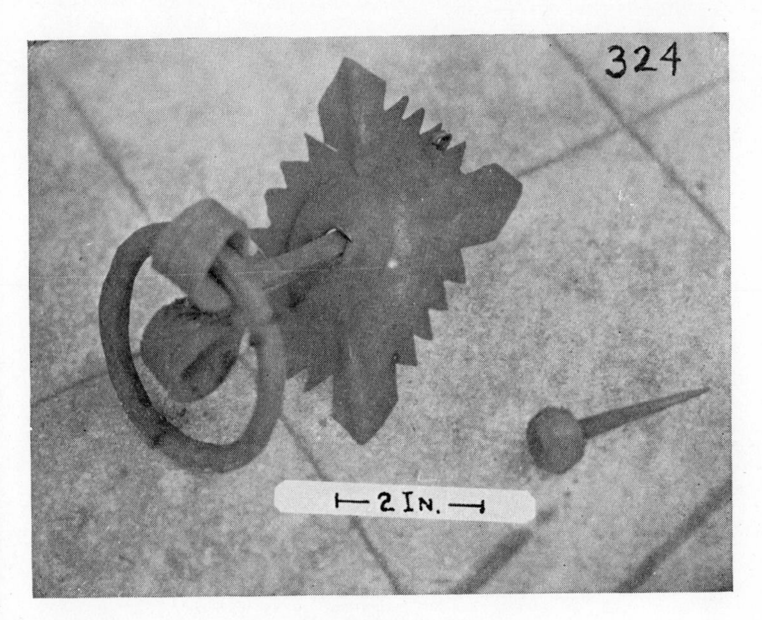

Fig. 455. Door Knockers.

zontally into two parts, much in use in the country. The upper part is kept open in the daytime to admit light and air and give egress to the smoke of the kitchen stove which rarely has a chimney. The lower part of the door is kept closed to keep out stray dogs, the pest of Chinese villages, and the small fry of the domestic animals.

The hinging of outside doors is always done with top and bottom corner pivots. For this purpose one of the long vertical side pieces of the door frame is prolonged at either end and the extending parts rounded to serve as pivots. There is a great variety in the outward appearance of these doors. Usually there is a pair of knockers, one on each wing. The wood is painted or lacquered, and the joints are entirely obliterated. Chinese painters use an elaborate groundwork of ox-blood and lime, which is followed with several coats of paint or lacquer. The securing of the door from the inside is done with a cross-beam, or a pair of wooden bolts, one above the other, which work in opposite directions (see Fig. 446). For additional safety a beam is often propped in a slanting position against the door at night, so that the upper part leans against the bolt and the lower rests against a wooden post which barely projects from the ground, or some other impediment to keep it in place.

The iron hinges in Fig. 444 represent a type from Kien Chang, Kiangsi province, near the Fukien border. They are employed sometimes on windows, and the upper half of horizontally double-winged doors. The "Dutch Door" in the center of Fig. 443 has one of the side posts of the lower half of the door extending upwards and terminating in the upper hinge-pivot. The upper half of the door is hinged to this post with hinges similar to the ones pictured in Fig. 444.

The door in Fig. 442 happens to be an inner door and the hinging as shown in Fig. 445 differs from the customary mode. It was the door of my bedroom in Feng Chen, Kiangsi, where I spent a few nights. The vertical bar can be pushed upward and the door then released from its hinge. In humbler dwellings, doors are frequently in demand in liu of mattresses whereon to spread the bedding. The flattened part of the hinge bar, facilitates the lifting of the bar and releasing of the door from the hinge. It is only in certain parts of

Fig. 456. Door Knockers in Place.

the country that iron hinges are in use, in others nobody knows anything about them.

Fig. 446 was photographed in Changshu, Kiangsi. Beside the double wooden bolt we see a curious wrought iron bolt, also a hasp and staple to be secured with a padlock. Less distinctly can be seen wrought iron door bands, which look like but are not hinges. These bands pass around and extend as far as here seen, on the other side of the door. They are structurally useful on a board door which being without battens needs as much lateral strengthening as possible.

FIG. 457. DOOR KNOCKER IN PLACE.

LOCKS

Fixed locks on doors of dwelling houses are not used very often in China. The reason is, as we have told before, that the Chinese home is usually peopled by several generations of a family with a generous amount of offspring and a multitude of servants, and that it would not happen in years that there was nobody at home, which would necessitate the locking of the front door.

On the other hand, with so many people in a house it is important to secure personal belongings in chests and individual rooms against relative and menial inquisitiveness or pilfering, and for this reason the padlock is very much in use in China. The very poorest people, who have not even a chest for their belongings keep always a set of clothing in the pawnshop for safekeeping. In spring they release their summer clothing and after changing about deposit the wadded garments until needed again in autumn.

The shape of the padlock shown at the top of Fig. 447, is preferred for chests, and we find the type made of brass or iron. Another type represented by one specimen in the lower half of the picture, is always made of wrought iron, and used for doors of stables and outhouses. To fasten them there are eye-bolts, one on each wing of a vertically double door, through which passes the thin bar of the lock.

There is quite a variety of padlock shapes, but the principle is the same in them all. A set of springs is compressed by pushing a key into the lock, and then it can be opened. The sketches in Fig. 447 show in detail the position of the springs, (*A*) when it is locked, and (*B*) when the springs are compressed by the key and the mechanism can be withdrawn from the barrel. I procured these locks at different places in Anhwei and Kiangsi, and photographed them in Kuling. They are all made of wrought iron.

The type of fixed door lock, shown in Fig. 449, is

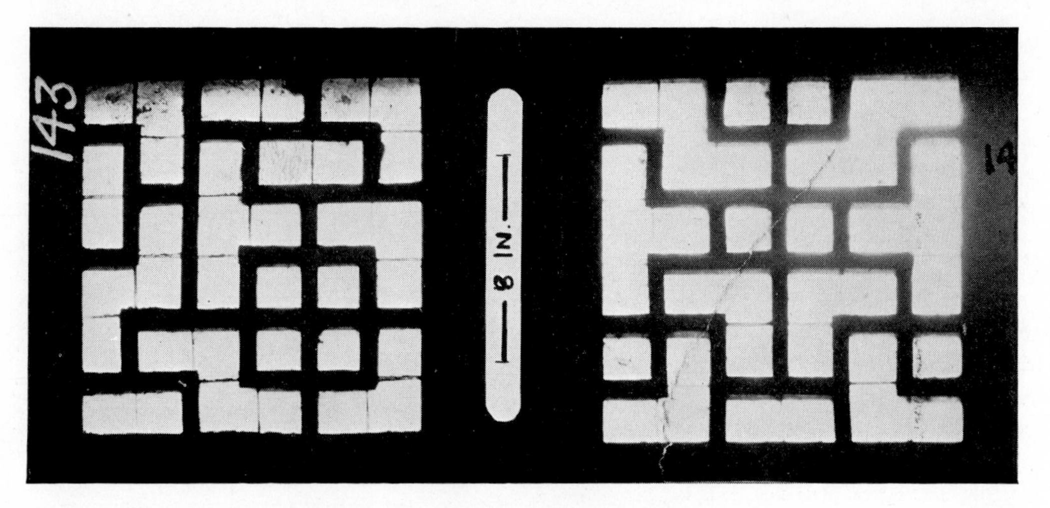

Fig. 458. Lattice Window with Sea Shells.

widely distributed in China. It is only found on garden gates, sheds, workshops, places for storage, where nobody lives, and which, when not in use, have to be locked from the outside. At a glance, therefore, we can tell that the door and door lock shown in Fig. 449 do not belong to a dwelling place. The one illustrated in Fig. 449 is composed entirely of wood and consists of the casing, the bolt and two tumblers. The bolt as photographed is drawn. Below it one can see the keyhole. The wooden key itself is hanging beside the lock. To open the lock the key is inserted and turned around. Then the two pegs seen projecting from the stem of the key, in their upward path, raise the tumblers inside the lock which rest in notches on the bolt, and the bolt can be freely pushed forth and back. No spring of any sort is necessary. The tumblers, when released by the key, fall back into place by their own weight. Fig. 449 was taken at Cha Tsuen, near Ningpo in Chekiang province.

Fig. 459. Lattice Work of a Chinese Window. Paper is pasted against this mortised and tenoned work formed of wooden strips. Viewing it closely it looks like a jumble but looking at it from a distance a pleasing pattern appears.

The lock just described can be manipulated only from one side of the door to which it is fastened. In Figs. 451 to 453 however, we are able to picture an unusual type for China, a lock, the main feature of which is a bolt, that can be drawn from the one side with the hand, and from the other by means of a key. It is very crude and exhibits very little mechanical skill. Fig. 451 presents the inner side of the door on which the bolt of this lock is fastened. A wooden case through which the bolt slides holds two tumblers, the ends of which are here seen in the right and left slots. These engage in the two exposed top-notches of the bolt, when the bolt is pushed home. The case with the mechanism of the lock, shown on the left, has

Fig. 460. Chinese Lattice Work Window Screen. Made of strips of wood mortised into each other and back-pasted with paper. Lighted windows of such pleasing pattern have an indefinable charm and make you stop and gaze at them in silent admiration.

Fig. 461. Bamboo Chair.

three slots, the two outer ones for the play of the tumblers. The middle one is the key-hole which passes through case and door. Fig. 452 gives a view of the door from the other side showing the vertical slot for the key-hole and lower down, a horizontal slot, which runs parallel with the bolt. The key is pictured in Fig. 453, together with a pointed iron pin. Assuming the lock to be closed, the method of opening it with the key from the outside is the following: Insert the key, prong-end first, into the key-hole and push it through until the two arms forming a semicircle are clear of the lock-case and door. Then turn the key in either direction a quarter turn. Now the position of the key will be as shown in Fig. 451. The next move is to pull the key backwards so that the two prongs or bits will enter the two tumbler mortises. Then a direct upward left of the key without further twisting will lift the tumblers, and clear the bolt for motion. Holding up the tumblers in this position, the iron rod, shown attached to the key, is inserted into the horizontal slot of the door, when by pricking its point into the wood of the bolt, the bolt can easily be pushed to open the door. The door can also be bolted or unbolted from the inside by lifting the tumblers and pushing the bolt with the hand. When the bolt is pushed home in the lock case the tumblers will fall into place by their own weight and the door is locked. The horizontal slot in the bolt shown in Fig. 451 gives clearance to a nail driven through the lock-case. This nail allows the bolt to be pulled only as far as the slot reaches and so prevents the bolt from being pulled out entirely from the lock-case. The key and pushing rod are made of wrought iron. The length of the key is 11$\frac{1}{4}$ inches, the width of its shaft 1$\frac{5}{8}$ inches with a thickness of one quarter of an inch. The pushing rod is 11$\frac{1}{2}$ inches long. The lock described was fastened to the door of a garden surrounded by high walls, in Kien Chang, Kiangsi province.

Chinese houses do not generally depend on locks for security. The main door as we have said is never

Fig. 462. Bamboo Chair.

fitted with a lock. In King Teh Chen, however, where whole establishments become deserted in winter, when all work in the porcelain industry ceases, the problem arises of how to lock the places of residence and business from the outside. This is done then by fitting several wooden locks of the type described under Fig. 449, and iron bolts secured with padlocks to the door. Quite frequently the owner goes a step farther, and walls up the recess of the door with bricks and mortar. This is an expedient also resorted to in places overrun with soldiery, who are ever intent on looting.

FIG. 463. WOODEN CHAIR.

For comparison the sketch, Fig. 454 is attached to show a lock which has been common in Europe since Roman times. It has scarcely passed out of the memory of peasants in Alsace and Hesse, and can to this day be found sporadically in remote parts of Germany, in countries around the lower Danube, and in Egypt.

DOOR KNOCKERS

Door knockers as shown in Figs. 455 to 457 are quite common in Kiangsi province. In Chekiang I saw similar ones, the doornails, however, were driven into the wood an inch or two below the hanging ring, so that the ring could never strike the nail head. This peculiar arrangement has been referred to under Fig. 56, on page 36.

Fig. 455 gives a typical example of a Chinese door knocker. A central pin terminating into two loops holds, in one loop, the ring. The escutcheon, a square plate also of wrought iron, is ornamented around the edges by notches, and the surface, in the manner of repoussé work, is raised in the center by hammering from the other side, likewise the four corners are adorned each with a raised rib in the same way.

In Fig. 456 we see two of these door-knockers attached to a two-winged door. The central pin penetrating the flat escutcheon and the isolated door nails seen below on the door face are driven through the door and the ends projecting on the other side are clinched.

Fig. 457 shows another pair of knockers in place, which are of cruder workmanship. Ring and central, double-looped pin are similar to the other specimens. The escutcheon serves also as a sounding body instead of a door-nail. It is interesting to notice that the outline of the escutcheon is a typical Roman form of ornamentation, compare for instance the Roman standards with the inscription S.P.Q.R.

The pictures of the three specimens of door-knockers shown in Figs. 455 to 457 were taken in Kien Chang, Kiangsi province.

WINDOWS

Berthold Laufer makes the statement that the Chinese learned from foreigners how to make glass as late as the fifth century A.D. (The Beginnings of Porcelain in China, p. 138, note 4, Chicago 1917). Giles in his Chinese Dictionary is more definite and gives 424 A.D. as the date when glass was first manufactured in China. S. W. Williams tells us that the manufacture of glass was introduced into Canton by foreigners in comparatively recent times. A customs' official told me that in Szechuan a native glass industry flourishes and that the products are bottles and window-glass. He thinks however that it was started by Jesuits. If this is correct the industry is not older than the 17th century. A Williamson gives data of a glass industry centering about Po-shan-hsien in Shantung. He visited the place in 1867 and found the natives making "excellent window-glass, blowing bottles of various sizes, moulding cups of every description and making lanterns, beads and ornaments in endless variety." He proceeds to say that "they also run it into rods, about 30 inches long, which they tie up in bundles and export to all parts of the country. The glass is extremely pure, they colour it most beautifully and have attained considerable dexterity in manipulation; many of the articles were finely finished." A hint as to the use of glass-rods we may take from a report of the sights of Peking by J. Edkins (1869) in which he describes the structure rising over the north altar of the Temple of Heaven, called Chi-ku-t'an, or altar for prayer on behalf of grain. "The windows in this structure," he says, "are shaded by venetians made of thin blue glass rods strung together. They are produced at the glass factories in Shantung."

From this account about Chinese glass it becomes evident that the making of window glass is a late accomplishment brought from abroad. In the interior even to this day glass is not used for the windows. Instead paper, silk or sea-shells are used. By far commonest is the use of paper. It would be too precarious to paste over a large window-opening merely a sheet of paper, therefore the opening is always filled out with a kind of lattice-work, dividing the space into various small panes. There is an endless variety of the arrangement of these panes, which form very pleasing and intricate patterns. Some typical ones are shown in Figs. 459 and 460. To make these wooden screens, against which the paper or silk is pasted from the inside, takes great skill and patience. The panes are not cut out from a solid wooden slab, as one might think, but are formed by wooden strips mortised into each other. The joints are so skillfully fitted, that even large screens appear very firm and solid.

In the Eastern provinces, near the sea, windows with their lattice-work covered by tablets of translucent sea-shells cut into rectangles, are not uncommon. Fig. 458 shows an example. These two screens, side by side, were on the upper part of the right wing of a vertically halved two-winged door. The same pattern reversed was repeated on the left wing of the door. The panels of the screens are covered with the shell tablets which nearly overlap each other. Thin strips of bamboo are laid over the joints of the shells, from one rim of the screen to the other, and fastened with wire nails through the sheets into the wood of the

Fig. 464. Arm Chair.

Fig. 465. Heated Stool.

Fig. 467. Brazier.

Fig. 466. Hand and Foot Warming Stove.

screens. The shell used is the *Placuna placenta,* a bivalve, native of the East Indies and China.

In the New Standard Dictionary (Funk & Wagnalls, N. Y., 1919) we find the word Window-shell or Window-oyster, the name for a translucent shell, with the remark that the expression is Provincial English or obsolete. Webster adds that such shells whose halves are very broad, thin, and translucent are said to have formerly been used instead of glass. From this it would appear that in rural England, many years ago, windows were in use similar to the one depicted in Fig. 458; similar only in so far as use was made of small apertures, not larger than could be covered by a single shell. If such shells were really used instead of glass, they might have been pieced together by lead as were the various colored bits of glass in making up the old stained glass windows.

In this connection I am reminded of a style of window in use in Europe in olden times, called Bulls' Eyes Windows. Round pieces of green glass, all of the same diameter but irregular thickness, looking very much like the bottom of a glass bottle, are put together with lead to form a pane. No doubt these panes were in vogue at a time when the manufacture of sheet glass was still in its infancy and very costly. Strips of lead, presenting the shape of the letter *H* in cross section were used for holding these glass disks together. I remember that in my child-

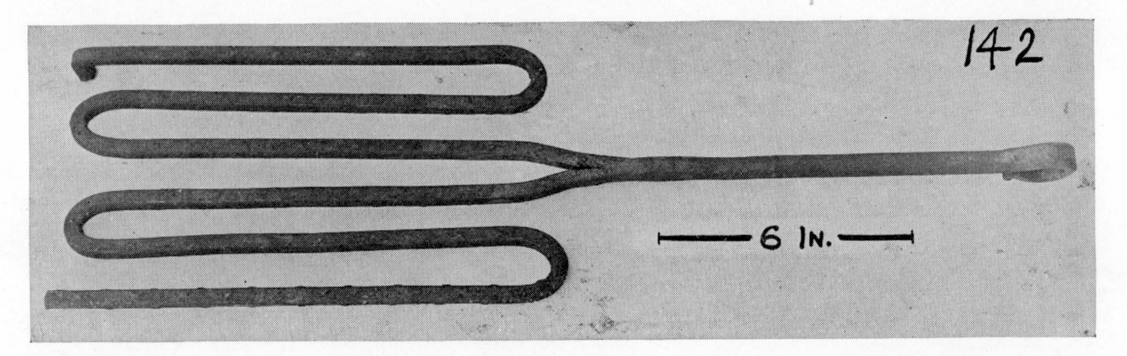

FIG. 468. FIRE GRATE.

hood days such strips of lead were still used for mending large window panes which were only cracked and not shattered.

In another interesting kind of window which I saw many times in Chekiang on old houses, the opening was filled with a stone screen. A solid block of stone, usually about 2 feet square, is set in the wall, with a round or square ornament which shows boldly, the background having been cut away right through the thickness of the stone. The opening can be closed on the inside with wooden shutters, which slide sideways between grooved moldings fastened to the wall.

The photograph for Fig. 458 was taken at Chao Ka Too, near Shanghai.

CHAIRS

Chairs are a luxury in the primitive home of the Chinese. Their place is taken by long and short "forms," benches such as our forefathers used in their houses several hundred years ago.

The learned sinologue, J. Edkins, writes that chairs were first used in China in the Buddhist period (1st century A.D.). We do not know how far A. H. Smith is correct who writes in his interesting book "Chinese Characteristics" (Shanghai, 1890), that the Chinese are the only Asiatic nation using chairs.

The few chairs found in a Chinese house in the country, are made of bamboo and have the shape depicted in Fig. 461 or Fig. 462. The type shown in Fig. 461 is more frequently met with. The construction is simple and sturdy. Two bamboo tubes, about 2 inches in diameter, are bent twice at right angles into the form of the letter *U*. Each *U* forms thus one pair of legs for the chair. In order to make this bend, part of the wood has been cut away leaving only a small strip of the wall of the bamboo tube. This strip is bent to a right angle, over a fire, otherwise it would break. Two shorter bamboo tubes of somewhat smaller diameter are then fitted at their respective ends horizontally into the bends mentioned and secured there with bamboo nails. Enough wood has been cut off under the bent strip to permit the insertion of these shorter tube ends which thus serve as front and back seat-rail of the chair. The stability of the four upright legs is further increased by rungs, two on each side, one in front, and one in back. The latter two are round bamboo tubes. The upper rungs on the sides are full-sized tubes large enough to receive the slanting arms of the backrest. The seat is

FIG. 469. PORCELAIN SLEEPING PILLOW.

Fig. 470. Bamboo Sleeping Pillow.

over about 7 inches of its length. The pointed ends are then pushed through holes in the seat-rail on each side of the chair, and rest in a smaller hole on each of the upper side rungs. Bamboo nails through the seat rails hold the bow of the backrest in place. Three vertical bamboo slats whose lower ends rest in a groove of the seat rail and whose upper ends are inserted in a similar groove in the bow serve as supports for the bow.

The chair shown in Fig. 462 differs from the one described in Fig. 461, only in the shape of the backrest, which is formed by two sidepieces secured to the chair in the same manner as the two arms of the backrest bow in the other chair, and connected on top by a horizontal cross-piece. This cross-piece receives, in round mortises, the ends of the sidepieces which are secured by bamboo nails. The three slats of the backrest are held in grooves in the same manner as in the other chair. The height of the seat of these chairs is usually not more than 14 inches.

There is quite a variety of other chairs in use, reflecting the refinements and riches of the people, made of expensive woods and sometimes elaborately inlaid with carved bone and shells. They can, however, not

formed of slats of bamboo each end of which is inserted between two transverse cross bars of bamboo mortised one above the other, into the front and back seat rails. The bow of the backrest on the chair, Fig. 461, consists of one piece of bamboo bent to form a curve. The bending is accomplished by cutting triangular sections from the bamboo tube, leaving a connecting strip, which bends until the surfaces of the incisions meet. This is a simple way of bending bamboo, and can be done without heating the wood over a fire. The ends of this bow are pointed by making a diagonal cut through the tube extending

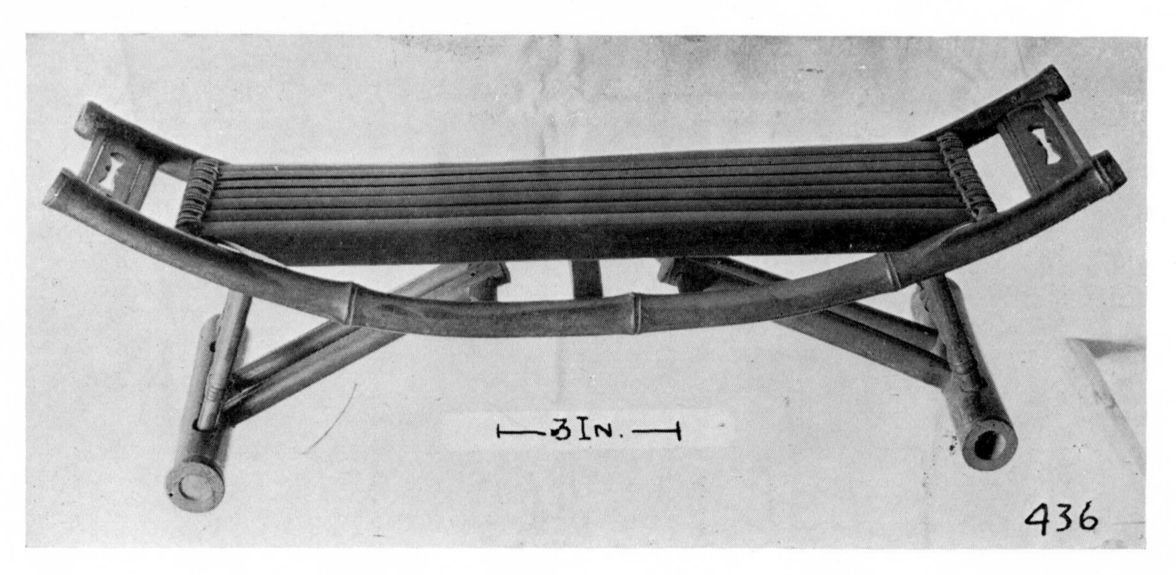

Fig. 471. Bamboo Sleeping Pillow.

be called typical. The photographs were taken at Cha Tsuen, Chekiang.

In Fig. 463 is shown another example of a Chinese chair from rural Kiangsi. It is made entirely of some kind of soft wood, while usually chairs are of bamboo. It is interesting to note that the mode of bamboo construction has been retained. Each pair of legs is formed of one piece of wood. To bend it at right angles the wood has been notched away so as to leave only a narrow strip, flexible enough to be bent at a right angle. The height of the seat from the ground is 20 inches.

Once I spent a few days with aboriginal people living in a wild mountain region north of Wantsai, Kiangsi. There I photographed the chair, Fig. 464, which was made by an itinerant carpenter. The peasants furnish the wood and engage a carpenter to make or repair furniture for them. He carries his tools and bedding with him and is given his meals at the places where he works. The whole chair is made of wood, the lower part is constructed like the bamboo chairs shown in Figs. 461 and 462. The back with arm rests reminds us of our windsor chairs. It has been suggested that our design influenced the Chinese but this is impossible since chairs of this type have been used for many centuries in China while the earliest specimens of windsor chairs do not go back much farther than the 18th century.

HEATING DEVICES

In Southern and Central China no provision is made to heat the houses in winter as the cold is not very severe. The Chinese protect themselves with warm padded clothing or furs. To protect the extremities hand and foot-stoves are in use, i.e., basins of earthenware or metal, filled with charcoal. Beside contrivances of general use and wide distribution one can see how some localities evolved their own peculiar methods for keeping warm. In an oil-mill in Kiangsi, a large drafty shed, the workers had a table around which they would sit to eat or to play games when the press did not require their services. Under this table in the mud floor was a square hole lined with bricks and filled with ashes and charcoal. I sat there myself wrapped in my overcoat on a cold December day and found nice warmth coming from below which spread around the lower part of your existence an agreeable atmosphere.

In the same district, near Teh An, Kiangsi, I saw

Fig. 472. Broom.

the heated stool pictured in Fig. 465. Even in winter on the farm the women have their duties outside the house. There are various productions of the field spread out on large wicker trays, or bamboo mats, to be dried in the sun, and the old granny sits by to keep the stray dogs, or the feathered tribe away. She has her spinning wheel beside her, and sits upon the heated stool with her feet drawn up, and resting on the edge close to the earthen charcoal basin in the lower part of the stool. Now and then she picks up the iron chopsticks, and stirs the embers into new activity. This stool, which may be compared to a bottomless tub, is 21 inches high, the diameter on the top 11¼ inches. The open cut on the side is 9 inches from the ground and the diameter of the bottom part 13½ inches. Through the lower part passes horizontally a wooden stick, resting loosely in square mortises in the side-staves of the tub, and on it reposes the earthenware bowl which holds the ashes and charcoal. The iron chopsticks are 7 inches long and the ends are united by a chain lest one member stray from the other. When not in use they are usually hung against the side of the stool by passing one of the pair through one of the decorative slats in the upper part of the stool.

In Ten Tai mountain range in Chekiang we found much in use a hand and foot warming stove like the one shown in Fig. 466. Otherwise there are no heating arrangements in the house except the kitchen stove and that is only used for cooking, not house warming. The people keep their bodies warm by putting cotton-padded garment upon garment. The cold is gaged by the amount of garments it takes to keep comfortable. Yesterday it was five coats cold, today it is only three. Only for the hands and feet they deem it necessary to apply external heat, and that is afforded by the hand-stove here shown which also many times becomes a foot-stove. The people carry these ember-bowls with them in and about the house, also when going to the fields or walking about the land, and calling on their neighbors. When they sit down, they hold the stove on their lap with their hands resting on the bamboo handle, or put it on the floor and hold their feet over it.

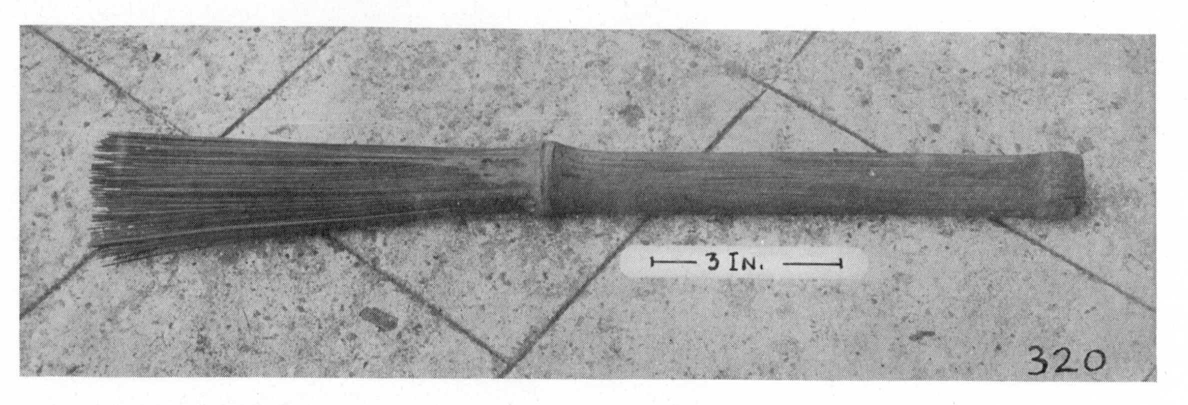

FIG. 473. BAMBOO KITCHEN BRUSH.

The stove pictured in Fig. 466 is an unglazed earthenware pot, about 7½ inches high, with widest diameter 8 inches, and 6 inches diameter on top, bound by bamboo strips which run up into the handle. The upper part of the pot is ornamented with conventional designs stamped into the clay. The bowl is over half filled with wood ashes; live charcoal or embers from a wood-fire are then put on top of the ashes. The Chinese press this stove into service for all kinds of other uses. The solid flat-irons elsewhere described, for instance, are frequently heated with this stove. At one place I saw it used as a nest for little chickens to keep them warm at night, the ashes having retained sufficient heat for this purpose. The photograph was taken at Se Aw, Chekiang.

The thought of a brazier is apt to set our imagination agoing and conjur up vivid pictures of the Arabian Nights. We fancy apartments resplendent with oriental rugs, where graceful figures recline upon gaily colored pillows around a brazier, from which fumes of fragrant incense rising in straight lines up to the high ceiling, mingle in semi-darkness with the tortuous forms of carved dragons and fabulous animals. Reality often destroys illusions. For if ever you were among those, who, grouped around a brazier in China, have tried to extract cheer and comfort from it, you must remember that you came nearer to swearing at than by it.

In Southern and Central China the winters are short, and the natives have never deemed it necessary to give serious thought to the providing of adequate heating devices. Miserable makeshifts are hand-stoves and sometimes the brazier, Fig. 467. The latter is usually placed under the table to keep the feet warm when the people sit around the table at meal-times, or for gambling, which for many Chinese, is almost as important as meals. A metal bowl, usually of cast iron, also sometimes, in more elaborate style of brass or copper, rests on a wooden stand with a perforated top, into which the bowl is set and held securely in place. The fuel used is charcoal. The height of the stand is 9 inches and the diameter of the bowl 22 inches. The photograph was taken in Changshu, Kiangsi. The fumes of charcoal never become dangerous on account of the airy, or rather drafty construction of the common dwellings.

Beside the large cooking stove there is usually a small stove to be found in the Chinese kitchen, built against the wall without any provision to carry off the smoke. A structure about 2½ feet high is erected, consisting of three brick walls like a chimney but with the front open. The top opening is usually just large enough to hold the brass tea kettle. A little lower down protruding from the back wall is a brick ledge and at the same height in front, extending from one side wall to the other, an iron bar or sometimes a brick arch. Ledge and bar, or ledge and brick arch, as the case may be, form the support of the wrought iron grate shown in Fig. 468. A wood fire is made on this grate, off and on during the whole day with brush wood, as it is essential to the well-being of the Chinese to have hot tea all day long. They would not think for instance of taking a trip or boat ride, without taking a tea kettle along, in a wooden box or basket, padded carefully with cotton to keep the tea hot for hours. The grate shown was made of a reinforcing bar, used in European concrete construction, (witness the wart-like protuberances), probably taken from some foreign building operation, the form however is quite typical. The handle serves to agitate the fire, shake down the ashes or to withdraw the grate from the hearth. The length, including the handle, is 22 inches, the width 6 inches. The average thickness of the square bar is ⅜ of an inch.

The photograph was taken in the Native City of Shanghai.

Fig. 474. Rush Wick Lamps.

PILLOWS AND BEDS

The upright position of *homo sapiens,* which distinguishes him from other mammals, finds its expression to a limited degree, in his sleeping habit when the head has to rest higher than the rest of the body. Because of this persistent habit, the reason of which remains unexplained, the pillow must surely be counted among life's necessities. We read in the Bible that Jacob used stones for a pillow, when night overtaking him in the open, forced him to find sleeping quarters without shelter.

In China people are not far removed from such primitiveness, and, in the heat of summer, one can see people sleep in the open, with all kinds of makeshifts for a pillow; a brick, a stone, a piece of wood, a pair of shoes, etc., when in all cases, the head rests a little higher than the rest of the body. Piles of timber where the one end is higher than the other, on account of the tapering from root end to trunk-top, are ever in favor with sleeping loafers or beggars, since because of the slant, the sleeper can rest, without a pillow. For the same reason a householder can now and then be seen, stretched out in front of his abode, upon a wooden door taken from its hinges and laid upon the ground, with one end propped up a little to gain the necessary slant.

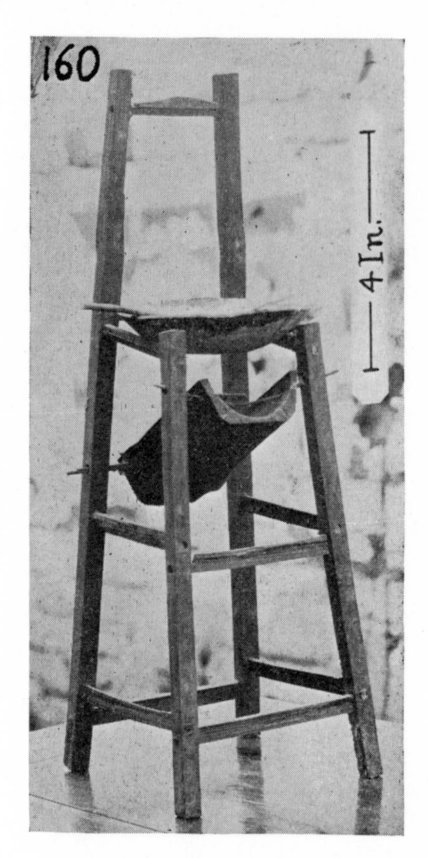

FIG. 475. WOODEN RUSH WICK LAMP.

There is a large variety of Chinese pillows for sleeping, with however one characteristic inherent in all: namely that they are extremely uncomfortable for occidentals. The Cantonese people are fond of using in summer a square box-shaped pillow of porcelain, one of these is shown in Fig. 469. It is considered very cooling. The dimensions are 6 by 5 by 2½ inches. It was given to me by a Cantonese family in Shanghai, but I am afraid that I have not so far shown sufficient appreciation to use it, not even in the heat of summer.

An ordinary bamboo pillow is shown in Fig. 470. By looking at it, one can imagine how admirably it fits the neck. It is 13½ inches long and a little over 4 inches high. I found it in an Inn in Tatung, Anhwei province, and procured it for a small consideration to take along as a souvenir.

In connection with sleeping appliances, a final word is necessary concerning bedbugs. They are a *sine qua non* in China, and the Chinese view it with apprehension if a person is not bothered by them: a healthy person must have bedbugs. All the poor victims object to, is too many. It is therefore quite frequently that one sees the bed-boards, or frames, with the cane, rattan, or chamærops cords, taken out into the open, in view of everybody, and plentifully besprinkled with scalding hot water. Bamboo pillows are similarly treated. Leather pillows don't lend themselves to such treatment and probably harbor always a few representative specimens to perpetuate the breed.

On a boat-trip in Chekiang, I saw the boat people spreading on the floor their bedding which consisted of a piece of wadding, about 3 by 6 feet in extent, enclosed in blue cotton cloth. In the day time it was rolled up and wrapped with a sheet of rush matting. The matting was put on the floor, and the wadding served as a cover. For a pillow these people took their upper garments and folded them up into a small bundle. I always envied such sufficiency, and yet my mode of inland travel was a close approach to such simplicity. Wadding to sleep upon and a feather pillow, two more items, gave me the feeling that I traveled like a gentleman.

Another more elaborate pillow, also of bamboo, is pictured in Fig. 471. It is even somewhat resilient and rather graceful in appearance, although a couch made in the same style we might view with more appreciation. The height in the center is 4½ inches, and the length 18 inches. It was bought from a secondhand dealer in Nanchang, Kiangsi. This latter example, Fig. 471, can be folded flat to fit conveniently into the bedding which any Chinese traveller carries with him.

All you can hope to find in a Chinese inn, is a place upon which to spread your own bedding. This may be a regular bedstead with an expanse of closely woven cane, rattan, or a surface of interwoven chamærops cords, fastened to the edges of a wooden frame, in the same way as our cane chair seats are attached in a row of holes along the edges. More common it is to find merely wooden boards, with some straw on top, either in a bedstead frame or on trestles. Pushing two of the square Chinese tables together, makes also a convenient bed, with the drawback, however, that one has to rise early to restore the tables to their legitimate use.

As we have learned already the Chinese like substance in their pillows and among other kinds use leather ones, lacquered and stuffed with chaff or bamboo shavings. They are about two feet long, with a square cross section, and are not a whit more comfortable than all the rest. Another kind, used by traveling merchants is a wooden box, covered with leather, in general outline similar to the bamboo pillow, Fig. 470. The curved top opens like a lid and the traveler upon retiring can store in the pillow all his valuables and be sure that nobody can get them without rudely awakening him.

BROOMS

A notable feature of the broom, shown in Fig. 472, is its renewability. The end of the wooden handle is bent over, probably with the aid of a fire and holds, in the fork of the bend, a bundle of straw. The upbent end parallel to the handle shaft, is tied to the latter with a rope to hold the bundle of straw in place. When the straw has been worn down, from frequent use the rope is loosened, a new bundle is put in place of the old one, and the rope once more tightened. Brooms are used in Chinese households, in the same manner as in the Western world. Long handled brooms like the one shown, are however, rarer than short handled brooms. With the latter, the Chinese have to stoop, a practice they don't seem to object to at all. Dust-pans are usually made of wicker or bamboo splints, similar to the scoops shown in Fig. 511. In the average Chinese house one finds only mud-floors, though sometimes, in bed-rooms, wooden floors. The floors are never washed. At meal-times bones and refuse are scattered upon the floor, only the most indigestible remnants of which are not snatched up by stray dogs, which always find their way into the houses at meal-times. The only cleaning a Chinese floor ever does get is with the broom, notwithstanding the fact that the floor has served as spittoon, handkerchief, children's toilet, etc., etc.

Broom-making is not a trade by itself. On the farms the peasants make brooms for their own use, and now and then some of the poorer folk will make quantities for sale and peddle them about the country. Brooms differ in material and workmanship according to locality. In the north, the stems of the kauliang or millet, are used extensively, and in the south, even splints of bamboo bundled together. The photograph was taken near Changshu, Kiangsi.

The brush shown in Fig. 473 is used for cleaning pots and pans. It was photographed in Fuchow, Kiangsi, and represents a common type, found extensively in China. It is made of a round piece of bamboo, the end of which has been cut longitudinally into many parallel slits to form the bristles. I include this sample here to show the principle of making a brush out of one piece of wood by merely fraying the end. The carpenter's brush dealt with under Fig. 373 is also of that type.

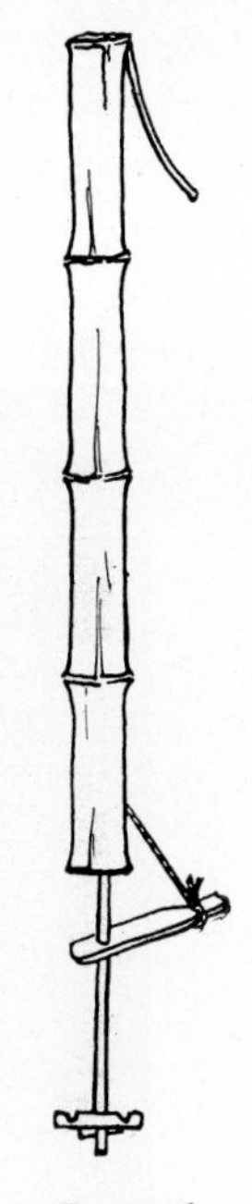

Fig. 476. Chinese Trammel.

About the Chinese brush pen, for writing, the tradition is current that it was invented in the 3rd century B.C., but it is hard to believe that no implement of a similar sort was replaced by it. The prototype of any brush is a wooden stick. Dipped into a medium and variously applied to trace lines the end would be apt to fray and then the application of paint would at once become easier. After such a practical experience the next step in the development might have been to fray the end of the stick purposely by making incisions. The invention of the writing brush in the 3rd century B.C. was probably then only another step in the development when hair tied to the end of a stick replaced the wooden fibres.

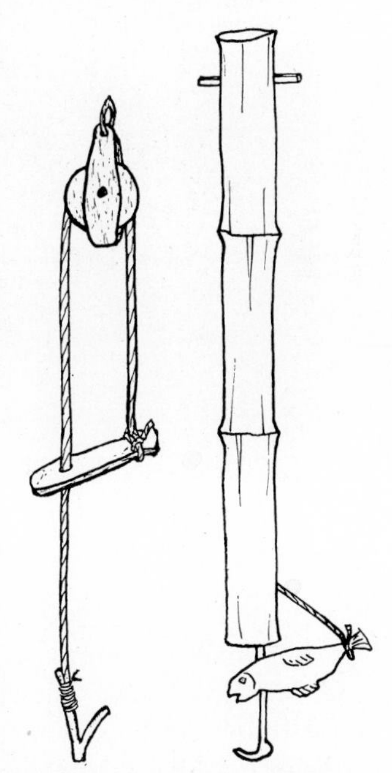

Fig. 477. Japanese Cooking Trammels.

LIGHTING

Fig. 474 shows three specimens of rush lamps which are now rapidly disappearing due to the introduction of kerosene in China.

A stand of porcelain, earthenware or brass serves to hold a small earthenware or brass dish which contains the oil. Two or three pieces of the pith of a rush, *Juncus communis,* are laid in the oil and allowed to extend a little beyond the rim of the oil container. Frequently a piece of iron curved to fit the shape of the dish, and long enough to protrude somewhat from the oil, is laid over the wicks to keep them submerged in the oil. The ends of the wicks extending from the oil are lit and as they burn shorter are pushed out from the oil with the piece of iron, which is grasped by the end projecting from the oil. The oil most frequently used as fuel for these lamps is derived from the soy bean, *Glycine hispidia,* and from rape seeds, *Brassica rapa.* Until the introduction of kerosene, rape oil was the cheapest and best illuminant known to the Chinese.

FIG. 478. LAMP STAND OF WROUGHT IRON.

Of the three lamps shown in Fig. 474 one is of porcelain, one of brass, and the one in the center of earthenware. Like many other Chinese articles lamps are made of various materials, the order as far as expense is concerned being usually wood, earthenware, porcelain, and then metal such as pewter, brass, copper, etc. The one made of porcelain is 11¾ inches high. On top rests an unglazed earthenware dish for the oil and wick. The largest diameter of this dish is 4 inches and its thickness ¼ of an inch. The stem of the porcelain stand is hollow and plugged in the middle to form an upper and lower hollow space. The bowl-shaped top of the stand has a hole ⅜ inch in diameter in its center communicating with the upper half of the hollow stand-stem. On the rim of the stand top at equal intervals are three small projections which form part of the stand, but are left unglazed. The loose oil dish rests on these projections which no doubt serve to keep the top of the stand from getting too hot when the lamp is burning. The decorations on the porcelain are applied by hand in blue under the glaze.

The earthenware stand in the middle of the picture is 6½ inches high. It is entirely formed of clay by hand, not upon a wheel, as closer inspection reveals. The stem is hollow but is closed tightly by the bowl-shaped top which also has three projections in this case glazed over like the entire outside. These projections extend a little above and beyond the side of the rim of the bowl-shaped top of the stand. The color of this glaze is of that smooth dead, robin's egg blue which is seen so frequently around Shanghai on cheap pottery. The bottom of the under-rim on which the lamp stands has three depressions, at equal intervals made apparently with the potter's thumb. The result is that the lamp does not stand upon a continuous circular rim but on three projections. These spaces probably served to prevent gases from accumulating in the hollow stem of the lamp when it underwent firing in the kiln. The lamp was built up of three pieces, the lower bowl, the stem and bowl-shaped top. The stem was formed by rolling together a flat thin piece of clay. The longitudinal lap-joint, carefully smeared over on the outside, and hidden by the glaze, can still be seen on the inside of the stem running from bottom to top in a straight line. A dish to contain the oil, not here shown, is likewise used with this earthenware lamp stand.

The brass lamp is 12½ inches high. The bowl-shaped top, with three copper pins projecting upward, is soldered to the solid stem. The foot of the lamp consists of an inverted brass cup soldered to the bottom of a shallow brass dish, 6¼ inches in diameter. The stem passes through a hole in the center of these two pieces and is riveted into place. All the different pieces composing this lamp-stand were cast. The ornamenting of the stem was done with a file. The two bowl-like pieces and the inverted cup-shaped foot, were finished in a primitive lathe with reciprocating motion.

The brass oil-dish for this lamp measures 3½

inches across on top. It has a flat piece for a handle with a little projection riveted into a corresponding hole into the side of the oil dish. To weigh down the wicks for this better grade of lamp and container, a piece of brass is used similar to the iron ones used for the cheaper earthenware lamps. I have not seen any of these wick weights; as is usual with discarded implements, the small accessories are lost first.

All three lamps were procured and photographed in Shanghai.

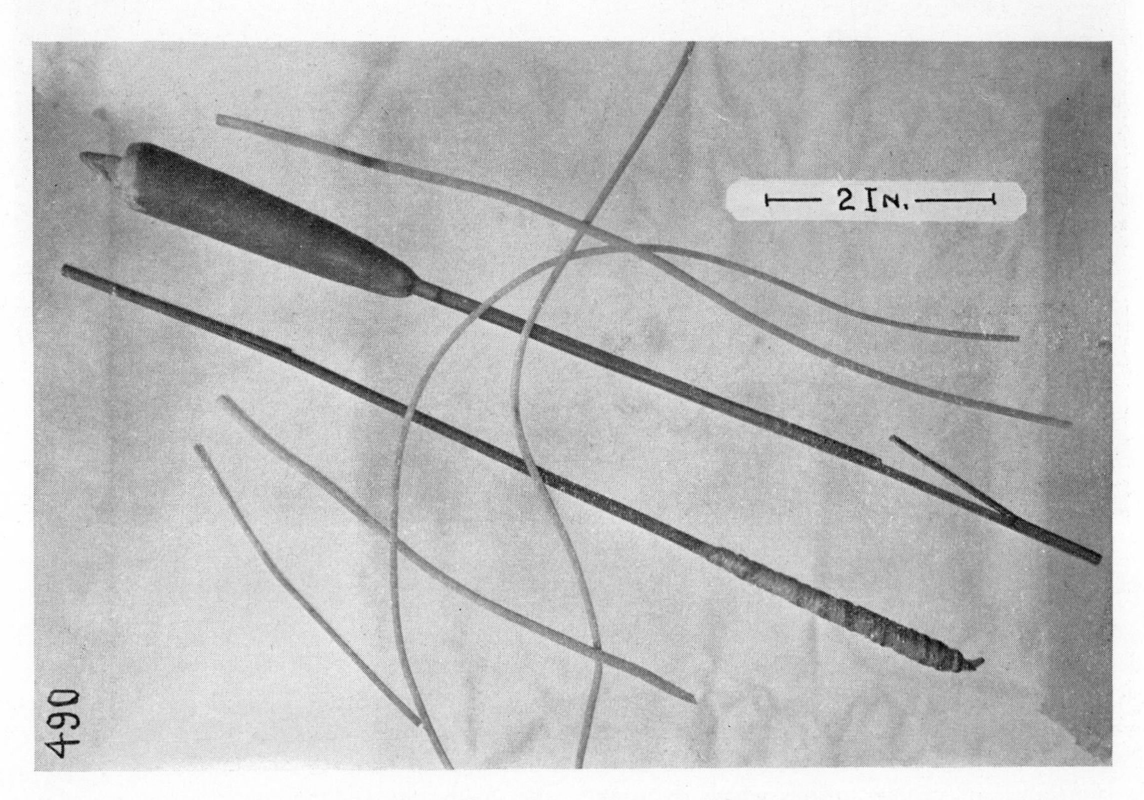

Fig. 479. Rush Wicks, Candle Core and Dipped Candle.

The simplest and most commonly used stands for rush wick lamps were made of wood and have generally disappeared. I found some of them still in use, in and around Sha Ho. One of them is shown in Fig. 475. The stand is composed of four upright legs, two of them 1 foot high, the other two 7¾ inches high; they are held together by rungs mortised with round tenons into the uprights. The distance between the upright legs at the base is 4½ inches. A porcelain bowl, 3¼ inches in diameter and ⅝ inch high, is used as an oil container and placed upon the stand. I did not see any wick-weights used with these lamps. The bowl is filled with oil and the rush wick simply laid into it with the ends extending. The oil-container sweats, that is, oil creeps up the wick to the edge of the container and oozes over forming drops on the bottom of the bowl which drip into the bamboo trough suspended obliquely between the legs of the stand. This trough is closed at its lower end by one of the natural division growths which separate the hollow stem of bamboo trees into different compartments.

The Chinese in whatever they do or make rarely strive for that perfection which we deem necessary in our industrial life. The free use they make of the word "about" testifies to this, also the typical expression "can do," which implies that perfection is neither expected nor desired. Keeping this in mind it is not surprising to see progress in many things come to a certain point and stop there abruptly. For the Chinese it has reached the "can do" stage and further development is arrested. An example in point is the oil-bowl of the rush wick lamps. Such dishes of unglazed clay have been used in the anterior Orient for more than 4000 years, also stands upon which to put the lamps. How long the Chinese have had them is hard to conjecture. The Chinese did not pay any attention to industries and crafts in their writings until about the Sung Dynasty (960-1280), and we get therefore scant information from their

FIG. 480. CANDLEMAKER'S WORKBENCH.

literature concerning the primitive industries and modes of living. One fact is certain, however, that the Chinese to this day use a little round bowl, be it of metal, earthenware or porcelain, for their lamps.

Extensive excavations in Palestine have brought to light lamp-bowls of various periods which show an interesting development from the simple bowl, with which the Chinese development stopped, to the closed oil-lamps with holes for a wick and for filling with oil. The development started with crimping the edge a little, as the earliest examples show, to mark the place for the wick. An example from Gezer, ca. 1500 B.C. shows the crimping more defined, and the next step to closing the top and leaving openings for wick and oil seems almost obvious, and yet it was not until the Hellenistic period (2nd century B.C.) that such examples occur, as shown by excavations in Palestine.

Fig. 475 was taken at Sha Ho, a small market-town in Kiangsi province.

In Changshu, Kiangsi, I saw an interesting lamp-holder suspended from the ceiling. Fig. 476 will aid in understanding the description. A bamboo tube, about 4 feet long is suspended vertically by a top hook from the ceiling. In it slides freely a wooden rod with a little notched block wedged on its end to which the oil lamp can be hung. A wooden catch-strip, with one end tied to the lower end of the bamboo tube acts as a brake. The other end of this wooden strip has a round hole large enough for the wooden sliding rod to pass through. By inspection of the picture the underlying principle may now be readily understood. The extending length of the sliding rod can be shortened by pushing it up into the bamboo tube, or lengthened by pushing it downward out of the tube. In that case it will be necessary to release the brake, that is lift the perforated end of the wooden piece which tightens the rod. The principle is one of friction. The more down-pull there is, the tighter will be the frictional force holding the rod in position. We would call such a device a trammel, because of its similarity to the adjustable iron rod with a hook for the suspension of a cooking-pot over the chimney fire. For many centuries past, the Chinese have reached a stage where they do their cooking on a built-up hearth, not on the open fire. Proof of this is furnished by graves from the Han Dynasty (206 B.C.-220 A.D.), which have revealed that at that period already cast iron cooking ranges were in use with a fuel door at one end and a chimney at the other, and with several pot holes on the upper surface. A trammel is under these conditions not necessary, so that in China we find such a device only used as a lamp-holder. In Japan, on the other hand, where the rural life has been much more primitive than in China until quite recently, we find that cooking in peasant houses is still done over an open charcoal fire, with similar trammels. Fig. 476 was sketched after a Chinese type seen in Changshu, Kiangsi.

The sketch Fig. 477 shows two trammels of the type still (1928) found in Japanese peasant kitchens, constructed on the same principle, as the Chinese lamp-holder, (Fig. 476). These trammels are suspended from the ceiling over the charcoal fire. The Japanese cooking trammel is made of bamboo or iron, and the small perforated piece which exerts the braking force is usually made in the form of a fish. Another Japanese type is shown on the left. Here over a pulley runs a rope, to one end of which a hook is attached to carry the load, namely a tea-kettle or cooking-pot. The other end of the rope, with a perforated piece of wood acts as a brake, like the key or rope slide used to tighten the guy rope on a tent.

The right figure represents a trammel from Nagasaki, a specimen of which was sent to the Mercer Museum. The left trammel, was sketched after a drawing by Hokusai, a Japanese color-print-illustrator of the early 19th century.

Fig. 478 gives a view of a lamp from the Lung Chuan District in Chekiang. In this region native iron occurs, and wrought iron lamps like the one shown here are therefore not infrequently met with. There are two parts to the specimen here shown, the stand proper with a catch-basin, and the cast iron bowl for oil and wick. The bowl rests upon a fixed iron ring, extending horizontally from the upright arm, which in turn terminates in a loop on top for hanging the lamp up against the wall. Below the lamp bowl is the catch-basin. The fuel is vegetable oil, and the wick the pith of a rush.

The adaptability of the lamp is three fold, it can be carried about in the house, hung up against the

Fig. 481. Candle Dipping Wheel.

wall, and stood upon its three legs. Three legs are most appropriate for a lamp which should stand solidly without shaking. Even on a rough, uneven surface a lamp, cooking pot, table, stool, etc., with three legs will always stand firmly.

The lamp shown belonged to a farmer of Ta Yao, Chekiang, a place famous for the making of Seladon porcelain in former centuries.

CANDLE MAKING

Candles are made in China by dipping. I have never heard of candles made with a mold. In earliest times beeswax only was used for making candles, but since the Tang (618-907 A.D.) and the Sung (960-1127 A.D.) Dynasties, other substances such as insect wax and vegetable tallow, have been employed.

The insect wax is the product of an insect, *Coccus Ceriferus,* which thrives upon several trees, mainly however upon *Fraxinus sinensis* and on *Ligustrum lucidum.* The insect nourishes itself from the sap of the tree, which it extracts from the small branches, and in turn it voids a whitish substance, the so-called insect wax, with which the branches become gradually covered. In August this substance is scraped off the branches. The crude wax is melted to separate it from impurities and is then poured into molds for cooling. It is sold in the shape of round cakes as it comes from the molds. The melting point is about 180° F. and its composition seems to be a ceryl cerotate. In its purified form it is translucent, white and highly crystalline.

The vegetable tallow is a white hard fat enclosing the seeds of the tallow tree, *Stillingia sebifera.* It melts at 112° F. and its chemical composition is palmitin with some olein. The seeds with their white covering are steamed in wooden cylinders with perforated bottoms. The steam enters through the holes in the bottom, and so softens the tallow that it can be separated from the seeds by gently beating them with stone hammers, or by pounding them in a mortar with a trip hammer. The beaten mass is sifted through hot sieves which retain the seeds. The fragments of the white seed-coverings, the vegetable

FIG. 482. CANDLE DIPPING WHEEL. The picture shows another candle dipping wheel, which was photographed to atone for the dimness of the one shown in Fig. 481.

tallow, are further pulverized in an edge mill. The resulting powder is still impure, being mixed with adhering particles of the seed pellicles, but purification is effected by pressing the mass through a cylinder made up of bamboo or willow rings, in an oil-press, similar to the one described under Figs. 133 to 139. The mass, forced through the rings, is first dark yellow, and turns white upon contact with the air.

The insect wax is the more valuable product and its use is therefore more restricted. For candles used in Buddhist worship a mixture is largely used of one part of insect wax to fifty parts of vegetable tallow. In my experience most of the candles used in China are dipped in vegetable tallow until they have nearly the required thickness and are then coated, also by dipping, with an outer layer of insect wax, which has been dyed red with alkanet root, green with verdigris, or left white in its natural state. This coating is an economic feature, inasmuch as it prevents guttering; the colors are added to fit the candles for festive occasions, red for happy events and white or green for funerals. Insect wax has a higher melting point (180° F. against 112° F. of vegetable tallow) and therefore keeps the liquid tallow confined near the flame and assures complete combustion. The top of the burning candle seems surrounded by a wall and this is the outer layer of insect wax which is consumed at a slower rate than the vegetable tallow. A combustion problem is thus ideally solved. Whether or not the stick wick, presently to be described, is a necessary feature to afford balanced combustion, I do not know. The only drawback of the Chinese candle is that it has to be snuffed from time to time. If this is not done the charred end will tumble over and make a mess of the candle by burning a pathway into the outer coating with a resultant flood of tallow. The peasants do the snuffing quickly with the fingers while otherwise brass snuffers constructed like sugar tongs are used.

There are two different types of candles used in China, one kind to be used on a pricket, and the other in a socketed candlestick, as here shown. The former seems to be prevalent in the coast provinces, Kiangsu, Chekiang, Fukien, while in the central provinces along the Yangtse, in Anhwei, Kiangsi, Hunan, Hupeh the candles which need a socketed candlestick are those preferably used. The wick or wick-basis of the candle is, conforming to its type, a hollow reed, adaptable for a pricket, or a solid bamboo stick for a socketed candlestick. The burning-part of the candle here shown appears as a swelling covering one fourth the length of this wick stick. The bamboo sticks for the solid bamboo wicks are split from a thick-walled bamboo stem and for rounding are pulled through a round, sharp-edged hole in a flat piece of iron. A number of sticks thus prepared are spread out upon the working bench and a line is drawn upon them with Chinese ink at right angles to their length. In this manner each rod will receive a little mark to determine the spot from which the winding of the rushes to form the candle proper is to commence.

Fig. 480 gives a view of the working bench. For medium sized candles such as those shown in Fig. 479, six rushes are taken from the heap on the bench and laid upon the square wooden board and flattened by rolling over them the round wooden stick, here seen lying on the board. They are then wound in a spiral over the spaced off end of the rod. To prevent the unwinding of the rushes from the bamboo wick rod, floss silk, pulled from the distaff, (conf. Fig. 247 for a detailed account of it) on the bench, is wound spirally up and down over the previously wound rushes, whereupon the wick stick is ready to be dipped.

There is a certain quality in the floss silk which makes it adhere where put, and therefore no tying is necessary. The Chinese have solved the problem of giving stability to the rushes in their own way; in old England, Ireland and Scotland, a narrow strip of the outer husk was left all along the rush pith, to give the latter the necessary strength.

The next step is to form the hook at the end of the wick stick which is necessary for hanging it, with the wound end downward, on the dipping wheel. The finished candle in Fig. 479 shows this suspension hook plainly. Near the unwound open end of the bamboo rod a cross-cut half through the wick stick is made with a knife, and the blade turned while still in the cut to split the blade beyond the incision and downward toward the stick-end for a short stretch. The split piece is then bent outward over the flame of an oil lamp, other wise it would be liable to break and not keep the position in which it forms the hook. Candles with a hollow reed center, have a supplementary pointed bamboo rod with a hook on it, pushed into the end hole.

For the purpose of dipping, the candle wick-rods, wrapped as described with their rush-wicks, are hung up on a dipping wheel, as can be seen in Figs. 481 and 482. A working-man sits in front of the wheel, takes down a wrapped rod, dips it, and hangs it upon another hoop on the same wheel. He turns the wheel to bring the sticks to be dipped in the hot wax in front of him until the wheel has made a complete revolution when the first one of the dipped rods, now hardened in the cool air, will again be in front of the worker. Now the cooled rods receive the second dipping, which is completed after another complete revolution of the wheel. Thus the work proceeds, by successive dippings, until the layers on the sticks reach the thickness required for the size of the candle. The final act is the dipping in a colored solution which gives color to the candle. The photograph was taken in Sinyu, Kiangsi.

Chapter V

TOOLS FOR ENABLING TRANSPORT

ROADS

IN OLDEN times, excellent wide roads were in existence in China suitable for chariots, coaches, and wagons of many descriptions. As early as the Chow Dynasty (1122-249 B.C.) the traffic necessitated the prescription of a uniform scale of proportion for wheeled vehicles, prohibition of "furious driving," and traffic regulations at crowded crossings. Various native records of the period 221-589 A.D. mention the use of carriages, which registered distances with a mechanical contrivance by which the wooden figure of a man struck a drum at the end of each li (1/3 of a mile). Present day conditions show a different picture especially in southern and central China where the two-wheeled cart is not known. The splendid roads are gone, and in their place, we find only narrow paths, scarcely wide enough for foot passengers and wheelbarrows. The Chinese peasant, ever intent to gain more ground for the cultivation of his crops, has gradually reduced the width of former highways, unhampered by a watchful government. In fact the greedy officials have winked at such encroachments, as long as they have been thereby enabled to exact increased contributions in taxes and in kind from the hardworking peasants. It must be stated, however, that my criticism refers to the old regime which ended with the establishment of the republic. Naturally changes did not come over night. While the monarchy was overthrown in 1911, the enlightened policies of the young republic have not had time to work appreciable changes for the general betterment of the country. It is only within the last five years that an extensive program of road building has been carried out.

Fig. 483. Chinese Wheelbarrow.

WHEELBARROWS

In Central and Southern China where the roads are too narrow for wheeled carts the most widely used conveyance for transportation is the wheelbarrow. While there are many kinds of wheelbarrows, the one

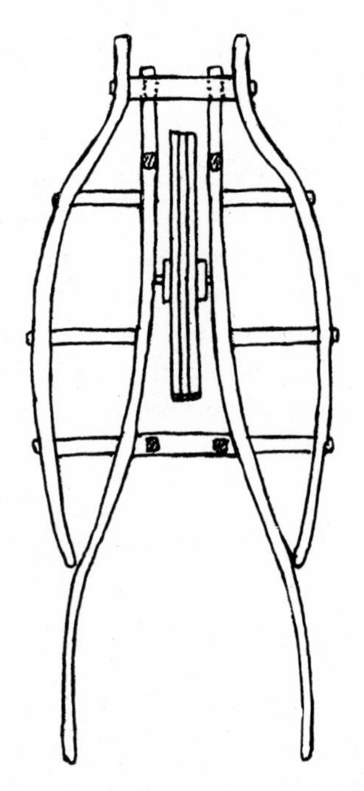

FIG. 484. DETAIL OF CHINESE WHEELBARROW CONSTRUCTION.

shown in Fig. 483 is typical of them all; the principle being always the same, i.e., one large wheel surrounded by a framework, guarding the upper part of the wheel from contact with merchandise or persons transported. Two long shafts, held at a proper distance from each other by two crosspieces, terminate in the handle-bars, and form the basis of the whole vehicle. Into them is mortised the lattice work which surrounds the wheel. On each side a carrying frame is formed by curved bars attached to the main shafts by crosspieces. The accompanying sketch, Fig. 484, will make this clear. The wheel, about 3 feet in diameter, is made entirely of wood and has two iron bands around the hub, and an iron tire. The axle is made of some very strong wood. From the frame of the wheelbarrow two pieces extend downward with the bearing holes for the axle. This looks rather precarious, and yet these pieces stand up splendidly under the heavy strain of immense loads and the considerable bumping over the miserable roads. These wheelbarrows are masterpieces of joinery and special care is bestowed on the selection of the best grades of hard wood for all parts.

Besides transporting goods with these wheelbarrows, the Chinese use them also for passengers. I have seen as many as six people on them, three sitting on each side with their feet dangling down. If only one passenger is conveyed the driver balances the wheelbarrow skillfully with the wheel tilted at a considerable angle from the vertical. If a peasant wants to take a pig to the market, he saves himself all the trouble of guiding the recalcitrant beast, by tying it upon the wheelbarrow and wheeling it to the market.

This description would not be complete without mentioning the squeaking of the unoiled axle, a nightmare to foreigners, which does not bother the Chinese in the least. In Shantung and Honan, sails are frequently used on wheelbarrows. A large sheet of cloth

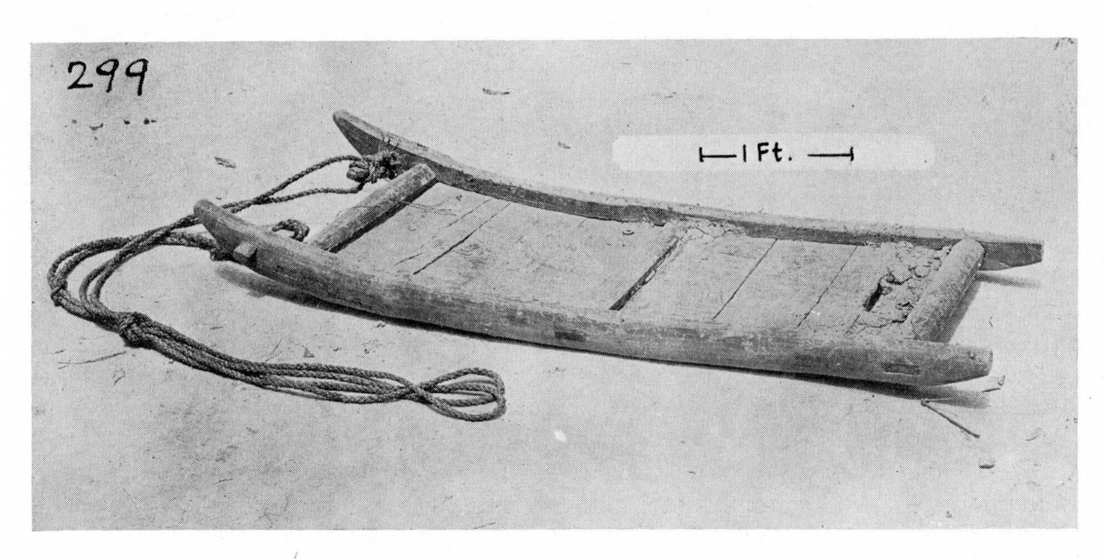

FIG. 485. SLED FOR TRANSPORTING MUD.

is set on a framework in front, which can be raised or reefed at will, the ropes being attached to the handlebar close to the driver.

The photograph was taken in the yard of a farm about 20 li west from Te An, in Kiangsi Province.

Fig. 487. Chinese Grass Cart as Used on the Poyang Lake in 1925.

SLED

Among the devices relating to Chinese transportation must be mentioned the sled which no doubt preceded the wagon in its development. Fig. 485 gives a primitive example. It is used for shifting mud from one part of a field to another, when levelling the surface for rice-growing. The fields must be perfectly level to allow of uniform inundation. For the runners of the vehicle naturally curved pieces of wood are selected. They are held together by four crosspieces mortised into the runners. The intervening spaces are filled with boards which rest loosely in longitudinal grooves cut in the runners, in the manner in which panels are held in place. At the end where the runners curve upward wooden pegs have been placed to fasten the rope. Earth is heaped upon the platform, and a draught animal is required to drag it about over the field. For loading and unloading, shovels are employed. The length of the runners is about 5 feet, the width of the whole contrivance is 2 feet 3 inches. It was photographed on a farm about 5 li from San Ho, Anhwei, where we were the guests of a retired official, formerly the secretary of the General of Amoy.

Fig. 486. Chinese Grass Cart Used on the Poyang Lake.

CARTS DRAWN BY ANIMALS

The two-wheeled cart is a vehicle of North China. In former times it seems to have been common all over China. Through the neglect of roads it disappeared gradually and survived only in North China under the sway of the court in Peking, where the important business of victualizing the capital was sufficient urge to keep the roads leading from and to it in good repair. A. Semedo, a Jesuit of the 17th century, observed that public carriages in China disappeared about the 16th century, at which

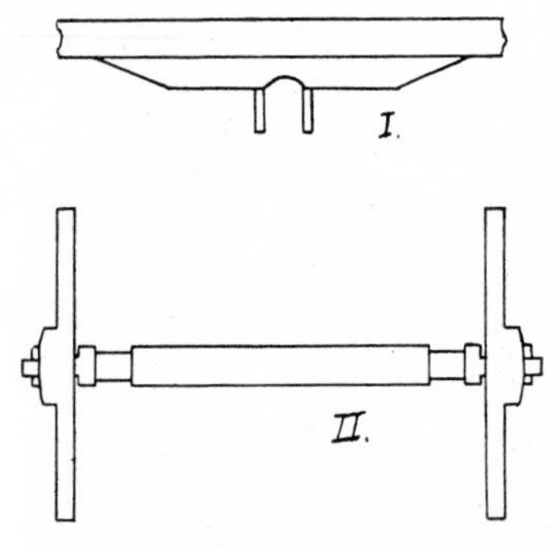

Fig. 488. The Axle Bearings of a Poyang Grass Cart.

time they were introduced in Europe.

Before describing the two-wheeled cart as it is used in Shantung, I shall refer to the use of primitive carts on the mud-flats of the Poyang Lake, Kiangsi, the first two-wheeled carts I saw in China. Being contiguous to the Yangtse River, there is towards summer an enormous rise of water in the lake, something like 30 feet, which subsides again towards winter. On the extensive mud-flats which are then exposed, starts a luxurious growth of reed-like marsh grass, this is harvested for fuel, and then, after that, a short curly grass is taken up with the hoe with much of the soil attached. The latter is used for fertilizing the fields, and protecting, against night frost in January, the young tobacco plants grown in the neighborhood of the lake.

The cart, Fig. 486, is transporting reed grass, and the persons at work with it are males in spite of their skirts.

The cart recalls conditions in Europe in the middle ages and reminds me of a statement made by a German historian (Gustav Freytag) who said that around 1200 A.D. carts were few and the Alsatians used wagons without any iron. Wagons with iron trimmings came later from Swabia into Alsatia. These all-wooden Chinese carts form no doubt also a link with ancient times. Huang Ti (2697 B.C.) is said to have invented carts and indeed there occurs a word for cart among the oldest Chinese signs. According to Giles (A Chinese Biographical Dictionary, London and Shanghai 1898, p. 269), Hsi Chung, 20th century B.C., a descendant of the Yellow Emperor, is said to have been Master of the Horse under the Great Yü and to have been the first to employ horses as draught animals. The statesman and first statistician Kuan Chung of the 7th century B.C. counts the cart among the implements necessary for the peasant. An ode in the

Fig. 489. Shantung Cart for Passengers and Merchandise.

Fig. 490. Shantung Passenger Cart.

Fig. 491. Horse Stirrups.

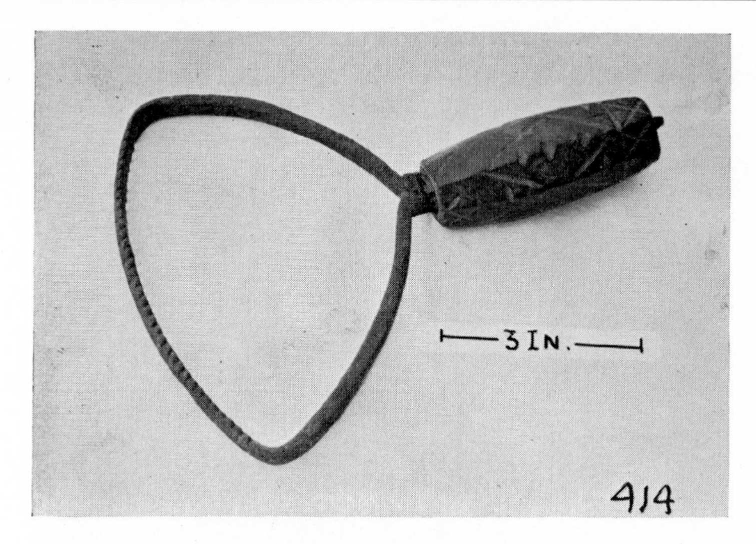

Fig. 492. Chinese Curry-Comb.

Shi-King, describing a battle between the Chinese and the Huns in 827 B.C., a contemporary account, speaks of the well-made war carriages, nicely balanced before and behind. The latter characterization fits the Chinese cart where the body should be well balanced upon the axle of the two wheels. Fig. 487 shows another example of one of the primitive Poyang carts used for transporting fuel and grass, from the far stretching marshes to the boats. In their primitiveness these vehicles seem the prototype of all two-wheeled carts. The wheels about 5 feet in diameter, are built up of solid planks joined together with dowels and two dovetailed crosspieces. The plank in the middle is left thicker in the form of a central block, to form a kind of nave or hub. The axle is a rough beam squared at both ends to fit into square mortises in the wheels. The extending part of the axle is secured with a wooden pin. The platform of the cart rests on the axle, in such a manner that the axle can freely turn with the wheels. The axle is firmly fixed to the wheels and turns only as they turn.

The picture shows clearly the primitive wheel which is here mended with a few iron cleats, but originally there was not a particle of iron used on the cart. The yoke which rests upon the neck of the water buffalo is tied to the ends of the shafts. The shafts are prolonged with beams tied to the original shafts and it seems likely that formerly these carts were drawn by men only.[1] Mules are not used in the district at all. The wheels are about 5 feet in diameter. The cart was photographed at the Poyang Lake, Kiangsi.

No. I of the sketch Fig. 488 shows one of the bearings of the underside of the platform of the cart. The platform consists of two large shafts about 15 feet long, running parallel, at one end connected with the yoke which is tied to it. There is sufficient space between the shafts for the draft animal, but further behind the latter, the shafts are connected with crosspieces which, with boards lying upon them, parallel with the shafts, form the body of the cart. Each shaft under the body of the cart has a short strengthening beam pinned to it with two parallel wooden pins. These pins extend about 6 inches downward (see sketch No. I), and fit over a bearing which is merely a rounded space on the axle. On No. II of the sketch these rounded places are plainly indicated.

The cart Fig. 489 a typical specimen of those used

[1] "Wheel carriages were first introduced by the Emperor Tay-yu, the founder of the Hia dynasty, 2205 B.C. At this early period, however they were not, it appears, drawn by horses, but by men. Their use was in a great measure restricted to royal and noble families. The cars in which the Emperor rode were invariably drawn by twenty men." (J. H. Gray, "China," London 1878, Vol. II, page 177.)

Fig. 493. Coasting Junk of Shantung.

in North China, stands unhitched in a Chinese farm yard. The shafts are propped with a stick to keep the cart in an upright position. The wheels, about 4 feet in diameter, are ponderous affairs, with hub, spokes, fellies and iron tires. The fellies are studded on the sides with large-headed nails to prevent wear and instead of continuous hoop tires, are covered with detached iron plates in three sections. This cart was photographed in Weihsien, Shantung. The axle does not turn with the wheels as in the Poyang grass cart (Figs. 486 and 487) but as with European carts, the wheels turn on the axle. The roughly squared axle fits between parallel pins a few inches apart, projecting downward from the underpart of the shafts. These pins fit into grooves cut on the sides of the axle, and in this manner the axle keeps in place and is prevented from revolving. The hub, about 10 inches in diameter, is strengthened by two iron bands and the circular opening is lined with a sleeve of iron. The spokes are mortised into the hub and the fellies. The body of the cart is built lightly of framework and covered with white or blue cotton cloth which is further protected from rain by an additional covering of oil cloth or oiled paper. Little windows are fitted on the sides with black gauze and nowadays sometimes even with glass. The shafts extending on the back furnish space for baggage. The passenger on the inside spreads out his bedding upon the board floor, and has to sit in a cramped and uncomfortable position with crossed legs, or with legs stretched straight from the sitting body, both of which positions are most uncomfortable for foreigners not used to it. Springs, of course, the cart has not, and on a rough road you get shaken up, until every tooth in your head seems to become loose and shake as the bones in a dice-box. The driver usually sits at the opening of the cart on one of the shafts with his feet dangling down.

Fig. 494. River Boat of Kiangsi.

Fig. 490 shows another example of a Shantung cart with a mule in harness. The draft animal in this province usually is a mule. The leather harness is not unlike the American harness and consists of collar, saddle, breeching and, in some cases, traces. The girth is frequently a piece of rope. The shaft ends are attached to the saddle to keep the vehicle balanced. As

FIG. 495. VIEW OF SHIPBUILDING YARD.

the cart has no brake the breeching has to serve to hold back the load going down hill. The baggage space at the back must not be loaded to the point of destroying the balance, otherwise the mule is lifted into the air. The driver's seat on the shaft is indicated by the pad shown in Fig. 490. Underneath it hangs a bamboo bottle with heavy vegetable oil for lubricating the axle bearings. The end of the axle around which the wheel revolves is protected by an iron sleeve so that iron bears upon iron. An iron linch pin keeps the wheel in place on the axle. The cart was photographed in Weihsien, Shantung province.

The two carts shown are for passenger service and goods. Carts exclusively for transporting goods have no top structure. The Chinese two-wheeled cart is looking back upon a history of several thousand years, and is now gradually approaching the end of its usefulness with the advent of road improvement and motor cars.

HORSE FURNITURE

Of the various articles belonging to the equipment of horses in China, I shall here deal with the stirrup.

The first mention of a stirrup in the Occident appears in a book attributed to the Roman Emperor Mauricius, called Ars Militaris, which was written in the 6th century A.D. In China stirrups are much older, B. Laufer [2] noticed them on a sculptured stone of the Han Dynasty, and F. Hirth [3] calls attention to the mention of stirrups in Chinese writings of the year 477 A.D. The form then was a metal ring fastened by a leather strap to the saddle. The typical Chinese form of the present day is shown in Fig. 491. The pair on the left is of cast iron and the single one on the right of brass. The height of the cast iron pair is 6½ inches, the foot-rest is elliptical with a diameter of 5 inches one way, and 5½ inches the other. The dimensions of the brass stirrup are 5¼ inches high, and a diameter of 3 and 4 inches. Near Tsao Hsien, Anhwei, I noticed once very primitive stirrups on donkeys, consisting of a piece of wood, about 6 inches long, 1½ inches wide and ½ of an inch thick, held at each end by a piece of rope which led up to the saddle where they were fastened. The stirrups shown in Fig. 491 were photographed in Kienchang, Kiangsi.

[2] B. Laufer, "Chin. Pottery of the Han Dyn.," Leyden, 1909.
[3] F. Hirth, Verhandlungen der Berliner Anthropologischen Gesellschaft, 1890.

Fig. 496. View of Shipbuilding Yard.

The place where stirrups originated seems to be somewhere in Central Asia. Thence they spread East and West. The incursions of Asiatic hordes in the 4th and 5th centuries brought them to Europe. The oldest specimens recovered from European graves of that period, however, are in form and decoration quite advanced, and point to a long period of previous development which must have taken place somewhere else.

On the bronze reliefs from the gates of Shalmanesar dating of ca. 850 B.C. is depicted "the king whose sad lack of horsemanship is indicated by his riding straightened and with huge stirrups tied to the horse-blanket, not in the only fashion known to the oriental expert, with hunched-up knees and bareback." (Quoted from Olmstead, History of Assyria, New York 1923).

The curry-comb, Fig. 492 now in the Mercer Museum, was procured in Kienchang, Kiangsi. A wrought iron bail has on both sides incisions which form ridges like dull-saw-teeth. The ends

Fig. 497. Shallop Propelled with Scull.

Fig. 498. Coasting Junk of Shantung.

of the bail rest in the wooden handle, which is furnished with grooves giving a decorative effect and affording at the same time a firm grip.

The Chinese apparently have no spurs. I never saw any and there seems no word for spur in the Chinese language. Of the Turks and some Central Asiatic tribes it is said that their stirrups with sharp corners offer a good substitute and make up for the absence of spurs which however cannot be applied to the Chinese stirrups which have round contours and no sharp corners.

WATER WAYS

Among the earliest records of the Chinese we find references to the improvements of water ways. The legendary rulers Shun and Yü, it is said, deepened the rivers and in times of floods made channels and canals to conduct the flood waters to the streams and to the sea.

Of the Han time we have more definite information. An engineer, named Shih Lu, constructed a canal 60 li in length with 36 locks, through the mountainous country of Hai-Yang, Kuangtung province. The first attempts to connect the two great rivers with a canal was also made in the Han time. The energetic Yang Ti (605 to 617 A.D.) built a great system of canals amounting altogether to nearly 5000 miles. The Grand Canal connecting the Huang Ho and Yangtze River was also brought to perfection by him. It was 40 steps wide and the banks were lined with solid stone.

Today, as one travels through the country, signs of thousands of years of water-borne traffic are everywhere in evidence. Bewildering networks of canals, f.i., stretch over the lowlands around Ningpo and Fenghwa in Chekiang province and it seems a puzzle how the boatmen find their way through that maze. High-arched bridges span the canals for easy passage of boats and night traffic is aided by the piers of the bridges being painted white. As a boatman comes along at night and approaches a bridge he looks for the painted piers and steers his boat safely through the narrow opening. Boat-traffic in some cases goes up a river to near its source and there a portage is established to connect with another stream beyond the mountain.

Fig. 499. Seagoing Fishing Junks.

Sometimes one can discern the path of dry and silted-up canals. Consulting the map one usually finds that the abandoned and forgotten canal had at one time served a good purpose by connecting important rivers or by considerably reducing the distance between points on a tortuous stream. The queerest sight is to see a beautiful arched bridge in the midst of level land without approaching roads, surrounded by tilled fields. The well-built pile of masonry has endured while the neglected canal has altogether disappeared.

Fig. 500. Seagoing Cargo Boats.

At one time we proceeded in a sampan on a fresh water canal in Chekiang. Finally we arrived at the end of the canal and had to pass over a lock into the Young River. The tide runs into this river a considerable distance and as it was then just passing out we had to wait the turn as our man-propelled sampan could not go against the strong

Fig. 501. Shipbuilder's Thong Drill, Method of Working by Two Men.

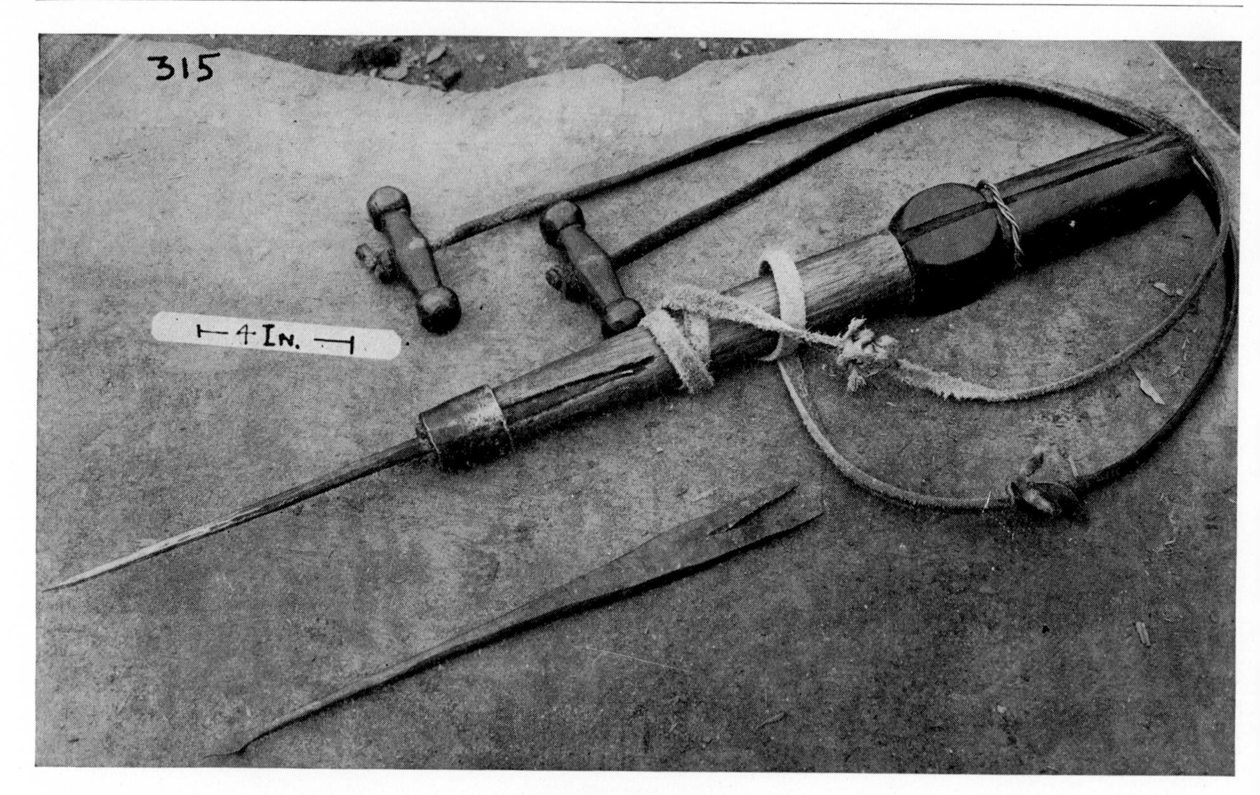

FIG. 502. SHIPBUILDER'S THONG DRILL.

FIG. 503. SHIPWRIGHT'S LINE MARKER.

current of the tide. The lock, a mere mud ramp, is of very simple construction and serves to keep the level of the freshwater canal constant. The canal approaches the river at right angles and is dammed in to a width of about 10 feet. At the narrowest point mud is heaped up and a board stuck on edge across the ridge of the lock. If a boat wants to pass, the board is taken out of the mud, ropes are fastened on each side of the stern and the ropes wound up on each side of the lock upon horizontal beams which have four arms sticking out. These arms are pushed by the lock-tenders. After our boat was thus pulled up the mud barrier halfway, it tilted forward and slid gracefully down into the Young River. The loops of the ropes which were laid around the boat slid off by themselves.

Fig. 504. Chinese Shipbuilder's Caulking Tools.

BOAT BUILDING

Chinese historians gave thought to the origin of boats and tell us that observations of falling leaves floating on the water led to the idea of making boats. The great Yü of the Hsia Dynasty, ca. 2205 B.C., who usually has to do historical service in such cases, is blamed for having made the first dug-out, adding rudder, bamboo cover, stone anchor, the sail and mast. Another source says that the need of fishing led to the construction of boats, which were made of wood of the cypress, willow or pine.

Boat building in China seems an independent development. The people have found specific conditions and have adapted their boats accordingly. As the conditions change from region to region we find an endless variety of minor differences. There are boats with flat bottoms for use in shallow rivers, some with highly curved bow and stern for the rapid mountain streams with treacherous rapids, to take sudden jolts gracefully. Some have the galley fore and some aft. River boats have usually only one mast for sails, and for towing, the line is fastened to the top of the mast. Towing is exclusively done by man-power. Some boats are covered with arched matting, and to pass from one end to the other, one has to crawl through under the matting which is only high enough to sit under, while other boats have the half-round matting cover narrow enough to leave a walk on either side along the gunwale. This walk is then used for upriver poling, where steep banks make towing impossible. The best boats are built in Southern China, where there is an abundance of timber suitable for boat building. Boats are always built up of planks. In some parts they are constructed entirely of camphor wood which is peculiarly resistant against rot and other injurious influences. In other parts the braces and knees are of hard wood and the sheathing of soft wood. The planks are flat on the inside, but unhewn and left in their natural state on the outer side where exposed to the water.

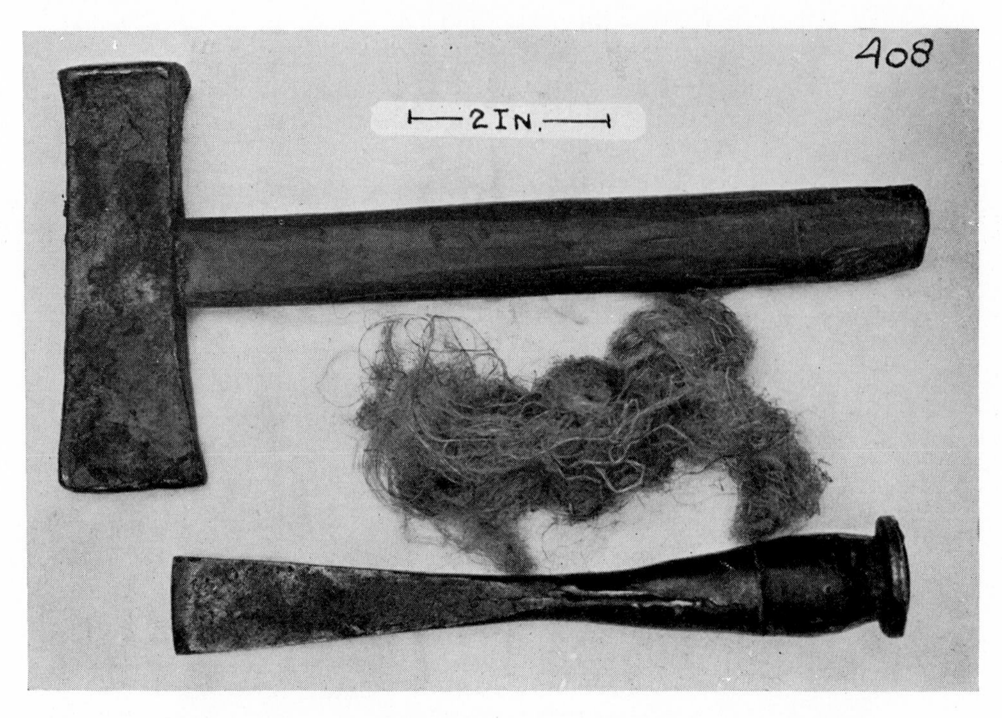

FIG. 505. CHINESE SHIP-BUILDER'S CAULKING TOOLS, HAMMER, OAKUM AND CHISEL.

Chinese boats sometimes have oars, two handled by one man, but the rower stands facing the bow and with the full weight of his body pushes the oars which hang in a loop made of a strip of leather and are fastened to a stick projecting from the gunwale. In this way he has the advantage of seeing where he is going without turning around. In the Ningpo (Chekiang Province) district a foot-power boat is quite popular. It is small and used for rapid conveyance of passengers. The boatman sits at the stern, pushes two oars with his feet, leisurely handles a small oar for steering, which he holds under his arm and which extends behind him over the stern into the water and now and then puffs at his pipe. He is barefooted and the oars have instead of handles pedal-shaped knobs which offer a convenient surface to be pushed with the sole of the feet and then are guided back with in-curved toes which from use seem to have become prehensile.

On top of the mast there is usually a triangular strip of cloth serving as a weather vane, a necessary guide for the boatman handling the sails. Sails are made of matting mostly in the South, and to a greater extent of cotton cloth in the central and northern parts of China. Ropes running through blocks are used for hoisting the sails and are sometimes made waterproof with a mixture of pig's blood and oil. The hull of a boat, after caulking is soaked with wood-oil, varnished or painted. The painting is not done with brushes. The painter gets a handful of silk or cotton waste, dips it in the paint, and then smears it over the wood, disregarding his hands which get all full of paint.

Fig. 493 presents the stern of a Chinese coasting junk, photographed in Tsingtao. The large rudder, here shown with its vertical rudder-post, can be raised or lowered by means of the horizontal winding bar of the windlass placed across the top of the stern. The tiller has been removed from the rudder post for convenience in unloading. The two landing planks which extend into the air from the open stern, are pulled out, and laid slantingly to reach from the ground to the stern and for loading or unloading the coolies have to pass upon them under the windlass.

A peculiarity of Chinese boats is the side sheathing. Instead of using planks flat surfaced on both sides, rough planks which show on the outer exposed side the round unhewn part of the original tree are employed as a protection against ramming, not so much on the open sea, as in the rivers and marts where so many boats congregate and where scraping past, and knocking against each other is of frequent occurrence. Fig. 493 and 498 show the unhewn log faces referred to quite plainly.

The completed hull of a boat is seen in Fig. 494 laid on its side to be caulked. The watertight compartments are shown plainly, a feature already noticed by Marco Polo, which in the form of bulkheads, has comparatively recently been introduced into our western shipbuilding. To the left behind the boat can be seen the start of another boat, the bottom boards upon trestles and the partitions, or bulkheads, if you will, at set intervals.

Two boats are seen under construction in Fig. 495, the farther one appears with the hull pretty nearly complete, while the one in front still needs some planking to be nailed upon the partitions which can be seen at set intervals. The stern of both of them is on the left and when finished they will be pushed into the river to the right, bow first.

A wonderful accomplishment in building Chinese boats is this dividing of the hold into watertight compartments. When a boat runs upon a rock and springs a leak or is rammed by another the flooding is usually confined to one compartment, and does not endanger the whole ship. In Fig. 494 between the watertight compartments plainly indicated, the intervening hold spaces are for storing merchandise, and the ceiling above the apartment partitions will be covered with boards forming a deck upon which is the space for passengers who are protected against sun or rain with matting which by means of wooden arches erected for its support covers the central part of the boat. Fig. 494, as well as Figs. 495 and 496 show pictures from a shipbuilding yard at Fuchow, Kiangsi province.

A nearer view is shown in Fig. 496 of the stern of the same boat which we saw in the background in Fig. 495, taken however, from the other side. A rectangular light spot in the curvature of the high-swung stern, marks the opening through which the rudder projects into the water when the boat is finished. The shed on the left is covered with matting similar to that which is used as a covering for smaller boats.

Fig. 497 was photographed in the junk harbor of

FIG. 506. ANCHOR.

Fig. 507. Mariner's Compass.

Tsingtao. It represents a shallop being sculled by two Japanese. With the exception of sailing and towing, sculling is the most common method of boat propulsion in China. This scull is called "yuloh" by the Chinese. In smaller boats a "yuloh" at the stern serves both for propulsion and steering. This is the case with the small boat shown in the picture. The straight oar has a handle which forms an obtuse angle with the oar. At the edge of the boat where the scull seems to rest a knobbed iron spike extends from the wood and its round knob fits into a corresponding hollow in the oar, thus forming something like a ball joint, around which the scull is moved from side to side. The scull can easily slip from this pivot and is therefore secured with a rope at the handle end, straight down to the floor where the rower stands. It is not as easy to handle a scull as it looks. The proper twist at each stroke is attained only after some practice. The twist turns at each stroke the flat part of the oar against the water. The scull has therefore besides the action from side to side a motion around itself which is aided by the smaller handle extending at right angles from the main handle. This smaller auxiliary handle is a feature of Shantung, I never saw it in Central China. The rower always stands at the side of the scull as in Fig. 497. Smaller sailboats in a calm are also propelled with sculls, which are then worked from the side of the boat one on each side of the stern. Sometimes also two more are worked from the deck at the bow. In this case a wooden beam is fastened to extend horizontally over the gunwale, and on this beam rises the spike with the round knob. The scull hangs down parallel with the boat side, sufficiently away from it to allow of free action to and fro.

Fig. 498 gives a closer view of the sturdy rudder which can be raised and lowered by means of the roller beam of the windlass which stretches horizontally across the highest rear part of the stern. The windlass is turned by means of levers inserted into holes of the windlass beam. The hole for the tiller can be seen on top of the vertical rudder post. From

Fig. 508. Carrying Pole.

the stern extends the long scull or sweep which is used to propel the sail boat in calms, or harbors where through restricted space no advantage can be taken of the wind. The photograph was taken in the junk harbor of Tsingtao.

A feature of rudders in South China is to have a few perforations through the large board surface that swings in the water so as to have it respond more easily to the action of the tiller.

The two-masters, Fig. 499, with low, painted stern have far extending rudders, and are complete sea-going junks. The fishing nets have been hung up on the masts for drying. The photograph was taken in the junk harbor of Tsingtao.

FIG. 510. MANURE BASKETS.

The junks in Fig. 500 which carry cargo from one port to another along the coast are seen from the side. The sails, an expensive part of the equipment, are let down and covered up for protection when not in use. A conspicuous feature of these boats are the carved eyes on the bow, which are necessary in the belief of the Chinese, to enable the boat to see where it is going. The photograph was taken in the junk harbor of Tsingtao. It is an interesting fact that Chinese boats have no names.

FIG. 509. CHARCOAL-BURNER'S FAGOT CARRIER.

To the right can be seen the eyes near the bow. There is one on each side, and, as above noted, the Chinese explanation for these is, that the boat could not see where it was going if it did not have them. I heard once of a missionary who had studied Chinese boat-life, who said that all along the China coast where the Arabians had traded in the middle ages one can find the custom of furnishing the boats with eyes. He meant to imply that the custom originated in the Near East. A Greek vase of Athens made about 400 B.C. and kept in a museum in Munich shows Charon in his boat ready to convey a departed soul over the Styx to the Netherworld. His boat shows distinctly an eye on the bow. A coin kept in the British Museum of the time of the Roman Empire (B.C. 29-284 A.D.) shows also a boat with an eye. It is quite plain therefore that the idea was prevalent in the Mediterranean in olden times.

Building of boats in China is mainly carpenter work. The tools used are then those of the house carpenter and we show therefore only a few which are conspicuously different. There is the Ship-builder's Thong Drill, Fig. 501, the principle of which is simi-

FIG. 511. WICKER BASKETS FOR CARRYING ALL KINDS OF LOADS.

lar to the bow drill described under Fig. 365. Two or three men are needed to handle it. One of them, absent in this picture, holds the bit stock, or rather the revolving piece on top of it, and one or two men pull the leather thongs. If only one man pulls, then the thong pulling is done as shown in Fig. 501. Another man, of course, is then supposed to hold the drill and guide it. We could, however, not persuade any of the working men to pose for doing this.

The details of the Thong Drill can be seen in Fig. 502. The bit, forked at one end is placed into a corresponding slot of the bit-stock, and an iron ferrule forced over it, to keep it firmly in place. The handle revolves freely upon the bit stock. Photographed at Fuchow, Kiangsi.

Fig. 512. Frame for Carrying Firewood.

R. Forrer [4] pictures the epitaph of a Christian coffin maker of the 4th century, upon which working-men are shown using a drill in ornamenting a stone sarcophagus. The mode of procedure is similar to the Chinese drill shown above. One man holds the drill and the other pulls the thongs to revolve it.

The shipbuilder, as if to emphasize that he has nothing in common with the ordinary carpenter, has a line marker (Fig. 503) of his own design. It is in the shape of a boat, quite appropriately, and really more compact than the ordinary line marker shown previously under Fig. 372. The boat has two compartments, the one for the roulette and the other for the inkwell. The latter is filled with ink-saturated silk or cotton waste. The string passes through it and is inked in this way. A necessary complement is always the brush which is used with the square or ruler to mark shorter lines. At the end of the string is a wooden plug driven down with a hammer for fastening the line. The carpenter takes the little boat in his hand and, walking away from the starting point of the line to be drawn, lets the hemp or silk cord pass out from the roulette and inkwell. Stretching the cord taut and twanging it produces the line. After the performance is finished, the string can be wound back onto the roulette by turning the prolongation of its axle, which penetrates the side of the little boat, and is bent to form a crank. The photograph was taken in Fuchow, Kiangsi.

BOAT CAULKING

Caulking is an important part of boat building. The step from the simple dugout, to a boat sheathed with wooden planks, was only possible after a method had been found to keep the water from penetrating the joints of the wooden planks. In the western Orient this problem had been solved by the use of asphalt, which was found at Is, in the northern part of old Babylonia, and at el-Muqaj-jar, the Ur of the Bible. The Europeans also use asphalt for caulking, and may have derived the knowledge from the Orient. The name for caulking in German is "Kalfatern" (French, calfater, It. calafatare), a word of Arabian origin, introduced by the Italians into the Western languages, and an old German word for asphalt is "Judenpech" (Jews' pitch) which also suggests an Oriental derivation.

The Chinese have since olden times been expert ship-builders of composite boats and are therefore well acquainted with caulking. As binding material they use generally a kind of putty made of wood-oil (pressed from the seeds of *Aleurites cordata,* a common tree of China) and lime, mixed together by pounding in a stone mortar. In the coastal provinces, a few other media are known for caulking, as *dam-*

[4] R. Forrer, "Reallexikon," Berlin 1907.

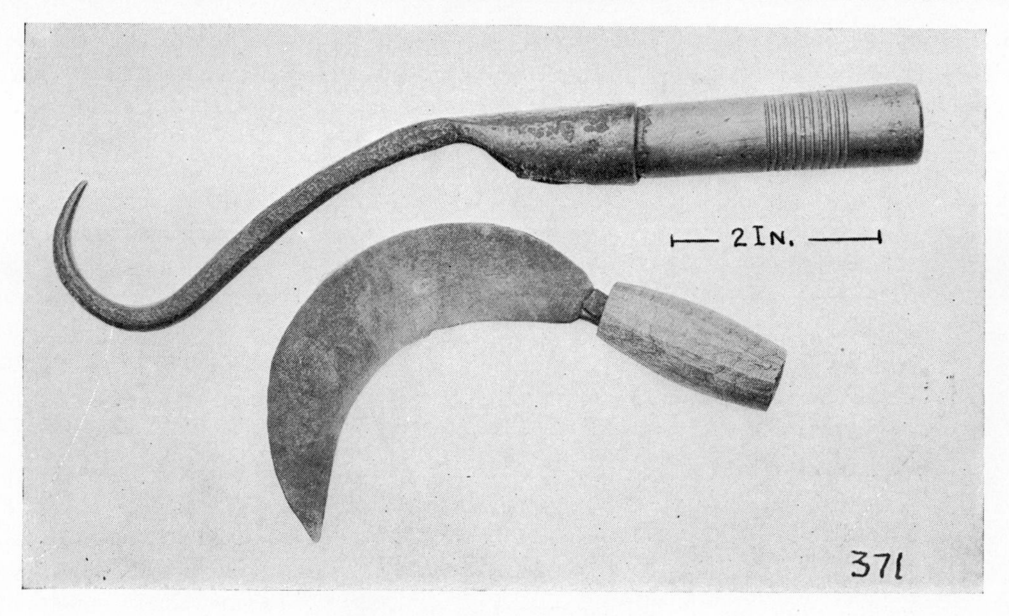

FIG. 513. BALE-HOOK AND KNIFE.

mar, imported from Borneo and Singapore, *gum animi, gum elemi,* and a resinous mass derived from *Canarium pimela.*

Fig. 504 shows all the tools necessary for caulking. The picture was taken in Tatung, Anhwei. The tools are lying on the side of a boat which has been tilted over to be repaired and have the leaky seams caulked. There is first the hammer with a square poll and dull chisel-like edge. The slot and hole are apparently of no significance, although we were told that the slot is used for pulling nails. Ordinarily the hammer is plain and without slot and hole, like the one shown in Fig. 505. Fig. 504 shows the caulking-irons, namely two chisels, one with a narrow and the other with a wider dull edge for driving bits of waste hemp into the seams. Oakum (from Anglo-Sax. a-cumba, meaning combed out), waste hemp, or the fibres of old, untwisted, tarred hemp rope is also the material for caulking in the Occident. The fisherman in China, who repairs his own boat, makes use of old torn fish-nets, beaten soft and cut into strips, for stuffing the seams. Finally, the stuffed seams are smeared with the putty, a quantity of which is here shown resting on a kind of wooden palette. A wooden spatula sticks out from the mass. A stubby hand-broom, for cleaning the seams, completes the set of tools. Fig. 505 which shows a more representative hammer, was photographed in Fuchow, Kiangsi.

The hulls of Chinese boats are in the South usually built of camphor wood, a tree by no means very plentiful in China. The greatest economy is practiced in its use and even defective trunks are sawed into boards, the outlines of which present sometimes irregular and fantastic shapes. The Chinese, patiently laboring, fit

FIG. 514. OIL BASKET.

Fig. 515. Row of Oil Baskets.

Such oil-lutes or cements have since ancient times served wood-workers for filling and priming the wood previous to polishing, varnishing or painting, and they, no doubt, were the ones who established the custom of puttying window panes, a custom which spread and became at once popular before a fitting name had been found for the substance used.

ANCHOR

Fig. 506 shows a typical Chinese boat anchor. It is about four feet high and made entirely of wrought iron. The shaft ends in a bowl-shaped knob into which the different arms or flukes are welded. The other upper end of the shaft, has an eye with a ring

the boards together very skillfully, with now and then the insertion of a graving piece, a piece of wood set into a defective place in the bottom or side of the boat also called graven piece or dutchman. Altogether the task of the caulker is a formidable one.

The original meaning of putty (from Old French potee, calcined tin) is a polishing powder or calcined tin. It would be interesting to establish since when panes of glass have been fixed into window sashes with what we now call putty; probably not before the 18th century. Compositions of glazier's putty are given as a mixture of linseed oil with whiting (precipitated chalk) and tin-, lead-, or zinc-oxide; or a similar combination with air-slaked lime instead of the whiting.

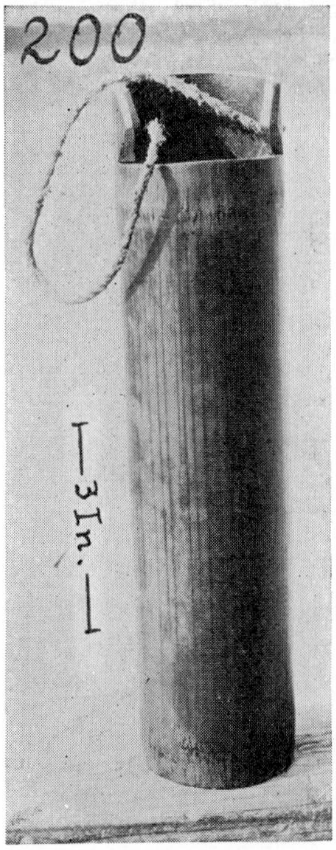

Fig. 516. Oil Container.

Fig. 517. Kong or Large Earthenware Jar for Storing Water or Night Soil.

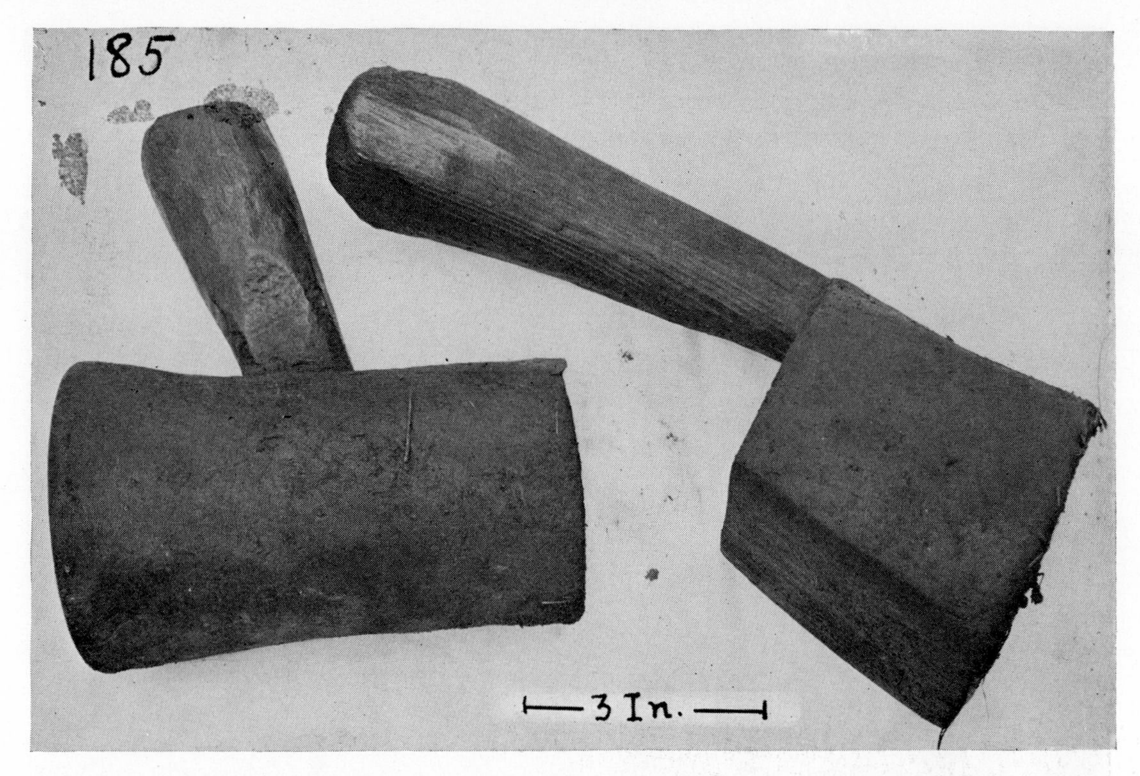

Fig. 518. Potter's Clay-Beating Hammers Used in Building Up Large Vessels of Plastic Clay Without the Use of the Potter's Wheel.

Fig. 519. Potter's Hammer-Stamps for Decorating the Outside of Earthen Vessels.

Fig. 520. Potter's Wheel for Making Smaller Earthenware.

for fastening to the anchor chain. Iron chains are used almost exclusively in connection with anchors. This is the more noteworthy, since in the Occident the use of chains for anchors was not at all common until the beginning of the 19th century, when gradually chains superseded the use of hawsers. There are larger anchors, than the one shown, and smaller ones, and the workmanship usually does credit to the Chinese artisan. The anchor shown I photographed in Changshu, Kiangsi.

Marco Polo speaks of wooden anchors, which the traders from Southern China used on their boats plying between Chinese ports and the Malay Archipelago. De Mailla in his "Histoire Generale de la Chine" (Paris 1783), tells us that these anchors were of iron-wood and quite in favor with the Chinese because the iron ones were subject to strain. Wooden ones I never saw, but stone anchors I have met with now and then, a stone roughly round like a mill-stone with a wooden staff rammed into a hole in the center, and a rope attached to the free end of this staff. Ferryboats sometimes have them, and this contrivance is put on the shore with the rope attached to the boat to keep it from drifting off.

MARINER'S COMPASS

There is a story occurring again and again in early Chinese literature about a "south-pointing chariot." Ambassadors come by sea from India and Syria disembarked in one of the sea-ports of China and were conveyed overland to the Imperial court at Sian-fu in Shensi. To guide them on their way home they had received from the Duke of Chow (died 1105 B.C.) among other presents five chariots with a south-pointing contrivance. While this early use of such a contrivance is considered legend by the historians, we find the definite mention of it in the still extant writings of Han Fei (died 233 B.C.). He says that the early kings constructed the "south pointer" to fix the position of morning and evening. There is further Kuei-ku Zzu, a philosopher of the 4th century B.C. who speaks of the people of Kaifeng Fu who used a south-pointing chariot when they brought jade from far away regions. In another place he speaks of "lodestone attracting a needle" and in a cyclopedia of the 10th century he is quoted as having told the story that the Duke of Chow constructed the "south-pointing chariot" to guide strangers who had brought tribute on their way home. The references to this contrivance are so persistent that the story cannot altogether be ignored. The Chinese have also a definite conception of how the contrivance was constructed and show it in a jade figure which is pictured in several works of reference. It shows the figure of a man with outstretched hand pivoted upon a horse's head and we must assume that the figure through the agency of a lodestone pointed in a southward direction. From the 11th century on we come to firmer ground, and even if it is not proved that the magnetic needle was then used to show the junks their way at sea it was already a time honored tool in the hands of geomancers, the "Wind and Water Doctors." These experts, for valuable consideration, have to be consulted in finding proper sites for graves, for houses and temples, and make elaborate calculations with the south-pointing needle in conjunction with data from their philosophy, astrology and chronology. Evil influences are in their belief due to disregard of the influence of Feng-shui (wind and water) and the people, firmly believing this, are the prey of these geomancers. For our technical investigations it is interesting to hear how the south-pointing needle was formerly employed. In records written about 1115 A.D. it says that "if one rubbed a needle with lodestone it would point to the south, but that it would always deviate a little to the east and not show due south. To prepare the contrivance, one had to single out a fine thread from a new skein of silk floss and fix it with half a candareen of bees' wax on the middle of the needle, the latter to be hung up where there was no wind. The needle would then always point to the south. By sticking the needle through a piece of lamp wick (which in China is made of pith), thus causing it to float on the water, it would also point to the south with a slight deviation." [5]

The eastern deviation of the magnetic needle was already pointed out by Shen Kua, who wrote about the year 1068. The first mention in Europe of the deviation of the needle by Pierre de Maricourt (1269) comes therefore two centuries later than the Chinese record.

Of the use of the compass at sea we hear first in

[5] This quotation and the preceding references to Chinese literature are from "The Ancient History of China" by F. Hirth, New York 1908.

Fig. 521. Specimens of Earthenware Made at the Pottery Near Teh An, Kiangsi.

FIG. 522. POTTER'S KILN FOR BURNING EARTHENWARE WINE JARS.

the 12th century. In 1122 A.D. a Chinese ambassador going with his retinue to Korea in eight boats kept a diary and mentions the use of the compass, a needle floating in water to find the proper course.[6]

In Europe occur references to the compass in the works of Alexander Neckam, an English scholar, who wrote in the latter half of the 12th century. He describes it as a needle placed upon a pivot and a necessary part of the ship's outfit. The Chinese form was also known, as we find from a satire of Guyot of Provins, a French poet, known under the title "La Bible de Provins," written about 1205 A.D. He speaks of the mariners who use as a guide a needle stuck into a straw and floating upon water. They rub the needle upon an ugly stone and then it points to the North Star, and the Mariners know the right way to take.[7]

In view of the facts quoted it seems difficult to say just who invented the compass. The Chinese surely had a notion of it long before anybody else. The mention of a pivoted needle occurs first in Europe, the pivoted jade-figure of the Chinese seems a later conception. The Chinese themselves relate that they improved their compass in the 16th century by patterning it after a Japanese compass which they had taken from a Japanese junk captured on the Chinese coast. Ever since that time they use the dry compass with the needle turning about a pivot. The Japanese had learned how to make them from the Portuguese.[8]

Fig. 507 shows a Japanese compass as it is used today by the simple fishermen going out in their sailboats around Nagasaki. The dial is divided into 24 parts with 12 Chinese characters, the same as the Chinese compass. The characters are the so-called horary signs, used also for dividing the day into 12 periods of 2 hours each. The compass is south-pointing, and shows thereby its close relationship to the Chinese conception. The diameter is 4½ inches and the height of the box 2 inches. The box is of turned wood, has a lid (not shown) and on the circle between glass and the circular band with the Chinese characters are four holes penetrating the box with which the compass can be fixed in the proper place on the boat. The compass needle is steel with a brass pivot in the center and rests upon a steel pin stuck in the wood.

[6] Journ. Peking Oriental Society, II, 151.
[7] Chambers' "Book of Days," 1864.
[8] Journal Peking Oriental Society, II, 152.

CARRYING LOADS

By far the most important implement used in Chinese transport is the carrying pole. Even for the smallest bundle, when carried any long distance, the coolie will prefer the pole laid over his shoulders, with the bundle at one end, and a brick at the other end, for keeping the balance, rather than carry the package in his hand.

The commonest form is the bamboo pole shown lying on the ground in Fig. 508. It is usually about 5 feet long. Remarkable is its strength, considering that it is only part of a bamboo tube, cut down to less than half of its circumference. In fashioning this pole, the ends are notched to prevent the rope to which the load is tied, from slipping off. In carrying it, the smooth round part rests on the shoulder. Such a pole is suitable for carrying a combined load of from 100 to 120 catties (about 135 to 160 lbs.). For heavier loads a flat oaken pole is used with two wooden pegs on each end to prevent the rope from shifting. A carrying coolie has to be on the road with his load from 12 to 14 hours a day. The highest limit for carrying is 150 catties (200 lbs.). A coolie who cannot carry more than 60 catties is no good.

Another kind of pole, shown lying on top of a stool in Fig. 508, is used to carry bundles of brush-wood. The ends of the pole, shod with slightly down-curved iron points, are pushed into the bundles and the load is then shouldered. The pole is shown upside down, when in use it is held with the iron points curved upward. The part in the middle of the pole has been cut away to make it elastic, since the Chinese coolie, carrying no matter how heavy a load, must have it swing up and down, and for that purpose the pole must not be rigid. The length of the spiked pole is 5 feet 10 inches. The forged iron spikes are 8¼ inches long and have a socket which fits tightly over the ends of the pole. We took this photograph at Sha Ho, Kiangsi.

Another pole, used by charcoal-burners, is pictured in Fig. 509. I saw it used in Chekiang and in Kiangsi. A bifurcated pole, 6 feet long, holds, in the crotch of the fork, a board 27 inches long, which is tied to the crotch by a rope about 10 inches from one end; the other end of this board is encircled by another rope the ends of which lead to the prong-ends of the fork, where they are tied securely and kept from slipping by a notch. Thus a convenient shoulder bracket is formed upon which a fagot which is made up of sticks about 26 inches long is laid lengthways upon the board. The diameter of such a fagot thus carried, is roughly about 12 inches. Charcoal-burning is carried on in mountainous regions, and the charcoaler has to do considerable climbing in his search for suitable wood. This fagot-carrier, which is easily balanced on the right shoulder, needs only a strong hand to keep it in place, and is well designed to carry a heavy load with ease down the steep mountain sides. The implement, as shown in Fig. 509, was seen and sketched near See Aw, Chekiang Province.

Very heavy loads, like stones for building operations, are carried suspended from a stout hard-wood pole with each end resting on the shoulder of one man. An important feature of such two-man trans-

FIG. 523. PEWTER CAN FOR SERVING HOT WINE AT THE TABLE.

port, is the antiphonal chant, which invariably accompanies it. The heavier the load, the louder the shouting. China has the bamboo carrying pole in common with India, where it is called Banghy.

The peasants in China are ever on the alert to search for and collect manure for their fields. Young lads can always be seen on the roads with a basket dangling from each end of their carrying pole, armed with a small hoe to collect the droppings of farm animals. My interpreter posed for the picture, Fig. 510, showing the pole with baskets, and the little shovel for picking up the droppings. The type of the basket is prevalent for many uses (conf. Figs. 120 and 511). It is also similar to the winnowing basket or winnow-corb used formerly by our peasants. The little hoe is a heart-shaped bowl, about 5 inches long with a handle of liberal length so the manure collector need not bend down when picking up the droppings.

The baskets shown in Fig. 510 remind one of similar baskets which are used by Chinese laborers for removing earth when they are digging. In the accompanying sketch, Fig. 511, two views are given of such earth baskets. They have a wicker bail, rigidly attached and a handle on the high back of the basket. The laborer digging earth puts the basket as close to the place of digging as possible so that the soil which he loosens with his hoe drops into the basket. If this is not possible he pushes the earth or stones into the basket with the hoe, just as loose material can easily be pushed into a European dustpan. A shovel is never used for such work. When two of these baskets are full the laborer takes his carrying pole upon his shoulder, from each end of which dangles a hook, sometimes made of iron, but more commonly made of a forked piece of wood. This he hooks into the wicker bail of the basket and carries the two baskets filled with earth away. Arrived at the place where this material should be dumped he puts down the two baskets upon the ground and disengages them from the hooks upon the carrying pole. He still keeps the pole upon his shoulder, grasps the hook in front of him with his hands, and slides the hook dangling from the other end of the pole into the handle on the high back of the carrying basket and lifts it up. The balance is thereby upset and the material is dumped from the basket. After he has in this manner emptied both

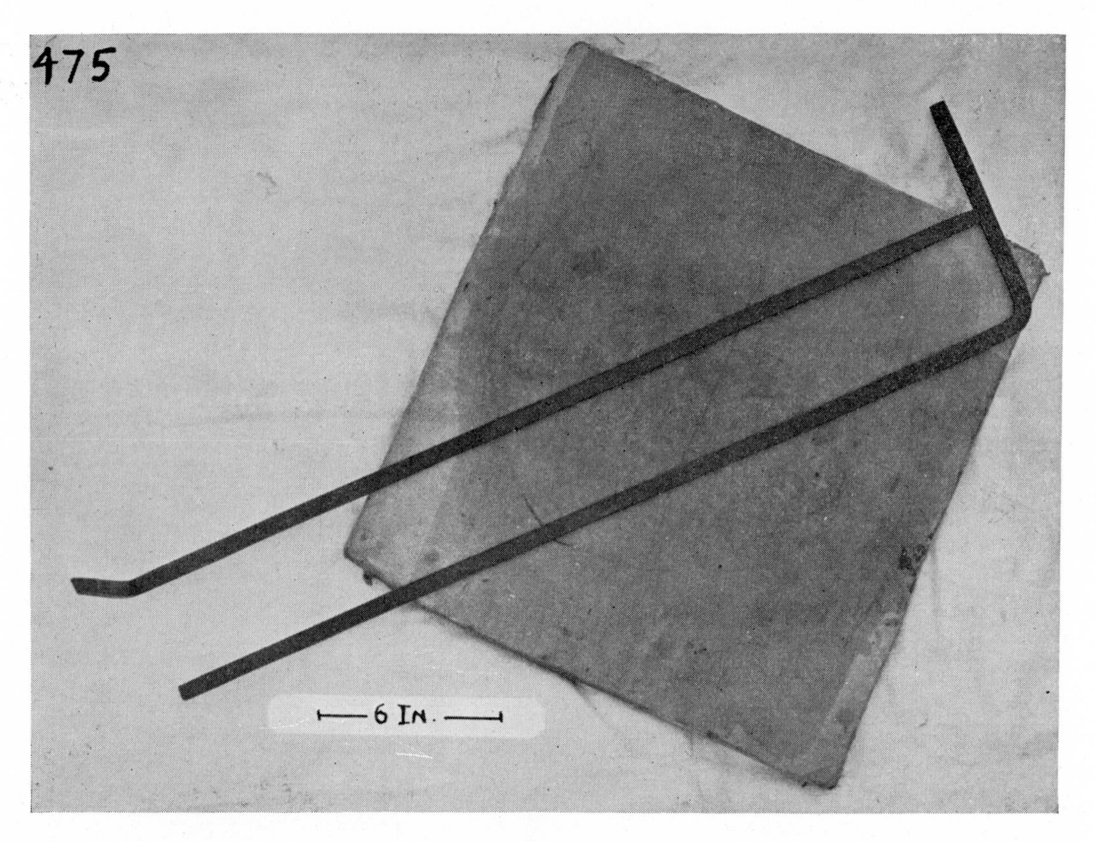

FIG. 524. PEWTERER'S TOOLS FOR CASTING THIN PEWTER SLABS USED IN BUILDING UP PEWTER VESSELS.

baskets he returns to the place of excavation or digging and resumes his work with the hoe, filling the baskets anew. It is usual for at least two men to do such work. One digs and fills the baskets and the other carries the filled baskets away. In this case, of course, there will be four baskets in use, two being filled, and another two being in the meantime carried away.

For transportation of chopped firewood in equal lengths of about 14 inches, the frame shown in Fig. 512 is used in many parts of China. The wood is piled up horizontally between the two uprights of the frame. Two of these frames are carried one hooked to each end of the carrying pole. The length of the frame is 4 feet. The specimen shown was photographed in King Teh Chen, Kiangsi, where it is used for carrying loads of firewood by the thousands to the porcelain kilns.

In December, 1923, we visited a wholesale drug establishment in Changshu, Kiangsi, a place noted for the barter of this commodity. The place is packed full of medicines, mostly herbs, roots, seeds, barks and dried flowers. One of the almost 3000 different drugs is deer horns and we are apt to smile about it, forgetting, however, that our forefathers made use of these too, as the name hartshorn indicates, an old appellation for a volatile preparation of ammonia, which was derived from the distilling of deer's horns.

Bales upon bales of drugs are received in these establishments carried by coolies or transported in native boats from all parts of China, mainly however from Szechuan. For their handling and opening the tools shown in Fig. 513 are in daily use. The bales are wrapped in rush-matting and are sewn together carefully. For moving them about the bale-hook is used, and the knife for ripping open the seams.

The hook along a straight line from the curve to the end of the handle measures 8½ inches. The metal part is wrought iron, with a socket for insertion of the wooden handle, which has parallel circular grooves to afford a firmer grip. The knife is a hook in another sense and may easily be mistaken for a reaping hook. The blade measures about 1 inch across the widest part. The bale-hook is very similar to the one

FIG. 525. CHINESE PEWTERER'S LATHE.

FIG. 526. PEWTERER'S TURNING-TOOLS. Used for smoothing the surfaces of pewter vessels on the lathe or in hand.

used by our longshoremen, there is, however, very little likelihood that it was adapted from a Western prototype. It is rather an illustration of an observation which we had many occasions to make, that like wants are met in like manner the world over in many, many instances.

CONTAINERS FOR LIQUIDS

A few words seem also in place about containers of liquids in general. Wine is mostly kept and transported in earthenware jars. Usually it is served hot at table, and then poured from pewter cans. Oil in many provinces is transported in large baskets.

Fig. 514 shows such an oil container from Shantung. A rectangular wicker basket, contracted on top to form a neck is lined on the inside with heavy tough paper which on getting saturated with oil does not leak. The contracted upper part is also lined with paper on the outside. The top is closed with paper after the basket is filled, or, as I saw it in Shantung, an earthenware bowl is set into the top opening, and the edge of the bowl, where it comes in contact with the mouth of the basket, is smeared with a lute of oil and whiting, a kind of putty.

Such containers remind us of our so-called carboys and demijohns. In these, however, a glass container is surrounded with wickerwork. It is interesting to note, that carboy and demijohn point to the Orient. The word carboy is said to be derived from the Persian qarabah (meaning demijohn) and the word demijohn from Damagan, a place in Persia once famous for its glassworks. In passing it is interesting to mention the Italian fiasco, known to us as the Florence flask or betty, a thin wine bottle woven over with straw or bast. Olive oil was formerly exported from Italy in such bottles.

The oil basket in Fig. 514 is 27 inches high, and 29 inches wide, in longest diameter, but measures only 18 inches in depth. The opening on top has a diameter of 7½ inches. These containers filled with oil are very heavy. A wheelbarrow takes two, one on each side, and to carry one requires two coolies, who suspend it from a pole whose ends rest on their shoulders. In Central Manchuria such baskets are also used for transporting distilled liquor. The specimen shown was photographed in Tsingtao, the same as Fig. 515 which gives a view of an oil-dealer's shop with oil baskets piled high in front on the sidewalk.

The use of ears or loop-handles on earthenware containers, we meet with in most primitive forms of pottery from neolithic periods in Europe. Some of the

Chinese present-day pottery does not show any change from these old forms. In regions where the glazing of pottery is either not known, or the glazing material cannot be procured, we find hand-shaped pottery with ears or loop-handles, shaped as they were thousands of years ago. The loops are now as useful as then. To take a crock with both hands to the spring and fill it with water is cumbersome, not to speak of the danger of spilling, while carrying it with one hand by a string is a more convenient and safe way. The hanging up of the containers by the string, also commends itself in view of the uneven mud floors, found in most Chinese houses, and we can well imagine that in prehistoric cave dwellings, the uneven floor prompted the same procedure.

The use of stoppers is not well developed in China. The ingenious way of pouring a few drops of oil on top of the liquid to preserve it from contact with the air, as practiced by the Italians, does not seem known in China. Porcelain containers for medicines have stoppers or plugs rolled of paper. The wine jars are closed with leaves, over which are placed cup-shaped covers of earthenware smeared with clay, to make the joint airtight. Botanists know of a Chinese cork-tree, *Phellodendron Amurense,* but I found no evidence that its bark is used for stoppers. A missionary writing in the sixties of the last century, speaks of the abundance of cork-trees in Korea, but not a word about their use.

In many places where foreign glass bottles have not replaced it, a bamboo bottle is used as an oil-container. I saw this especially in Kiangsi, and the one shown in Fig. 516 was photographed in Changshu, Kiangsi.

In a country where mainly oil is used for cooking, the oil-container must needs hold an important place in the household. The variety of the device, in form and material, is great, but most oil-containers have one characteristic in common, be the material wood or earthenware, and that is a means for suspending them from the ceiling or hanging them up against the wall. The bamboo tube shown, has a rope attached at the upper end, and earthenware containers have usually ears or loop-handles for receiving a string. By the same string the container is carried when it is taken to the shop to be replenished. In regions with foreign contact, glass bottles discarded by the thirsty white foreigner, are eagerly sought by the Chinese, to be used for oil and bean sauce, and are then handled in the same way, with a string tied around the neck.

The bamboo container is formed of a section of a tree with two of the natural joints, one near each end. The upper one is pierced and a rim above it left extending. Part of this rim is sawed off, to form a gutter for pouring. No stopper is used, as there is little danger of spilling when the container is hung up to the wall or ceiling. The height is 14 inches and the diameter 3¼ inches.

A Chinese characteristic is to buy supplies and provisions as they are needed. This is in accordance with a system where small tradesmen are continuously at

Fig. 527. Pewterer's Mold, of Sandstone, in Two Pieces, for Casting Ornamental Parts of Pewter Vessels.

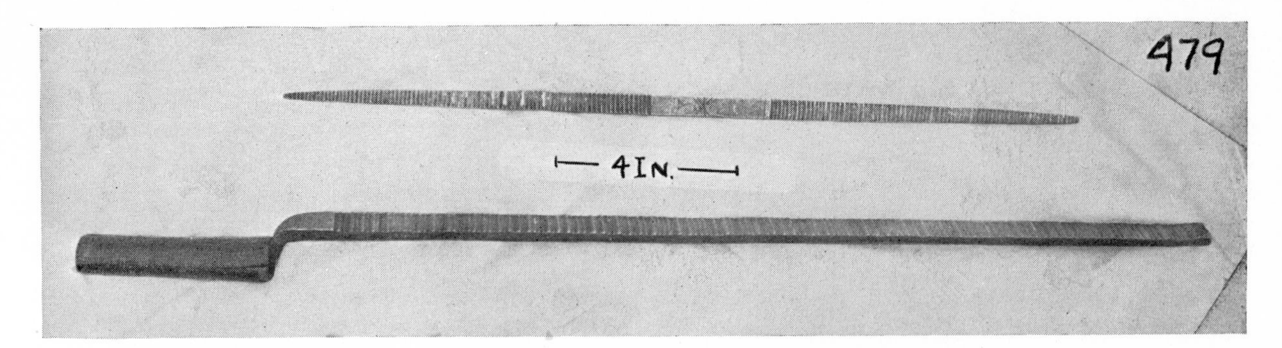

FIG. 528. PEWTERER'S FILES FOR SMOOTHING SOLDERED JOINTS AND ROUGH SURFACES IN MAKING PEWTER VESSELS.

work to meet the daily needs of the populace. The streets in Chinese cities are in consequence always crowded with hurrying people, servants, coolies, and children out on an errand to carry, transport or fetch one thing or another. In almost every block there is a hot-water shop. Whenever a bath is wanted in a household a coolie is sent to get two big pails of hot water, swinging from his carrying pole. If a hot kettle of tea is needed, a servant is sent to fetch the hot water from the shop around the corner. The wine for the meal is likewise procured in the pewter wine-can from the neighboring wine shop. And so with viands of all description. In this way containers of earthenware and pewter, and larger ones made by the cooper are ever in evidence as means of transportation and we shall therefore finish our chapter on transport with accounts of the making of earthenware, the pewterer's trade, and finally the cooper's.

MAKING OF EARTHENWARE WITH AND WITHOUT THE POTTER'S WHEEL

It was astonishing to observe in various places in Chekiang, the making of earthenware, from the

FIG. 529. PEWTERER'S STAKE.

FIG. 530. PEWTERER'S STAKE WITH BLUNT HORNS. FOR HAMMERING HOLLOW PEWTER VESSELS INTO FINAL SHAPE. This wrought iron pewterer's stake together with the wooden block into which it has been driven and tightened with molten pewter, is 21½ inches high.

smallest pieces to large vats, without the aid of the potter's wheel, by merely building up the ware with strips of clay. In Kiangsi, however, I visited a pottery where the wheel was used at least for smaller ware, although large pots were built up in the same manner as in Chekiang. It was on a winter morning that we reached an isolated pottery, 30 li, (10 miles), from Teh An, in a westerly direction. The owner was away, and we soon fraternized with the working-men, who willingly answered our inquiries, and never interfered with our taking pictures. As we were in the midst of it, the owner returned, and let loose a veritable deluge of reproach and vituperations upon the working-men for letting us invade his pottery in his absence. Glad for what we had gotten in the way of information and photographs, we departed rather sorry for the working-men, and the untimely arrival of the owner.

To start from the beginning, the raw material a ferruginous clay, which burns into a good red-brown color, is found in abundance in the neighborhood. The mode of digging, treading, tempering and kneading is primitive, and is the same as that previously described. The treading with bare feet enables the worker to feel any clods and stones, which he then picks out of the mass.

The most prominent article of manufacture at this pottery, near Teh An, was the kong, a vat of various sizes, the largest about 3 to 3½ feet high, used extensively by the Chinese for storing water or night soil. Fig. 517 shows a representative example. These kongs are built up while resting upon a round stand made of unglazed earthenware. The stand, also shown in Fig. 517, is 11 inches high and 13½ inches in diameter. The holes on the side are for picking up the stand. Intervening between the stand and kong is an unglazed disk with convex top. Stand and disk can be seen separately in Fig. 521, the disk to the left of the bench and the stand to the right. The convex top of the disk gives the bottom of the kong, resting upon it, a concave form. In building up such a vat the potter walks around it, encircling one loose strip of plastic clay, upon the other beneath it, until the desired height is reached. No inner form is used. After a strip is laid in place, the potter beats it down with a wooden hammer, and for obliterating the lines of jointure, he hits the sides with two wooden hammers, shown in Fig. 518, one from within the vessel, and the other from the outside.

Before I proceed to describe the making of smaller ware I shall mention the making of kongs out of very inferior clay as I saw it near Feng Hwa in Chekiang. The material forming the body of the ware is gray mud. The kongs are built up in the way described, and then they are coated, inside and out, with a veneer of excellent clay, which is brought from some distance, hence this economy. The clay is liquefied with water and applied, very much in the same way as is afterwards the glaze, i.e., with brushes on the outside and a hempen tassel on the inside. The latter is held in the center of the vessel and swung around in circular fashion so the ends pass like a brush over the inner surface of the vessel. Fragments of burned ware show distinctly the three layers, the poor material in the middle, then on both sides the veneer of good clay and over this the glaze.

The hammers for solidifying the built up earthenware are shown in Fig. 518. The one on the right of

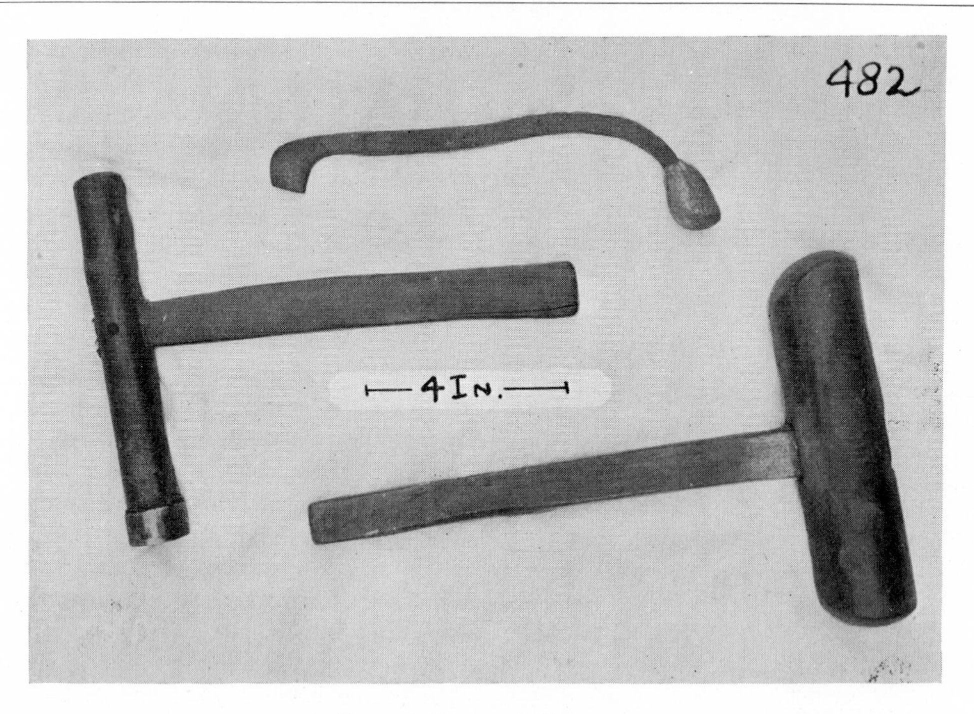

FIG. 531. PEWTERER'S HAMMERS.

the picture with the longer handle is fashioned of one piece of wood and used on the outside. The other hammer on the left of the picture has a handle inserted at right angles into a round wooden block. The end with the smaller diameter is used for hitting. The shapes of the hammers show that the one with handle inserted is more suitable for hitting a concave surface, while the one made of one piece of wood lends itself better for working upon the convex outer surface. The hammer for beating the inside is a section of a pine tree. It is dipped into water frequently to prevent the clay from sticking to it, and through the action of the water the pounding surface shows the annual rings raised, the softer parts of intervening wood having shrunk away. After a kong has been built up the inner surface is covered all over with imprints of the concentric rings from the hammer. The effect is quite decorative, which apparently was never intended.

Another and very much intended feature of the kong is a decorative band on the outside, near the top rim. It is produced by hammers with raised designs which are imprinted with one stroke. At the same time, of course, the potter deals the wall of the kong a blow from the inside with a plain wooden hammer, to save the wall from being broken or distorted. Three of these hammers are shown in Fig. 519. The two outer ones are made of slate, and the one in the middle, of unglazed burned clay. All the four faces of each hammer bear designs, about 3 inches square, which are the same as those used to decorate the side faces of bricks of the Han dynasty about 2000 years ago. It is probably hard for us to conceive that these designs form a living link with those early times and yet considering the isolation of the people using them today and the stubborn conservatism of the Chinese in general leaves no doubt that such is the case.

The kongs are next dried in the air, and then the glaze is applied with a brush. The composition of the glaze I could not learn, but it is administered in a rather liquid state and the dry clay greedily absorbs the water in which the finely powdered particles of the glaze are suspended, with the result that a thin film of the glazing material evenly covers the article. For covering the inside surface, a bundle of hemp fibres is dipped into the liquid glaze, and then held by the other end, it is swung around with a circular motion until the dipped end touches the inside walls of the kong, and sliding over it like a brush, deposits the glaze.

The making of smaller ware is illustrated in Fig. 520, showing the potter's wheel, and by Fig. 521 showing an array of some of the articles produced. Unfortunately, of the potter's wheel, I can give but a meagre description. It was in a dark shed, and while I was taking the picture, exposing it for ten minutes, the owner of the pottery returned, and made his presence known by high vociferation. My interpreter urged a hasty retreat, but I was determined to get the picture, come what would. For inquiries, of course, no time was left after this. The potter, manipulating his wheel, sits in front of it, with his feet stretched out, one on each side of the wheel. In the picture the place where he sits is obscured by a pot marked with concentric rings and covered with an inverted lid. The wheel is set in motion by means of the stick seen standing against the wall on the right with its lower end resting on the wheel. A true wheel with spokes forms the basis of the potter's wheel, the circumference is smeared with a mixture of clay, straw and hair, and an inverted porcelain cup is set into the clay near the rim. The concave base of the cup serves as a hold for the tip of the stick, when setting the wheel in motion. As the wheel is well balanced it spins for several minutes. The potter keeps the stick lying across his lap until he needs it again to give the wheel a new impetus. For this he gets up, and bending over the wheel, pushes it around vigorously with the stick about four or five times. Upon the hub of the wheel a round wooden disk is firmly fixed, and over this rises a frustum of a cone, shaped of clay, and air-dried, with a flat top. This top is sprinkled with wood-ashes, and the lump of clay to be worked upon, is rather set down with some pressure, than thrown down upon it, the usual practice at other potteries. Then the potter uses both his hands dipped in water to form the vessel and it looks almost like a conjuring trick to see the walls of the vessel rise up from the lump of clay. The finished vessel is taken, with both hands close to the base, and lifted off the wheel. The mode of cutting it off with a wire is not practiced. The vessel comes off easily enough on account of the wood-ashes applied. Loops, handles and spouts are formed by hand and applied afterwards.

Fig. 521 shows a few of the wares made at this pottery. The preserving jar on the right under the bench shows a secondary rim. The gutter formed thereby is filled with water and an inverted bowl is placed over the top of the jar with its rim submerged in the water. In this manner the jar is closed airtight, and yet any gases of fermentation which may form in the jar can easily escape, bubbling up through the water. The method of preserving salt-cabbage in this kind of jar seems to be confined to this locality. The unglazed kettle on the left of the bench top is used for boiling water. It gets covered with soot all over and this fills up all the pores and keeps it from sweating, a feature which unglazed vessels usually show.

More elaborate decorations on these kongs and on smaller ware, are produced at this pottery in the manner of sgraffito work by covering the outside with a light colored slip, and carving designs on it with a kind of graver. The dark colored clay is thus exposed, shows well, and gives a good contrast with the yellow slip. The sides of the warming pot, with octagonal circumference, shown in Fig. 521, has been treated that way.

The burning of earthenware wine jars is done in a

Fig. 532. Cooper's Clamp for Sawing Out Tub Staves.

long kiln or flue, which extends up a hill for about 500 feet. Fig. 522 taken at Cha Tsuen in Chekiang, shows the general aspect of such a kiln. This one appearing as a thatched shed, is used exclusively for the burning of wine jars, heaps of which are seen piled all around. At the lower end of the long thatched shed the woodfire is kept burning and at the upper end a brick wall which has square openings at regular intervals terminates the vaulted tunnel, or flue, forming the kiln. About 400 feet of the kiln is covered with a high thatched superstructure and the remaining portion with a low tiled roof appearing on the ground level at the left of the picture. On the one side of the flue about 100 feet apart are openings, altogether four, through which the ware is introduced and which are finally walled up. The roof of the flue is a round arch built of bricks. The height of the flue is about 8 feet and the width 10 feet. The ware to be burned is stored on the floor of the flue, apparently in any fashion, only with the large kongs care is taken that they stand level on the uneven mud floor. As props small square pieces are used, specially made for this purpose out of clay, and burned very hard. The space under the thatched structure is stacked with bundles of fir-boughs, which when burning the kiln, are inserted into small firing holes placed at set intervals all along the lower 400 feet of the flue. For twelve hours these twigs are fed into these openings in the arch to gradually heat the kiln uniformly. During the following twelve hours, wood billets are burned, but only on the hearth at the lower end of the kiln. Then firing is suspended, and the whole kiln let cool for from four to seven days according to extraneous conditions of moisture and temperature.

NOTES ON THE PEWTERER'S TRADE

The pewterer's trade is quite in evidence in China. The most common articles he produces are tea-kettles and wine-cans (conf. Fig. 523). Among others there are tea caddies with a tightly fitting cup-shaped lid to make them airtight, and a variety of shapes and sizes of this type of receptacle for storing spices, cookies, seeds, etc.; candlesticks for worship, oil bowls, wick weights, candelabra, parts of stills (see Figs. 212 and 213) etc.

The material is tin mixed with lead, both of which metals are found in some of the provinces of China. An alloy with much lead, is considered an inferior mixture, but its danger is not recognized, and lead-poisoning is not uncommon among wine-bibbers. The wine they imbibe is distilled rice wine, and in its manufacture the steam of the mash strikes a large pewter condensing surface, and here is where the wine gets poisoned if the pewter contains too much lead.

In some parts of China, notably Shantung, a base of fine red pottery is richly decorated by an overlaid tracery of pewter, in the shape of flowers, leaves and tendrils, enlivened by animals such as dragons, etc. A Chinese specialty is also the inlaying of brass parts into the body of the pewter, such as rings for attachment of handles or the like, or for further reinforcement of these parts of a vessel most exposed to wear, such as upon the foot, brim, edge of spout, etc.

The processes of decorating pewter are various. It does credit to the artistic

139

6 In.

Fig. 533. Wooden Dipper.

feeling of the Chinese that they have recognized the wonderful appeal of plain pewter of graceful design on which surface decorations would look out of place. We find therefore turned round shapes usually unadorned. Where decorations are resorted to they consist of designs executed in the mold and then cast, as for instance, the knob and parts of the spout in Fig. 523, or in designs incised with the graver on the surface. A pleasing effect is produced by covering the pewter with a coat of dark brown varnish and then incising designs, which cut through the varnish and expose the metal, an effect remindful of sgraffito decoration on pottery.

To cast flat sheets of pewter, which are needed to build up vessels, an earthenware slab is used, 13 inches square and ¾ of an inch thick, covered with stout paper. In Fig. 524 the slab is shown with two wrought iron rods which determine the size of the sheet to be cast. With the rods in the position here illustrated a long strip of pewter about 3 inches wide can be cast. The thickness can be regulated by placing the rods down flat or on edge. These rods are ⅜ of an inch wide and ⅛ of an inch thick. The one like an "L" which is lying on the slab is 21¾ inches long and the vent part 6 inches long. The other rod is 21½ inches long while the bent-up part at its left end is 5¼ inches long. As the rods are now lying on the paper-covered slab a strip with the edges sharply defined on three sides can be cast. It will be not more than ⅛ of an inch thick. The open end thins out gradually to a ragged edge, because the flow of molten pewter is not checked as it is on the other three sides.

When a tea-kettle is built up, a disk is cast for the bottom part and then hammered over a wooden form to assume the shape of a bowl. The side walls are formed of a long strip, cast as described above. The different pieces are assembled over a wooden sectional core and soldered together. It must be a sectional core so it can be taken out piece by piece from the finished kettle which has a belly larger than the mouth. The whole soldered piece enclosing the core is then attached to the head of the reciprocating lathe, shown in Fig. 525.

An assortment of pewterer's turning tools is shown in Fig. 526. They are all made of well-tempered steel and are about 1/16 of an inch thick. Pieces of pewter which cannot be turned in the lathe are finished with files and finally dressed by scraping with one or the other of the turning tools.

Fig. 527 gives a dimly photographed view of the two halves of a mold for casting smaller parts. It is made of a natural, finegrained sand-stone. There are two pewter projections on the left stone in opposite corners, to fit into corresponding holes on the other stone, so as to fix the patterns exactly face to face. The size of the stone is 4¾ inches square, and it is 1⅛ inches thick. It is customary for the pewterers to produce their own molds.

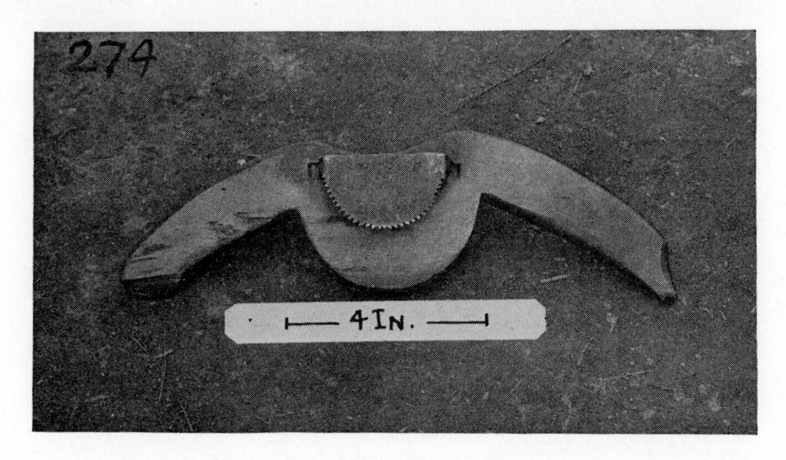

FIG. 534. COOPER'S CROZE.

Adjuncts such as spouts, handles, etc., are cast separately, and soldered fast to the body. The parts to be soldered are rubbed with resin. The soldering iron is rubbed upon a roofing tile (on the concave part) which has been strewn with powdered resin. Spouts for tea-kettles are cast in two halves, soldered together and the joints smoothed with a file and turning knife.

The long pewterer's file, the lower in Fig. 528, measures with the handle 27¼ inches in length, is ¾ inch wide and ¼ of an inch thick, and the short one (above) without a handle is 19¼ inches long, ½ of an inch wide in the center, and ¼ of an inch thick, and its cutting ridges are at right angles to its length. It is pointed at each end, on one half its surface is flat, while on the other it is convex, forming a half-round filing surface.

Important wrought iron implements for the hammering of hollow pewter ware are the stakes set upon wooden blocks, two of which are pictured in Figs. 529 and 530. The height of the one, Fig. 529, with sharply pointed horns, is 16½ inches, the horizontal metal part is 16½ inches long. Originally driven into the wooden block, it is held there with pewter which has been poured into the enlarged hole.

The Chinese artisan, ever an improviser, uses the contours of the wooden base block for hammering pieces of pewter upon it, as occasion arises.

Fig. 531 shows three hammers used by the pewterer. The upper one is constructed of an old soldering iron (conf. Fig. 36) with a lump of pewter at the handle end, and it serves to hammer, whenever it is necessary, on the inside of hollow ware, where another hammer could not be introduced. The hammer in the center is 9¾ inches long, 7¼ inches wide, and 1 inch in diameter. The metal cap upon the wood is of "pei t'ung," white copper, an alloy similar to German silver.

Finally, the third hammer is all of wood and the contact surfaces are considerably worn from use.

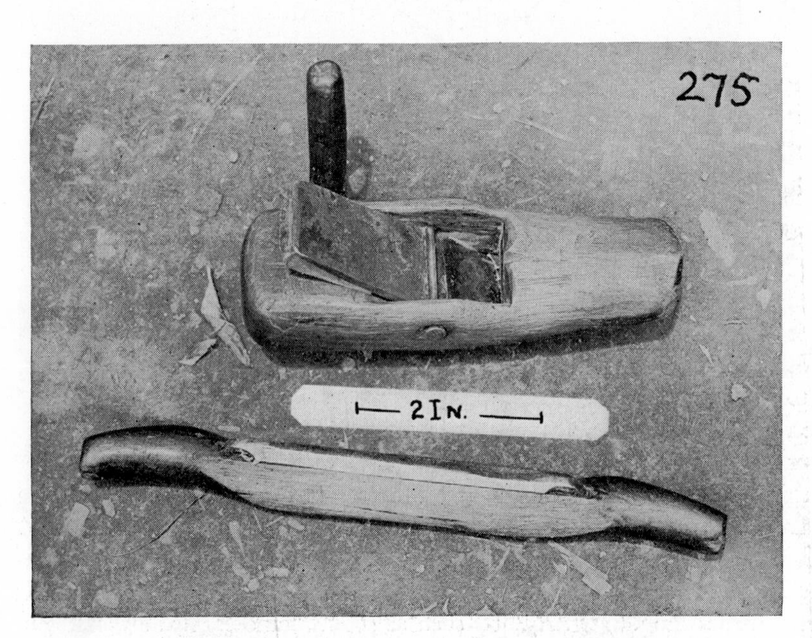

Fig. 535. Cooper's "Round Plane" and Draw Knife.

COOPER'S TRADE

The Chinese cooper makes pails, tubs, dippers, etc., articles which we class under white cooperage, but he makes no barrels, hogsheads or the like. While our coopers mostly use oak for staves the Chinese seem to prefer pine. The staves are usually not riven but sawed out, irrespective of grain when it comes to irregular profiles. Tubs and containers are often made with rounded sides and round turned-over rims. If it was not for the hoops which invariably hold together these containers they might with their smoothly lacquered surfaces, easily be taken by the casual observer for products of the potter. To saw out the staves from solid blocks of wood the cooper uses a method of holding down the block which is shown in Fig. 532.

The wooden block worked upon stands upright on a bench or wooden horse, and is held down by a wooden key with a side notch in which rests the top edge of the block. The key is tied to a fixed upright post, and a wedge driven in between post and key presses the latter firmly down upon the block to be sawed. The line of sawing is now marked on both sides of the strip, and sawing can commence. If the lines to be cut are straight, the board-saw is used, curved lines are sawed with the framed hand-saw with a narrow blade, in either case the saw is worked by two people one at either end.

The edges of the staves are carefully planed to make close joints, and dowels are used between the staves. Grooves are cut with a croze, near the bottom of the staves, for inserting the bottom disk of the tub. The edges of the bottom disk thus jointed are made tight with putty made from air-slaked lime and Chinese wood-oil. For smoothing the staves, a number of various planes, drawing knives, and spoke shaves are used. The hoops are made of strips of bamboo, for finer ware of cane. Projections such as handles and spouts are always part of a stave, fashioned with the stave out of one solid piece of wood. Fig. 533 shows this plainly. In the background of Fig. 169 two shallow tubs, can be seen one within the other standing on edge. The edges are rounded and resemble the crimped edges of molded clay ware.

The dipper, Fig. 533, has an interesting handle. It is easily carried by taking hold of the horizontal bar and easily tilted to pour out the contents. We saw this type in the mountain regions around Se Aw, Chekiang, where it is used for fetching water to the house from creeks or streams. The height of the body is 6½ inches, the diameter 11 inches, the height to the extreme end of the handle 13¾ inches. The spout and handle are parts of the staves, only the horizontal piece is mortised into the upright part of the handle. We saw a similar receptacle, with the same kind of handle, but without a spout, rather low and shallow, used for feeding chickens.

Fig. 534, shows a cooper's croze for making the grooves, into which the bottoms of pails, tubs, etc., are to be inserted. The diameter of the semicircular saw-blade is $2\frac{1}{2}$ inches. Two tangs project from it at right angles and they are wedged into the wooden holder at whatever distance is deemed necessary. Half of the teeth of the saw point towards the middle of its blade in one direction, and the other half in the opposite direction. We have noticed this arrangement already in the board-saw handled by two men. Here the purpose is similar, the saw cuts if pulled in either direction. The mode of handling is obvious. The wooden holder is made to rest against the edge of the staves near which the groove is intended to be cut. The space between saw-blade and holder determines the distance from the edge of the stave to the groove to be cut.

Fig. 535 shows a plane and a straight-edged draw knife. The plane has a bottom curved at right angles to its length. With it round, concave surfaces can be planed. A handle on the plane seems a necessity for the Chinese. The cooper's plane would be unwieldy with the double handle and has therefore only one, dove-tailed into the side of the plane, as shown in the picture. A foreign nail passes through the plane to hold the blade in place. Usually a pin of hard wood serves this purpose, or two shoulders which extend into the opening of the plane.

This little plane is worked in a direction away from the body according to the Chinese custom. There is another rather long plane which some coopers use upside down. The plane serves in this latter case like a work-bench. One end rests on the floor and the other is propped up with two wooden feet which give the plane a slanting position. The piece of wood to be planed is slid over the smooth surface of the plane against the protruding cutting edge in a direction toward the body of the worker.

The straight-edged drawing knife or shave has a blade 4 inches long. Tangs at right angles project from each blade end, and are wedged into the wooden frame. The instrument is held with both hands and drawn toward the body. The photograph was taken near Chichow, Anhwei province.

INDEX

INDEX

D

E

F

G

S

T